Kinships
of Animals and Man

An Animal Biology

By ANN H. MORGAN, Ph.D.

Mount Holyoke College

McGRAW-HILL BOOK COMPANY, Inc.

New York   Toronto   London

1955

KINSHIPS OF ANIMALS AND MAN

Library of Congress Catalog Card Number 55–6859

III

To

Elizabeth Adams

Professor of Zoology

in

Mount Holyoke College

Preface

Both living and non-living things are composed of strikingly similar substances. The living ones are not only composed of like substances but all living matter is put together in the same unique way. Kinships based on these similarities form the central theme of this book. The author's experience has indicated that the study of these relationships makes zoology more vital and interesting to the student.

The first chapter, "Relationships of the Living World," presents the general plan of the text and is its introduction. Part I, "The Foundation," tells of matter and energy as they occur in plants and animals, and familiar natural processes. It includes a discussion of atoms and molecules and references to the newer knowledge concerning them. This leads logically to the cell, as a sample of the complete organization of living matter and the focus of a great wave of contemporary investigation.

Relationships are persistently evident in our world and universe. Many of them are suggested in the *Kinships of Animals and Man,* and they are emphasized in the special discussions of Part II, "Ecology." Among these relationships are the competitions and unconscious cooperations of animals, the associations of animals in communities, and photosynthesis, the most important food-making process in the world.

Protoplasm must have water wherever it is. The inside of the animal body is wet. Structures and functions of tissues and organs are affected by the fact of their dependence upon fluid. In Part III, "The Internal Environment of the Body," the main systems of the animal body, invertebrate and vertebrate are studied with respect to their basic similarities. It is well known that modern medicine is the internal ecology of the human body.

Traces of history remain in animals and parts of animals showing the broken story of their evolution. "The Evolution of Animals" is a series of chapters which recount the great contribution of one or another group. Above all, evolution appears as a story of the continuity of life.

v

"Evolution and Conservation," or applied ecology, belong together in a final summary. Conservation is already taking its place as a part of Evolution.

I am grateful to all those who have made this work first of all a pleasure to me. There are more of them than I can name here.

First are my colleagues in the Department of Zoology in Mount Holyoke College; Professors A. E. Adams, E. M. Boyd, J. W. Kingsbury, C. Smith, I. B. Sprague and K. F. Stein. Dr. Adams has been generous beyond my telling in giving her time, scholarship and keen critical sense.

Others have read parts of the book and given suggestions that have greatly helped. These are: Dr. H. M. Allyn, former Dean of Mount Holyoke College; Dr. E. P. Carr, Professor of Chemistry, Mount Holyoke College; Dr. M. P. Cloud, Librarian of Peabody Museum, Yale University; Dr. E. T. Eltinge, Associate Professor of Plant Science, Mount Holyoke College; Dr. M. P. Grant, Professor of Zoology, Sarah Lawrence College; Dr. E. K. Moyer, Associate Professor of Anatomy, Medical School, Boston University; Dr. F. A. Saunders, Professor of Physics, Harvard University.

The original drawings except a very few of my own have been made by Shirley P. Glaser, Biological Artist of the Peabody Museum of Yale University. I have been fortunate in having the benefit of her ability and experience. Other illustrations, exclusive of my own photographs, are used through the courtesy of those whose names are written beneath them. The generosity of many authors in particular is a cause of my warm thanks.

There are many others whose interest and good wishes I have appreciated. Among them are Andrew Bihun of the National Audubon House; J. P. Hughes of the W. B. Saunders Company; my sister, Christine M. Kenyon; and my brother, Stanley D. Morgan.

Finally I give my hearty thanks to those who have helped to make my manuscript into a book. At first, Helen L. Goodwin, and later, Irene Mossman have typed the revisions with exacting accuracy.

Fortunately, the index of *Kinships* has been made by a biologist who is also a librarian, Dr. M. P. Cloud of the Peabody Museum at Yale University.

ANN H. MORGAN

Contents

Part V. EVOLUTION OF ANIMALS

Part VI. EVOLUTION AND CONSERVATION

1

Relationships of the Living World

This book is about animals, those that are regularly called animals and others, the human animals. The human ones descended from some now unknown ancestors of the apes, developed language and mind with ideas and became unique among all animals. It is about the relations of animals to one another, and to the plants upon which they depend, to water, to the sun, and to the earth about them. The organization and relationships inside and outside of animals are the keys to their existence. Inside, the secretion of a gland in one part of the body is carried by the blood and stimulates the heart and muscles in other parts. Outside, the seasons change, the woodchucks go into their holes for the winter and the bobolinks fly south.

Like the sun and the atmosphere and the soil, living organisms—the woodpecker in its hole in the pear tree and the fisherman and the fish—are composed of atoms and molecules. For every organism, life is a concern of matter and energy. It is not that its substances are so unusual; it is the way they are put together that makes living matter different from everything else.

Living matter occurs in cells. They are samples of its composition and activity, units of the architecture of plants and animals, rosebush and man. To the passing glance cells appear disarmingly simple although they are complex far beyond our present understanding. In many-celled animals the bridge over which all inheritable qualities pass to the next generation is in the content of two microscopic cells. By their union and the divisions which follow it, the billions of cells in the body receive their quotas of inheritance.

Plants and animals are bound together in a multitude of ways and the same fundamental processes of living are common to both. A cactus is nearer to human kin than a stone; the starvation of corn is not as spectacular as the starvation of cattle, but it also is a disaster.

On every hand animals depend upon plants directly and indirectly, for food, for shelter, even for decoration. Long before mankind made bouquets, the bowerbirds of Australia scattered blossoms on their courting grounds. Green plants carry on the great business of making the food that is essential to themselves and to animals. In spite of the schemes for providing the world with synthetic food, a cow will keep her mouth to the grass for some time to come. Plants also profit from the animals; many of them, including large numbers of fruit trees, do not produce seeds without insect pollination.

The two main ways to study animals are: with emphasis on their associations in groups of other living organisms, and with emphasis on the individual.

As associated organisms animals are considered among others of their own kind or of different kinds in environments of soil, water, or air, within a complex web of influences. The environment of the butterfly on the flower includes the sun, the rotating earth, and the atmosphere as well as the flower (Fig. 1.1). Ecology is the study of plants and animals in their home environments. It is discussed near the beginning and again at the end of this book,

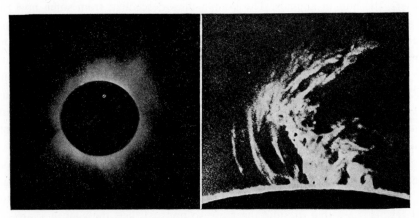

FIG. 1.1. Escaping energy, the heat and light of the sun. *Left,* the sun in total eclipse by the moon. The sun's corona of light streaming out great distances from behind the darkened moon. *Right,* part of the profile of the sun showing its prominences, great flames that extend hundreds of thousands of miles into space. All processes of living are related, directly or indirectly, to the capture of the radiant energy of the sun. (Courtesy, Mount Wilson and Palomar Observatories.)

but the relations of living organisms to their surroundings pervade all of its chapters. The animal body itself is a portable environment; the lungs and the heart carry on unique activities in their own special surroundings. The evolution of animals is a history of relationships.

Everybody has had experience with an animal in its home territory: clothes moths in flannel, skunks along the byways, or robins on the lawn. Everyone knows that plant lice suck up plant juices, that robins eat hugely of earthworms which in turn eat heavily of leaves and of soil rich in microscopic plant cells.

The watery homes of animals are exciting because they are relatively primeval. Wade into the border waters of a lively pond and you look down into a world in which animals are swimming, climbing, burrowing, eating plants, eating one another, mating, laying eggs, floating, and doing nothing but the basic business of living. The pond is affected by surrounding conditions but its swarming population is primarily adjusted to an ancient world of water. The tidal and surface waters of the sea contain populations which dwarf those of fresh water, but ponds and seas bestow similar benefits in the same great boon of water. Living substances must be wet. Life began in the water and all plants and animals are still bound by their need of water, even though many of them have moved into deserts. All plants and animals are subject to the chemical and physical features of their environments. The carbon cycle begins when plants take carbon dioxide from the air and build it into carbohydrate food. The atmospheric pressure in high and low places and the amount of oxygen in the air or water continually affect animals.

Ecological relationships—the fish to the sea, the bird to the air—pervade the evolution of animals and plants. They are apparent in a survey of the main groups of animals arranged with respect to their structures and activities. They also appear in special studies of certain animals as representative types, such as those of the ameba, hydra, grasshopper, honeybee, and frog. In this book each of these has been included with its own group of relatives instead of being considered as an isolated creature; no plant or animal lives unto itself alone. In the systems of the body and in their fundamental patterns animal groups show resemblances and relationships. The circulatory systems of all vertebrates are built on a similar ground plan. Except in protozoans and the simplest of multicellular animals, kidneys are tubular organs closely associated with circulating blood. From earthworm to man the body is a tube within a tube; in invertebrates the nerve cord is on the ventral side of the body; in all vertebrates it is on the dorsal side. Environment has been a sculptor. In environment and outward form a whale is fishlike; in internal anatomy it is closer to a squirrel.

Conservation is applied ecology. Not until good things are going or gone do we appreciate what they used to be. A stream runs clean and cold and well-fed trout cut through its currents. This home is right for them. No alterations are needed. Presently an upstream paint shop is established, the waste warms and poisons the water, supplies it with scum, bad smell, and gases that kill the trout. The need of getting back the clean, cold water is urgent for whatever fishes may still be alive. If the paint shop and the bad smell had not become a part of their environment, there would be many more alive. Conservation of our natural resources is growing daily more important. The kinships of animals and man extend in every direction and include all living organisms and the times and places which have made them and are still making them what they are.

The second way of studying animals is with emphasis on the individual. It is the study of the structure and function of tissues and organs, by examination and experiment. Every animal has an internal environment inherited from its ancestors through ages of evolution. Within the body all cells live in a watery environment as truly as do animals in a pond. The amount of water is continually regulated; chemical conditions—acidity, alkalinity, enzyme, and hormone actions are constantly balanced, unbalanced, and rebalanced; physical conditions are changed; temperatures shift, and pressures vary. Every animal body holds a special environment of which there is no duplicate and probably nothing in existence that is at once so complex, delicate, and generally durable. The release of energy in respiration, chemical regulation by the endocrine glands, and the excretion of the by-products of metabolism especially emphasize the balancing associated with these processes. As animals are examined, it becomes more and more clear that there are not thousands of separate facts to be learned, but a few associations and principles that apply to essentially similar things.

The Fields and Subdivisions of Zoology. The science of biology includes all living organisms. The term, actually meaning the science of life, Gr. *bios,* and *logos,* discourse, is used commonly and loosely, often with little understanding of its meaning. It may include only the plants and be called the biology of plants; it often deals only with animals, the biology of animals. In either case it is concerned with the general facts and principles of plant or animal life.

Zoology is the study of all aspects of animals, including their relations to each other and their environments in time and space. Other associated sciences are those particularly concerned with the environment, such as geology, physiography, oceanography, and meteorology which is concerned with conditions of the atmosphere. All of these are supported by physics, treating of the properties of matter, and by chemistry which deals with its constitution.

There are many subdivisions of zoology, the science of animals (including man). The principal ones are the following:

SUBDIVISIONS OF ZOOLOGY

Name	Description
Anatomy	Gross structure of the animal
Histology	Function and microscopic structure of tissues and organs
Cytology	Function and structure of the cell and its contents
Physiology	Function of the whole animal, or of its parts
Embryology	Development of the new individual

Name	*Description*
Genetics	Science of heredity dealing with characteristics arising from the behavior of genes
Ecology	Relationships of animals to one another, to plants, and to the environment; their home life
Taxonomy	Classification of animals and its principles
Zoogeography	Distribution of animals in space
Paleontology	Distribution of animals in time; fossils
Sociology	Societies of animals and man
Parasitology	Study of animals that live and subsist upon other animals or plants to their harm
Psychology	Study of the mind

Zoology is also divided into branches for the study of special groups of animals, such as:

Entomology	Insects
Ornithology	Birds
Protozoology	One-celled animals
Herpetology	Amphibians and reptiles

Part I
The Foundation

2
Life Is a Concern
of Matter and Energy

We live in a universe of substance and force. Everything that we can discern with our senses is either one or the other, matter or energy. So far as they are known, matter and energy are always associated. They are in the grass beneath our feet, the wind and the rain, our food and our use of food. Even a little understanding of the character and relationships of matter and energy throws light upon the lives of plants and animals; it may be the eyeshine of a cat in the dark, the song of a wood thrush, the drip of sweat from the skin, the heat of fever, the clinch of muscles.

Matter

Our bodies are composed of matter. It is all around us: books, plants, animals, sugar, smoke, gasoline, the earth, the planets, and the far-off galaxies, each of them like the Milky Way of which our own solar system is a part. What are these things? What is matter? A good deal has been learned about its structure mostly during the last part of the nineteenth and the first part of the twentieth centuries. In its analysis all the roads have led toward electricity. But nobody knows what matter is because no one yet understands electricity.

All matter is composed of invisible atoms; there are millions of billions of them in a drop of water, each one containing extraordinarily minute electrical particles. The electrical nature of living matter has been known in one way or another for a long time, but in recent years more and more evidences of it have been discovered. The Italian anatomist, Luigi Galvani (1737–1789) was observing a freshly killed frog hung from an iron fence by a copper wire hooked under the sciatic nerve when he noticed that the muscles twitched whenever the wind-blown legs touched the iron fence. Thus a century and a half ago Galvani discovered that living matter conducts electricity and recorded his observations in his essay, "Force of Electricity on the Motion of Muscles." Less than half a century later it appeared that living tissues not only conduct electricity but also produce it. Now rhythmically repeated waves of electrical charges are received over wires connected with metal plates placed against the human head, and the records of them are taken by recording mechanisms (Fig. 16.23). The existence of electrical brain waves is clearly established.

Energy

Energy is the capacity for action, the ability to do. Expressions of it are the jumping of fleas, the wriggling of a baby, the leap of a rabbit, the response of a tear gland. Just as life is known only through matter, so energy is measured only by its effect on matter, the size and the speed of a flea's jump.

Characteristics of Energy. Heat is the commonest form of energy. This is so generally true that measurements of energy can be stated in units of heat. The small calorie is the amount of heat required to raise one gram of water one degree centigrade at sea level pressure of nearly 15 pounds per square inch. Since the gram is too small to be a convenient unit, a large calorie has been adopted for general use. It is the amount of heat required to raise one kilogram (1000 grams or 2.2 pounds) of water one degree centigrade, also at sea level pressure.

Potential and Kinetic Energy. Usually energy can be in two forms, potential in the rabbit's readiness to jump, and kinetic in the actual jump. Atomic energy is seemingly of a different sort.

Potential energy is that contained in any object because of its position or shape or substance. Kinetic energy is that of motion. A fish hawk (osprey) hovering aloft over a lake has potential energy of position. This becomes kinetic energy as the hawk cuts downward to pick a fish from the water. The wiry threads wound around the eggs of certain mayflies have potential energy that becomes kinetic (Fig. 2.1). They are tightly coiled as long as the eggs are in the body, but they spring loose and catch on plant stems as soon as the eggs are laid in the water. Living cells hold potential energy of substances such as fat which may be transformed into the energy of heat. In a more particular sense the energy of substances is usually called chemical energy (Fig. 2.2). Energy is either stored or liberated in all chemical reactions. A coal fire is a chemical reaction in which chemical energy stored millions of years ago is liberated from the coal:

coal + O_2 (oxygen in the air) = CO_2 (carbon dioxide gas) + energy (heat).

Catalyzers are aids in chemical reactions, hastening them without entering or being affected by them. Many of them are known as enzymes or ferments and each one acts upon particular substances and under certain conditions. The

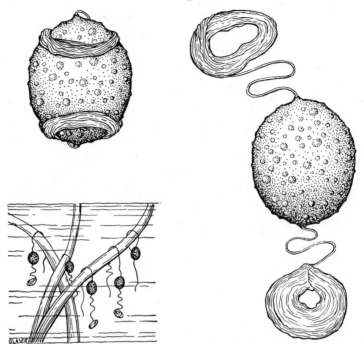

FIG. 2.1. Change from the potential energy of position to the kinetic energy of motion in the threads of a mayfly egg, the size of a sand grain. Before the egg is laid a wiry thread is coiled like a watch spring around each end of it; the energy in their coils is potential. Mayflies strew their eggs on lakes and streams. As the eggs touch the water the coils spring loose; in so doing their potential energy becomes kinetic. The threads catch on submerged twigs and the eggs are suspended above the mud that otherwise would smother them.

respiration of every living cell is a chemical reaction in which the chemical energy in the cell's substance is transformed into the energy of activity and heat.

Transformations of one kind of energy into another are constantly going on about us. The radiant energy of the sun becomes that which is stored in the simple sugars of green grass. Cows feed on grass and its stored energy is eventually transformed into milk for calves or babies.

Atomic Energy. The energy within the atom shows itself in qualities of cohesion. It is liberated when under special conditions one kind of matter is changed into another, e.g., nitrogen into oxygen. Such a change generally occurs in atoms in which the particles in the nucleus are numerous. They may be unbalanced for a long period and relatively unstable as in radium, uranium, and thorium. Such atoms cannot hold themselves together and their radioactivity is a long, continued breaking apart.

The beginnings of the knowledge of radioactivity moved rapidly. In 1895 Röntgen concluded that some active radiation emitted spontaneously from

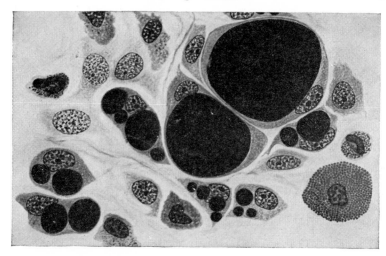

Fig. 2.2. Chemical energy stored in a globule of fat. Fat cells from connective tissue underlying the skin of a rat. Fat stained black. (After Maximow. Courtesy, Gerard: *Unresting Cells*. New York, Harper & Bros., 1940.)

uranium had fogged photographic plates protected by light-tight envelopes. He coined the word radioactive to describe the activity. In February of the next year Henri Becquerel read a paper before the Academy of Science in Paris in which he announced that compounds of uranium were able to affect a plate through an envelope that was proof against light. The radiations were called x-rays because they were not understood. Following Becquerel's discovery his one-time student, Marie Curie, succeeded in isolating minute quantities of two highly radioactive new elements from uranium minerals, to which she gave the names polonium and radium. In 1899 Becquerel showed that the rays from uranium could be separated into two types, alpha rays easily absorbed by a few sheets of paper, and beta rays able to penetrate thin aluminum. In 1900 Villard discovered still a third and more penetrating radiation from uranium minerals, the gamma rays. By 1913 Rutherford and Soddy had coordinated the various processes and proposed a theory that the nucleus of the atom was spontaneously disintegrating. They suggested that the nuclear disintegration was explosive and showed that during the process particles of matter and energy were lost. Since that time the knowledge and use of atomic energy have become important in many fields of biology; x-ray photographs are routine items in medical practice; exposure to controlled quantities of x-rays is a common treatment of cancer; Muller's experimental radiation of fruit flies produced inheritable differences in generation after generation of their offspring; and the use of radioactive tracers has opened a new era in biological investigation.

Atomic energy is now a tool in world politics; perhaps it is more true that world politics is a tool of atomic energy. The most startling display of energy that had ever been known to the world occurred on August 6, 1945, when an atomic bomb exploded over Hiroshima, Japan, and uranium atoms (U-235) broke apart and unloosed their extraordinary power.

Structure of Matter

The physical states of matter are more or less easily changed by conditions about them. In shifting temperatures, the state of water may be a gas, fluid, or solid, i.e., vapor, rain, and sleet in quick succession. The composition of matter is not thus easily changed, the elements and their compounds, the atoms and molecules. Atoms are the incredibly minute, organized units of matter that are the building blocks of elements.

An element is composed of one kind of atom for which it is named, oxygen, carbon, calcium, and so on. One hundred elements are known, mainly discovered in nature: certain radioactive ones have also been created experimentally. The elements are distributed unevenly. Four of them, oxygen, carbon, hydrogen, and nitrogen constitute 96 per cent of living matter; less than 20 make up 99 per cent of the atmosphere, the ocean, and the earth's crust.

Molecules are usually the units peculiar to an element or a compound. Molecules of elements contain two or more atoms of the same kind. Molecules of compounds have two or more different kinds of atoms. The molecule of water has two atoms of hydrogen and one of oxygen (Fig. 2.3).

Molecules are continually attracted to one another by intermolecular force that is electrical rather than gravitational. They are in constant motion, in a random jumpy dance. They are too small to be visible and the dance cannot be seen but can be felt as heat. When a substance is cold, e.g., ice, the dance is slow; when hot, e.g., boiling water, the dance is extraordinarily rapid. Turn an electrical current through a cold iron and the dance of the molecules is changed from the slow to rapid rate. The motion never stops. The lounger in

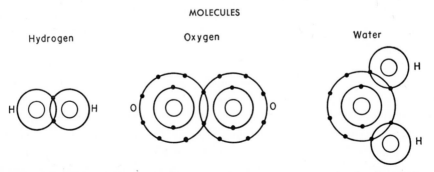

FIG. 2.3. Diagram of the formation of a molecule of water by the sharing of electrons between two atoms of hydrogen and one of oxygen. Electrons are the particles that take part in chemical reactions.

Boston Common and the dead bench on which he sits both abound in speeding molecules (Figs. 2.4 and 2.5).

Characteristics of Atoms. Nobody has seen the atoms. Their existence was assumed by John Dalton (1766–1844) and it has been proved by patient, skillful experimentation with radioactivity and other means.

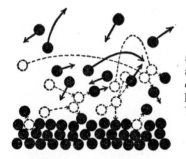

FIG. 2.4. Molecules are continuously repelled and attracted in a random jumpy dance. Those in a thin gas move in free curves. Those in a fluid or a solid are packed together as if in a crowded hall. (Courtesy, Gerard: *Unresting Cells.* New York, Harper & Bros., 1940.)

The relatively small center body or nucleus contains practically all of the atom's mass. Electrically negative particles rotate around it. In comparison with their size, they swing through space relatively as great as that in which planets rotate about the sun (Fig. 2.6). The nucleus is composed of protons carrying positive charges of electricity and neutrons that carry no charge. The sum of their masses is the weight of the atom. The electrical charge of the nucleus indirectly controls the nature and behavior of the atom. Atomic nuclei are bound together by a force that was unimagined until experimental splitting demonstrated its reality. As interdependence permeates living organisms, so interdependence of parts is the keystone of the atoms that are the foundation of living matter.

Within the space around the nucleus are particles called electrons, so light that they are ignored in the computation of atomic weight. Each carries a negative charge of electricity and spins like a coin that is spun upon a table top. It is generally believed that electrons revolve around the nucleus, but their spinning is independent of it. The number of electrons in an atom governs its chemical properties. Electrons, for example, determine that one atom of oxygen will unite with two atoms of hydrogen to form water (H_2O).

ISOTOPES. Isotopes are different forms of atoms existing in the same element (Fig. 2.6). They have nearly the same chemical properties but differ in the number of neutrons in their nuclei. Since the weight of an atom is the sum of the numbers of its protons and neutrons, the isotopes of an atom have different atomic weights. For example, hydrogen has three known isotopes: hydrogen, atomic weight 1; deuterium (heavy hydrogen), atomic weight 2; tritium, atomic weight 3. Isotopes that have few neutrons in their nuclei are called light isotopes and those with the most neutrons heavy isotopes. In general the heavy isotopes are less stable, since an excess of neutrons weakens the cohesion of the nucleus. Those that do not readily change are called stable isotopes; the radioactive isotopes give off nuclear energy. Isotopes have been detected in nature and many radioactive ones have been made in laboratories.

The separation of isotopes is a means of exploring changes that take place within the nuclei of atoms. One of the problems in dealing with isotopes is to separate out the kind which is to be used. In some cases this is easy; in others it is extremely difficult. In the distillation of water the vapor which first condenses is water containing the light isotope of hydrogen. Later the heavy water

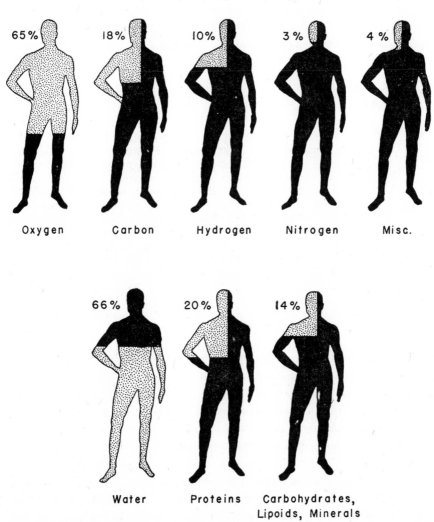

65%	18%	10%	3%	4%
Oxygen	Carbon	Hydrogen	Nitrogen	Misc.

66%	20%	14%
Water	Proteins	Carbohydrates, Lipoids, Minerals

FIG. 2.5. *Top,* Percentages of different kinds of atoms in the human body. Included under miscellaneous are, in order of decreasing amounts, calcium, phosphorus, potassium, sodium, sulfur, chlorine, magnesium, and iron. *Bottom,* Percentages of different kinds of molecules in the human body. (Modified from Moment: *General Biology.* New York, Appleton-Century-Crofts, 1950.)

containing a heavy isotope of hydrogen also distills. Isotopes of uranium are not procured by any of the easier methods; skill, persistence, and elaborate equipment are required.

Isotopes are also put to various uses, in war, in biological investigation, and in medicine. The atomic bombs of the Second World War contained isotopes of heavy atoms with unstable nuclei that flew apart establishing chain explosions of tremendous destruction. The political condition of the world has established an association of isotopes and war. There is hope that this may sometime give place to great constructive uses. To the world at large, atomic bombs have almost hidden the importance of the radioactive isotopes that are being used as tracers in living plants and animals.

Hydrogen atom

Deuterium atom

Helium atom

FIG. 2.6. Diagrams of the structural plan of the atom. As they are at this date generally named the particles inside the nucleus are: the protons (+) that carry positive charges and the neutrons (0) that carry no charges; the electrons outside the nucleus bear negative charges. Hydrogen atoms have one proton and one electron. Deuterium atom, an isotope of hydrogen (heavy hydrogen) consists of a nucleus with one proton and one neutron, and a single electron moving around it. Helium atom, the nucleus consisting of two protons and two neutrons, has two electrons moving around it. Helium gas is used in dirigible balloons.

IONS. Atoms may gain or lose electrons and are then known as ions. If electrons are lost, the ion is positively charged; if they are gained, it is negatively charged. Ions combine more readily than electrically neutral atoms. Water facilitates the splitting of substances into ions. Living organisms are largely water and many substances are present in them chiefly in a dissolved state. In solution many of these dissolved substances split into simpler ones and ions are formed (Fig. 2.7). When crystals of common salt (sodium chloride, NaCl), a component of the blood of all animals, dissolve in water, the ions of the sodium (Na^+) already present in the lattice of the crystal are separated by the attraction of the polar molecule of water. The crystal framework is thus broken and the ions are free in the solution. Their formation in salt solution is expressed by the formula, $NaCl = Na^+ + Cl^-$.

Because of the positive and negative charges of ions, the living body can conduct electricity. When the opposite poles of a battery are placed in water, the sodium ions (Na+) are attracted toward the negative pole where they acquire electrons and their positive charge is neutralized. The chlorine ions (Cl−) are attracted toward the positive pole, give up an electron and become neutral atoms. The moving ions conduct an electrical current and thus establish a complete circuit. Any substance which thus ionizes in water is called an electrolyte because of its ability to conduct electricity.

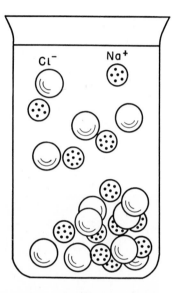

FIG. 2.7. Diagram of the ionization or dissolving of salt in water. When sodium chloride (salt) is put into water the atoms Na (sodium) and Cl (chlorine) separate and become electrically charged wandering atoms or ions, Na+, Cl−. The movements of the sodium ions (+) and chlorine ions (−) conduct an electrical current in water. In general, water promotes the formation of ions and ions promote chemical reactions.

The properties of electrolytes depend upon the kind of ions which they produce in a solution. On the basis of the simpler theory of electrolytes there are three classes: acids, alkalis, and salts. The degree of acidity or alkalinity of a compound depends upon the degree to which it ionizes in water, that is, the degree to which the molecules yield positive hydrogen ions (H+) or negative hydroxyl ions (OH−) in the solution. Acids are electrolytes that as a group form positively charged hydrogen ions, giving the acid its sour taste. Hydrochloric acid ionizes in water:

$$HCl \rightleftharpoons H^+ + Cl^-.$$

The alkalis or bases form negatively charged combinations of oxygen and hydrogen, the hydroxyl ions, OH−. The alkali, sodium hydroxide, ionizes thus:

$$NaOH \rightleftharpoons Na^+ + OH^-.$$

Some compounds of protoplasm yield both H+ and OH− in solution. The third class of electrolytes is the salts whose ionization produces neither H+ nor OH−. Sodium chloride is an example:

$$NaCl \rightleftharpoons Na^+ + Cl^-.$$

Many of the important characteristics of cells, such as the permeability of their membranes, their irritability or response, are associated with the existence of electrolytes either within or outside them. The sensitiveness of the animal organism to hydrogen ions is apparent in scores of cases; in a large number of animals the control of respiration is through the hydrogen-ion concentration of the blood. Hydrogen-ion concentration (symbol pH) of substances in their surroundings is also of greatest importance to living organisms; the range of many aquatic animals, certain protozoans, insects, and fishes is limited by it; so is the range of earthworms.

TRACERS. The use of radioactive isotopes as tracers for investigating life processes is probably one of the most significant developments in modern biological work. Such a possibility had been recognized for some years but was limited by the fact that all the work had to be done with heavy elements such as lead, bismuth, and mercury. The isotopes chosen are labeled by exposure to radiations from a radioactive element. After this treatment they give off radiations for a longer or shorter period. The ease of this modern technique is comparable to locating a white penny among ordinary copper ones. They are introduced into plants and animals in various ways (Fig. 2.8). For exam-

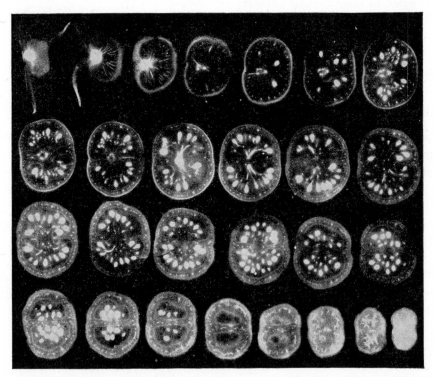

FIG. 2.8. The presence of radioactive tracers shown by radioautographs in slices of tomato, especially in the seeds. The vine from which the tomatoes were taken was grown in a solution containing radioactive zinc (Zn^{65}). This was taken up throughout the plant and affected the photographic plates like light. (Courtesy, P. R. Stout, University of California.)

ple, in the body of a rabbit they may be carried in and out of organs, into cells and perhaps out again.

The travels and destinations of such labeled isotopes are detected most commonly by the now familiar Geiger-Müller counter. This apparatus detects and amplifies each radioactive disintegration of an atom. The number and rate of disintegrations are a measure of the amount of labeled material present. In general the use of tracers is directed toward investigations of the constant buildup and breakdown, and the come and go of chemically active molecules in the living organism. In this way it has been learned that thyroxin, the iodine-containing amino acid that is so important in the functioning of the thyroid gland, is manufactured by muscle and in the intestine as well as in the thyroid gland. Recent studies on the metabolism of rabbits by means of radioactive isotopes have shown that radioactive phosphorus administered to adult animals enters their bones and the enamel and dentine of their teeth. This shows that such hard substances, deposited in early youth, do not stay unchanged for a lifetime, but are continually exchanging material with the circulating blood.

States of Matter

Molecules are continually affected by the attraction of their neighbor molecules. Their relative sizes and the distances between them determine the strength of their mutual attraction and the state of the substance in which they are contained whether gas, liquid, or solid (Fig. 2.9). Changes of matter from one state to another involve a change in energy, usually the giving off or absorption of heat.

In gas, the molecules are scattered away from each other; their movements are rapid and disorderly and they take zigzag turns into their surroundings. The volume of a gas is dependent upon temperature and pressure. The gas spreads through all available space but is compressible because it does not

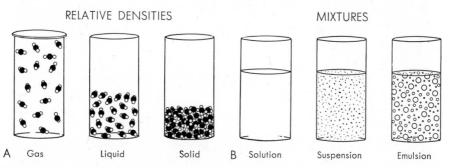

RELATIVE DENSITIES   MIXTURES

A   Gas   Liquid   Solid   B   Solution   Suspension   Emulsion

FIG. 2.9. *A.* Diagrams showing the relative densities of molecules in a gas, liquid, and solid. *B.* Diagrams of mixtures: solution thoroughly dissolved and homogeneous; suspension with particles of one substance undissolved; emulsion with very large undissolved droplets.

actually fill the space. Air is a gas and its density varies with the compression, with the pressure and temperature of the atmosphere. In high places where pressure is lessened, its molecules are relatively far apart and it may be too "thin" in oxygen to be adequate for respiration. In liquids, the molecules are closer together. In a solid, such as iron, the molecules are crowded together in patterns. Solids have fixed shape and volume.

The behavior of water molecules is very exceptional. Down to 39° F. they draw closer together; between 39° F. and 32° F. they move apart. Thus, ice expands and floats, forming a protecting cover to the animals beneath it (Fig. 5.17).

Surface film. Surface films are composed of molecules that are attracted only by those at and close to the area where one substance comes in contact with another, such as water and air (Fig. 2.10). Molecules below the surface are attracted equally from all directions. Surface film occurs on all bodies of water and forms the boundary of such units as soap bubbles and raindrops. It is important in the lives of many small aquatic animals. Certain insects, such as the water striders, forage on the upper face of surface films that bend but do not break with the pressure of their feet (Fig. 2.10). Snails glide over the underface of the film and hydras are often buoyed up against it.

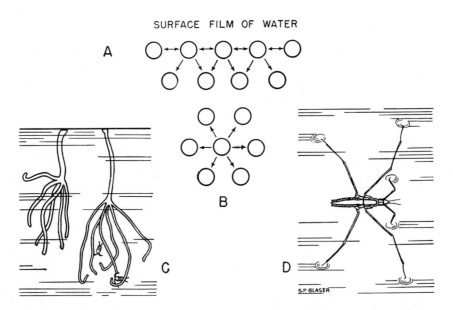

FIG. 2.10. The surface film of water. *A,* In surface film molecules of water are attracted only by those at the surface or just below it. *B,* Molecules below the surface are attracted evenly from all directions by other molecules. *C,* Hydras rest against the surface film in the topmost water where oxygen is plentiful. *D,* Water-striders skim over the surface film of quiet water and their feet make the dimples that cast shadows on the brook bed.

MIXTURES OF SUBSTANCES

Mixtures of substances may be of different kinds and states, those of solids, liquids, gases, or a solid and a gas (Fig. 2.9).

Solutions. These are homogeneous mixtures. We usually think of solutions as aqueous since natural water is a solution containing dissolved air. Bubbles of air leave water when it is heated, appearing just before it boils. When it is freezing bubbles of air appear and are caged in the ice. Glass is also a homogeneous mixture, in spite of its hardness, a true solution.

Suspensions. The particles of at least one of the substances in a suspension are larger than molecules and remain undissolved. One or several kinds of substances, or different states of one or more of them may be suspended in another substance. Suspensions include various types of colloids all of which consist of one or more substances dispersed in another. There is no escape from colloids. We consume them as food, breathe them as fog and smoke, and are composed of them.

Colloids. These are gelatinous substances that include two or more components: (1) a solid in a solid—the ruby glass of cathedral windows usually containing metallic gold; (2) a solid in a liquid—sodium chloride (salt) in water; (3) solid particles in a gas—blue cigarette smoke; (4) a liquid in a solid—natural pearl, which is water in calcium carbonate (a secretion of

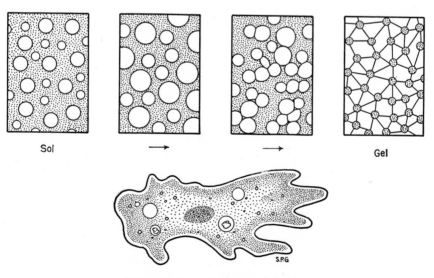

Sol   →   →   Gel

Movement of ameba accompanied by
changes sol to gel and reverse

FIG. 2.11. Diagrams of the colloidal states, sol and gel. In the sol state the particles and droplets (white) move about freely in fluid. In the gel state the surfaces of the droplets are in contact and the substance is jellylike. The protoplasm of an active ameba constantly changes from sol to gel and reverse.

oysters), natural opal, water in silicates; (5) liquid in a liquid—gelatin in water (gelatin may be a liquid or solid); (6) liquid in a gas—fog. Fog and mist are actually solid particles in gas since the water molecules are gathered on solid particles. It has been noted that at 6 A.M. the air over London may be clear and at 9 A.M. there may be a dense fog. The onset of the fog is largely due to the smoke that has provided particles on which the water gathers.

The most important of all mixed substances is protoplasm. It is a colloid, the most complicated, most studied, and still largely unknown one without which life does not occur. This colloid varies in consistency; when it thickens its droplets swell, come closer together, and become a gel; when it thins, the droplets do not absorb water, are smaller and farther apart, and form a sol (Fig. 2.11). Protoplasm is a reversible colloid that may change from sol to gel and return. Such changes may be seen through the microscope in any ameba. White of egg is a gel when heated but it will not return to a sol.

Emulsions. Although containing larger droplets than most colloids, emulsions are similar to them. Familiar emulsions are whole milk, egg yolk, and mayonnaise dressing.

Diffusion and Osmosis

Diffusion is the movement of a gas or liquid from points of greater to those of lesser concentration continued until an even distribution is achieved throughout the available space (Fig. 2.12). Mice find the cheese from the

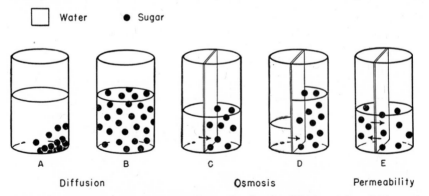

FIG. 2.12. Diagrams illustrating diffusion. In simple diffusion (*A* and *B*), molecules of sugar without any barrier become evenly distributed among the molecules of water in consequence of the motion of both. In osmosis, the diffusion through a semipermeable membrane (*C* and *D*), the molecules of water can pass through the membrane in either direction. They continue to do so until their number is equal on each side of the membrane. Thus, the level of the sugar solution is raised. The molecules of sugar, imprisoned by their larger size, continue to hit against the membrane in their random movements exerting the force called osmotic pressure. In the complete permeability (*E*) both kinds of molecules pass through the membrane at the same rate and the solutions have uniform content on each side.

particles of it diffused in the air. Skunks have few enemies because of the diffusion of their scent. The success of the great perfume industry is dependent upon human responses to the diffusion of its products, the various perfumes.

Osmosis. The diffusion of water or of certain gases through membranes that permit certain simpler molecules to pass, but not the more complex and larger ones, is osmosis. A membrane which does this is said to be semipermeable.

Living cells are enclosed by semipermeable membranes containing submicroscopic pores through which certain molecules can pass and others cannot. The rate of passage varies with the kind of membrane and the material on the two sides of it. Such membranes regulate many functions of the body such as the exchange of oxygen and carbon dioxide, the absorption of food, and the constant come and go between cells and body fluids. Two liquids that contain equal concentrations of dissolved substances are called isotonic. When living mammalian blood cells are examined microscopically they are usually immersed in a solution of 0.9 per cent NaCl in imitation of the body fluids whose salt content is isotonic with the cell content.

An example of osmotic diffusion or osmosis through an artificial membrane illustrates this principle (Fig. 2.12). The membrane is permeable to molecules of sugar as well as water, but so much more so to the latter that equal amounts of sugar and water on each side are never reached. Red blood cells puff out like pillows (called laking of blood) if the salt content of the plasma becomes too much reduced, that is, hypotonic. This is because molecules of water enter them, establishing an equal concentration with the too watery plasma (see Chap. 12). If the salt content of the plasma is too high, i.e., hypertonic, the water is drawn out and the cells wrinkle.

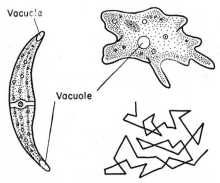

Vacuole

Vacuole

FIG. 2.13. Brownian movement occurs in the contents of vacuoles of an ameba (*right*) and of the green alga Closterium (*left*). With the high power of a microscope the zigzag pathways of the larger particles can be traced. The Brownian movement is due to bombardments of usually invisible particles striking unevenly against the larger ones.

Brownian movement. This motion is an irregular agitation of particles of different sizes. The molecules constantly jostle against relatively huge particles, striking them unevenly on one side or another. Many of them are very small molecules and others are large molecules. The molecular motion is invisible, but that of the larger particles is evident with the high power of the microscope. The motion occurs in gases, fluids, and especially in colloids including protoplasm. It is common in the vacuoles of algae and protozoans (Fig. 2.13). It was discovered in 1827 by Robert Brown, an English botanist, who saw the motion in a fluid in which pollen grains were suspended. Like other diffusions, Brownian movement is an example of kinetic energy.

3
Living Matter and Cells

No one has ever found anything alive apart from matter. We see the evidences of matter in the protoplasm of every plant and animal: sunflowers turn toward the sun; bees gather about nectar; the ticket line moves toward the show. All of these beings are composed of matter uniquely organized in protoplasm and active in an equally unique process of living. Protoplasm reproduces itself; like produces like but never duplicates itself. A cat has kittens, not squirrels. Her kittens grow and they have kittens, and so, on and on, cats and kittens. None of them repeats its mother or father or grandparents but each one shows its origin.

Protoplasm occurs in cells. The cell is a sample of the complete basic organization and activities of protoplasm. It becomes more and more evident that nonliving and living states blend together since the most complex protein molecules have certain characteristics of protoplasm. The submicroscopic gene that carries hereditary qualities is believed to be a protein molecule that, like a living organism, reproduces itself. Whether viruses are alive or not is still debated; it appears however that they have many of the properties of living matter and are very active. Protoplasm came into being in a very remote time but even now in the nucleoproteins there may still be a twilight zone of originating protoplasm.

Protoplasm

General Features. We seldom see naked protoplasm. Generally we see and touch the dead remains of cells in the outer layer of skin, scales, feathers, and hair. The softness of a kitten's fur is all due to dead cells. Most animals shed such dead cells seasonally; human molting or shedding goes on the year round. No plant or animal is entirely alive. Cells contain nonliving as well as living structures; freckles are groups of cells holding lifeless pigment that has been deposited within them. Protoplasm looks fundamentally similar wherever it occurs. A dozen cells flecked from the lining of one's own mouth

and a living ameba shifting its shape through the water on the same microscopic slide can be seen to have many differences. Their differences are not
surprising, but that their respective protoplasm should look so much alike is
unforgettable.

Protoplasm is a glassy fluid jelly that suggests the white of an egg be-
sprinkled with translucent particles and globules of liquid whose sizes and
arrangement change, at one time forming an open network, at another crowded
together (Fig. 2.11). Even through the microscope protoplasm often appears
inert. It is never really so as long as it is alive and after that it ceases to exist.
Dead protoplasm is only the somehow disorganized remains of protoplasm
and a contradiction of its name.

Structure. Protoplasm consists of a watery solution (hyaloplasm) in which
salts and other substances are dissolved and in which solid and semisolid
bodies are suspended. Many of these are molecules, mainly proteins that are
invisible through ordinary microscopes; others are clearly visible droplets.
Water may pass into protoplasm, making it more liquid, or out of it leaving
it less so. Under osmotic pressure (Fig. 2.12) minute amounts of solution
pass in or out of the droplets by way of their surface films which play the
part of semipermeable membranes. The numbers and sizes of the suspended
bodies constitute a relatively enormous surface, all of it inviting to chemical
and physical changes (Fig. 3.1).

Protoplasm is an exceedingly complex colloid. At one time it may be as
fluid as water (sol state) and at another a jelly (gel state) depending upon

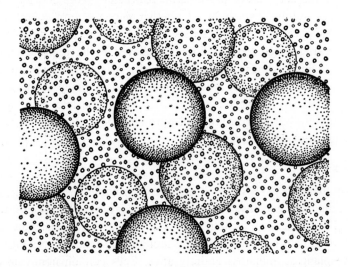

FIG. 3.1. In keeping with their colloidal nature, even minute particles in protoplasm present a relatively enormous surface to the molecules which continually
jostle them. (Courtesy, Gerard: *Unresting Cells.* New York, Harper & Bros.,
1940.)

conditions around it such as the degree of temperature, its chemical environment, and its age, or phase of life. The streams of protoplasm which pour like water into the forming pseudopodia of an ameba are in the sol state; their borders are changeful, now sol, now gel. If the cell membrane is broken slightly, a little of the sol will flow out and "set," thus healing the wound.

Chemical Characteristics. Protoplasm has substantially the same chemical content in all plants and in the great procession of animals whether jellyfish, redbird, or man. The four elements, oxygen, carbon, hydrogen, and nitrogen make up 96 per cent of living matter. No element occurs in protoplasm which is not also present in nonliving substance. It cannot be recalled too often that it is not the content of protoplasm but the way it is put together that is unique.

WATER. The most abundant compound in active protoplasm is water, in general terms of weight at least 75 per cent of it. A jellyfish may be 96 per cent water, a paramecium 80 per cent. The gray matter often called the "thinking part" of the adult human brain is at least 80 per cent water; in early youth the percentage of water is still greater. The water content of a cell is controlled by the living membrane which encloses it. Protoplasm has a water-regulatory power which resembles that of gelatin in that it takes in water and swells to a limited amount and no more. Water heats slowly and holds its heat. Thus the temperature of an animal with its high water content rises slowly and tends to hold its level. Water works toward a temperate climate for protoplasm, whether it is in the body cells of a fish or surrounding the fish in a stream. Certain very important changes in the water content of their protoplasm make animals of low metabolism relatively cold-hardy, such as the numberless cold-blooded ones, insects and others that withstand temperatures of zero (F.) and far below. As winter approaches their protoplasm loses water, but this is only part of the cold hardening. The water which remains is not all in the same state; it may be free or bound, more of one than the other. Free water is water that contains truly dissolved materials and acts as a dispersion medium for them. In both plants and animals it transports digested foods and waste products and forms a liquid base for secretions. Bound water is held in a loose chemical combination with other molecules. Ordinarily bound water does not freeze. Free water freezes readily forming ice crystals, which because of their size and pressure kill the protoplasm. Studies on the bound and free water in gelatin and egg-white show that part of the water freezes when the temperature reaches $-6°C$. ($21.2°F.$) while what remained did not freeze even at $-50°C$. Thus, for the beetle that must endure a northern winter there are striking advantages in having a content of bound water.

CHEMICAL ACTIVITY. Water is the closest approach that we have to something which dissolves everything. This is the basis of its prominence in diverse metabolic processes, of its power to shape the earth's surface, and its efficiency in the digestive tract, in the washtub, and in the factory. Chemical reactions are hastened by any agent that finely divides a solid, and this happens when water divides a lump of sugar. Living depends upon chemical reactions, both continual and intermittent, all of them together making up the grand process of metabolism, the chemical changes in which water is a constant attendant. Water conducts electricity; when salt is added it does so much more readily. Thus, protoplasm is an efficient conductor since a variety of salts occurs in it and especially in body fluids, the latter being similar to sea water in their salt content.

ATMOSPHERIC GASES. The gases of the atmosphere are soluble in water and therefore in protoplasm. Nitrogen (N_2), abundant in the air (79%), is always present in living cells but is chemically inactive; in pure form it does not take part in metabolism although its compounds, e.g., proteins, do so. On the other hand, oxygen, varyingly abundant in the atmospheric air (about 21%), takes an essential part in oxidation in the cells. Carbon dioxide, usually 0.03 per cent in the air, is produced as a by-product of oxidation in protoplasm. Although a by-product in the respiration of both plants and animals, carbon dioxide is essential for photosynthesis in plants (Chap. 4), and in small amounts for important functions in the respiration of animals.

MINERAL SALTS. Protoplasm doubtless came into existence in sea water and mineral salts must have been included in it from the beginning. It contains a variety of salts; sodium, potassium, calcium, and magnesium are the chief positively charged ions, and chloride, carbonate, phosphate, and sulfate are the common negatively charged ones. Mineral salts are important in maintaining the osmotic balance between protoplasm and its environment, in regulating the passage of water into and out of the cell. Calcium may take part in the change of protoplasm from a sol to a gel state.

ORGANIC COMPOUNDS. The most important difference between inorganic and organic compounds is in the carbon content of the latter. This is so universal that carbon is the one element with which organic chemistry deals. Carbon is present in some inorganic compounds, but it is present in all organic ones. Virtually every organic substance will char if hot enough and yield charcoal, that is, carbon. Roast pork and apples can be burned to charcoal; chicken fat and chicken feathers make a lively fire.

Protoplasm contains many organic compounds which continually shift through interactions with one another. The most abundant of these are carbohydrates, lipids or fatty substances, and proteins. They constitute the main part of food and are included in the discussion of foods and digestion (Chap. 11), but their distribution and importance make many other allusions to them essential. Certain fundamental facts about them may be appropriately taken up here with protoplasm.

Carbohydrates. All protoplasm is believed to contain carbohydrates. Those of one group (pentoses) are one of the main components of the chromatin in the nuclei of all cells. Other than that important role, carbohydrates are not actually a part of protoplasm but are only contained in it. Their great function is the immediate supply of energy, of which they are the chief source for all living organisms.

The familiar carbohydrates are sugars and starches, the cellulose in the walls of plant cells, pectin, and glycogen or animal starch stored in animal cells (Fig. 3.2). Cellulose gives stiffness to plant stems and forms most of the fiber of cotton. Pectin, a carbohydrate of fruit, insures the stiffening of jelly. Starch in plants and glycogen in animals are the reserve food supply of the cells. They occur in the watery solution of protoplasm and the molecules come and go through cell membranes (Fig. 3.3).

All carbohydrates contain only carbon, hydrogen, and oxygen. In forming them, untold numbers of green plants capture the energy of the sun, the source of energy for all living matter, and use this energy to combine carbon dioxide with water, thus creating the energy-packed food, glucose, and the by-product oxygen.

The simplest of the carbohydrates are sugars, all of them more or less sweet. They include the simple sugars, pentoses with five and hexoses with six carbon atoms ($C_6H_{12}O_6$), the latter including glucose (also called dextrose). This is an almost universal protoplasmic fuel. It is the form of sugar present in human blood in which the essential blood-sugar content is about 0.1 per cent. One of the compound sugars (polysaccharides) is table sugar (sucrose, $C_{12}H_{22}O_{11}$) from sugar cane and sugar beets. It is the commonest sugar in the nectaries of flowers, easily tasted in violets and columbines. Sucrose is produced by the union of a molecule of glucose with one of

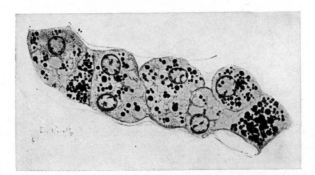

FIG. 3.2. Glycogen (black) or animal starch in human liver cells. It is stored in many kinds of cells but is most abundant in the liver and muscles. Soluble in water and therefore in protoplasm it is a quickly available food. (Courtesy, Bremer and Weatherford: *Textbook of Histology,* 6th ed. Philadelphia, The Blakiston Company, 1944.)

fructose and the loss of a molecule of water—glucose ($C_6H_{12}O_6$) + fructose ($C_6H_{12}O_6$) — H_2O = sucrose ($C_{12}H_{22}O_{11}$). When it is hydrolyzed sucrose gives one molecule of glucose and one of fructose.

Other compound sugars are starch, glycogen, and cellulose. These contain units of simple sugars combined into large molecules. Starch is the common storage form of carbohydrate in plant cells and glycogen or animal starch in animal cells. The molecules of both are too large to go through the cell membranes, but protoplasm can hydrolyze both and obtain glucose with its smaller molecules.

Fats. Fatty substances take part in the composition of cell membranes and therefore in their selective permeability (Fig. 3.3). In animals they constitute the principal supply of food. They produce more energy per gram than carbohydrates but oxidize more slowly and are less quickly accessible. Fat persons get hungry just as soon as lean ones. Fats are the backlogs of the fire of which carbohydrates are the kindling. Fats are abundant in animals and by no means absent in plants. They may be in the cells, as in bacon, or in the secretions that cells produce, as in cream, or in the wax of honeycomb.

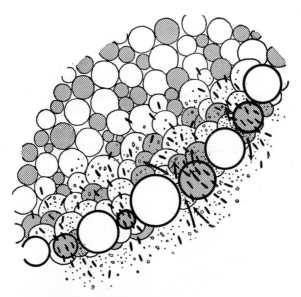

Fig. 3.3. Diagram of a cell membrane where there is continuous activity, constant separation of what shall and shall not pass in and out of the cell. These processes are discovered by chemical analysis. Here, the cell membrane is shown cut so that its inner surface is at the left and its outer edge at the right. Lipoid (fatty) particles are shaded, protein particles are white. Water channels (arrows) permit water and other smaller molecules to pass. Larger molecules are blocked by the small pores but those that are soluble in fats may enter the lipoid (shaded) particles of the membrane, mix with their molecules and thus pass in or out of the cell. (Courtesy, Gerard: *Unresting Cells.* New York, Harper & Bros., 1940.)

Fats resemble carbohydrates in being composed only of carbon, hydrogen, and oxygen but differ in the proportions of each of these, the hydrogen atoms being twice as numerous as those of carbon and the amount of oxygen relatively small. Fats are colloids, relatively insoluble in water. They liquefy at various temperatures, oils at room temperature or lower, others near the body temperature of the animals in which they occur. Those of snakes and other cold-blooded animals liquefy at relatively low temperatures.

The complex phosphorus-containing fats (phospholipids) include lecithin, abundant in egg yolk, in nerve tissue, in bile, and blood. The steroids, another group of fatty substances, include cholesterol, well known in the bile and gallstones. The male and female sex hormones are also related to these fats. Certain vitamins are associated with them; the growth vitamin A and vitamin D, which prevents rickets, occur especially in butter and cod-liver oil and in green vegetables; the fertility vitamin E is in butterfat and lettuce.

Proteins. All protoplasm contains proteins. They are the keystones in its organization and next to water its most abundant compound. Different proteins occur in different kinds of cells. The proteins of every species of organism evidently differ from those of every other. The kinship of animals is recorded in the proteins of their blood. Proteins in the blood of whales that have lived in the sea for countless generations are more like those of their relatives, the land mammals, than of their neighbor fishes. Proteins are prominent in the nuclei of all cells. Chromatin, the chief physical basis of heredity, is composed of nucleic acid and extraordinarily complex proteins. The nuclei of the male and female sex cells together contain most of what determines the inherited qualities of an offspring, maybe its chance to become a codfish or a senator.

Proteins are the most complicated and various of all substances. They are composed not only of carbon, hydrogen, and oxygen, like the carbohydrates and fats, but include nitrogen, sulfur, phosphorus as well. Their molecules are very large, often containing thousands of atoms, and are complex, and variable like living matter itself. This means variety of structure and enables protein to interact with many other substances and to share continually in the metabolism without which life ceases.

Proteins are constructed of chains or groups of smaller molecules called *amino acids,* the simplest of which is glycine ($C_2H_5O_2N$) which can be synthesized in the body. Molecules of proteins are too large to enter cell membranes, but those of amino acids go through them freely and form within the cell the kind of proteins which are characteristic of it (Fig. 3.3). By varied combinations of about thirty-odd amino acids, a variety of protein molecules enormous beyond imagination is achieved. They not only differ with every species but with every individual. This is shown in many ways, such as the usual difficulty in skin grafting, even between nearly related persons as contrasted with its success between identical twins. The variety of proteins is no less remarkable than their constancy. One remembers the whales that after thousands of years in the ocean still have blood proteins similar to their near kin on land. In the inheritances of plants and animals proteins have not only kept their basic patterns for millions of generations, but countless variations have been added, making their constancy all the more remarkable.

Enzymes, Vitamins, and Hormones. These are associated with other subjects that are discussed later, the first two with foods and digestion, the hormones with endocrine glands. All known enzymes and many of the vitamins and hormones are proteins or intimately associated with proteins and all are catalysts.

Enzymes are vital catalysts of living matter affecting the rate, and even initiating chemical reactions of all cells. Their importance is realized in light of the fact that they participate in the breaking down of proteins into amino acids, of starch molecules into simple sugars, and of fats into fatty acids and glycerol before any one of them can go through a cell membrane (Fig. 3.3).

CHARACTERISTICS OF PROTOPLASM

The physical basis of life is made of common materials largely composed of a few of the most abundant substances in the earth and atmosphere, all of them easily attainable. Its organization is in the highest degree complex, a continuous series of reactions which follows a permanent general pattern with details that are related to particular surroundings. It has its own characteristic organization and punctuality, precision of arrangement, and interdependence of parts. Plants and animals exist in multitudinous variety yet they are fundamentally similar. They all have the capacity for the composite of continual chemical changes called metabolism.

Protoplasm has a capacity to change and yet hold its stability: in its content of water, an almost universal solvent; in its abundance of proteins; in its colloid structure, with variability in size and shape of particles allowing large total areas of exposure to surrounding influences and subject to continuous movement. It is susceptible to external and internal influences and consequent shifts in the phases sol and gel. It has rhythms and continuity of income and outgo of materials, resulting in a balance maintained between constructive and destructive changes.

Cells

Cells are the units of the architecture of plants and animals. A cell is a bit of protoplasm containing a nucleus without which it cannot grow or reproduce itself (Fig. 3.4). As long as it lives the cell constantly builds and burns in the unceasing chemical changes of metabolism.

A cell is enclosed by thin protoplasmic layers forming a semipermeable membrane. This membrane is the lifeguard of the cell. It is permeable to certain dissolved substances but impermeable to others, a constant control over what may enter or leave the cell. The plant cell produces on its outer surface a definite wall that is not living, an important difference between it and the animal cell.

Cells may live independently of others and if so each behaves like a complete organism, as an ameba does. In multicellular animals each cell is continually affected by its relations with others, and by the behavior of the whole cellular community comprising the animal of which it is a part. A cat consists of billions of cells, yet when it springs on a mouse it moves as a single organism.

Origin and Importance of Cells. Every cell originates from a preexisting one and in no other way. This is a complex process during which the new cells receive equal amounts of this essential substance of a parent cell. Every

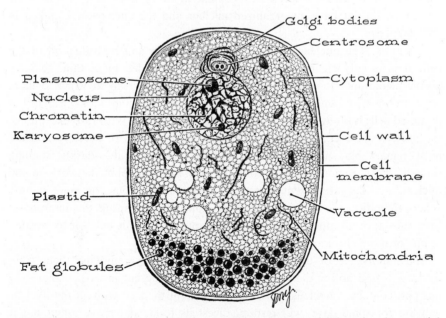

FIG. 3.4. Diagram of body cell. Some of the parts are visible only after special preparation and very high magnification. Plasmosome is another term for nucleolus. The karyosome is a body of nuclear substance. Organoids such as the centrosome, chondriosomes (mitochondria), Golgi bodies, and fibrillae are parts of the cell that have particular functions. Plastids are characteristic of plant cells. There may be many nonliving inclusions, e.g., droplets of water; and granules of yolk: the yolk of a hen's egg is loaded with these. The inner cell membrane, an extremely thin layer of protoplasm, is ordinarily invisible. It is in close contact with the porous outer cell membrane (or "wall"); in animal cells the inner and outer membranes are together and commonly called the cell membrane. (Courtesy, Stiles: *Individual and Community Health.* New York, The Blakiston Company, 1953.)

multicellular animal begins its existence as a single cell which soon divides into two. Each of these grows and divides into two, and thus in the majority of the cells the repeated growing and dividing go on as long as the animal increases in size, whether it is a flea or a cow. This reproduction of cells is entirely independent of sex.

The characteristics of a many-celled animal are the expressions of its cells acting together. A bird flies and its sensory cells react to light, gravity, and air currents; its nerve cells carry messages to and from the brain; its muscle cells contract; its body consumes more oxygen and releases more energy as flight demands it. The responses of its cells are the links between the bird and the world about it.

Structures and Functions. Interphase means that the cell is in a phase of life between divisions. In this phase, also called the resting stage, the cell is resting from division. It is not in any sense resting from respiration and other routine metabolic processes. Certain structures are typical of animal cells though all are not necessarily present in every kind (Fig. 3.4). Some plant cells do not have an organized nucleus and the chromatin is naked in the cytoplasm.

NUCLEUS. The nucleus is essential to the growth and reproduction of the cell. It is usually clearly defined and sharply bounded by a thin, scarcely visible membrane. It contains a foundation of nuclear sap in which definite structures are suspended. In living cells the nuclear sap looks watery; in prepared cells it often shrinks away leaving open spaces. With rare exceptions, the nucleus alone contains chromatin, the physical basis of heredity and the most remarkable substance of protoplasm. The delicate, darkly staining threads, the chromonemata or color threads form a webby network in the nuclear sap. They represent the future chromosomes. One or more minute spherical bodies, the nucleoli, are often conspicuous during the interphase; their substance disappears during cell division, much of it being incorporated in one or more chromosomes.

The importance of the nuclei has been shown by removing them from living cells and noting the results. An ameba can be cut in two so that only one part contains a nucleus. After such treatment the part without the nucleus will live for some days, will respire, digest its food, and move about but it does not grow or reproduce. On the other hand the part containing the nucleus grows, replaces the lost part, and finally divides as usual. All well-established cells have nuclei at some time during their life history. The red blood cells of man and other mammals have no nuclei when mature as they usually are when in circulating blood. However, nuclei are always present when the cells are first formed.

CYTOPLASM. As already defined, the cytoplasm is all of the cell except the nucleus. The ground substance of cytoplasm is a clear semifluid, the hyaloplasm (Fig. 3.5). In living cells it looks like white of egg; in stained ones it is usually granular, sometimes with and sometimes without a delicate network running through it.

The cytoplasm is enclosed by the protoplasmic semipermeable membrane, mentioned earlier in this chapter as the lifeguard of the cell. It controls the passage of everything that comes in or goes out of the cell, water, the respiratory gases, digested food, and other materials. Likewise it regulates the disposal of waste substances from the cell.

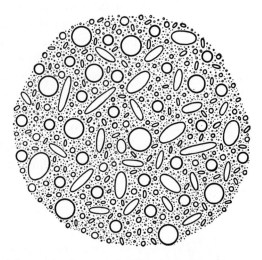

FIG. 3.5. A bit of seemingly homogeneous protoplasm in a clear space in the living cell. Very highly magnified it shows particles such as protein molecules and others that are jostled about by molecules of water and other smaller molecules. (Courtesy, Gerard: *Unresting Cells.* New York, Harper & Bros., 1940.)

The semipermeable membrane has submicroscopic holes through which smaller molecules, such as those of water and amino acids can freely enter or leave the cell. The passages are too small for the larger molecules. However, those that dissolve in fat merge with the fatty substances in the membrane and pass between their molecules and into the cell (Fig. 3.3). Such fat substances include alcohol, ether, and many organic compounds. Molecules of these, among them alcohol and anesthetics, may enter in such numbers that they clog the surfaces of the cells and slow down their normal activity. Brain cells are especially rich in fat and take in alcohol or an anesthetic and are strongly affected by them, while muscle and other kinds of cells may be undisturbed. Thus, the cell membranes figure at the cocktail party as well as in the hospital.

In both animal and plant cells, but more commonly in the latter, there may be vacuoles, evidently surrounded by ultradelicate semipermeable membranes and usually containing liquid.

The cytoplasm contains the organoids which reproduce themselves, thus exhibiting one of the fundamental characteristics of living matter. It also contains nonliving cell-inclusions (Fig. 3.4).

ORGANOIDS. The centrosome consists of a spherical mass of specialized protoplasm called the centrosphere and at its center are either one or two minute, deeply staining bodies, the centrioles. During the interphase of the cell the centrosome is almost always located just outside the nuclear membrane (Fig. 3.4). It plays an important part in cell division and at that time divides into two parts from each of which rays extend simulating a star. Centrosomes have been found in practically all animal cells except nerve cells, but are not present in those of higher plants. Chondriosomes (mitochondria) are threadlike or granular bodies (lipoproteins) scattered through the cytoplasm, visible in specially treated cells and sometimes in living ones (Fig. 3.4). It is generally agreed that they are physiologically important although details of their function are unknown; in actively secreting cells they increase in size and number. The Golgi substance is an irregular network located near the nucleus, first discovered by Golgi, an Italian physician (1898), in nerve cells and later found in almost all the cells of vertebrates and in many invertebrates, especially in glands. Its nature continues to be debated. Fibrillae are fine threads that extend in a definite direction in the cell and may have a supporting, conducting, or contractile function (Fig. 3.6). Cilia and flagella are thin cytoplasmic processes extending from the

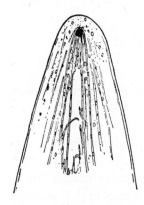

FIG. 3.6. Extremely minute fibrils stretched by a microdissecting needle (black spot) pulling out one side of the living cell (a malarial parasite, Plasmodium). (From Seifriz. Courtesy, de Robertis: *General Cytology*. Philadelphia, W. B. Saunders Co., 1949.)

surface of the cell and are used in locomotion or to create currents of fluid. Flagella are relatively long; there are few of them to a cell and different ones lash independently. One group of protozoans, the flagellates, are so called because they swim by means of flagella. Cilia are short and there are many on one cell. They move in unison, rhythmically. Paramecium is the most familiar ciliated protozoan though there are many others. In multicellular animals surfaces are often covered with ciliated cells: the lining of the human trachea, the gills of clams, the gullet of a frog. Gills of fresh, as well as salt water clams, are good material for the study of ciliary movement.

NONLIVING CELL-INCLUSIONS. In animal cells the most abundant of these is stored food: yolk granules and oil globules in eggs, glycogen in other cells (Fig. 3.4). In gland cells the materials to be secreted are often held in the cells as droplets or granules. Crystals, pigment, and droplets of water and waste matter are common cell-inclusions.

Shapes and Sizes of Cells. The shape of a cell depends upon the viscosity of its protoplasm, the pressure from other cells, and upon its function (Fig. 3.7).

Most cells are microscopic, with dimensions of a few thousandths of a millimeter (1 mm. = $\frac{1}{25}$ of an inch). Certain nerve cells of man and other large mammals have processes that extend from the cell bodies in the nerve

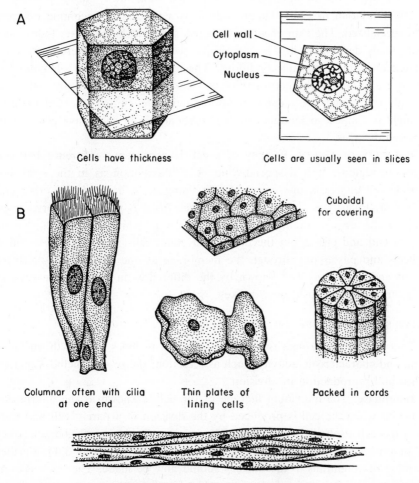

Cells have thickness   Cells are usually seen in slices

Cuboidal for covering

Columnar often with cilia   Thin plates of   Packed in cords
at one end   lining cells

Elongated in the direction of the pull

FIG. 3.7. Shapes of cells. In a multicellular organism most of the cells are pressed together, often flattened, or six- or eight-sided. It has been recently maintained that packed cells are actually 14-sided. This is apparent only under special conditions and observation. *A*. Diagram of a cell cut in section as cells are commonly studied. *B*. The shapes of these cells, muscle and others, are correlated with their special functions and also affected by crowding.

cord along the whole length of the leg. The largest single cell is the unfertilized egg, commonly called the yolk, of an ostrich's egg. The egg cells of birds, reptiles, and amphibians are all large because of the yolk stored in them. Relatively large or small body cells are characteristic of different groups of animals. Cold-blooded amphibians with low metabolism have larger body cells than warm-blooded birds and mammals whose body temperature and metabolism are high. A horse has smaller cells than a salamander and literally lives faster because it has a relatively greater cell surface exposed to body fluids bringing in oxygen and food and taking away waste.

Differentiation of Cells. Differentiation is a process of becoming different and specialized. The skin of an embryo fish seems to be all alike; then scales and glands develop in it. The possibility of difference was there, but it appeared only under certain conditions. The epitheliomuscle cell of hydra has become specialized for contractility at one end. Shapes and sizes of cells, already mentioned, are results of differentiation. They are inherited patterns brought out and also modified by the surroundings of successive generations through the ages.

POLARITY OF CELLS. Polarity of a cell is consistent—difference between opposite regions. It is a special kind of differentiation as in the epitheliomuscle cell of hydra, one end useful as lining or as a gland, the other end muscular. Polarity is almost universal in cells as it is in all living organisms. Among the diverse examples are nerve cells in which the impulse enters at one end and passes out the other, and gland cells in which the secretion collects and passes out through the membrane at one pole. The polarity of plants and animals is well known by the differences in the opposite ends as in a turnip, a rose bush, or a donkey.

PHASES IN THE LIFE OF THE CELL

Every cell goes through two phases: the first includes its growth, metabolism, and characteristic activity, such as secretion; the second includes metabolism and reproduction by division.

Interphase. The individual lifetime of the cell is known as the interphase. It begins when the cell is produced by the division of a parent cell and lasts until the cell itself divides or dies. The structure and general characteristics of an animal cell have already been described and shown (Fig. 3.4). Further mention of conditions in the nucleus should now be made. The nucleus contains a tangle of threads of chromatin, the latter containing genes, the bearers of hereditary traits. The chromatin threads are double, made up of two slender strands, the chromonemata or colored threads in which lumps of chromatin, the chromomeres, the probable locations of groups of genes, are arranged irregularly. The two chromonemata are actually two future chromosomes lying so close together that the doubleness is difficult to discover.

Each pair of chromonemata was formerly a single thread (potential chromosome) with genes arranged along its whole length. As a thread doubles, each gene makes a duplicate of itself out of materials lying close to it. As a result of this a new string of genes, forming a new thread, lies close to the old one and is identical with it, gene for gene, in every part (Fig. 3.8). This creation of new genes, as pointed out by H. J. Muller (1947), "should perhaps be regarded as the most remarkable process in nature; it consists of the simultaneous creation, under the guidance of each gene, of a new gene in its own image, lying next to itself and built out of materials lying around it" (Fig. 3.8). Now having the layout of its future chromosomes, each with its quota of genes, the nucleus is ready for reproduction.

Reproduction of Body Cells—Mitosis. Cell division usually includes that of the nucleus and cell body. However, the nucleus may reproduce when the cell body does not and a multinucleate cell results. The cause of cell division is not understood. If it were, the cause of cancer would be known, since that is a disease of too rapid and usually abnormal cell division.

Mitosis is the almost universal method of cellular reproduction. The only significant exception is the variation of it called meiosis which occurs regularly in the multiplication of sex cells. Mitosis is the precise rearrangement, doubling, and separation of nuclear material by which two new nuclei are formed that are quantitatively and qualitatively similar to each other and to the nucleus from which they came. By means of it each daughter nucleus receives an equal share of every substance which was in the parent nucleus. It is a continuous process having four main stages; each stage has its own characteristics but each merges into the one following (Fig. 3.8).

PROPHASE (PREPARATION). Features of the interphase gradually change. The knotted chromonemata are more distinct with the members of each pair clinging together. At first each pair forms an irregular open spiral. Then the coil tightens, shortens, and is filled in with darkly staining substance finally forming a chromosome. At the same time the centrosome just outside the nucleus is active. It divides, and, if the cell has two centrioles, they move toward opposite poles of the nucleus. If there was but one centriole during the interphase, it now divides and the two new ones move apart. In either case the area between them contains lines of protoplasmic particles. These form the mitotic spindle, a double cone that at first lies a little outside the nuclear field and later extends directly across it. This region is now occupied by the chromosomes among the lines of the spindle and directly between its dynamic poles. The nucleolus may still be visible, but it looks soft as its substance begins to diffuse, seeming to scatter.

METAPHASE (MIDWAY). The chromosomes are balanced midway between the poles of the spindle (Fig. 3.8). Each one of the two chromonemata in a chromosome has at exactly the same level a special point (centromere) of

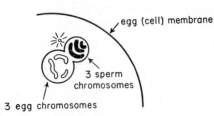

1. Egg shortly after fertilization becomes the first cell of the embryo.

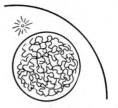

2. The nucleus formed by the coalescence of sperm and egg nuclei. Interphase.

3. Soon after duplication of the chromosome threads. Early prophase.

4. Chromosomes shorter and thicker. Aster dissolving the nuclear membrane. Later prophase.

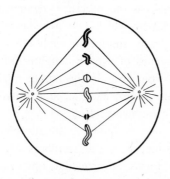

5. Lines from centrosomes are attached to each chromosome at a given point. Early metaphase.

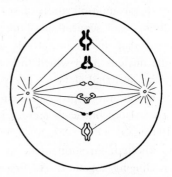

6. Lines of force from centrosomes exert a pull that separates "sister chromosomes". Later metaphase.

7. Pulling apart of two identical groups of chromosomes. Body of cell dividing. Late anaphase.

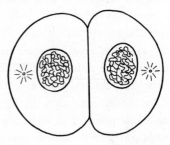

8. Two separate cells, each with a nucleus of tangled threads as in 2. Interphase (Telophase omitted)

attachment to the spindle. This "owes its existence to a particular gene lying at that point" (Muller, 1947). When it is at the center the chromosome is V-shaped with the tip of the V in contact with a line of the spindle. Sometimes it is fairly near the end and the chromosome then hangs J-shaped on the spindle, or, if very close to the end, it is rodlike. During the early part of the metaphase the centromeres are apparently repelled from the poles of the spindle and moving toward the equator they draw their chromosomes with them. There, all the chromosomes become arranged exactly half-way between the poles of the spindle at the midplane in an equatorial plate. The chromosome and its duplicate are still in contact (Figs. 3.8 and 3.9).

ANAPHASE (SEPARATION). Each chromosome and its duplicate begin to separate always starting at the centromeres which are responsive to the forces of the attraction of the spindle. The members of each pair of chromosomes gradually draw apart until they become entirely separated and each one moves toward the nearer pole. During this journey the centromere is always in front, pointed toward the pole (Fig. 3.8). Late in the anaphase the chromosomes are in two identical groups, one at each end of the spindle. In each group the chromosomes of the parent cell with their genes are all represented.

In animal cells the division of the cytoplasm starts from the outside and

---

FIG. 3.8. Diagrams showing changes in the nucleus during the reproduction of a cell by mitotic division such as occurs in every cell of a growing body, or in parts of the adult, except in the later divisions of maturing sex cells. *1.* Part of an egg shortly after its fertilization. Three chromosomes (black) represent the inheritance from the male parent, and three (in outline) the inheritance from the female parent. The descendants of these six chromosomes occur in all the cells of the new individual. The star-shaped centrosome is a center of force. *2.* Interphase or "resting stage" with the chromosomes uncoiled in threads so ensnarled that individual chromosomes cannot be identified except with great difficulty. *3.* Early prophase. Each thread has doubled and now consists of two identical strands, thickened by means of the ultra-fine coiling of the strands. The centrosome has divided and there are now two centers of force. *4.* Late prophase. The chromosomes are mates, shortened and lying side by side. Every one of the thousands of genes contained in one is duplicated in the other. The centrosomes are moving to opposite sides of the nucleus and the nuclear membrane is dissolving. *5.* Early metaphase. Lines of force from the centrosomes have become attached at given points (centromeres) to the respective mates, called identical chromosomes. This has forced them into positions on an equatorial plane half way between the centrosomes. *6* and *7.* Late metaphase and late anaphase. The apparent lines of force exert a pull on the centromeres, thus separating the identical chromosomes, and drawing the respective mates toward the opposite ends of the spindle formed by the lines of force. *8.* Division completed. Interphase. (Telophase omitted.) The two identical groups of chromosomes are pulled near to the centrosomes and cell membranes separate the cell body into halves. The fine coils of the chromosomes unwind in threads similar to those in *2.* This process occurs in the telophase stage not shown here. With the attainment of two new cells in the interphase stage, the reproduction is completed.

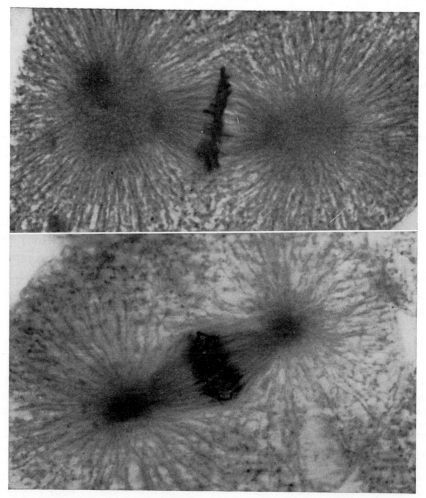

FIG. 3.9. Stages (metaphase and anaphase) in the mitosis of cells of a white fish embryo. Microphotographs of stained and sectioned cells at an enlargement of about 700 times. Note the lines of force that compose the spindle and radiate from the centrosome in the metaphase, and the dimming of the spindle and the new cell membranes in the anaphase. (Courtesy, General Biological Supply House, Inc., Chicago.)

the membrane separating the two new cells extends inward in a plane at right angles to the spindle. In plant cells it starts from the center as a cell plate and extends outward.

TELOPHASE (RECONSTRUCTION). The chromosomes in each nuclear group uncoil and lengthen into knotted chromonemata. The spindle and at the same time the rays about the centriole disappear. If two centrioles are characteristic of the interphase each centriole now divides; if not, each one remains single. The nucleolus becomes visible again and the boundary of the nucleus regains its sharpness. The daughter cells are now complete growing cells in the interphase stage.

The time required for the complete process of cell division varies greatly with the kind of cell and the surrounding conditions, especially temperature. A cell of a salamander's heart observed living in tissue culture completed the process in two hours. The process may be much quicker.

RESULTS OF MITOSIS. Two cells are formed that are identical with one another in respect to every gene and every chromosome. This is accomplished first by the doubling of the genes in the chromosomes, and then by the separation of the chromosomes and their inclusion in the new nuclei. The remainder of the cell may or may not be equally divided. In the growth of a multicellular animal, whether hydra or man, mitosis is repeated hundreds to billions of times, and each time hereditary qualities originally received from the parents and contained in the first cell are distributed equally to new cells.

In amitosis the nucleus simply constricts into an hourglass shape and then separates into two parts without forming chromosomes. This is a very rare arrangement which occurs only under unusual conditions, especially in degenerating cells.

Reproduction of Sex Cells—Mitosis and Meiosis. Body cells reproduce exclusively by mitosis. Germ or sex cells reproduce by mitosis and meiosis.

The reproduction of sex or germ cells in males and females includes an increase in numbers from a few original germ cells, a reduction to half their number of chromosomes, i.e., from the diploid to the haploid number, and changes in the shape and size of the cells (Fig. 3.10). The all-important genes inherited from the parents of the individual and present in the chromosomes of his or her original germ cells are distributed so that each gamete (egg and sperm cell) has an inheritance from its ancestors, even remote ones. The process in the male is spermatogenesis, the history of the sperm cell from its earliest stage to maturity, and in the female, oogenesis, the history of the egg cell. There are differences in size and numbers of the mature sex cells in the male and female, but the changes in their nuclei are essentially similar.

SPERMATOGENESIS. The original primordial germ cells in the male divide repeatedly by mitosis, gradually producing great numbers of extremely minute, nearly spherical cells called spermatogonia. These have the diploid (or body) number of chromosomes; half of them were in the male cell or sperm and half in the female cell or egg when fertilization occurred.

Suppose, for example, that a primordial germ cell has six chromosomes, three derived from each parent (Fig. 3.10). Such cells divide mitotically, producing several generations of cells called spermatogonia, each one of which contains six chromosomes. A change then occurs beginning with the maturation or meiotic divisions. First the cells become relatively larger and are called primary spermatocytes. In the prophase of the first meiotic division

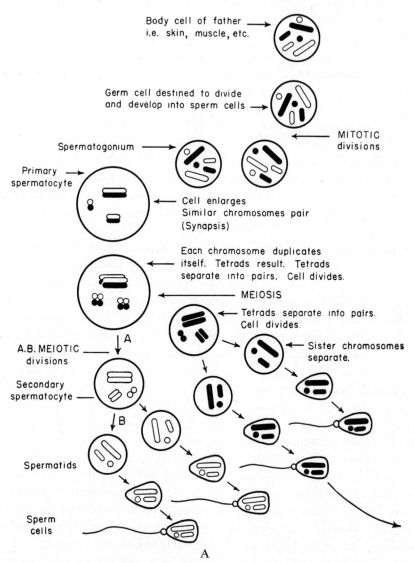

Distribution of chromosomes in the development of
sperm cells. Dark chromosomes = male inheritance.
Light chromosomes = female inheritance.

Body cell of father
i.e. skin, muscle, etc.

Germ cell destined to divide
and develop into sperm cells

MITOTIC
divisions

Spermatogonium

Primary
spermatocyte

Cell enlarges
Similar chromosomes pair
(Synapsis)

Each chromosome duplicates
itself. Tetrads result. Tetrads
separate into pairs. Cell divides.

MEIOSIS

Tetrads separate into pairs.
Cell divides.

Sister chromosomes
separate.

A.B. MEIOTIC
divisions

A

Secondary
spermatocyte

B

Spermatids

Sperm
cells

A

FIG. 3.10. Diagrams showing the behavior of the chromosomes during (*A*) the
development of the sperm cell (spermatogenesis) and (*B*) the similar features in
the development of the egg cell (oogenesis). In each sex cell the process includes:

Distribution of chromosomes in the development of egg cells. Light chromosomes = female inheritance. Dark chromosomes = male inheritance.

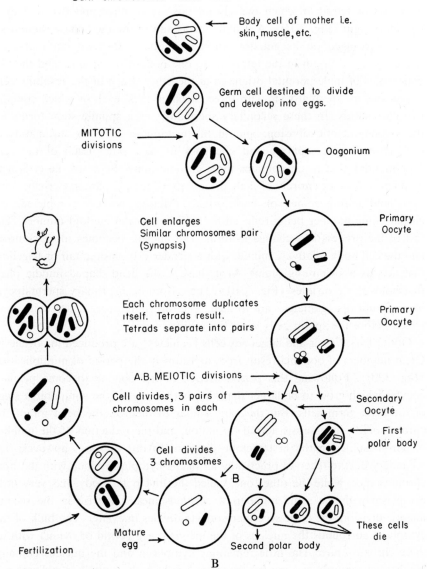

Body cell of mother i.e. skin, muscle, etc.

Germ cell destined to divide and develop into eggs.

MITOTIC divisions

Oogonium

Cell enlarges Similar chromosomes pair (Synapsis)

Primary Oocyte

Each chromosome duplicates itself. Tetrads result. Tetrads separate into pairs

Primary Oocyte

A.B. MEIOTIC divisions

Cell divides, 3 pairs of chromosomes in each

A

Secondary Oocyte

First polar body

Cell divides 3 chromosomes

B

These cells die

Fertilization

Mature egg

Second polar body

B

an increase in number of chromosomes by MITOSIS and a reduction in the number of chromosomes by MEIOSIS. For simplicity six chromosomes are used here for body cells. Cells of the human body have 48 chromosomes.

the two chromosomes of each similar or homologous pair, one derived from the male and one from the female parent, come together and lie parallel to one another. This is called synapsis. Soon each chromosome duplicates itself as in mitosis, so that there is a cluster of chromatids (potential chromosomes), a quartet or tetrad in which two chromatids are of male and two of female parental origin (Fig. 3.10). A spindle forms and in the metaphase the tetrads become arranged on its equator. In the anaphase, the two chromatids of female parental origin in the tetrad go to one pole of the spindle and the two chromatids of male parental origin go to the other. Each of the resulting cells is a secondary spermatocyte with three chromosomes, each of which contains two chromatids. In these secondary spermatocytes a spindle soon forms for the second meiotic division, and in the metaphase the two chromatids of each chromosome separate and one goes to each pole. Each of the cells (spermatids) that result contains three chromosomes. Some of the cells may hold chromosomes entirely of male or entirely of female parental origin; some may hold chromosomes of both origins. Meiosis is now completed, the chromosome number being reduced by half, i.e., to the haploid number. The rest of the process is a change in form. The nucleus becomes more compact and the cell body relatively minute with a slender cytoplasmic tail or flagellum that acts as a swimming organ. At its base is the bead-shaped middle piece that holds the centrioles (Fig. 3.10). Thus, from each primary spermatocyte four sperm cells (gametes) are formed. The foregoing process is usually completed before the sperm cells leave the testis.

OOGENESIS. Fewer and larger sex cells (gametes) are produced in oogenesis. Great numbers of oogonia result from divisions in the period of multiplication (Fig. 3.10). Following this period certain of the oogonia become primary oocytes which grow to be larger than the spermatocytes, the comparable stage of the male germ cells. But they are similar to them in the behavior of the chromosomes, in synapsis, tetrad formation, and the reduction of the number of chromosomes in the first meiotic division. In this division, however, one secondary oocyte receives practically all of the cytoplasm along with its three chromosomes, while the other one, called the first polar body, has very little cytoplasm with the same number of chromosomes. Likewise in the second meiotic division, the large secondary oocyte divides unevenly. The bulk of the cytoplasm surrounds the nucleus of the incipient egg (ootid or ovum) with its three chromosomes. The little remaining cytoplasm and the nucleus containing three chromosomes compose the second polar body, actually a rudimentary egg. The first polar body goes through a division that parallels the second meiotic one. Thus there are three polar bodies and the egg, each with three chromosomes assorted as in spermatogenesis (Fig. 3.10). The polar bodies with their loads of precious hereditary substance eventually degenerate and come to nothing. The egg keeps its form and is enlarged by its supply of yolk.

In different species of animals the production of polar bodies may occur inside or outside the ovary.

With the fusion of the nuclei of sperm and egg that occurs at fertilization, the number of chromosomes is returned to six, that of the zygote, the first cell of the new individual.

Part II
Ecology

4

Plants Provide for Themselves and the Animals

The existence of the living world depends upon green plants since they alone make the food that is essential both to themselves and the animals. Through the long past animals became agile of movement, swimming, running, or flying, developed keen senses, and became alert to their surroundings. Great numbers of them fed upon plants, and as time went on many became carnivores and devoured their fellow animals. But none of them could make their own food from the chemical elements about them. Human beings are no better off than other animals. Although they have extraordinary capabilities, their existence finally depends upon the carbohydrate foods, the sugars and starches that green plants make by photosynthesis. After years of study it now seems that photosynthesis may be understood, but to furnish the world with food is another and probably much more difficult matter.

The meals of Eskimos are far removed from the cabbage patch, yet they too originate in plants. Eskimos live on seal meat and fish and birds, but ultimately all these are fed by the microscopic plants which swarm in the arctic seas. The seals and the birds feed upon the fishes; big fishes eat little fishes and both devour little copepods by billions; and finally copepods feed exclusively upon microscopic plants, mainly diatoms (Fig. 4.1). Thus, the substance of the Eskimo's diet is in origin mainly digested diatoms. For the dweller farther south in America or Europe the food chain is different, usually beginning with grass and ending with beef, or starting with diatoms and ending with codfish. Grass can live without cattle and diatoms without codfishes but no animals can exist without plants somewhere in their food story. Plants and animals are fundamentally similar. A sunflower and a horse look strikingly different; yet they are both living organisms existing basically in the same way.

51

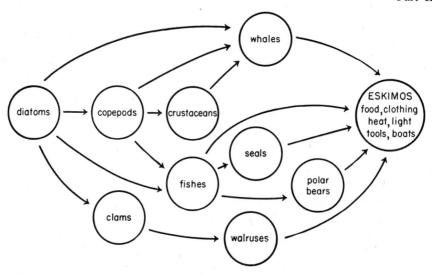

Fig. 4.1. In their own way of living Eskimos are finally dependent for food upon diatoms and other algae, the microscopic plants that crowd the surface waters of the arctic seas. The dependence is indirect but sure, just as farther south human dependence for beef steak is upon plants. (After Transeau and Tiffany: *Textbook of Botany*. New York, Harper & Bros., 1940.)

Plant and Animal Relationships

Building Materials and Protection. Plants furnish building materials for all animals from insects to man. Wasps bite off wood fibers for their paper nests, a host of insects lives within burrows in stems and tree trunks. The habits of land birds would be changed beyond recognition if those birds did not perch and nest in trees, or nest and feed in grass and mosses. There is scarcely a mammal, short of ocean-going whales and their kin, that does not at some time take to plants for shelter. Hundreds of field mice live among the grasses of empty-looking fields; the wildcat climbs a tree for a meal of young birds; in South America trees furnish the bandstands for the howling monkeys and the hammocks for sleeping sloths. In the noon heat of the tropics the silent forest is populous with hiding animals.

With the main exceptions of beavers and man, mammals do not use wood for building. Man is the great builder with plant fiber. From the time human animals left their caves they began to make earthen and wooden houses and long before that they must have used windbreaks of wood. The prehistoric lake-dwellers lived in wooden houses raised on piles above the lakes, ideal for safety as well as for fishing at home.

Throughout history plants have supplied humanity with wood for boats and wagons, and fibers for ropes and cloth. In recent years the elegant and versatile rayons and plastics have been produced mainly from plant products. The existence of all this outfit of civilization hinges upon a microscopic structure peculiar to plants, their strong cell walls composed of cellulose, or cellulose impregnated with lignin if the tissue is woody.

The Plant Cell Wall. Plant cell walls have long provided heat and power for humanity (Fig. 4.2). Whether lignified or not, cellulose burns rapidly in combination with oxygen; its stored energy is released in the form of heat and it is converted back to carbon dioxide and water. When cellulose is subjected to heat and pressure for long periods of time it undergoes chemical changes; hydrogen and oxygen are removed and solid carbon remains. This is what happened in the ancient swamps and forests where peat, lignite, and coal were formed, one or another product depending upon the material and the stage of the carbonization. Coal exposed longer and under the right conditions becomes graphite; exposed still further and properly conditioned, it crystallizes as pure coal, or with extreme hardness as diamonds. The heated live coal of the open

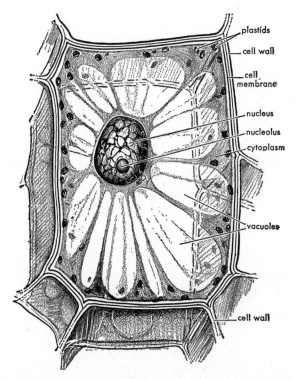

plastids
cell wall
cell membrane
nucleus
nucleolus
cytoplasm
vacuoles
cell wall

FIG. 4.2. Typical plant cell. In plant cells the cytoplasm occupies a relatively small space and the central part contains one or more large vacuoles filled with watery solution containing many substances related to the life processes of the plant. The vacuoles are separated from the protoplasm by an almost invisible semipermeable membrane (or tonoplast), a lively and important region of exchange of substances. In contrast to animal cells those of plants have a prominent cell wall strengthened by cellulose, made woody by lignin. (Courtesy, Rogers, Hubbell, and Byers: *Man and the Biological World,* ed. 2. New York, McGraw-Hill Book Company, 1952.)

fire is "alive" in so far as it is freeing energy gathered from the sun and stored in plant cells millions of years ago. Neither coal nor diamonds are modern upstarts: both have long been important to humanity, in fires for the tempering and molding of metals, in various techniques, and in tokens and jewelry.

Distribution. There are many ways in which plants depend upon animals. Most animals can travel around freely; plants cannot. Plants are carried about by the natural forces of air and water and by animals. Thus insects carry pollen (male sex cells) and cross-pollinate the flowers as they seek nectar and pollen in one after another (Fig. 4.3). Birds carry seeds across land and water often to germinate safely in distant regions. Plants are directly dependent on the content of the soil and animals fertilize this with their excretions and disintegrating remains.

Photosynthesis

Green plants are, with exceptions such as nitrifying bacteria, the only self-supporting organisms on the earth. They accumulate energy from the sun and

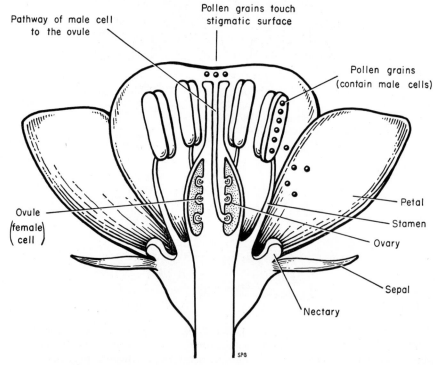

FIG. 4.3. The parts of a typical flower. Insects visit flowers to gather nectar and pollen. The nectaries are at the bases of the petals and many flower-visiting insects must brush against the pollen-bearing anthers in order to reach the nectar. In moving around they transfer the pollen containing the male cells to the stigma of the flower or other flowers of the same kind and thus bring about the fertilization of the ovules (eggs).

FIG. 4.4. Carolus Linnaeus (1707–78), the Swedish botanist, at age 25, in Lapland dress, holding his favorite, the twin-flower (*Linnaea*) and equipped with a collecting kit for his Lapland journey. Linnaeus made one of the great contributions to natural sciences, the two-word naming (binomial nomenclature) of plants in 1753 and of animals in 1758. His work made way for the natural arrangements of living organisms. (Courtesy, Greene: *Carolus Linnaeus.* Philadelphia, Christopher Sower Co., 1912.)

store it as chemical energy in carbohydrates (starches, sugars). The process of photosynthesis or carbohydrate-making is the greatest chemical industry in the world with the widest importance of all biochemical reactions. It is carried on by all chlorophyll-bearing plants from microscopic algae to the largest trees. Red and brown seaweeds and plants of various other colors contain chlorophyll cloaked with pigments. Although the manufacture of food by land plants is enormous, it is estimated that 90 per cent of the total is produced by the large (seaweeds) and small algae of the ocean (Fig. 4.5). They constitute the basic food supply of the great animal populations of the seas. In general, the plants themselves use a good deal of the food which they produce. Much of it is decomposed into water, carbon dioxide, and mineral salts by the decay of leaves and plant bodies in water and on land, and is used over again by the plants.

Materials and Conditions. The natural conditions for photosynthesis include the presence of chlorophyll, the energy of sunlight or artificial light, water, and

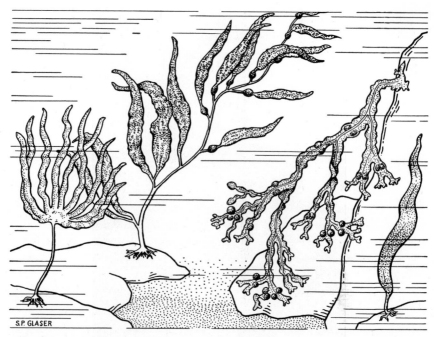

S.P. GLASER

Fig. 4.5. Common brown seaweeds that are great food producers. From left to right, fan kelp, Laminaria; giant or vine kelp, Macrocystis; bladder wrack, Fucus; ribbon kelp, Nereocystis. (Not drawn to scale.) Seaweeds constitute a large percentage of the basic food supply of the seas. On the rocks between the tides where they abound they furnish food and holdfast for hosts of small animals.

carbon dioxide. The chlorophyll occurs in chloroplasts usually rounded green bodies in the tissues of leaf and stem. It is a complex protein, in higher plants consisting of two pigments, a blue-green one, chlorophyll a ($C_{55}H_{72}O_5N_4Mg$) and the less abundant yellow-green, chlorophyll b ($C_{55}H_{70}O_6N_4Mg$). The chemical content of chlorophyll is in many ways similar to that of the hemoglobin of blood except that iron occurs in the latter instead of magnesium. In the higher plants chlorophyll is almost always associated with yellow pigments, the carotenoids, and the various xanthophylls related to carotene. Their function is not wholly known; if they are concerned with photosynthesis they are far less important than chlorophyll. Carotene and xanthophyll are much more stable; the rich yellow autumn colors of birch and elm leaves are exultant witnesses that these colors endure after chlorophyll has broken down.

The Process. During photosynthesis the kinetic energy in light is changed to the potential chemical energy of food. Carbon dioxide is mainly absorbed from the atmosphere. It enters the leaf through the millions of pores or stomata, diffuses through cell membranes in a dissolved state, and goes into the chloroplasts (Fig. 4.8). Water enters chiefly through the roots. In the presence of chlorophyll and with the aid of the energy of light, the carbon dioxide and water unite to form glucose ($C_6H_{12}O_6$), the simple sugar from which all the organic compounds of plants and animals are eventually derived. The chlorophyll itself is not used up and is evidently a catalyzer that hastens other chemical processes.

Green plants include the seed plants, and the mosses, ferns, the green algae, and the lichens, many first named by Carolus Linnaeus in his two-name system (Fig. 4.4). As already noted, besides these there are other plants whose chlorophyll is blanketed with various colors, as in the deep red, yellow, or variegated *Coleus* often called foliage plants. The pigment of red and brown seaweeds also effectively clothes the chlorophyll as does the brown cloak of the microscopic diatoms of fresh and salt waters. Although the process of food-making in these plants is not clearly worked out, it is certain that pigments other than green ones take an important share in it. One investigator has observed that in red seaweeds the light absorbed by red pigments is more efficient in photosynthesis than that absorbed by the green of chlorophyll. The food product in blue-green algae, for example, is not glucose but glycogen which is also found in fungi (bacteria, molds, mushrooms, and rusts) and in the tissues of animals. The tons of rockweed washed by the breakers on many headlands press home the estimate that "90 per cent of the photosynthesis on earth is carried out, not by green land plants, but by the multicolored sea algae" (Fig. 4.5).

Studies of Photosynthesis. In 1772 Joseph Priestley discovered that a plant produced oxygen. He piped air into a glass jar from another jar in which a mint plant was growing. Then he put a lighted candle in the empty jar and the candle, being well supplied with oxygen from the plant, went on burning. Later he took the candle out and put a mouse into the same jar. The mouse breathed comfortably and Priestley wrote of it, "nor was it at all inconvenient to a mouse which I put into it" (Fig. 4.6). In 1779 Jan Ingenhousz, a court physician to Empress Maria of Austria, observed that plants "corrected the bad air" in which they were growing. He wrote of his observations, "I found that this operation of the plants is more or less brisk in proportion to the clearness of the day and the exposition of the plants." Julius R. von Mayer, who formulated the principle of conservation of energy, first stated in 1845 the physical function of photosynthesis as the conversion of light energy into chemical energy. Photosynthesis is a subject of joint chemical and biological inquiry in which new discoveries are made from month to month, and sunlight has created sugar from carbon dioxide and water.

Organization of a Green Plant

Essential Needs. Plants are light-seeking, light-directed organisms. They have four essential needs, light, air, water, and certain minerals. The sun sheds its energy in light and heat upon the earth. It creates currents in the water, winds in the air, quickens the activity of water molecules that scatter as vapor,

In sunlight a green water plant
gave off bubbles (of oxygen).

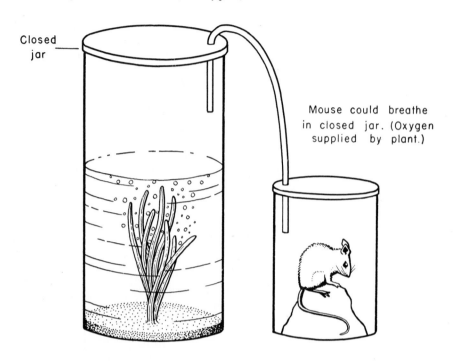

Closed jar

Mouse could breathe
in closed jar. (Oxygen
supplied by plant.)

PRIESTLEY'S DISCOVERY

FIG. 4.6. The chemist (England, 1733–1804), Joseph Priestley kept a plant growing within a glass jar connected with another jar in which he kept a mouse. The
mouse breathed on comfortably because the plant provided it with oxygen, a
product of its photosynthesis. (Data for figure from *Memoirs of Joseph Priestley,*
1:253. London, J. Johnson, 1806.)

and activates the photosynthesis of green plants. Thus the sun surrounds plants
with light and keeps air and water circulating about them. Plants may have
all of this without going after it as the majority of animals do. Light bathes
the whole plant from above or from one or more directions; the branches
reach out for light and the leaves take positions to receive it. Light does not
penetrate deeply into the tissues, but leaf surfaces are spread out and the
chlorophyll is always near to them (Fig. 4.8). The spread of maple leaves to
receive light is a marvel of efficient arrangement. The essentials for a green
plant's existence are in two layers of its environment. Light and air are above;
there the plant is green and its stem upstanding. Water and minerals are below; there the plant is colorless and its roots are pliant.

The Individual. The plant has a particular form recognizable as characteristic of its species and of itself—the barrel cactus of the southwestern desert, the American elm, the jack-in-the-pulpit. There is a strict division of labor in the plan of the body; different parts perform particular functions such as protection, support, and water transport (Fig. 4.7). The plant body has two main regions, the shoot system of stem and leaves which is intimate with the atmosphere and the root system which is correspondingly intimate with the soil.

Stem. The stem or axis is a support and a highway. Its first function is the raising of leaves to the light, of flowers upward for light and pollination, of seeds in position for better dispersal. Its second function is the distribution of water and nutrient solutions and gases throughout the plant. In most plants, the stem is a cylinder that tapers at the top and gives off branches that are

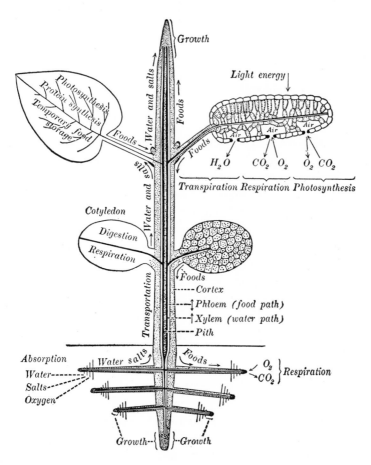

FIG. 4.7. A diagram indicating the main structures and functions of a seed plant, the bean. The first leaves (cotyledons or seed leaves) are richly stored with protein and contribute only slightly to photosynthesis. (Courtesy, Woodruff and Baitsell: *Foundations of Biology,* ed. 7. New York, The Macmillan Co., 1951.)

ultimately continuous with the veins of the leaves. Stems vary in circumference: the stem of a California redwood is thick enough for a car to drive through; that of the young maidenhair fern has a hair's thickness. Stems are squat in turnips and tall in royal palms.

The main layers of the stem are the cambium, and the phloem, and xylem, the latter two named from the Greek words for bark and wood. Cambium is the vital growing layer from which the other two layers originate, the xylem from its inner and the phloem from its outer side. In tree trunks the wood is composed of xylem and most of the bark of phloem. The xylem holds the supporting tissue and tubes through which water and dissolved substances are conducted from root to leaf. The phloem contains tubes through which manufactured foods are distributed especially from the leaves to regions of the plant where they are stored or used. The epidermis covers the stem and is continuous over the leaves and roots. Tons of water mixed with mineral nutrients ascend from the soil and through the tubes of the xylem into the veins of the leaves. Great quantities of food made in the leaves pass through the veins and stem by way of the tubes of the phloem. The pattern of conduction in xylem and phloem is essentially the same whether in a buttercup or an oak tree.

Sugar cane, potatoes which are underground stems, and tree trunks are stems that have million-dollar values and high places in history. Except for the plant stems that made his ships, Columbus would not have crossed the ocean nor the Norsemen set foot upon American shores. A few plant stems made the raft Kon-Tiki on which six men crossed the Pacific Ocean.

Leaf. A leaf is a thin blade, greener on the upper than the underside and freely exposed to light and air. Continuous with its petiole or stem is the stiffened vein or group of veins from which other more delicate ones branch off and hold the leaf outspread. The unique function of green leaves is photosynthesis. Water from the plant stem is conducted to the leaf, and carbohydrate food from the leaf to the plant stem. There is great variety in the shapes of leaves, but, whether they are simple or compound they all fit three types: the rounded leaf like that of the nasturtium, the linear leaf like the grass blade, and the cone-shaped one such as the elm leaf.

Microscopic openings of stomata occur in the otherwise waterproof epidermis, especially on the lower side of the leaf (Fig. 4.8). Each opening is between two specialized cells of the epidermis, called guard cells because changes in their size and shape determine whether the stomata are open or closed. Water enters through the root hairs and passes out mainly through the open leaf-stomata and to some extent through the cuticle, in the process of transpiration. Of the total quantity of water absorbed by the roots, as much as 98 per cent escapes by transpiration. Stomata also regulate the exchange of gases between the air and leaf. If the leaf is well lighted they are open and

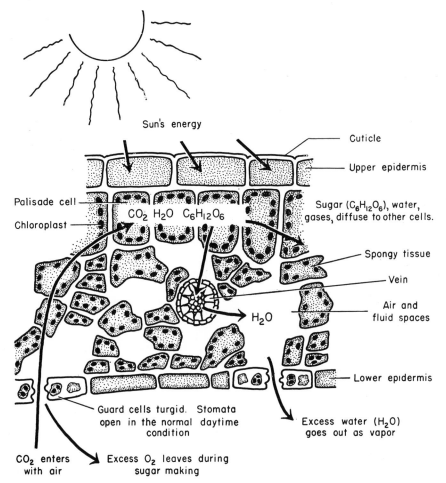

Sun's energy

Cuticle

Upper epidermis

Palisade cell

CO_2 H_2O $C_6H_{12}O_6$

Sugar ($C_6H_{12}O_6$), water, gases, diffuse to other cells.

Chloroplast

Spongy tissue

Vein

Air and fluid spaces

H_2O

Lower epidermis

Guard cells turgid. Stomata open in the normal daytime condition

Excess water (H_2O) goes out as vapor

CO_2 enters with air

Excess O_2 leaves during sugar making

FIG. 4.8. The leaf blade. The essential structures are: the upper and lower covering layers or epidermis; the cells of the palisade and spongy tissue containing the chlorophyll that carries on photosynthesis; the veins that are the highways of transportation between leaf and stem (the xylem ducts transport water and the phloem carries food). Each stoma is a breathing pore leading to the air spaces in the spongy tissue. The guard cells on either side of the pore regulate its size according to the moisture and the amount of oxygen and carbon dioxide exchanged.

photosynthesis is in full swing. The bean-shaped guard cells are then rotund with stored sugar and water which the sugar has attracted by osmosis. Their plumpness causes them to pull apart and thus to form an opening between them; when they collapse the opening closes. Other conditions within or without the leaf affect the guard cells, especially scarcity of water. The stomata are then closed and what water there may be left in the leaf is kept from passing out in transpiration.

Respiration occurs in all cells of the leaf as it does in the root, the stem and other parts of the plant. Within the green leaf the upper layers of cells hold an

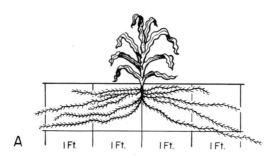

A

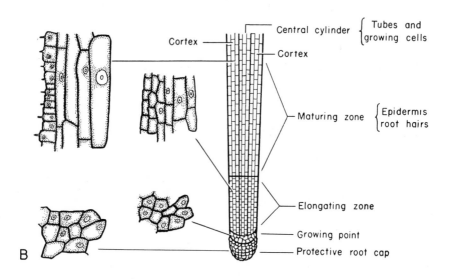

Central cylinder $\left\{ \begin{array}{l} \text{Tubes and} \\ \text{growing cells} \end{array} \right.$

Cortex

Cortex

Maturing zone $\left\{ \begin{array}{l} \text{Epidermis} \\ \text{root hairs} \end{array} \right.$

Elongating zone

Growing point

Protective root cap

B

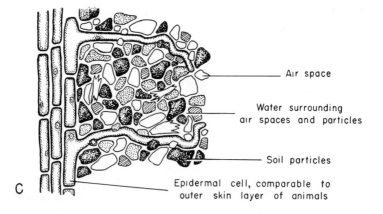

Air space

Water surrounding
air spaces and particles

Soil particles

Epidermal cell, comparable to
outer skin layer of animals

C

abundance of chlorophyll (Fig. 4.8). Here the leaf is greenest and the light falling on it is strongest. These cells are the all important food-makers, the links between the energy of the sun and the living world. The lower layers contain spongy cells of odd shapes and hold less chlorophyll than those of the upper layers. They are loosely packed in clusters with air spaces in between. This region of the leaf provides for the income and circulation of gases and the outgo of water. Extra water is also eliminated in droplets (guttation) from openings at the tips of the veins of grasses, corn and many other plants. In early morning the droplets hang in beautiful symmetry on the edges of the leaves of strawberries and jewelweeds. During the day some water is lost from the leaf and at night moisture in the air condenses on its cool surface. The main supply of water is always from the root.

Root. The main functions of the root are the anchorage of the plant, the absorption of water and mineral matter, the storage of manufactured food and sometimes of chemicals, e.g., nicotine is produced in the roots of tobacco plants and transported to the leaves. The spread of surface necessary for absorption also makes it an efficient anchor in the soil (Fig. 4.9). The root is the extension of the stem and resembles it in having long tapering branches and an essentially similar structure, although the pattern of the conducting tubes is different. Although roots are various in size, form, and structure, they have no such diversity as the leaves and stems, for conditions in the soil are less variable than those in the air.

Of all the material which the root absorbs the most important is water. It is a great part of the plant substance and as essential for the processes of living as it is in animals. Absorption occurs exclusively in the microscopic root hairs in the white terminal parts of roots, the ones whose injury in transplanting is followed by the familiar wilting of the plant. Near the tip of each new root, hairs are continually forming, a little farther back they are constantly dying. The root hair is a single cell of the epidermis. It grows outward in a hairlike projection that turns and twists about the particles which in any moist soil are clothed in a thin capillary film of water (Fig. 4.9). The root hair is an osmotic mechanism (Chap. 2, p. 22). Water and salts enter it but sugar does not pass out. Although each root hair is virtually microscopic, their total area is a marvel of expansiveness. In one species of grass the total length of root hairs

---

FIG. 4.9. *A.* The root system of a corn plant. (After Weaver.) *B.* Diagram of a section of a root tip and its different zones. Cells of the root cap are worn off and replaced by new ones from the growing zone above it. The force that pushes the root through the soil is the lengthening of cells in the elongating zone. Epidermis, root hairs, and the ducts of the food-transporting phloem and the water-transporting xylem all develop in this zone. (After Woodruff & Baitsell: *Foundations of Biology,* ed. 7. New York, The Macmillan Co., 1951.) *C.* Root hairs are branches of epidermal cells. In every well-grown root billions of root hairs take in water from the films of it that surround particles of soil wherever there is moisture on the ground.

held within one cubic inch of soil has been estimated to be four-fifths of a mile.

Root pressure pushes sap to the top of the tallest trees. It acts under various conditions, in trees of tropical rain forests where there is no evaporation from the leaves, and in trees of temperate climates before the leaves appear in spring. In some parts of our country the maple sugar season is the time of the first great lift of sap from its winter storage in the roots of sugar maples. Root pressure is all-important to plants. Details of the causes of it are complex and not completely understood. Root hairs are the first actors in root pressure because they carry on the absorption of water from the soil. About one-third of the pressure is believed to be osmotic and two-thirds metabolic, that is, due to respiration and other life processes.

Reproduction

Higher plants reproduce asexually and sexually. Some species reproduce more often or exclusively in one way, some in the other. Young strawberry plants develop from creeping stems which grow from the parent; grass plants spread out many sprouts from older plants. The white potato of the dinner table is a food-filled underground stem. When used for planting it is cut into pieces each containing an "eye" or bud from which a new plant grows. In most higher plants both methods of reproduction are common which is never the case in higher animals. A strawberry plant buds forth a new plant; a cat never buds off a kitten.

The root, leaf, and stem are concerned with the vegetative functions, the intake of food and water, digestion, respiration, and asexual reproduction; the flower with sexual reproduction. In higher plants sexual reproduction is more important than asexual. Any bouquet of flowers—roses, orchids or butter-cups—is a cluster of reproductive organs. Although sexual reproduction differs greatly in detail in plants and animals, its essential features are the same.

Flower. The flower is the reproductive organ of the plant. The more or less conspicuous parts are the sepals, petals, stamens, and pistil. The latter two are directly and the others only indirectly concerned with the formation of male and female sex cells and their union in the process of fertilization. Flowers differ greatly in the position and form of the parts and whether male and female cells are borne on the same or different plants of a species. They are often in the same flower as in the diagram (Fig. 4.3). The stamen consists of the stalk supporting the anther and its pollen sacs. When it is mature, the pollen sacs break open and liberate the pollen grains within each of which there are two male sex cells. These are equivalent to the male sex cells (sperm) of animals. The pistil (or pistils) usually consists of a central stalk with a sticky tip, the stigma. At its base is the ovary containing the ovules, the female sex cells equivalent to eggs. The union of the sex cells is brought about in one way or another, such as by the locations of the parts, or by insects. The male cells come in contact with the stigma and make their way down through the stalk of the pistil to the ovary. Finally one of them reaches the ovule and enters it. The subsequent fusion of the male and female cells within the ovule is fertilization. These are the essentials of the journey of the male cell and its union with the female, with many complexities omitted and numbers of irregularities unmentioned. The fact remains that the behavior and function of the primary sex cells are strikingly the same in plants and animals.

Seed. The seed is an embryo plant which has developed from a fertilized ovule. A fruit is a growth around one or more embryos (seeds) which protects them and is a common means of their dispersal.

Similarities of Plants and Animals

1. *Cells.* Their basic material is protoplasm organized in cells.

2. *Food.* Their main food and chief sources of energy are carbohydrates—starches and sugars. Amino acids, the "building blocks" of proteins, are essential to them. Water is a vital need.

3. *Metabolism.* The basic processes of respiration and of digestion and assimilation are similar. Excess products of metabolism are mentioned below.

In the respiration of plants and animals oxygen enters the cells and unites with carbohydrates, fats, and lastly with proteins. Oxidation, i.e., chemical burning occurs. Chemical energy is released as activity and heat. Carbon dioxide and water are formed.

During digestion food is changed to simpler chemical compounds. During assimilation the digested food becomes part of a specific kind of protoplasm. For example, food assimilated by the chromosomes in certain cells of an oak tree acquires the characteristics of the appropriate substances in those chromosomes; food assimilated in the chromosomes of certain cells in a goat does likewise.

In both plants and animals, certain excess by-products may be stored. Examples of these are digitalis in foxgloves, opium in poppies, calcium carbonate in earthworms. The use of these, if any, to the producing organisms is not clearly understood. Certain other by-products may be used; carbon dioxide by green plants in photosynthesis, and by animals in small amounts as a stimulus to breathing and as a control of the force of the heartbeat.

Differences between Plants and Animals

1. *Locomotion.* The majority of plants do not move from place to place. The majority of animals move about freely.

2. *Food.* Green plants make carbohydrates by photosynthesis. Animals take carbohydrates from plants. Plants are the chief makers of proteins which they elaborate from amino acids. Animals take proteins from plants and other animals.

3. *Metabolism*. Even in higher plants the rate of metabolism is low. In active respiration the temperature of plants may rise only slightly above their environment. In higher animals the rate of metabolism is high. The temperature of birds and mammals is usually much higher than that of their environment.

In the majority of animals, there are special organs of excretion by which nitrogenous waste products of metabolism are eliminated. In plants, there are no such organs. The only approach to an excretory product in plants is probably the excess by-products of metabolism such as opium (see similarities of plants and animals). There are no excretory organs in plants.

4. *Hormones*. Plants produce relatively few hormones and these have general effects, such as, growth of stem and growth of root. Animals produce an elaborate and delicately adjusted series of interacting hormones which have specific effects, such as, thickness of skin.

5. *Responsiveness*. In plants, the ordinary cells are variously responsive, e.g., to light, to temperature, in some regions more than others. In animals, special sensory cells are highly responsive to one or another kind of stimulus, e.g., the rod cells and cone cells of the eye.

5
Animals and Their Environments

Animals abound in great numbers. Thrust a stick into a large ant nest on a July day and millions of ants pour out, many carrying white packages that taken altogether contain myriads of their eggs and young ones. Sea birds scarcely have room to sit on their eggs during the great gatherings of the breeding season (Fig. 5.1). Populations of animals, except the human ones, seem to stay about the same size, but those that have been carefully observed have proved quite the opposite. The dips and peaks in the populations of one kind of animal also affect others. In Labrador in a recent year the numbers of field mice ran up to a peak and the hawks and snowy owls grew fat; in another year they almost vanished becoming so scarce that the snowy owls flew down to New England for better eating.

Animals enter every part of the earth except craters of active volcanoes and places poisoned by civilization. They abound in the damp tropics. Microscopic organisms crowd the surface waters of arctic seas, for cold water holds more oxygen than warm water and food is abundant. On their journey into the Antarctic members of the Robert Scott Expedition found emperor penguins incubating their eggs, holding them on the tops of their feet in the dark of the antarctic winter "with the temperature seventy degrees below frost and the blizzards blowing."

The Numbers of Species. The term species is commonly used but difficult to define. Animals of one species resemble one another, interbreed with one another and do not usually interbreed with animals of other such groups. The number of described species is still growing. For birds and mammals it may for the present be nearly complete; for protozoans and insects it is far from that. Frequent estimates suggest that only ten per cent of all insects is yet accurately described. In 1946 the total number of known living species of animals was figured at about one million (Fig. 5.2).

Variety and Similarity. Large numbers of animals have basic similarities; they also have many less fundamental differences. Likenesses and differences

67

Fig. 5.1. Abundance. Gannets nesting on ledges of Bonaventure Island, off the coast of the Gaspé Peninsula, on rocks as high as a 20-story building. A gannet is about the size of a duck. (Courtesy, Allan D. Cruickshank, from National Audubon Society.)

make classification possible. Animals may have two or four or more legs; insects have six; spiders have eight; there are a hundred or more in millipedes. The bones of the arms and legs of a man are arranged like the comparable bones in the legs of a horse (Fig. 9.14), but in other ways the legs are different. Such structures are correlated with the history of their environment, human arms and legs with ancestors that climbed trees and the horse's legs with ancestors that ranged the swamps and the plains. Various noses are adapted to various functions in addition to smell; an elephant can give itself a shower bath with its nose (Fig. 5.3).

Sizes of Animals and the Environment. Animals of a given species vary relatively little in size. Size, proportions, and structure of the body and environment are mutually related. Water lifts and supports weight as air does not; boats can anchor and float but airplanes cannot poise in the air without special devices. Many animals can swim, but few can fly. Aquatic animals are often larger than their terrestrial near-relatives and literally lean on the water

Protozoans	30,000
Sponges	3,000
Coelenterates	9,000
Flatworms	6,000
Roundworms	3,000
Echinoderms	4,800
Molluscs	40,000
Annelids	6,000
Crustaceans	25,000
Arachnoids	30,000
Centipedes	2,000
Millipedes	6,000
Insects	660,000
Fishes	15,000
Amphibians	1,900
Reptiles	4,000
Birds	25,000
Mammals	15,000
Total	892,000

ARTHROPODS

CHORDATES

Fig. 5.2. Diagram showing the approximate number of living species of animals. The grand total is often given as one million. Numbers differ greatly with the methods and time of counts. New species of insects are being discovered even in familiar places; probably only a fraction of all the tropical insects have been described. (Courtesy, Hunter and Hunter: *College Zoology*. Philadelphia, W. B. Saunders Co., 1949.)

for support. Giant grasshoppers are small compared to the largest lobsters, their marine relatives. Blue whales, the largest living animals, are ten times as long as elephants, more than twenty-five times heavier, and, like large ships, are helpless when stranded (Fig. 5.4).

Only the smallest mammals burrow or live in grassy runways. The pigmy shrews are very small, one of them, *Microsorex hoyi winnemana,* total length with tail, 3.12 inches, is the smallest mammal known in North America. Nocturnal and mouse-like but more slender it travels comfortably in a runway half an inch wide.

FIG. 5.3. Noses are adapted to many uses in addition to smell and breathing. A ground mole bores its way wedging with its nose and digging with its feet; mice and other rodents use their noses as wedges; anteaters probe into anthills. The noses of elephants are general tools, for shower baths, lifting logs, and picking up nuts; a pig's snout is a living plow.

Form, Symmetry and Segmentation. The symmetry of animals is the arrangement of structures with respect to a point, a line or a plane. In radial symmetry the structures are placed like the parts of a wheel in relation to its center. In bilateral symmetry the right and left sides correspond to one another. Symmetry is correlated with an animal's way of life, especially its lack of locomotion or kind of locomotion. Hydras, corals, jellyfishes, and others are radially symmetrical. Such animals move about slowly or are attached like the corals. In sea anemones and starfish and their kin bilateral symmetry appears within the radial; that is, the wheel or cylinder shows a division into two parts. This is a persistence of the bilateral symmetry of their free-swimming young. The majority of animals, and all the vertebrates, are bilaterally symmetrical (Figs. 5.5, 5.6). They move about freely, often with great speed,

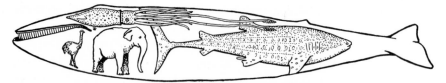

FIG. 5.4. The relative size of the blue whale (length, 90 to 100 feet), whale shark, and giant squid. All of them live surrounded by the lifting capacity of buoyant salt water. The ostrich and elephant receive no such support.

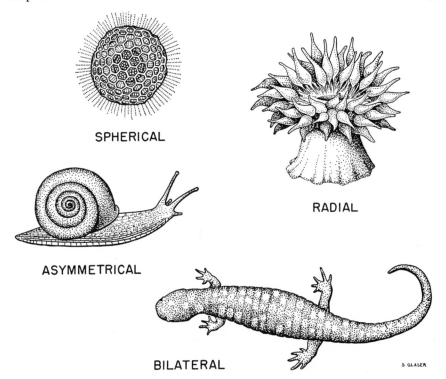

SPHERICAL

RADIAL

ASYMMETRICAL

BILATERAL   S GLASER

FIG. 5.5. Types of symmetry. *Spherical,* a protozoan (radiolarian) floats in water that presses against it equally on all sides; *radial,* a sea anemone, its shape common in animals that are attached for most of their lives; *asymmetrical,* in a snail that no plane will divide into halves; *bilateral,* in a salamander, in animals that move about freely, and are mainly symmetrical on each side of a plane extending the length of the body.

and the brain and sense organs are always at the end that arrives first. Scarcely any animal is perfectly symmetrical, whatever the type; all tailors know that the human ones are a little one-sided.

SEGMENTATION. The bodies of all animals from earthworm to man are segmented, i.e., partitioned into sections that are joined together in a series. The segmentation may be conspicuous inside and out, as it is in the earthworm; it may be mainly on the outside as in the abdomen of an insect; or prominent in certain structures such as vertebrae and ribs. The arrangement has the advantage of making parts of the body more independent of one another; it is an insurance lessening the disaster of injury to the whole body. If one or more segments are hurt, others can carry on. Segmentation gives flexibility to long slender bodies such as those of worms. It allows great variety by the modification of different segments for different functions, as in a lobster, in which some segments bear swimmerets while others bear mouthparts and eyes.

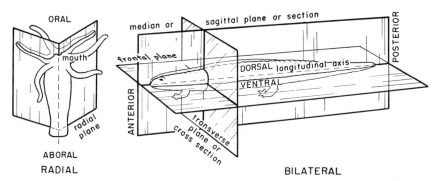

FIG. 5.6. Axes, planes and regions in animal bodies.

Environments

Rhythms of Sun and Moon. The lives of all plants and animals are interwoven with the rhythms that originate outside the earth, their income of energy from the sun, the changes of the tides, and shifts of climate. Patterns of living change from hour to hour as the earth rotates on its axis in its journey round the sun. Evening with its own ways comes to a countryside as it is turned from the sun. If it is New England and early June, the wood thrushes sing through the sunset and afterglow; the whippoorwills begin calling when the hedges are black; the mosquitoes are enlivened by the subdued light and the dampness. From moment to moment animals as well as plants respond punctually and precisely to changes in light and atmosphere.

The gravitational attraction between the sun and the earth and the moon and the earth constantly pulls upon these bodies, its strength varying with their respective positions in their orbits. On land its effect is relatively slight but upon the sea it is the basic cause of tides. Sun and moon both take part in the changes of the tides, but the moon, being much nearer the earth, has the stronger influence upon them. With many variations there are in general four tides on every seashore, two high and two low ones in each period of 24 hours. The tide rises and water that has swept the ocean bottom floods over the tide pools bringing additions to the already crowded communities of animals, some of them to eat, others to be eaten. Each little group is continually changed by flooding and ebbing water. Everything that belongs to the sea waits on the tides. Fishermen in harbors put out their seines for the fishes that follow the rising tide. Great ocean steamers wait at their docks until the tide rises.

The Sun, a Great Provider. The sun sustains life upon the earth, providing living organisms with heat, light, the energy stored in food, and indirectly with water. The sun is a great furnace of transmuting atoms, extraordinarily different from the earth yet with a similar chemical content. According to certain theories the earth originated from a torn-out piece of it. It is the source of

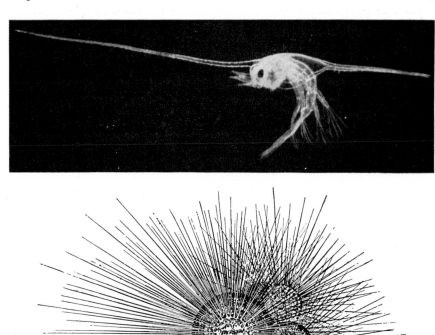

FIG. 5.7. Types of marine plankton, the great population of minute plants and animals that live in the surface of the seas and includes the eggs and developing young of the majority of marine animals. *Top*, the larva of the porcelain crab like other plankton organisms is translucent and bears outgrowths that serve as floats characteristic of animals of the plankton. (Photograph by D. P. Wilson, Marine Biological Lab., Plymouth, England.) *Bottom*, the protozoan, *Globigerina bulloides*. Enormous numbers of these live among the plankton in the surface waters of the sea. Their chalky frames and fine spines dropping through the water for millions of years have formed the globigerina ooze of many parts of the ocean bottom. (After Murray and Hjort. Courtesy, Coker: *This Great and Wide Sea*. Chapel Hill, N.C., Univ. of N. Carolina Press, 1947.)

practically all the energy on earth, excepting atomic energy. It is the prime mover of the winds because it heats different places unevenly and this sets currents of air in motion. As heat it lifts water by evaporation eventually to form clouds and be distributed in rain. With its energy plants make the food for which directly or indirectly all animals including man struggle unceasingly.

Types of Environment. THE LAND. Terrestrial animals of various groups are described briefly in Part 5.

THE SEA. The greatest numbers of living organisms in the world are the plankton that live in the surface waters of the sea. They are small, mainly minute and microscopic plants and animals that drift with the currents. No plants are so completely open to the energy of the sun. No mixed population of animals is more uniformly short-lived and prolific. In no other place are there, in season, such multitudes of floating eggs and swimming young (Figs. 5.7, 5.8).

The richest population in numbers and kinds of animals visible to the naked eye lives between the tides and near the bottom out to depths of about 400 feet. Hosts of them are attached to rocks and seaweeds; or crawl and burrow on the bottom (Fig. 5.9 and 5.10). Farther from shore are the larger free-swimmers (nekton), the fishes; coastal waters are the main fishing grounds.

The deep water of the open sea from the surface well into its depths is the home of the largest fishes, the giant squids, sea turtles, and the mammals, porpoises, dolphins, and great whales. Except for the whalebone whales all

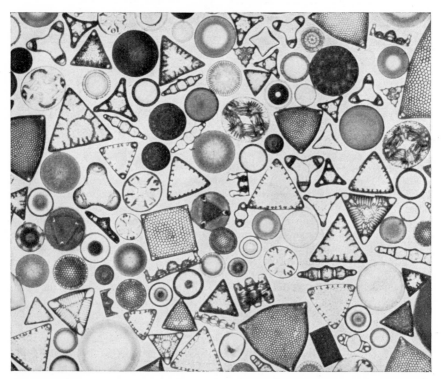

FIG. 5.8. Photograph of marine diatoms. Their beauty and variety are due to their silicious shells. Diatoms of fresh waters are less various but equally beautiful and important in the economy of their environments. (Courtesy, Paul B. Conger, United States Museum, Washington, D.C.)

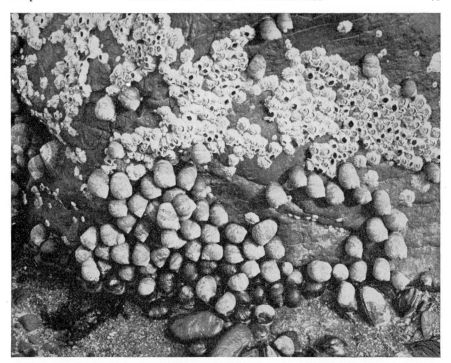

FIG. 5.9. Hosts of animals cling to the rocks and seaweeds between the tide lines. Common rock barnacles (*Balanus balanoides*) (*above*), and edible periwinkles (*Littorina litorea*) (*below*). Periwinkles are about the size of cherries. In British shore resorts "winkles" are roasted and sold like peanuts in America. (Photograph by D. P. Wilson, Marine Biological Lab., Plymouth, England.)

of these live upon one another and the offspring of one another (Fig. 5.11).

Salt water is a far better support and carrier than fresh water. The eggs of marine animals float easily; those of fresh-water animals often drop to the bottom, are attached to vegetation, or carried about by the parent. The young ones climb, creep, and hold onto whatever comes their way.

PONDS AND LAKES. Healthy ponds and the coves of lakes usually hold goodly populations; in midsummer they teem with them (Figs. 5.12, 5.13). Ponds are smaller than lakes. They are defined as bodies of water so shallow that green plants can grow attached to the bottom even at the center. Lakes are too broad and deep for this. Near the borders of ponds and the protected shores of lakes the plants are food depots and shelters for invertebrates, snails, climbing fingernail clams, innumerable crustaceans, and aquatic insects. There are a few resident vertebrates, chiefly frogs and turtles. The plants have partly or completely submerged stems—blue-blossomed pickerelweeds, arrowheads, rushes, and waterlilies. All of their stems are coated with green algae and bacteria (Fig. 5.14). Yellow perch, bass, and pickerel come among them to forage.

FIG. 5.10. With every high tide the tide pools and surrounding rocks are flooded with water carrying millions of little plants and animals that are fit for food. During low tide the pool dwellers are busy consuming the meal. They are attached and slow moving protozoans, bryozoans, barnacles, tunicates, and many mollusks often along with a few crabs, starfishes, brittle stars, and sea urchins. (Courtesy, the American Museum of Natural History.)

Chemical Conditions

Plants and animals are continually taking materials from their environments and making them into their own bodies. Certain substances and conditions must be present around them. Whether in arctic or tropic regions, in water or on land, these essentials are: sufficient energy from the sun for the plants to synthesize food, enough oxygen for respiration, enough water, the chemical elements which take part in protoplasmic activities, and certain physical conditions, such as temperature and pressure.

FIG. 5.11. Larger free swimmers (nekton) of the open coastal waters. *Upper left,* dolphins, length up to 12 feet; North Atlantic sea turtle (loggerhead), 100 to 200 pounds. *Center,* swordfish, 250 to 400 pounds. *Bottom,* blue-fin tuna (or marlin), up to 600 pounds. Not drawn to scale.

Carbon Cycle. Carbon, a main element in protoplasm and its products, is available only in small amounts. Ordinary air contains about 0.035 per cent of carbon dioxide by volume and only a quarter of this is carbon. From this small amount, plants obtain all they use and in turn become the source of carbon for all organisms. The sources of free carbon dioxide are plant and animal respiration, decay of the bodies of plants and animals, and the release from burning oil and coal. From all these sources it is automatically returned to the atmosphere. The only way that it gets back to protoplasm is by green plants.

Plants take carbon dioxide (CO_2) from the air and with the help of energy from the sun during photosynthesis, produce the valuable food, carbohydrate. When a carbohydrate unites with oxygen, the energy of action and heat and carbon dioxide are set free, the latter in part a waste product respired into the air. One branch of the cycle is thus complete. In another branch of the circuit, carbon is built into the protoplasm. It is locked within the cells until they die, decompose, and free it into the air to unite with oxygen as carbon dioxide (Fig. 5.15).

Oxygen Cycle. Plants and animals take oxygen (O_2) from air or water in

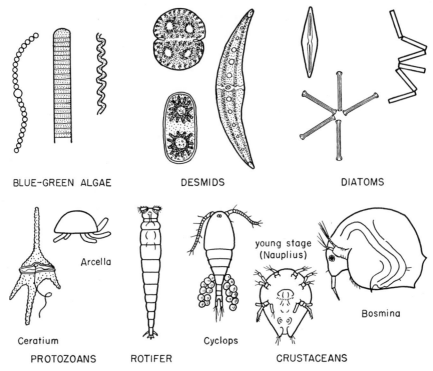

BLUE-GREEN ALGAE   DESMIDS   DIATOMS

Arcella

young stage
(Nauplius)

Bosmina

Ceratium   Cyclops
PROTOZOANS   ROTIFER   CRUSTACEANS

FIG. 5.12. Important groups in fresh-water plankton. Blue-green algae, common in lakes especially in hot weather, sometimes turn color and create "red water"; green algae (desmids) and diatoms, present the year round with spring and other upswings of abundance; protozoans, few; rotifers, many; crustaceans, abundant, creating the basic fish food.

respiration. They return it to the atmosphere in combination with carbon as carbon dioxide and with hydrogen as water. In addition green plants release oxygen in photosynthesis. In an aquarium properly arranged for plants and animals, the output of carbon dioxide from respiration and of oxygen from photosynthesis is balanced.

Nitrogen Cycle. The great reservoir of nitrogen in the atmosphere (78.03 per cent of volume) is an inactive associate of oxygen and carbon dioxide. The nitrogen dissolved in bodies of water comes mainly from the atmosphere. Its cycle is more complex than that of carbon because living organisms do not release nitrogen in a form that green plants can use. It is released from animals as nitrogenous waste such as urea $(CO(NH_2)_2)$ and from decaying tissues after death (Fig. 5.15). Saprophytic bacteria attack these and produce ammonia. Other bacteria feed upon the ammonia, combine oxygen with it, derive energy from the oxidation, and produce nitrites (NO_2)—upon which they feed. Still other bacteria (Nitrobacter) attack the nitrites and, through anaerobic (without free oxygen) respiration, derive energy from them and

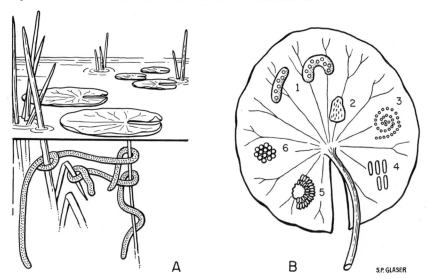

Fig. 5.13. Stems and leaves of pond lilies are nurseries for hatching eggs and young animals, mainly invertebrates. *A*, strings of jelly that shelter minute eggs of midges. *B*, eggs: on the under side of a lily leaf: *1*, snail; *2*, water mite; *3*, caddis fly; *4*, whirligig beetle; *5*, beetle (Donacia); *6*, beetle, the waterpenny (Psephenus).

convert them into nitrates (NO_3)—that are taken up by green plants, and finally converted into the amino acids and proteins of green plants. Blue-green algae are now known to fix nitrogen and the process may be even more general than this. Many commercial fertilizers contain nitrates.

Nitrogen-fixing bacteria are able to fix free atmospheric nitrogen in nitrogenous compounds which can be used by green plants. Some of these bacteria live in the soil, estimated at least two billion to a teaspoonful in garden soil; others live in nodules on the roots of clover, peas, and beans. The value of these plants in building up the nitrogen supply in the soil is recognized by farmers who rotate crops of clover with corn in order to supply the soil with nitrogen which corn exhausts. Denitrifying bacteria occur in some soils. These reverse the nitrifying process and reduce nitrites to free nitrogen which is then released into the atmosphere. This is the nitrogen that is compounded with water and brought to the earth in an electrical storm. The bolts of lightning fix the nitrogen as nitrites and nitrates that are brought to the earth by the rain.

Mineral Cycles. These include the time in which iron, phosphorus, or other minerals are in the crust of the earth and in the body of a living organism. Calcium carbonate ($CaCO_3$) or lime is a good example for it is widely distributed in nature and an important component of bone. The developing embryo of a mouse receives lime from its mother and after birth from its food, notably milk. Lime is maintained in the body of the mouse, chiefly in its bones, as long as it lives. Exactly the same storage of lime occurs in an elephant ex-

Fɪɢ. 5.14. The web of feeding habits among the animals of pond and lake borders: frogs on immature insects, snails, small fishes, crustaceans; pickerel on insects, fishes; turtle on tadpoles, frogs.

cept that a larger amount is involved and for a much longer time. Large amounts of lime and other minerals are temporarily stored away in plants and animals.

Water Cycle. The internal environment of the body is completely dependent upon the come and go of water. It enters the body bearing traces of iron, iodine, sulfur, or salt from the external environment. It leaves the body carrying the wastes of metabolism that are records of protoplasmic activity. Water rises in vapor from the sea and land, floats in the atmosphere as clouds, condenses, falls as rain, and runs down from the highlands to the sea again. Water is a traveler. Like mineral matter it is taken into plants and animals but it never remains in them. Whether they are pine trees or cattle, living organisms take in relatively large amounts of water that gradually filters completely through their bodies.

Physical Environment

The chief physical influences upon plants and animals are gravity, pressure, temperature, and light.

Gravity. Its weight, actually the earth's pull, greatly affects an animal. The bridge-type of four-legged animal is a four-cornered support of the body against the pull of the earth (Fig. 9.11). Birds are the master adjusters to the force of gravity. No other animals approach them in lightness and strength, due to the air-filled outpocketings of their lungs that extend into the bones, their rapid elimination of waste products, and the lightness of feathers (Chap. 36).

Pressure. The medium in which animals live presses upon them continually from every point, upon their forms, actions, and the amount of gases which they hold.

The atmosphere of the earth is like a haystack (Fig. 5.16). At the bottom or sea level its content is closely packed; the atoms of oxygen are near together. At sea level an animal, like every other object, carries 14.7 pounds of atmospheric pressure on each square inch of the surface of its body, and this pressure so evenly permeates its body that none is felt. At 20,000 feet (300 feet lower than Mt. McKinley) the same animal would be exposed to pressure less than half that of sea level. In spite of their high oxygen demand in breathing, birds fly through air of low oxygen content probably securing an adequate supply because of the speed with which they drive into it. At 18,000 feet mules in South America carry riders without great difficulty, and this is said to be due to their frequent stops during which oxygen accumulates in their blood. Anyone acquainted with them knows that mules have the same sagacity at sea level where they also make frequent stops.

Water is about 775 times more dense than air and consequently heavier. It is peculiar in that it becomes denser and heavier as it cools to a temperature of 39.2° F. (4° C.). When colder than that it is less dense and lighter, finally floating as ice. Because of this the pond is covered with a blanket of ice below which fishes can disport themselves in safety (Fig. 5.17).

The pressure upon an animal in water is the weight of a column of water extending above a given area of its body plus the atmospheric pressure above. The pressure on a fish in Lake Tahoe in California, over 6,000 feet above sea level, is far less than that on a codfish in the Atlantic Ocean. At great depths of the ocean the pressure is several tons per square inch. It does not crush the animal because the fluids in its body are under the same pressure as the water surrounding it. Pressure compresses gas which expands when deep-sea fish are

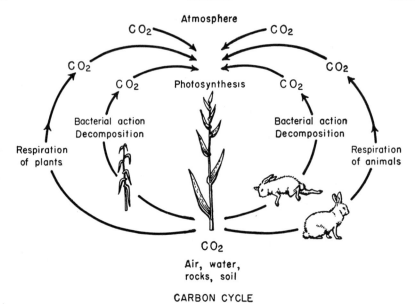

Atmosphere

CO_2 CO_2

CO_2 CO_2

CO_2 Photosynthesis CO_2

Bacterial action   Bacterial action
Decomposition   Decomposition

Respiration   Respiration
of plants   of animals

CO_2

Air, water,
rocks, soil

CARBON CYCLE

Free nitrogen N_2 is made available
to plants and animals (fixed) by
certain bacteria. Also fixed by
lightning and washed to earth.

Free nitrogen
N_2

Earth   Death   Excretion

N_2 bacteria in   Used by plants
root nodules   to build protein

Plant and animal
residue

Denitrifying   Nitrates (NO_3), salts
bacteria
Decay   Nitrate bacteria
N_2 fixing   produce
soil bacteria   Ammonia (NH_3)

Nitrite bacteria produce

Nitrites (NO_2), salts

The processes from free nitrogen to protein
are carried on mainly in the ground

NITROGEN CYCLE

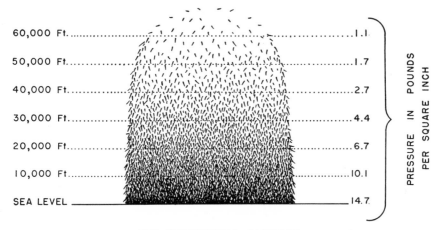

60,000 Ft.	1.1
50,000 Ft.	1.7
40,000 Ft.	2.7
30,000 Ft.	4.4
20,000 Ft.	6.7
10,000 Ft.	10.1
SEA LEVEL	14.7

PRESSURE IN POUNDS PER SQUARE INCH

THE ATMOSPHERIC HAYSTACK

FIG. 5.16. Atmospheric pressure illustrated by stacked hay showing the weight it would carry at various heights to 60,000 feet. The proportions of the gases in the atmosphere do not change at different heights but their total amount does. This is why the air is thin in high places.

brought to the surface, just as gas expands when a bottle of compressed fluid pops. When deep-sea divers rise to the surface rapidly the pressure on the nitrogen in the blood is released too quickly; it gathers in bubbles in their muscles and joints producing a condition known as the bends (Fig. 5.18).

Temperature. Except for those that live in hot springs, plants and animals can live only within a narrow range of temperature and can endure relatively low temperatures better than high ones. Many tropical animals cannot bear extreme exposure to the sun's heat. In zoological gardens ostriches, crocodiles, and snakes have often been killed by heat. Birds have the advantage in their cooling devices of air sacs and mammals of panting and sweating.

Wherever there are severe winters, animals resort to various ways of avoiding or meeting them. Birds go to warmer regions or remain in the cold and depend on heavy feeding to keep up their metabolism; many mammals, rabbits, foxes, and others are active but must have abundant food; other mammals hibernate, put on layers of fat in the fall, and live at a kind of physio-

---

FIG. 5.15. Chemical cycles. *The carbon cycle.* Respiration of plants and animals returns most of the carbon to the air as carbon dioxide. The storage of carbon in coal and oil is an important exception to the general rule that the carbon used by the green plant in photosynthesis returns to the air. Coal is largely carbon derived from the cellulose of the trees about 250 or more million years ago. Carbon is also captured in the calcium carbonate ($CaCO_3$) of clams, crabs and others.

The nitrogen cycle is much more complex than that of carbon. The main reason is that many organisms do not release nitrogen in a form that can be immediately used by green plants. They can use it when it appears as certain inorganic salts, particularly nitrates.

A

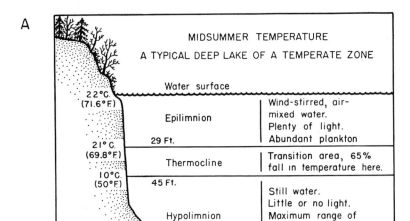

MIDSUMMER TEMPERATURE
A TYPICAL DEEP LAKE OF A TEMPERATE ZONE

22°C. (71.6°F)	Water surface	
	Epilimnion	Wind-stirred, air-mixed water. Plenty of light. Abundant plankton
21°C. (69.8°F)	29 Ft.	
10°C. (50°F)	Thermocline	Transition area, 65% fall in temperature here.
	45 Ft.	
	Hypolimnion	Still water. Little or no light. Maximum range of temperature for year about 40° F.
5.5°C (41°F)	128 Ft. Bottom	

B

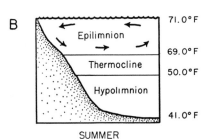

71.0°F
69.0°F
50.0°F
41.0°F

SUMMER
Layers as in A. Wind blows surface waters. Temperature shift in thermocline.

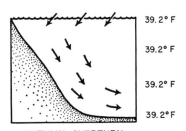

39.2°F
39.2°F
39.2°F
39.2°F

AUTUMN OVERTURN
Cold winds blow and chill surface waters. Their temperature changes to 39.2°F. They fall and mix.

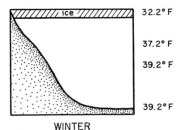

32.2°F
37.2°F
39.2°F
39.2°F

WINTER
Ice cover is a boon to population beneath it. Plankton sinks with heavy water.

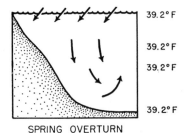

39.2°F
39.2°F
39.2°F
39.2°F

SPRING OVERTURN
Ice melts. Surface water changes to 39.2°F, is heavier and falls, mixes and displaces lower waters. Stir brings plankton to surface.

logical low gear for which little or no food is needed. In winter the water is warmer than the air; frogs stay in muddy pond bottoms but do not drown because they take in enough oxygen through the skin for their lowered metab-

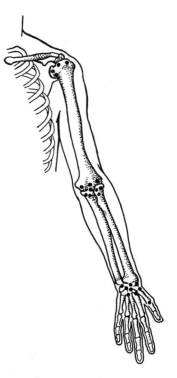

FIG. 5.18. Bubbles of nitrogen gas (black) collect at the joints when a person, e.g., a deep-sea diver, rises suddenly into greatly lowered pressure.

olism. Insects go through a special cold-hardening, partly by loss of water and the production of bound water which does not freeze except in extraordinarily low temperatures. Earthworms burrow below the frost line and gather in clusters conserving heat and moisture. Lady beetles spend the winter in companies

---

FIG. 5.17. *A*, midsummer temperature of a lake. Water contracts with cooling and becomes heavier but only to 4° C. (39.2° F.). When warmer or colder than this it becomes lighter.

Water takes its place in layers according to its weight which is dependent on temperature.

B, sections of a lake showing the seasonal changes in temperature. *Summer*. The light is stronger but the diatoms decrease probably because of inadequate nourishment and perhaps of silica since the thermocline seems to bar the way to chemical substances that might otherwise well up from the bottom. *Autumn*. With the mixing of the water and disappearance of the thermocline there is an upward diffusion of nutrient salts. Another increase of diatoms occurs, not so great as in spring since the sunlight is weaker. *Winter*. The lake is covered with ice which is water at its lightest and coldest. *Spring*. Light increases and with it an increase of diatoms called the spring pulse, of great importance in the food supply of all young animals.

FIG. 5.19. Social hibernation of ladybird beetles. With the first frosts the beetles fly to the ground and then to trees searching for holes in which they gather by hundreds. Animals that are solitary in summer may be social in winter. (Photograph by Carl Welty.)

though they are solitary at other seasons (Fig. 5.19). Cold as well as sex encourages sociability.

Light. Light is necessary for vision but there are other ways in which it concerns animals. Like plants they are deeply affected by longer or shorter days. This shows in their breeding seasons, in the migrations and seasonal changes of color in birds, and in the color changes of snowshoe rabbits, and other northern animals. In general, animals are responsive to light whether they have light-perceptive organs or not, but lenses are present even in certain protozoans. The majority of higher animals probably find their way chiefly by vision, but by no means entirely.

The amount of light that enters water depends upon the direction of the rays, which differs with the time of day and year, the amount and clearness of the water through which the rays pass, and the intensity of the light. In relatively clear water, one-third of the light is generally lost in about three feet and three-quarters of it in 16 feet. At depths of 2,000 feet or more the ocean is completely dark except for the luminescent animals, mainly fishes.

Biological Environment

The neighboring plants and animals compose an organism's biological environment. Whether the organism is a crocus in a mountain meadow, a parasite in human blood, a squash bug on the vine, or a citizen in the town, it is concerned with a biological environment, human or otherwise. The animals of an environment are roughly divided into producers of food and competitors in the consumption of food. Some of the consumers are predators that rob and kill.

Search for Food. Numerous and widely distributed animals are apt to live on common foods. Rodents—squirrels, field mice, and rabbits—all abound in great numbers; so do the shrubs, grasses, and clover which they eat. Grasshoppers and crickets live surrounded by grass and grain. At the height of their season the only grass-eaters that compete with them in open fields are cattle and sheep. During the great migrations of grasshoppers nothing stands in their way (Chap. 30). Birds, small mammals—shrews, ground moles, and chipmunks—commonly prey upon them. But their reproductive capacity is so high that these predators do them the good turn of keeping the population to a size which the space and food can support. Animals multiply greatly in regions where they have few or no competitors for the particular food on which they live. This is strikingly true of penguins in the Antarctic. The same principle applies to nocturnal animals such as owls and skunks that hunt by night when there is less competition.

Biological environments obviously depend on the chemical and physical ones. Plant populations rely particularly upon water and temperature and animals follow the plants. Animals abound at river mouths to which the river brings rich organic deposits. Rivers and their valleys have always determined the location of animals just as they have always determined locations for mankind.

Size of Food. Man is the only animal that can catch all sizes of animals, from frogs to cattle, oysters to whales, and use them for food. He can eat small, large, and medium-sized animals indiscriminately: an important control to have over the environment. The scavengers—vultures (turkey buzzards), lobsters, pigs, and chickens—approach mankind in the variety and sizes of food which they appropriate. With the exception of parasites and scavengers, other meat-eaters must deal with food that is adequate but not too large to be manipulated. Fierceness and skill may take the place of size in capturing prey, so may social behavior. Packs of wolves will attack a moose but a solitary wolf seldom does so. Millions of South American army ants will set upon and kill small mammals but no one of them could do it alone.

Food Relations. The food relations of a community are exceedingly complex, changeful, and affected by factors in the immediate environment as well as others far outside it. The complexity of the human food market is an example with its many and remote causes of undersupply and oversupply and resulting prices. The food relations between animals are expressed as food chains, food webs, and pyramids of numbers (Fig. 5.20, 5.21). A food web is

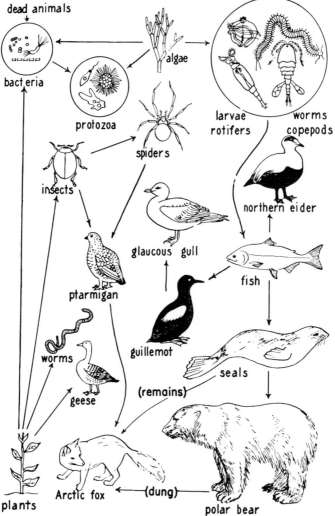

Food-web on Bear Island in the Arctic zone. (Simplified from Elton.) The arrows are read as "eaten by," e.g., "bacteria ⟶ protozoa" means bacteria are eaten by protozoa.

FIG. 5.20. In food webs the successive eaters are usually larger, e.g., insect, ptarmigan, fox, but fierceness, cunning or group action may take the place of size, e.g., in army ants, wolves, and wild dogs. (Reprinted from *Readings In Ecology* by Ralph Buchsbaum, by permission of The University of Chicago Press. Copyright 1937.)

literally what eats which in a community of animals or of animals and plants. Plant-eating animals are the basis of any community; they serve as food for the small carnivores which are in turn eaten by the larger ones. Such a series of food links is a food chain. In a pond bacteria and unicellular plants are the basic supply. Beginning with them, smaller animals are eaten by larger ones, protozoans by minute crustaceans and the fry of fishes, and these by aquatic insects and so on to the large fishes and turtles. If they die in the lake their bodies are returned to the bacteria; if they are caught and taken elsewhere they may become part of another food chain. In any long food chain, the successive eaters are not only larger in size but fewer in number. There are few sparrow hawks compared to the number of sparrows, few owls to the number of field mice, one fox to dozens of rabbits.

In communities of animals there are many more small adults than there are large ones (Fig. 5.21). What seems obvious is borne out, in broad lines, by analyzing a definite area of a community, counting the animals of various sizes and measuring the totals by bulk or weight. The result is a pyramid of numbers. Such a pyramid applies particularly to predatory animals. It shows that smaller animals have a higher reproductive capacity than large ones and are

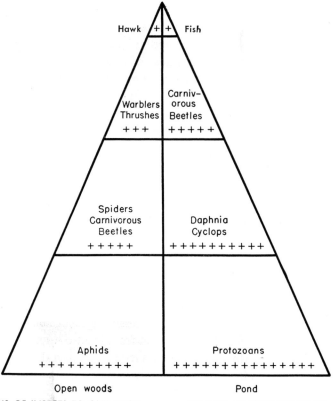

FIG. 5.21. A pyramid of free living animals in one area. Plus signs express abundance of types of animals. The smallest ones are most abundant. They supply food to carnivores that are larger in size and fewer in number and these in turn supply other carnivores that are still larger and fewer.

generally the prey of larger ones, that there are great numbers of small animals and relatively few large ones. This food situation is very complex. It clearly involves sizes of food; it also includes feeding equipment such as cilia, teeth, and claws, all sorts of locomotion, and kinds and extent of territory covered in hunting food, as well as shifts in population due to cataclysms from the action of weather and humanity. The food relations of animals, actually the connections between the soil and the beefsteak, are exceedingly important to human economy.

Protective Resemblance and Mimicry. Protective resemblances are characteristics that seem to make life safer for animals in their own environments. Such protection is a debatable subject which has much to be shown for it and considerable against it. It is a pattern of colors that makes an animal unrecognizable against its home background. A brown streaked sparrow is lost among the twigs of a brush pile; katydids are as green as the leaves beneath them; ground squirrels (gophers) and prairie chickens are streaked like prairie grass; fishes that swim in and out between bright-colored corals are also brightly colored. Polar bears are white. Snowshoe rabbits and weasels (white phase is ermine) are brown during the short northern summer and white in winter. There are vast numbers of animals whose coloration does conceal; there are also many in which it does not. There are animals whose coloration seems to have no significance in their survival. Throughout the Arctic there are two color phases of arctic foxes, one of them is brown in summer and white in winter; the other is grey or black in summer and blue or black in winter. Both the blue and white phases interbreed and are common and successful in the same areas of Greenland and Alaska.

Camouflage is the painting or screening of boats, buildings, other objects, or persons so that they are lost to view in the background. It was first widely used in World War I. Its principles were based upon those of protective coloration suggested by a British zoologist, E. B. Poulton, and later developed by an American artist, G. H. Thayer, and published in his finely illustrated book, *Concealing Coloration in the Animal Kingdom*. The first of the principles is counter-shading, a generalization of the fact that in the great majority of animals the back is dark and the underparts are pale. By painted models Thayer showed that any object so colored is less conspicuous on being strongly lighted from above and with dark reflection from below. Another principle is related to the break-up of a familiar form such as that of a dark-colored bird whose head is separated from its body by a white ring around the neck.

Colors of animals are often strikingly different in the two sexes, the males usually the more brightly colored, especially in birds, fishes, and insects. Sexual coloration is often associated with endocrine secretions and is mentioned further in connection with them (Chap. 15).

6
Mutual Relationships of Animals

Whirligig beetles spin and turn in companies on the pond surface; a hundred starlings swing into a treetop; swarms of gnats rise and fall in quiet air; men and women join in a folk dance. These are all social beings, those of each group sharing particular surroundings. Animals express their sociability by being in the same place at the same time.

Two kinds of behavior, competition and natural cooperation, are characteristic of sociability.

Competition and Cooperation

Competition occurs when there is a common demand on a limited supply. A certain amount of it is stimulating and healthy. An unlimited competition is dangerous to individuals and communities. Its basic cause is the overproduction of animals, human or otherwise. During the spring breeding season many small ponds are populated with toads and each female lays about 15,000 eggs in a clutch. Presently the water swarms with toad tadpoles. All these tadpoles have insistent appetites for the algae of the green pond scum that overspreads the water. At the start there is an abundance of algae as well as tadpoles but it thins out as the eating goes on. Then competition begins. Some of the tadpoles manage to get food, but many of them starve. If they were fighting animals, there would be conflicts along with the starvation. In all communities plants and animals compete for such essentials as earth, water, food, warmth, and light as well as for less necessary things. Competition is commonly accompanied by a struggle for power and dominance usually gained by one or a few individuals.

Competition is usually keenest between those of the same species since they have the same wants; two rabbits go for clover, but a sheep eats grass and a cat eats birds. The overpopulation, sparsity of food, and starvation of individuals that occur in nonhuman animals have been matched in human ones throughout history. Competition is reduced by differences of diet: among

FIG. 6.1. The overpopulation of rabbits in Australia, too many for the space and food available, a prime cause of competition and ultimate destruction. This tele-photo lens picture shows how rabbits denude the pastures and drink the water holes dry. (Courtesy, Australian News and Information Bureau, New York.)

birds, as in seed-eaters and insect-eaters, among larvae of insects, e.g., tomato worms and cabbage worms. The rabbits of Australia, a country almost without predators, have repeatedly overpopulated the land, devastated vegetation, and brought themselves to starvation (Fig. 6.1).

Cooperation, conscious or unconscious, is the behavior of plants or animals which benefits the lives of those about them. Animals may produce a flourishing population beneficial to all concerned. They easily pass this point however, by multiplying to such an extent that they are hungry and sick for want of food and space. Thus their cooperation may be turned to disoperation. Examples of cooperation are plentiful. In winter bees crowd together in clusters within the hive and thus conserve the heat in their bodies. Northern musk oxen stand close together, heads down, against attacking wolves; geese band together with outstretched necks to hiss their disturber. People join in applause by clapping their hands together; tent caterpillars join in making their web and mending it when it is torn; beavers work together on their winter lodge and their food stores (Fig. 6.3).

Competition and cooperation are fundamental biological principles. Competition has long been recognized as such, especially since Darwin based his Theory of Natural Selection upon it. Although the importance of cooperation had been suggested by certain European workers, its prevalence and the

FIG. 6.2. Cooperation. Tent caterpillars and their community web. The young caterpillars spin a dragline of silk from the time they hatch. After a few days of feeding and trial spinning they begin to work together constructing the nest, at first a small night tent, then a larger one a foot and a half or more long. They leave the tent in the day time and creep in single file to a feeding place leaving a trail of silk behind them. (Photograph by Lynwood Chace. Courtesy, National Audubon Society.)

soundness of the principle have been demonstrated in recent years by the observation, experiments, and conclusions of the eminent American ecologist, W. C. Allee and his co-workers (Suggested Reading, Chap. 6).

Varieties of Partnerships

Partnerships may occur between plants, between animals, or between plants and animals.

Symbiosis. Living together is known as symbiosis. This is a general term that includes all aspects of physiological and ecological association (Fig. 6.4). It is often difficult to determine the exact nature of the relation between two organisms that live together, whether it is a neutral affair or an advantage to both partners. In either case, symbiosis would describe it. Commensalism, mutualism, and parasitism are types of symbiosis.

FIG. 6.3. Cooperation. Beavers' lodge and winter food storage—a community project. The lodge and passageway to the pond bottom are shown as if cut open and the ice bound pond as if in section. The two beavers working below the water line must frequently come up for air. (Courtesy, Hamilton: *American Mammals.* New York, McGraw-Hill Book Co., Inc., 1939.)

COMMENSALISM. Meaning at the same table, commensalism was originally applied only to sharing the same food. It is now used for neutral associations which do not seem to affect either partner. A classic example is the sea anemone that rides about on the shell of the hermit crab and thereby gains wider range for forage, but does not eat the same kind of food as its host. Less familiar is the mahout beetle that rides on the head of a worker termite and takes bits of food as it is passed from one termite to another (Fig. 6.4).

MUTUALISM. A symbiosis that benefits each partner is mutualism. Honeybees and many flowering plants aid one another to the point of dependence. Honeybees eat nothing but flower products. And as they collect the nectar and pollen they distribute the latter, usually to flowers of the same kind because they grow together. Thus the bees cross-pollinate them. Many flowers are so formed that they can be pollinated only by insects. In nature the yucca lily (Spanish bayonet) and the yucca moth (Pronuba) are entirely dependent upon each other (Fig. 6.5). The lily is pollinated by the moth, which thrusts a blob of pollen onto the pistil. Thus she effects the fertilization of the ovules and then lays her eggs in the ovary where the larvae can feed on the ovules. The plant does not suffer, for more seeds develop than are eaten by the larvae of the Pronuba. Yucca lilies are native to southern North America but are cultivated farther north, since they are easily pollinated by hand.

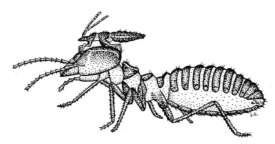

FIG. 6.4. A minute beetle, *Termitonicus mahout,* that rides on the heads of the workers of the termite, *Velocitermes beebei,* and takes bits of the food as it is passed from one worker to another. An example of symbiosis, a general term that includes a variety of partnerships. (Redrawn after Allee *et al.: Principles of Animal Ecology*. Philadelphia, W. B. Saunders Co., 1949.)

One of the most remarkable examples of mutualism is that between wood-eating termites and certain species of protozoans. The protozoans live protected within the intestines of the termites and in turn actually digest their food for them. Bits of the cellulose food are taken in by the protozoans and changed to sugar (dextrose) which is squeezed back into the intestine and absorbed by the tissues of the termite. Experiments have shown that termites cannot survive long without the protozoans unless they are given a diet other than cellulose. On the basis of the evolutionary history of termites it is estimated that these intestinal intimacies have existed for 150 million to 250 million years.

PARASITISM. Another form of symbiosis in which an organism lives on or in and at the expense of a larger plant or animal, called the host, is parasitism. The parasitic mistletoe grows on a tree, commonly an oak. Animal parasites are always small in comparison with their host and usually numerous. The parasite obtains food, protection, or transport from its host, often all three of these.

Parasitic animals are discussed in the chapters dealing with the groups to which they belong. These are especially: Chapters 21, Protozoa (sporozoans, e.g., malaria); 25, Flatworms (tapeworms, *et al.*); 26, Roundworms (trichinae, hookworms, *et al.*); 28, Annelids (leeches, *et al.*).

The relationship of parasitism costs the host its substance and the parasite its independence. People who must have special food are restricted in their travels; so are fleas and bedbugs.

The Host, a Living Habitat. Plants and animals have three major dwelling places: terrestrial—on or in the earth's crust, aquatic—in fresh or salt water, and on or in living organisms.

Parasites occupy living habitats. In them there are special places in which various parasites thrive, such as the skin or the liver, just as different seashore animals thrive in tide pools or in mucky sand.

Living habitats offer ready food and protection, within limits. Parasites must

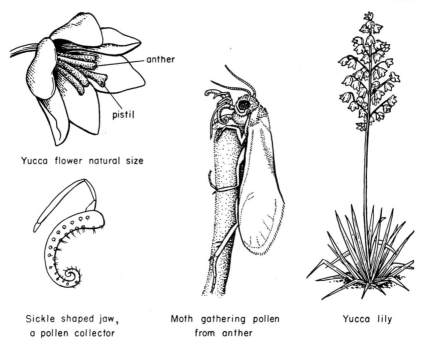

anther

pistil

Yucca flower natural size

Sickle shaped jaw,
a pollen collector

Moth gathering pollen
from anther

Yucca lily

MOTH AND LILY, MUTUAL BENEFACTORS

Fig. 6.5. Mutualism, a partnership that benefits each member. The yucca lily, *Yucca filamentosa,* whose stalks of white flowers grow four to six feet high in the eastern and much higher in the western United States. When the female moth visits a flower she thrusts her long ovipositor into the ovary and deposits an egg beside each of the several ovules (eggs). Then she climbs to the tip of the pistil and carrying pollen that she has collected from some other flower she pushes it into the stalk incidentally making it possible for the transported male cells to fertilize the ovules of the flower she is visiting. After fertilization the ovules develop into seeds; some of them are eaten by the larvae of the moth but others that are untouched propagate the plant.

hold their places, often against pressure, lack of oxygen, and the defenses of their host. If parasites of digestive tracts did not have a protective immunity to digestive fluids they themselves would be digested. Parasites must reproduce and be distributed in such a way that the young ones can enter into new hosts of the right type and at the right time. Trichinae, the minute worms resting in the pig's muscle, must arrive still alive in a human stomach by way of a sandwich or a sausage. It is a great gamble, but not a rare feat for trichinae in the United States (Fig. 6.7 and 26.5).

Development of a Food Habit. Parasitism is primarily a food habit and parasites are mainly chronic predators. Typical free-living predators are larger than their prey, kill it quickly, and devour it soon. A cat pounces upon a mouse, and if hungry, kills and eats it at once. Cats, foxes, and hawks are typical predators. Parasites are smaller than their host, feed upon its substance persistently, and chronically weaken or gradually kill it. A field mouse can supply blood to a moderate population of lice without great injury. But an excessively large population results in great competition among the lice and the death of the mouse from loss of blood. Like tax collectors after more income the lice must then find another mouse.

Development of Parasitic Living. In the early stages of parasitism the incipient parasites visit their hosts only for meals. Blood-sucking leeches clamp their suckers to the flesh, insert their jaws, suck blood until they are satiated, and then drop off into the water. Such a meal supplies a leech with food for several weeks. The blood-sucking mosquitoes, always female, spend even less time on their hosts and simply take a firm stand on the skin while they suck up the blood (Chap. 30). In certain species mosquitoes do not lay their eggs until after they have had a blood meal. In laboratories where they are reared they are allowed to bite a human victim whenever eggs are needed for experiment. Such mosquitoes have taken a long step into parasitism

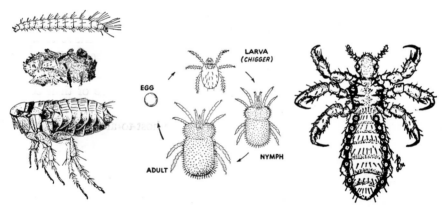

FIG. 6.6. Ectoparasites; examples of parasitic life on the external surface of the body: fleas, lice, chiggers. *Left,* the common rat flea, *Nosopsyllus fasciatus* (after Bishopp): upper, the nonparasitic larva and pupa that live near the host, not upon it; lower, the blood-sucking parasitic adult (female) that stays much of the time feeding on its host, slips easily between the hairs, has great ability to spring on and off its host, and is able to adopt a human one temporarily. *Center,* common chigger, or jigger mite, harvest mite, *Entrobicula alfredugesi.* The exceedingly minute six-legged parasitic larva that bores into the skin, liquefies the local tissue and sucks up the fluid. After feeding the mite is no longer parasitic but drops to the ground and develops the free living eight-legged stage. Chiggers are distributed from New York to Minnesota and are pests in the southern states attacking all land vertebrates including man. *Right,* human head louse, *Pediculus humanus,* var. capitis. Adult showing the claw and thumb that lock around the hairs. Lice are highly adapted for clinging and blood sucking and do both throughout their life history. (*Left,* courtesy, Matheson: *Medical Entomology.* Ithaca, N.Y., Comstock Publishing Co., 1950. *Center,* courtesy, Stiles: *Individual and Community Health.* New York, The Blakiston Company, 1953. *Right,* courtesy, Herrick: *Household Insects.* New York, The Macmillan Co., 1916.)

in being so seriously dependent upon the special diet of warm blood that the species will die without it. Male mosquitoes do not show any such trend toward the habit; they still drink fruit juices. Fleas and sucking lice represent steps in increasing parasitism in the persistence with which they stay on their host. Fleas stay on a dog most of the time; they also frequently jump off. Lice stay on except by accident. Their claws lock onto the hairs of the mouse or other host and they cling fast as fleas never do. Chiggers go still further. They are the parasitic larvae of certain kinds of mites that actually burrow into the skin (Fig. 6.6).

The parasites so far mentioned are a few of the great host of ectoparasites that attack the outsides of animals and represent the earlier stages of parasitism. Endoparasites spend most of their lives inside the bodies of animals and represent the extremes of adjustments to parasitic living (Fig. 6.7). The easiest way for an endoparasite to enter an animal is by way of the mouth along with food or drink. Other possible entrances are into the breathing organs, the excretory ones, the reproductive organs, and through the skin.

Life Histories. Whatever their habit, animals go through various phases during their life spans. The embryo of any animal is very different from the adult; young animals may live in one environment and later move to a very different one. Parasites often change from one host to another while in their egg or larval phase of life. This is especially difficult for endoparasites which have to take advantage of the habits as well as the structure of their second hosts in order to enter them.

A parasitic animal may pass directly from one host to another of the same

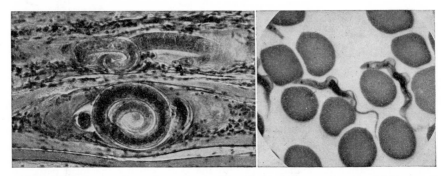

FIG. 6.7. Endoparasites; phases in the life of two endoparasites in which parasitism is highly developed. *Left,* trichina worms: *Trichinella spirella,* coiled and dormant among muscle cells, an example of the phase of waiting, characteristic of many endoparasites. *Right,* trypanosomes: *Trypanosoma gambiense,* a protozoan blood parasite. (Fig. 21.10, trypanosomes and West African sleeping sickness.) They reproduce in enormous numbers in the blood of man and in the big game of Africa and are transmitted by the tsetse fly. The multiplicity of their populations and dependence upon a second transmitting host are characteristic of many endoparasites. (Courtesy, General Biological Supply House, Inc., Chicago, Ill.)

species, in which case it has a direct life history. Such parasites may live through their entire lives in one host, producing eggs and larvae which in turn live and reproduce in the same place. Many of them are usually carried out of the body with waste from the intestine. They then await the chance of getting into the mouth of another individual; this is the usual history of pinworms (*Enterobius vermicularis*), common parasites of children (Chap. 26). In contrast to such direct life cycles are the indirect ones of parasites with hosts that belong to two or more different species. Larvae of these parasites develop to a certain stage in one host, such as a sheep. But they cannot develop further unless they are cast out of the sheep's intestine at the edge of a pond where they can enter certain pond snails, their intermediate hosts. In the snails they develop to a particular stage in which they leave the snails, swim about in the water, and finally onto the wet grass around it. In this stage and in no other are they able to infect another sheep when swallowed (Fig. 25.11). These parasites, called flukes, prove that gambling is a very ancient and enduring practice.

Certain important variations apply to both direct and indirect life histories of parasites. Some species with direct life histories can live parasitically in several related animals, such as sheep, cattle, and others that chew the cud; while other species, such as the human hookworm, can live only in one type of host. Parasites with indirect life histories spend part of their lives in an intermediate host before they can pass to the definitive host in which they reproduce. An example of indirect life history is that of the liver fluke of sheep; the intermediate host is a snail in which the parasite is immature; the definitive hosts are sheep in which the flukes reproduce.

Effects of Parasitic Life on Parasites. Parasitic animals have to contend with many difficulties and risks. Such gamblers stake their lives on finding their hosts and maintaining themselves upon or within them. They accomplish this by an enormous production of sex cells, by the development, in many species, of male and female organs in the same individual, making fertilization of the eggs more certain, and by parthenogenesis, the production of young from unfertilized eggs. It has been calculated that the beef tapeworm of man produces between 50 and 150 millions of eggs a year. American hookworms probably release about 6 to 20 thousand eggs per day. Numbers are also increased by asexual reproduction. In certain parasitic wasps one egg divides so as to produce several embryos. The single-celled malarial parasite produces many new individuals by division. It has been estimated that these parasites (*Plasmodium vivax*) can produce about 40 thousand parasites to every cubic millimeter of the host's blood. Eventually parasites kill their host and destroy their own welfare by overpopulation, just as too many gasoline stations kill a business.

Some Important Parasites of Man. Parasites occur in all the main groups (phyla) of animals. Parasitic members of the phylum chordata are extremely rare, e.g., hagfishes and a few blood-sucking bats. Of the invertebrates, the protozoans, roundworms, and flatworms are deeply committed to parasitism. Among parasitic arthropods the insects are best known, such as fleas, lice, bed-bugs. They are transmitters of disease-producing parasites and are themselves in the earlier stages of parasitism.

The life cycles of various parasites are described and figured in Part IV with the groups to which they belong. The accompanying list shows the occurrence of some important animal parasites of man (Table 6.1).

Table 6.1

SOME IMPORTANT PARASITES OF MAN

	Parasite	Means of Transmission	Disease in Human Host or Other Mammal
Protozoans (*Chapter 21*)	*Endamoeba histolytica* *Plasmodium* (various species) *Trypanosoma gambiense*	Ticks Bodily contact Water Anopheline mosquitoes (female) Tsetse fly (*Glossina*)	Tick-borne relapsing fever Syphilis Amebic dysentery Malaria (various types) African sleeping sickness
Flatworms (*Chapter 25*)	*Schistosoma mansoni* et al. Blood flukes *Taenia saginata* Beef tapeworm *Taenia solium* Pork tapeworm	Water, snails Cattle, beef muscle Pork muscle	Bilharzia in about 50 per cent of population of Egypt, also in other tropical countries Inhabits intestine, muscles Inhabits intestine, muscles
Roundworms (*Chapter 26*)	*Ascaris* *Ascaris lumbricoides* *Enterobius vermicularis* Pinworms *Necator americanus* American hookworms *Wuchereria* *Trichinella spiralis* Trichinae	Soil, food, clothing Clothing Water, soil Mosquitoes (several genera) Hogs, rats, et al. (in pork, sausage, etc.)	Ascariasis Enterobiasis Hookworm disease Filariasis Trichinosis

Animal Communities

Organization of Groups. Aggregation is a general term for a group of organisms of the same or different species, associated but not organized into societies. Many of them are examples of natural cooperation and as such were cited at the beginning of this chapter in connection with cooperation. Un-organized groups like these were doubtless the beginnings of complex societies such as those of ants and termites. Animals congregate because their environ-

FIG. 6.8. Hundreds of white pelicans rising and thousands still to rise from a preserve on Lake Washington, State of Washington. A typical aggregation of animals associated because something in the environment has beckoned them. (Photograph by Hugh M. Halliday. Courtesy, National Audubon Society.)

ment drives or beckons: the cold of winter, the heat of summer, the dark that starts the crows crowding into their roosts, the low tide that leaves new forage for the gulls, the lakes kept as safe stopping places for migrating waterfowl (Fig. 6.8). Animals are brought together by accident; starfishes, snails, and others thrown on the beach enmeshed in seaweed. The spring gatherings of frogs and toads and the shoals of spawning fish are aggregations stimulated by climatic conditions and breeding habits.

Social Organization of Animals. Among invertebrates social organization reaches its highest development in the insects—termites, wasps, bees, and ants. Their organization has a complexity comparable to that attained by vertebrates but of an entirely different character. It is a strictly defined and inflexible division of labor in which the various needs of the community are attended to by individuals whose structures and functions mark them, with rare exceptions, inescapably as members of particular castes with special work to do. Among bees such specialists are the queen, the workers always females, and the male drones (Chap. 30).

Organization of Vertebrate Groups. This is based upon three general principles: the holding of territory, social hierarchies in which dominance and power exist in a graded order from highest to lowest, and leadership-followership.

TERRITORIAL RIGHTS. Birds take possession of a parcel of good habitat, sing loudly from a prominent perch and defend it against trespass, driving off members of their own or other species. American song sparrows sing special proclamations of their ownership of territory and defend the mating and nesting grounds by fighting. The willow wrens that migrate into England every spring have a regular system of dividing up their usual territory into roughly equal parts, and the males fight among themselves for their respective rights.

SOCIAL HIERARCHIES. Groups in which one individual dominates all the others have been observed in birds, rats, cats, dogs, apes, and human groups. A dominance known as peck right, observed in small flocks of domestic hens, has been investigated mainly by Allee and his co-workers. In these flocks one particular hen pecks any other hen without being pecked in return, that is, she is dominant with peck right over the whole flock. Below her a small group of hens peck those of lower social levels than themselves without receiving return pecks. Below them again, similar levels occur down to the lowest level, the hen which is pecked by all others yet does not peck back. During observations each hen was tagged for identification by colored leg bands and other markings. Observations were taken with great care and repeated many times. The dominance of a hen was generally first established by fights. Ailing hens and those newly installed were in the low levels, and regular members which were taken from the flock lost their positions by being absent. Similar social hierarchies or grades of power exist among flocks of male fowls. Flocks of white-throat sparrows represent social hierarchies similar to those of domestic fowls but are less fixed.

LEADERSHIP AND FOLLOWERSHIP. The leader of a group may or may not be its dominant member. The leader is the individual that will not desert the group in any emergency and that its members will follow. It is the experienced "knowing" animal, not necessarily the largest or fastest. In herds of Scottish red deer a stag is ordinarily the dominant member, but in crises the males leave the group and a female assumes leadership. With real leadership the

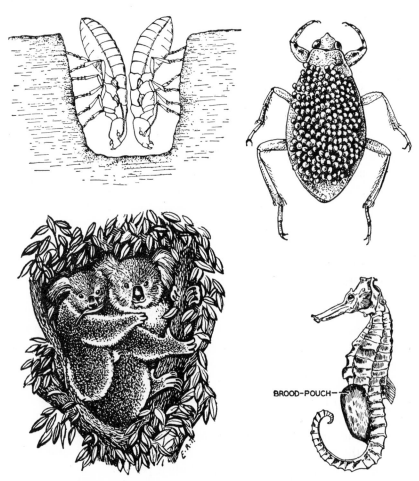

BROOD-POUCH—

Fig. 6.9. Relations of parents and young. *Top left,* termite, *Hodotermes turke-stanicus,* king and queen beginning to dig the burrow that will lead to an elaborate underground nest with thousands of occupants of which they will be the parents (After G. Jacobson). *Top right,* male water bug, *Pelostoma flumineum,* with developing eggs glued to his back by the female. Such nursery-bearing males can be found commonly in ponds during the summer. *Bottom left,* Koala, Australian teddy bear. Female first carries the young one in a pouch like that of the kangaroo, then on her back. Adults are about two feet long. *Bottom right,* male sea horse (Hippocampus) with brood pouch in which the developing young are carried (After Boulenger). (Termites courtesy, Wheeler: *Social Life in the Insect World.* New York, Harcourt, Brace & Co., 1923. Waterbug courtesy, Morgan: *Fieldbook of Ponds and Streams.* New York, G. P. Putnam's Sons, 1930. Seahorse courtesy, Rand: *The Chordates.* Philadelphia, The Blakiston Co., 1950. Koala courtesy, Young: *The Life of Vertebrates.* Oxford, Clarendon Press, 1950.)

followers are dependent upon the leader, and the leader upon the followers in a way which is not the case with the dominant animal or with the pseudo leader which chance may place temporarily at the top. Interdependence between leader and followers is complete in the queen honeybee and the workers, and is very marked in other social insects. Male bees are the least social members of the hive. After the mating season, male deer separate from the rest of the herd and forage for themselves. On the other hand, the females are accompanied by the young ones wherever they go. Many similar habits point to the female as the deeply social influence in groups of animals.

The Family. Both parents may take part in rearing the young. The male water bug carries the eggs stuck to his back until they hatch; the male seahorse has a brood pouch where the female deposits the eggs which he carries until the young ones swim out into open water; male birds usually take their turn at bringing food to the nest (Fig. 6.9). In general, however, the mother and young relations are more stable and intimate, more truly social. Mother and young have a comparatively long association in widely different types of animals. Female spiders carry nurseries of spiderlings on their backs; crayfishes and lobsters swim about for many weeks with eggs and then young ones hanging on their swimmerets; for days the female robin keeps close company with her young ones, showing them what it is to listen for earthworms and how to tackle them. A great company of young mammals are carried or trail beside their mothers, young kangaroos or joeys, skunklets, bear cubs, and fawns. They explore the surroundings from their shelter of maternal care. They imitate the turns of their parents and gradually take part in the customs of their kind. They are products of family associations, mothers, and some times both parents, and young. Thus the family constitutes one of the bases, though not the only one, from which society has sprung. Competition and cooperation exist in the family as they do in other groups.

PART III

The Internal Environment of the Body

7
Tissues

In multicellular animals, cells live crowded together and constantly affected by one another. Whether similar or different they cooperate closely in the organization of the animal. Differentiation, the modification of certain parts for certain functions, and cooperation are fundamental properties of their structure and activity. The body of a flying bird and the body of the pilot of an airplane are both great companies of cooperating cells.

Cells are associated in groups, the tissues and organs, and these in turn in systems. The study of groups of cells is histology or microscopic anatomy.

Tissues, Organs, and Systems. Tissues are groups of similar cells with the intercellular substances which they may produce. The substances may be of hardly noticeable amount as in epithelium, or conspicuous as in bone, or fluid as in blood.

An organ is an association of tissues all of which cooperate toward the performance of one or more particular functions. The heart is an organ that consists largely of muscle; it is covered and lined with epithelium; nervous tissue acts in the control of its pulsation; and connective tissue holds the other tissues together.

A system is a group of organs which collectively perform certain related functions. The digestive system is concerned with intake of food, its preparation for absorption, and elimination of undigested waste substances.

The animal body, like the plant, is built of groups of cells that form tissues, of tissues that form organs, of organs forming systems, and of systems that compose the whole body.

The tissues are discussed in this chapter. The organs are included with their respective systems.

Classes of Tissue

There are four types of tissues, grouped according to their structure and function: epithelial, connective tissue including blood and supporting tissues, muscular, and nervous tissue.

EPITHELIAL TISSUES

Epithelium covers the outer surfaces of the body, lines its cavities such as lungs, alimentary canal, the coelom or body cavity, and the blood and lymph vessels (Fig. 7.1). It forms glands and the essential parts of the sense organs —sensory cells in the eye and nose.

Epithelium is an essential guardian of the integrity of the body. It has a general and vital part in metabolism since all substances which take part in metabolic activity must go through epithelial cells. All digested food is absorbed through epithelium, mostly in the small intestine. The amount of water contained in an animal is controlled through epithelium, in the skin, alimentary canal, and kidneys. In the liver and kidneys it takes part in excreting waste substances. It secretes such varied products as oyster shells and pearls, the chitinous cover of insects, the digestive fluids of all multicellular animals, and the hormones of glands such as the thyroid and the pancreas. It is directly the protection against all manner of mechanical and chemical injuries. It was

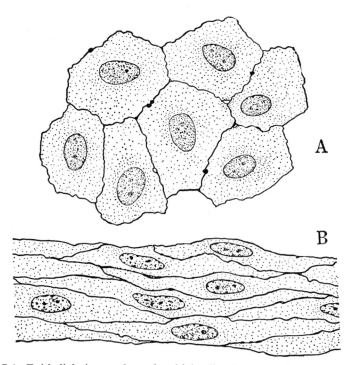

FIG. 7.1. Epithelial tissues through which all substances that take part in the metabolism of multicellular animals must pass. *A*, simple flattened or squamous epithelium from the surface of the mesentery of a guinea pig; *B*, lining of a small vein of mesentery. Intercellular cement is darkened by the preparation. ×1200. (Courtesy, Nonidez and Windle: *Textbook of Histology*, ed. 2. New York, McGraw-Hill Book Co., Inc., 1953.)

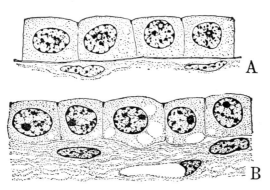

Fig. 7.2. Cuboidal or low simple columnar epithelium; *A*, lining of a collecting tubule in the kidney of a monkey; *B*, in the thyroid gland of a monkey. These cells produce the thyroid secretion. ×1200. (Courtesy, Nonidez and Windle: *Textbook of Histology*, ed. 2. New York, McGraw-Hill Book Co., Inc., 1953.)

due to the epithelium on their bodies and in their kidneys that the animals of ancient time could leave the sea and gradually become adjusted to living in fresh water or on land. The epidermis or outer layers of human skin which is formed of epithelial cells is in general about as thick as tissue paper. Yet a bit of vinegar dropped on broken and unbroken skin are vividly different experiences. In certain regions, the epidermis is many-layered, as on the palms of

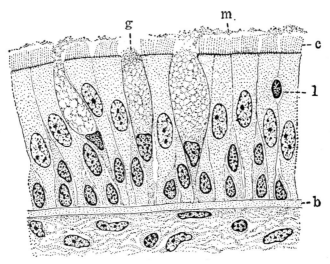

Fig. 7.3. Columnar epithelium with motile cilia (*c*) lining the trachea of a monkey. Mucous or goblet cells (*g*) secrete the mucus (*m*) that passes through the membrane at one end of the cell and spreads over the inner surface of the trachea. The delicate non-cellular basement membrane (*b*) separates the epithelium from the loose connective tissue beneath. A lymphocyte (1) is migrating through the epithelium. ×1200. (Courtesy, Nonidez and Windle: *Textbook of Histology*, ed. 2. New York, McGraw-Hill Book Co., Inc., 1953.)

the hands, and thick and tough in the footpads of cats and dogs; the cells are heavily cornified in fingernails, in the horns of cattle, in the hoofs of horses, the outer shell of turtles, the hair of mammals, and feathers of birds. New epithelial cells are formed as others are worn out or injured. Otherwise we should be walking records of our encounters—scrapes, burns, and pinches. Regeneration is constantly going on in skin and its outgrowths of feathers and hairs. The snake's skin comes off in one piece, the human skin in little fragments; feathers are shed in late summer, human skin at any time.

Different Kinds of Epithelial Cells. These are classified according to their shapes—flattened, cuboidal, columnar, and arrangement in single or multiple layers, simple or stratified (Table 7.1). A single layer of simple flattened (or squamous) epithelium lines blood and lymph vessels including the heart (Fig. 7.1). Cuboidal epithelium lines the ducts of glands (Fig. 7.2). The cells of columnar epithelium are tall prisms or cylinders (Figs. 7.3, 7.4). They form the lining of the small intestine where they secrete digestive juices and absorb the digested food. All columnar cells have polarity, that is, are different at their two ends. In ciliated columnar cells the polarity is conspicuous since they bear a large number of cilia only on their free surfaces. Cilia beat with rapid effective and slower recovery strokes, always bending in one direction. The movements travel over the surface in waves which rapidly succeed each other at regular intervals. This occurs in the lining of the human trachea with the stronger stroke toward the mouth. Cilia on the gills and lips of clams wave particles of food toward the mouth. In the oviducts of mammals they create currents which move the eggs toward the uterine cavity (Fig. 18.14).

Stratified flattened epithelium of the skin is several layers thick; the outer

Table 7.1

FORMS AND FUNCTIONS OF EPITHELIUM

Name	Form	Examples
Simple	Flattened	Mesentery of frog; in man, lining of capillary
	Cuboidal	Lining salivary gland in insect; lining normal thyroid of frog
	Columnar	Lining food cavity of hydra; small intestine of cat
Ciliated	Columnar	Pharynx of frog; human trachea; gill of clam
Stratified	Cells in layers, outer ones flattened	Skin of frog and man

Name	Function	Examples
Glandular	Digestive secretion	Small intestine of mammals
Sensory	Response to vibration, light, chemicals	Lateral line organ in fishes, tadpoles; rod and cone cells of human eye; chemoreceptors in jellyfishes
Germinal	Origin of sex cells	Seminiferous tubules in testes of frog, cat, man; ovary in hydra, grasshopper

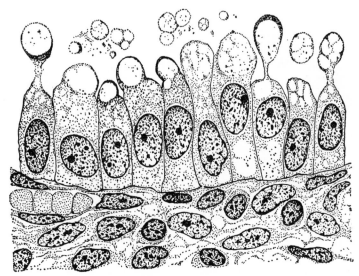

FIG. 7.4. Simple columnar cells in a gland in the human uterus. Droplets of the secretion have collected at the ends of the cells and are about to pass through the membranes; other droplets are free of the cells in the cavity of the uterus. All the epithelial cells have polarity, most striking in the ciliated and glandular ones. Preparation by Dr. G. N. Papanicolaou. × 1200. (Courtesy, Nonidez and Windle: *Textbook of Histology*, ed. 2. New York, McGraw-Hill Book Co., Inc., 1953.)

ones are dead and horny (Fig. 8.2). They are constantly being worn away at the surface and replaced in the deeper layers. Stratified epithelium is extremely thick in the footpads of large carnivores—tigers, lions.

Connective Tissue, Including Blood and Supporting Tissues

Connective tissue contains a large amount of nonliving intercellular substance, fibers in connective tissues, tough resilient chondrin in cartilage, hard rigid substance in bone, and the fluid plasma in blood (Fig. 7.5).

Connective tissue connects and binds together the tissues and organs of the body. It seems ever present, penetrating into glands and muscles along with the blood vessels, and binding nerve and muscle fibers into compact bundles. If all other tissues were destroyed, the body with its organs would keep its shape because of connective tissue. During dissection its whitish sticky strands have to be pushed aside and torn. In beefsteak and roast beef such strands display their tough and threadlike quality. Surface wounds are closed mainly by connective tissue and scars of all kinds are chiefly composed of it.

Loose areolar or open tissue is the papery fastening which must be torn as one skins any animal, especially birds and mammals. This most generalized connective tissue supports and surrounds other tissues and is a living packing material in the body.

The substances which other tissues receive from the blood and lymph—

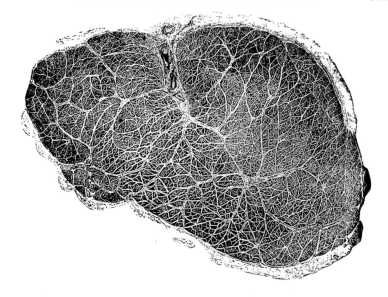

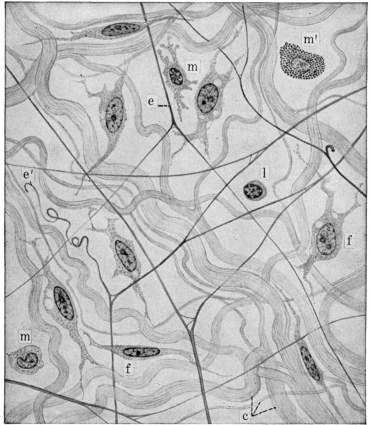

(*Legend on facing page*)

oxygen, food, water—and the metabolic products which tissues pass on to the blood and lymph must all go through connective tissues. Like epithelium it is a screen through which substances pass to and fro. The characteristic of the body known as its constitution is probably connected with properties of the loose connective tissue. Abnormal growths such as tumors persist or fail to develop, depending to some extent on the reactions of this tissue. In its defensive response the phagocytic cells called macrophages (large eaters) which originate in it are the main actors. These cells are scattered throughout the body and are ordinarily quiet, but if properly stimulated, as by infection, they become mobilized like an army, enlarged, and active.

The structure of loose areolar connective tissue is typical of all connective tissue (Fig. 7.5). It is composed of: (1) cells, such as macrophages, fibroblasts (associated with the formation of fibers); (2) nonliving collagenous white and elastic yellow fibers; (3) a thin jellylike ground substance. Collagenous fibers are so-called because they contain a protein, collagen, which on boiling yields glue and gelatin. In areolar tissue they run in all directions, are very flexible and resistant, but are not elastic. They are really bundles of very, very fine cross-striated fibrils, but these are invisible except by special techniques. Elastic fibers appear as single strands, branched and like rubber bands; when a pull is released they return to their original length. Areolar tissue pulls the skin into place after it has been pinched up from the back of the hand, more quickly in a younger than an older person; it also surrounds organs. Dense areolar tissue, the dermis of the skin, is the fibrous part of leather.

In many ligaments and tendons collagenous fibers are predominant and compactly arranged according to the strains put on them. They are densely woven like felt in the sclerotic coat commonly called the white of the eye. Connective tissues often contain very few collagenous white fibers and many yellow elastic ones, the latter so abundant that the whole tissue is elastic. This is the case in the nuchal ligament of grazing animals: a strap of ex-

---

FIG. 7.5. Connective and supporting tissues. *Top,* cross section through the human tailor's or sartorius muscle showing how muscle cells are held together by a web of interlacing strands of connective tissue, the white lines in most cross cuts of meat. This muscle is the longest in the body originating on the hip, crossing the thigh obliquely, extending down the leg, and attached to the inner side of the shin bone. *Bottom,* microscopic structure of the loose areolar connective tissue of a kitten, spread out and stained to show its parts. This tissue tears like paper as one skins an animal, a tissue with many open spaces. *c,* non-living collagen (or protein) white; *e,* elastic yellow fibers; *f,* fibroblasts, the cells associated with production of the fibers; *l,* lymphocytes; *m,* macrophages, the cells that consume bacteria and foreign particles; *m¹,* mast cells, function unknown. (*Top,* courtesy, Maximow and Bloom: *Textbook of Histology,* ed. 6. Philadelphia, W. B. Saunders Co., 1952. *Bottom,* courtesy, Nonidez and Windle: *Textbook of Histology,* ed. 2. New York, McGraw-Hill Book Co., Inc., 1953.)

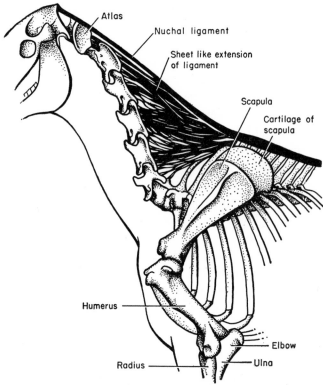

FIG. 7.6. Nuchal ligament of the horse, a strap of tough, yellow elastic fibers, often called whetleather, highly developed in grazing animals.

tremely tough yellowish tissue, sometimes called whetleather, which extends along the back of the neck (Fig. 7.6). In the larger arteries these nonliving elastic fibers form a large part of the wall. In older animals they lose their elasticity.

Certain connective tissue cells are storage places for fat. In adipose tissue or fat each cell is so filled with the fat globule that the nucleus and cytoplasm are pushed into a thin rim around it (Fig. 7.7). Fat enters and leaves the cell in soluble form. Fat cells border the blood vessels, often great masses of them in the mesentery of the human abdomen constituting the so-called fatty apron. Blubber, the fat of whales, has long been a valuable source of oil; for the whale it is a great insulation against cold as well as a store of food. All insects contain more or less fat, especially caterpillars and various pupae. The weight of full-grown larvae of honeybees is 65 per cent fat, due to rich diet and no exercise.

Supporting Tissues

Cartilage and bone are living tissues with cells that produce the substances giving these tissues strength and rigidity.

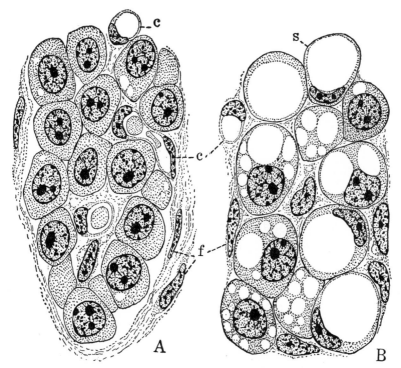

FIG. 7.7. Development of adipose (fatty) tissue in the larynx of a newborn kitten; *c,* blood capillaries; *f,* nucleus of developing fibers (cells); *s,* signet fat cell. *A,* in a region in which fat droplets (white spots) have appeared in only one cell; *B,* another region in which fat droplets almost fill the cells crowding the cytoplasm and nucleus against the cell membrane so that the shape is like a signet ring. Cells containing large amounts of fat are found in connective tissue almost everywhere throughout the body. (Courtesy, Nonidez and Windle: *Textbook of Histology,* ed. 2. New York, McGraw-Hill Book Co., Inc., 1953.)

Cartilage. The intercellular substance of cartilage is firm and gumlike. Normally it contains no lime but with age may gather deposits of it. Hyaline, glassy cartilage or gristle, occurs in the higher vertebrates in many regions, such as the ventral ends of the ribs, the joints, end of the nose, the rings of the trachea (Fig. 7.8). The cells are surrounded by their semitransparent secretion in which there are no blood vessels. Yellow elastic cartilage contains a network of elastic fibers and is more flexible and elastic than the hyaline type (Fig. 7.9). It constitutes much of the external ear of mammals, such as man, bats, donkeys. White fibrous cartilage composes the intervertebral discs which act as cushions between the vertebrae (Fig. 7.10). Those of the human body are subject to various disarrangements especially in the lumbar region where there is most pressure upon them.

Bone. This is a supporting tissue composed of bone cells surrounded by organic material, collagenous (protein) fibers, and inorganic salts (Fig. 7.11).

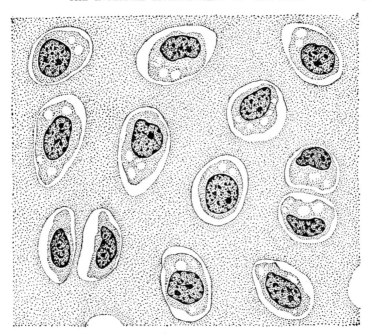

FIG. 7.8. Hyaline cartilage from the head of the thigh bone (femur) of a puppy. The cells (chondrocytes) secrete the glassy substance surrounding them and from which they have shrunken away. Nourishment filters through the cartilage to the cells. (Courtesy, Nonidez and Windle: *Textbook of Histology*, ed. 2. New York, McGraw-Hill Book Co., Inc., 1953.)

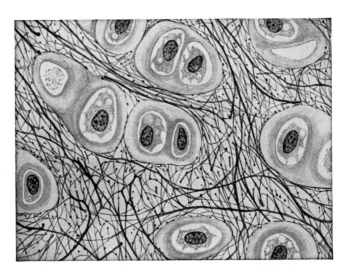

FIG. 7.9. Yellow elastic cartilage from a pig's ear; groups of hyaline cartilage cells are isolated by the hyaline substance which holds a meshwork of the elastic fibers of connective tissue. The springback of the human ear when pulled is due to these fibers. (Courtesy, Nonidez and Windle: *Textbook of Histology*, ed. 2. New York, McGraw-Hill Book Co., Inc., 1953.)

These salts are largely calcium phosphate and calcium carbonate. Two types
of structure are found in most bones, compact bone and latticed or spongy

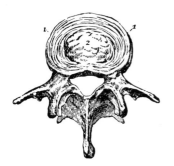

FIG. 7.10. The intervertebral disk or cushion between the vertebrae mainly composed of white
fibrous cartilage. A human vertebra seen from
above with part of the intervertebral disk adhering
to it. The outer side of the vertebra is down; in
life the hole contains the nerve cord. *1*, rings of
fibers arranged in layers; *2*, a small central body
of cartilage (nucleus pulposus). (Courtesy, *Quain's
Elements of Anatomy*, ed. 11. New York, Longmans, Green & Co., 1915.)

bone. The Haversian system is the unit of bony structure (Fig. 7.12). Its odd
name comes from that of Clapton Havers, an English anatomist, who described the system in the 17th century. The unit is an irregularly cylindrical
structure with a central or Haversian canal containing nerves and blood

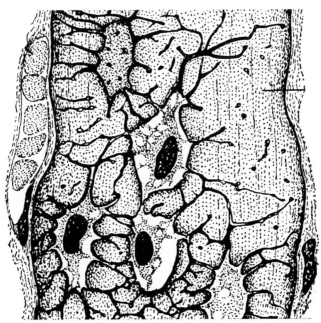

FIG. 7.11. Bone cells in a thin section of human thigh bone (femur) with bone
cells and their processes highly magnified; the naturally colorless nuclei have been
deeply stained. The bone cell lies in a minute cavity (lacuna) with its living
processes extending into extremely fine canals (canaliculi) which branch out in all
directions through the intercellular substance often connecting with those of other
cells. Materials pass through these to and from the cells, ultimately to blood vessels. (Courtesy, Nonidez and Windle: *Textbook of Histology*, ed. 2. New York,
McGraw-Hill Book Co., Inc., 1953.)

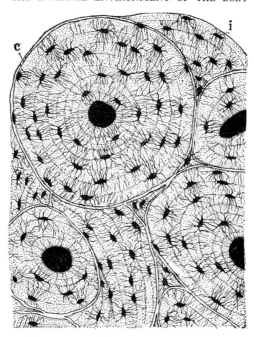

FIG. 7.12. Microscopic structure shown in a cross section of human dried compact bone, one complete unit of bony structure (Haversian system) and parts of
others. In life the central or Haversian canal (black) contains nerves, blood and
lymph vessels; the lacunae, also black, contain the bone cells. All nourishment and
oxygen come to the bone cells by way of the canals. Layers of bone surround each
canal like successive coverings of a cylinder. (Courtesy, Nonidez and Windle:
Textbook of Histology, ed. 2. New York, McGraw-Hill Book Co., Inc., 1953.)

and lymph vessels. The blood vessels of the Haversian canals are connected
with those in the marrow or with larger vessels entering and leaving the bone.
Thus, when young, even compact bone proves to be a living tissue through
which body fluids can circulate. Respiration occurs in bone cells and consequently metabolism does also, the latter at a lower rate than in other tissues.
In the finest structure of the bone around the Haversian canal the fibers
are wound spirally and are thus made stronger as the fibers of rope are
strengthened by twisting. In spongy bone the "lattices" are like bridges which
increase the strength against blows and breakage. The intercellular substance
of bone acts as a storage for calcium and phosphorus. There is continual interchange of calcium between the blood and bones which keeps the calcium
content of the blood constant. Insufficient calcium and phosphorus cause
rickets, a softening of the bones. In small children this may be a cause of
bow-legs.

Bone marrow is a soft cellular tissue in the central cavity of long bones
and the spaces of spongy bones. There are two closely related kinds, the
yellow and red. The yellow marrow that fills the central cavity of long bones

is chiefly fat. Red marrow occurs mainly at the ends of long bones. It contains fewer fat cells and is characterized by the development of red blood cells and granular white ones. Great numbers of these are continually passing into the blood and a comparable number of worn-out cells is withdrawn. This is an instance of the regulated economy of the body which breaks down comparatively seldom.

Blood and Lymph

Blood and lymph, its supplemental fluid, are tissues comparable to connective tissue and the skeletal tissues, bone and cartilage, to which they are related. As here described, there are four types of connective tissue in each of which the cells are surrounded by abundant intercellular substance. In ordinary connective tissue the substance is gelatinous; in cartilage, it is tough and jellylike; in bone, hard; in blood and lymph, a liquid in which the cells float freely.

As far as its origin and related tissues are concerned, the discussion of blood should be included at this point. Instead it is given in Chapter 12, Blood and Circulation, and is thus placed with the vessels that carry it through the body.

MUSCULAR TISSUE

Muscle cells are so elongated that they are commonly called muscle fibers; thus, the terms muscle cell and muscle fiber are used interchangeably. A muscle fiber is living matter; a connective-tissue fiber is not. Muscle fibers, that is, muscle cells, contain fibrils (myofibrils) within their cytoplasm; the shortening of these is the contraction or muscular action. Muscle cells are usually in bundles held together by connective tissue. Muscle has a high degree of contractility. This fundamental character of protoplasm is evident in the movements of an ameba and the action of its contractile vacuole, as well as in the movements of all other animals. Contraction of protoplasm is accompanied by chemical and physical changes.

Chemical Composition of Muscle. About three-fourths of muscle is water. Of the remainder about four-fifths is protein; the other one-fifth includes carbohydrates and fats, nitrogenous substances (urea, creatine), lactic acid, pigments, enzymes, and inorganic salts. The most abundant protein is myosin which makes up most of the contractile myofibrils. The carbohydrate is largely glycogen, the ready-to-use food stored in many tissues. When a muscle has been excited and fatigued its store of glycogen disappears and an equivalent amount of lactic acid takes its place. When the oxygen supply is renewed and after oxidation occurs the lactic acid is reduced and a proportional amount of heat results. Muscles contain a red pigment, muscle hemoglobin or myoglobin, which has an even greater affinity for oxygen than has the hemoglobin of blood cells. It is abundant in the "red" muscle of birds and mammals and the heart muscle of all vertebrates.

Types of Muscle. There are two main types: smooth, unstriated, or involuntary; and striated, skeletal or voluntary. Cardiac (heart) muscle, although striated, is involuntary and contracts rhythmically.

SMOOTH MUSCLE CELLS. These spindle-shaped cells occur in sheets held together by connective tissue (Fig. 7.13). They include muscles in blood vessels, in the urinary bladder, in the bronchial tubes of the lungs, in the alimentary canal, and in other structures not under voluntary control. The contraction of the iris of the eye in bright light is due to the contraction of smooth muscle. The contraction of smooth muscle causes goose flesh, the erection of hairs on the arms resulting from fear or cold, and the vivid lift of hairs on a cat's tail.

STRIATED OR SKELETAL MUSCLE. This is the muscle attached to the skeleton, the voluntary type that comprises the bulk of muscle in the body. Most of the meat that we eat is voluntary muscle, cut in slices, actually cross-sections, taken at right angles to the length of the muscle cells (Fig. 7.14). Striated muscle differs from the smooth type in the size and shape of its cells. The most conspicuous microscopic structures are the alternating light and dark crossbands of the cells. Striated muscle fibers are regarded as giant multinucleated cells. Some very long ones have about 100 peripheral nuclei. Each muscle cell contains a bundle of contractile fibrillae. In insects probably all muscle is more or less striated. Striations are prominent in the flight muscles of the honeybee when spread thinly on a slide in their fresh condition.

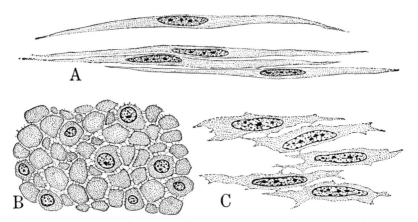

FIG. 7.13. Smooth muscle. *A,* fibers (cells) from a frog's bladder; *B,* cross section of smooth muscle from the bladder of a kitten; the muscle cells are held together by connective tissue; the section misses the nuclei of many cells; *C,* branching smooth muscle cells in the aorta of a dog. × 900. (Courtesy, Nonidez and Windle: *Textbook of Histology,* ed. 2. New York, McGraw-Hill Book Co., Inc., 1953.)

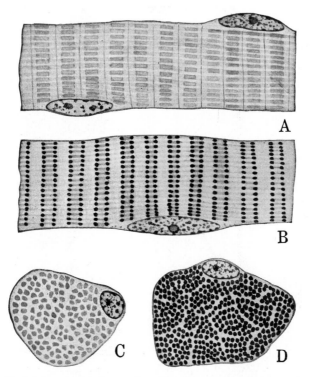

FIG. 7.14. Skeletal or striated muscle cells. *A* and *B,* in long section; *C* and *D,* in cross section. Note the nuclei with large nucleoli. The differences in appearance are due to different methods of preparation, an example of what often happens to preserved material. (Courtesy, Nonidez and Windle: *Textbook of Histology,* ed. 2. New York, McGraw-Hill Book Co., Inc. 1953.)

RED AND WHITE MUSCLE. The cells of dark red muscle (dark meat) contain an extra amount of muscle hemoglobin (myoglobin), and abundant cytoplasm. This muscle also has a large blood supply and is usually active for long periods of time. Pale muscle fibers (white meat) contain less cytoplasm, less myoglobin, and have a smaller blood supply. The color of muscle also varies with the animal; in birds, red and white; in rabbits, red and white; in nearly all human muscles, a mixture of both types.

CARDIAC MUSCLE. In all vertebrates the heart is composed of a network of striated muscle fibers. They are unique in being branched and having centrally placed nuclei and intercalated, or literally, inserted discs, that is, dark bands that cross the fibers at irregular intervals whose function is not known (Fig. 7.15).

NERVOUS TISSUE

The functioning of nervous tissue is due to two properties of protoplasm: irritability, the power to react to various chemical and physical stimuli, and

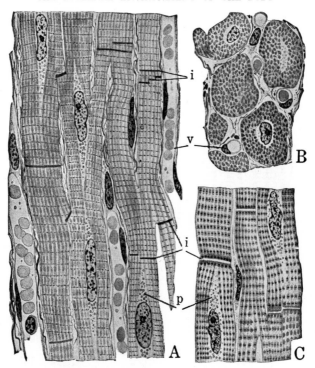

FIG. 7.15. Cardiac muscle. *A* and *B*, ventricle of a monkey's heart; *C*, from a human heart. *i*, intercalated disks, the cross bands that are characteristic of heart muscle; *p*, granules of pigment; *v*, blood capillaries carrying rich supply of blood. (Courtesy, Nonidez and Windle: *Textbook of Histology*, ed. 2. New York, McGraw-Hill Book Co., Inc., 1953.)

conductivity, the ability to transmit the reactions from one place to another.

The nerve cell or neuron is the structural unit of the nervous system. Its striking feature is the extension of the cell body into processes. These include two types: the relatively short dendrites through which the changes known as nerve impulses move toward the cell body, and a single process, the axon, through which nerve impulses move away from the cell body (Fig. 7.16). In different parts of the nervous system the cell bodies vary widely in size and shape but all of them have certain characteristics in common. They have prominent nuclei, no centrosomes, fine fibrils which become visible in the cytoplasm with special stains, the neurofibrils, and irregularly shaped bodies, the Nissl or tigroid bodies. The state of the Nissl substance is a sensitive indicator of the condition of the nerve cell. It is depleted in infections such as poliomyelitis, in intoxications, and exhaustion, and is reformed during recovery from illness or during sleep. In all but the simplest animals, such as hydra, the nerve-cell bodies exist only in ganglia and in the gray matter of the brain and spinal cord.

Nervous tissue is mentioned here because it is one of the four main types of tissues. Since nerve cells are peculiarly related and interdependent as a whole system, the general discussion of them is given with The Nervous System, Chapter 16.

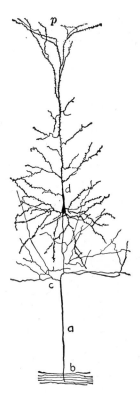

FIG. 7.16. Nerve cell from the cerebral cortex or gray matter of a rabbit. The axon gives off numerous branches and then enters the white substance, within which it extends a long distance. Only a small part of the axon is shown in the drawing. *a,* axon; *b,* white substance; *c,* collateral branches of axon; *d,* descending or apical dendrite; *p,* its terminal branches at the outer surface of the brain (After Ramon y Cajal. Courtesy, Maximow and Bloom: *Textbook of Histology,* ed. 6. Philadelphia, W. B. Saunders Co., 1952.)

Important Reactions in Tissues

Inflammation. The defense reaction of living tissues to an unfavorable condition such as an infection is evidenced by inflammation. Its general results are redness, swelling, heat, and pain at or near the site of the injury. The region becomes congested and swollen by an accumulation of body fluids and their associated cells. There is increased activity of these cells; this and the greater supply of blood produce a local heat rise. The congestion with pressure on the nerve endings results in soreness and pain.

There is an efficient cellular defense against inflammation. Cells which produce antibodies or antitoxins and may be phagocytic are scattered everywhere in loose connective tissue and in the blood and lymph. In the loose connective tissue there are many capillaries from which increased numbers of leucocytes migrate to the inflamed areas (Fig. 7.18). The neutrophils move in first and act quickly; monocytes enlarge and, along with the now

FIG. 7.17. Drawing of a leucocyte (neutrophil) at half-minute intervals showing its ameboid movement, and the intake of bacteria (black dots). The nucleus (black) is many-shaped. (From Best and Taylor: *The Living Body,* ed. 3. Copyrighted by Henry Holt and Co. Reprinted with their permission.)

active macrophages (connective tissue), attack and take in the poisonous alien matter. The ability of these cells to adjust themselves to a different situation is characteristic of protoplasm and a keystone in the body's defense against injury. As the inflammation decreases, healing begins. Scar tissue forms with new connective tissue cells and white collagenous fibers. Some of the macrophages remain in resting condition among the new connective tissue

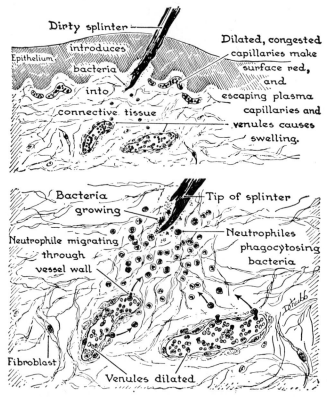

FIG. 7.18. Diagrams to show how leucocytes (neutrophils) migrate from small congested blood vessels to combat bacteria introduced into the tissues by an injury. (Courtesy, Ham, *Histology,* ed. 2. Philadelphia, J. B. Lippincott Co., 1953.)

cells. In the walls of adjoining blood vessels, cells (endothelial) multiply and form branches which extend into the scar tissue, their presence accounting for the "red scar." By this time the surface of the scar is covered by epithelium. Contraction of the white fibers reduces the capillaries and the "white scar" results.

Bruises. Such bruises as a black eye are produced by blunt objects which crush blood capillaries and other tissues. The capillaries bleed; the hemoglobin of the accumulated blood breaks down, causes the black and blue and later the greenish colors.

Fever. There may be a general response to injury in a fever involving the whole body. It results in an increase of metabolic activity and a consequent rise in temperature. High temperature is a dependable sign that something unusual is going on in the cells of the body.

Hypertrophy. The enlargement or hypertrophy of a particular region or organ may be due to enlargement, i.e., hypertrophy of individual cells and/or increased number of cells, i.e., hyperplasia. If one kidney has been removed, the other usually enlarges with more cells and does extra work.

Atrophy. This is a degenerative process in which cells diminish in size and number. It is sometimes due to lack of blood or nervous control. A common example is the degeneration in leg muscles following the destruction of parts of the nerve cord in infantile paralysis.

8

An Agent of Evolution—
The Body Covering

Skin is a meeting place, the frontier between an animal and its surroundings, a region of come and go, of shutting in and out.

The body coverings of animals are strikingly different: tenuously delicate in a jellyfish, tough enough to stop bullets in a rhinoceros. They include such contrasts as the ectoplasm of an ameba, the ciliated pellicle of paramecium, the simple slimy skin of earthworms, the thin skin of birds, the leathery skin of mammals. The multiplicity of structures that have developed from skin is a record of its many functions that usually help and sometimes hinder animals that live surrounded by shifting climates and shifty neighbors. Skin glands secrete the shells of oysters, the chitinous exoskeletons of grasshoppers, the scales of butterflies, the slippery mucus of fishes and frogs, the watery sweat of mammals, and the oil that waterproofs the feathers of birds. Cellular outgrowths of skin form the claws of owls and tigers, horns of cattle, beaks of birds and turtles, and hair—bent and crinkled in the wool of sheep and straight on a monkey. Although less significant than the kidneys, the sweat glands are also excretory organs. Sweat is similar to very dilute urine; in man it contains about 99 per cent water, about 0.08 per cent urea and some other salts. Skin is more or less resistant to disease and to the entrance of bacteria and parasites. The mucus secreted from the skin glands of fishes and the cornified layers in the skin of land animals are among its defenses.

Pigment is deposited in skin cells making patterns—the spots on leopard frogs, the stripes of zebras, which disguise their owners against the background of their homes. Certain cells of the skin are sensitive to touch, others to temperature, to chemicals, some of them to light. Animals, human and nonhuman, learn much about their surroundings through their skins.

126

General Structure of Skin

Skin consists of one or more layers of cells which cover the outside of the body and make a sheath over the delicate tissues beneath. Thus the outer layer of protoplasm that covers unicellular protozoans is not related to skin except in function. In all multicellular animals the outermost covering is a layer of epithelial cells, the epidermis. This is the only layer present in the invertebrates, except the starfishes and their near kin (Fig. 8.1). In the vertebrates there is also an underlying connective tissue layer, the dermis, sometimes called leather skin, because when properly prepared it is leather (Fig. 8.2).

Epidermis. The epidermis is composed of several layers of epithelial cells. The inner ones next to the dermis form a growing zone (malpighian layer) where new cells are constantly being formed and pushed outward by the pressure for space. As this occurs they are gradually flattened and outspread (Fig. 8.2). In fishes and other moist-skinned animals even the outermost cells stay alive for considerable time, but in land animals they become dry and lifeless. Amphibians and reptiles molt the old epidermis in one piece; birds lose their old feathers; and mammals continually shed little fragments of skin. The constant flecking off of the human scalp in dandruff must be familiar to everybody, in advertisements if not otherwise. Epidermal cells become horny by deposits of the protein called keratin (horn). Keratin is prominent in land dwelling vertebrates, in hair and feathers, horns of cattle, footpads of dogs, and hoofs of horses. The "horny hands of toil" are actual facts.

Many glands originate in the epidermis although they usually enlarge and

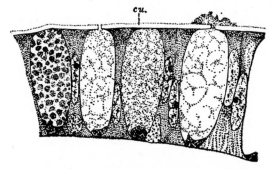

FIG. 8.1. A section of the epidermis and cuticle of an earthworm highly magnified. It shows four mucous cells in different stages of secretion, all swollen with the mucus which has pushed the nuclei to the bottom of the cells. It finally pours out through microscopic pores, one at the end of each cell, and spreads over the cuticle (*cu*). Mucus keeps the surface of the body moist, makes skin respiration possible, lubricates the skin and lines the burrow in which the worm lives. (Courtesy, Dahlgren and Kepner: *Principles of Histology.* New York, The Macmillan Co., 1908.)

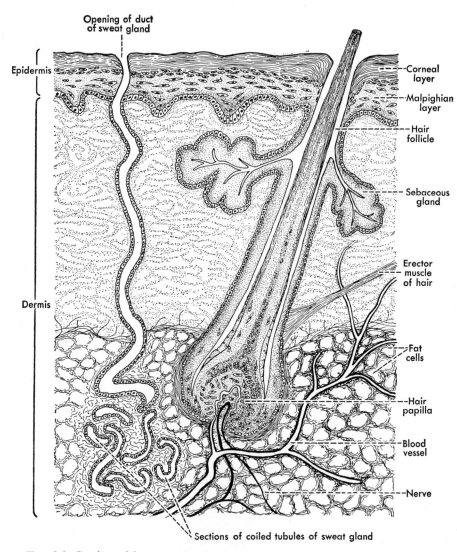

Sections of coiled tubules of sweat gland

FIG. 8.2. Section of human skin showing the two layers, epidermis and dermis, characteristic of all vertebrates. The outermost corneal layer of the epidermis composed of the horny remains of cells is gradually shed in small bits and replaced by new cells from the growing (Malpighian) layer beneath. Cells of this layer contain the pigment that is responsible for dark complexion. As shown in this figure a hair is a shaft of cells that arises from a layer of epidermal cells that form a narrow pocket in the dermis from the bottom of which a core of cells grows upward and forms the hair shaft. Sensory cells, nerves, and the erector muscle provide for the sensitivity and movement of the hair, and sebaceous glands for the oil. (Courtesy, Gardiner: *Principles of General Biology*. New York, The Macmillan Co., 1952.)

push down into the dermis (Fig. 8.2). Their great variety includes the stinging cells of hydra, wax glands of honeybees, the mucous glands whose secretion earthworms leave behind them in shiny trails, and the mucous glands that make the slipperiness of fishes. More familiar are the oil glands of hair and the sweat glands whose products have become the symbol of human toil, the lacrymal or tear glands, and the mammary glands which produce food for all young mammals. The activity of these glands is deeply associated with human experiences. The epidermis has earned a high place in human history; Sir Winston Churchill gave it two-thirds of Blood, Sweat and Tears.

Dermis. The dermis is the inner and thicker layer of the skin, the one where the prick of a needle first hurts (Fig. 8.2). The bulk of it is composed of the crisscrossing fibers of connective tissues familiar in leather. Dermis is a nutrient layer containing lymph and blood capillaries and fat cells, the latter often extremely abundant. There are many nerve endings in it; the autonomic (involuntary) nerves control the contraction and dilatation of the capillaries and consequent paling or flushing of the skin. The dermis is the scene of blushing. Heat regulations also occur there; blood may be spread out and cooled in the dilated surface capillaries or driven into the warm deeper parts of the body when they are contracted. The colors of frogs and other lower vertebrates are mainly due to pigment-bearing cells (chromatophores) in the dermis. Epidermal structures, glands, and feather and hair follicles project into the dermis where dermal structures such as blood vessels, nerves, and smooth muscle are associated with them (Fig. 8.2).

Skin Derivatives

Such notable developments from the skin layers as horns, claws, nails, and hoofs should be added to the scales, feathers, and hair already mentioned. Teeth have a history of close association with the skin and in certain sharks there are rows of them just outside as well as inside the mouth cavity. The plates of whalebone that hang from the upper jaw of toothless whales are composed of cornified epidermal cells.

Epidermal Glands. The epidermis contains glands. Lobsters, grasshoppers, and every other arthropod are completely clothed in the secretion of their epidermal glands. Natural pearls are epidermal secretions as are shells of the giant clam (*Tridacna gigas*) weighing 300 pounds or more, often used as basins for holy water.

Scales. The scale of an insect, a butterfly, or moth is a minute plate of cuticle secreted by one or more epidermal cells. It is solely a secretion and does not contain any cells. The "hairs" and spines of other invertebrates are similar. In contrast to these, the scales of bony fishes and other vertebrates are composed of cells that originate from groups of skin cells.

Certain members of each class of vertebrates bear scales except the amphibians, and in them scales are unknown. Most fishes and all reptiles are more or less covered with scales; birds have them on their legs; many mammals bear them on their tails—mice, rats, ground moles, opossums, beavers, and armadillos have them on their bodies and tails (Fig. 8.3). Fishes and reptiles are the typically scaly animals. In the yellow perch, salmon, and other bony fishes, the scales grow out from pockets of connective tissue in the dermis and overlap one another like shingles. Fishes do not molt and scales keep growing and wearing off as long as the animals live. The scales of reptiles are formed by the thickening and hardening of the cornified epidermis. Those of turtles lie flat over the bony plates beneath; those of snakes partly overlap one another. Turtles never shed their scales but each one increases in size as the animal grows. The cornified scaly epidermis of snakes and lizards forms a complete armor that is shed in early summer. It is then that reptiles appear most sleek and burnished in their new skins.

Feathers. These are slender upgrowths from the dermis. A feather carries the epidermis with it and at its base sinks into a depression or pit in the skin. Feathers are cellular structures but only near the level of the skin do they remain alive as the feather grows. Nearly all of the feather consists of cornified walls of microscopic air spaces that once were living cells. Thus each feather is an extraordinarily complex horny air trap, an insulation, whose light weight is only a part of its great efficiency. The habits and successes of birds are peculiarly bound up with their feathers. (See also Chap. 36.)

Hair. The most striking development of mammalian skin is hair, an insulation as characteristic of mammals as the feathers of birds. Among the very few almost hairless mammals are the armadillo, the hippopotamus with a few bristles around the snout, elephants, and whales that are covered with hair before birth but afterward have only a few bristles about the lips.

A hair is a shaft of purely epidermal cells which projects outward obliquely from its bulb-shaped root that extends down into the dermis (Fig. 8.2). Below the surface of the skin a hair is a column of rapidly multiplying cells;

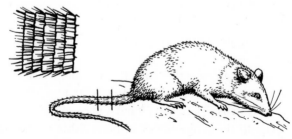

FIG. 8.3. Hairs and overlapping scales on the tail of a rat, section of it magnified.

the outer ones form a pit or follicle sunk in the dermis; the inner ones develop into the horny shaft which extends out as the hair. A minute papilla of dermal cells containing blood capillaries and nerve endings projects into a cup in the root and furnishes nourishment in this spot where growth is very rapid. Sebaceous glands feed oil onto the hair, sometimes in superabundance. An involuntary muscle extends from near the base of the hair to the epidermis. When this muscle contracts it pulls on the base of the hair and makes it "stand up." In thickly furred animals this increases the insulating power of the coat. Standing hair on the back of a dog's neck is a warning; on human skin it is only "goose flesh," and no indication of danger to others, meaning only that its owner is scared or chilly. It is too sparse to create any insulation from the cold and is a sign of kinship to furred animals rather than a protection. Above the skin a hair is composed of the dead and horny remains of cells (Fig. 8.4). Pigment, most commonly black, is distributed along the rod in varying degrees of abundance, causing the different shades of brown and black hair. When the papilla of the hair does not supply materials for pigment, the hairs are gray or white. Air vesicles are frequent in white hair; it is an air trap, in a feeble way, like a white feather. Hairs are also like feathers in being shed at regular intervals. Human hairs are among the exceptions in being shed irregularly; healthy human hairs of the head are estimated to live a few years, eyelashes only a few months. A curly hair is slightly flattened and shorter on one side than the other like a shaving; a straight hair is a perfect cylinder.

Claws, Nails, and Hoofs. These are all structures of cornified skin (epidermis) (Fig. 8.5). Their development is similar to that of hairs; they are

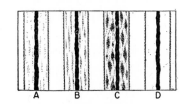

FIG. 8.4. *Left,* diagram of a human hair showing the characteristic shape of the cuticular scales (F), colorless in all animals unless the hair has been dyed. Scales composed of dead or cornified epithelial cells are arranged like shingles with their free margins always directed toward the end of the hair. The main thread of the hair (medulla, *C,* and cortex, *D*) consists of compressed remains of cells, through which pigment is distributed. *A,* fusi or air vesicles; *B,* pigment granules; *E,* cuticle. *Center,* sections of hairs from the human head showing the distribution of pigment granules in hair of different colors. The color or absence of color depends upon the hair's content of pigment and air. Loss of pigment makes the hair look gray; when it contains much air, it is silvery white. *A,* cream buff; *B,* befza brown; *C,* black; *D* white. *Right,* hairs from various mammals have characteristic scales; hair of a star-nosed mole, percheron horse, sheep, and other. (Courtesy, Hausman, *Scient. Monthly* **59:**195–202, 1944.)

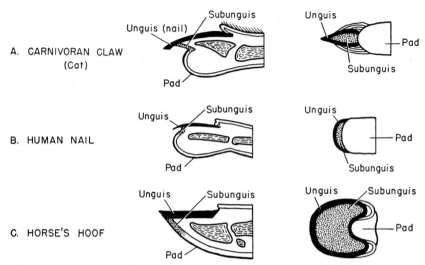

Fig. 8.5. Diagrams of claws, nails and hoofs seen in section and from beneath. All of these are modified scales, an unguis or scale above and a subunguis or cushion below. Thus, the front of a horse's hoof is a modified nail essentially similar to the claw of a lizard or a human fingernail. (Redrawn after Walter and Sayles: *Biology of the Vertebrates,* ed. 2. New York, The Macmillan Co., 1949.)

actually fused hairs. Lizards, turtles, and birds have claws as do many mammals, but nails belong solely to a few mammals. A claw fits like a hood over a terminal joint and beneath it is a pad of softer tissue. A nail is a thin horny plate growing on the upper side of the end of a finger or toe. The human fingernail is like a broad flattened claw on the upper surface of the fingertip. None of these structures is molted but broken nails are regenerated. The hoof of a horse is a claw which has become a greatly thickened sheath for the toe-tip.

Horns and Antlers. The horns of cattle, sheep, goats, and Old World antelopes are outgrowths of bone covered by thick layers of cornified epidermis and, like claws and nails, are tough and resistant to chemicals. Horns are not shed and are never branched.

The antlers of deer, reindeer, moose, and elk are annual growths of bone. Deer shed their antlers when they are about two years old and every year after that. At first the bony outgrowth is covered with hairy skin, later the skin is resorbed and the spike of bone breaks off. In the second year the antler develops in the same way, is shed, and in each following year the process is repeated with new branches added (Fig. 8.6). Growing antlers are said to be "in the velvet" because their skin is thickly covered with short hairs. They are hot and feverish to the touch due to the large blood supply and the almost explosive expenditure of heat in their rapid growth. Giraffes, which are close relatives of the deer family, do not shed their stubby antlers, that remain in the

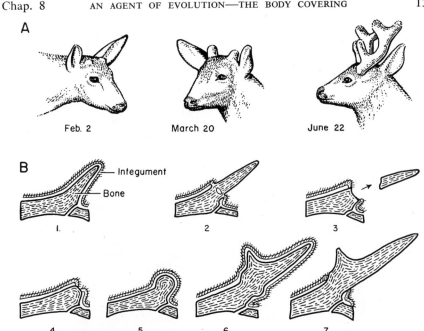

FIG. 8.6. Antlers of male mule deer. *A*, usual annual growth: Feb. 2, March 20, June 22. *B*, structure and shedding; diagrams of sections. *1*, growing prong in the velvet, i.e., covered with hairy skin; *2* and *3*, skin worn off and antler shed; *4, 5, 6*, regrowth and mature condition in which the bone is bare. Each successive breeding season is marked by new antlers; to a certain limit older animals have more prongs. (*A*, redrawn from Hamilton: *American Mammals*. New York, McGraw-Hill Book Co., 1939. *B*, redrawn from Walter and Sayles: *Biology of the Vertebrates*, ed. 3. New York, The Macmillan Co., 1949.)

velvet stage throughout life (Fig. 8.7). Antlers of deer, reindeer, moose, and elk are not composed of horn at any time.

Functions of Skin

Skin is a protection from heat and cold: by pigment in cells (frog); by coverings of feathers (birds) and hair (mammals), with few apparent exceptions—whale, armadillo, et al.; by erection of feathers and hairs securing greater insulation from cold because of the increase of air space between them; by fat associated with the deep layer (dermis)—the blubber of whales and other marine animals.

The amount of water in the body is regulated by the control of its entrance through the skin (frog), resistance to its passage through the skin by chitinous coverings (many insects) and by cornified layers and fat (mammals), by scales (fishes and reptiles), by feathers and hair, by oil or wax glands (in birds especially water birds, cockroaches, certain beetles, bees, ants, and aphids).

Skin resists the entrance of parasites and diseases by special thickened areas,

FIG. 8.7. Masai giraffe. Although giraffes belong to the deer family they never shed their stubby antlers which are knobs of bone permanently in the velvet. (Courtesy, New York Zoological Society.)

e.g., soles of the feet, pads, hoofs (man, elephant, horse), by scales (fishes, reptiles, feet of birds), by feathers and hair, by secretions (mucus in fishes, frogs and toads, mild poisons of hydras, caterpillars of gypsy moths).

The skin is a receptor of stimuli through sensory cells and nerve endings, sensitive to touch, heat, cold, and pain.

Skin takes part in the heat regulation of the body: in mammals through control of surface blood vessels, through evaporation of sweat from the body surface (man, horse), by coverings of the body, i.e., by hair, or feathers.

Vitamin D is produced through irradiation or the exposure to sunshine of oils in skin and on feathers and hairs. In licking their fur mammals secure irradiated oil containing vitamin D involved in the metabolism of calcium and phosphorus.

Sweat glands located in the skin excrete products of metabolism, such as water, small amounts of urea, and certain salts.

In certain invertebrates (earthworms, planarians, et al.) the respiratory gases pass through the skin.

9

Protection, Support, and

Movement—Skeletons

Skeletons provide protection and support. The advantage of having a skeleton is made most vivid by the animal which does not have one. Jellyfishes drift and in calm seas can even swim. But let them be thrown on a sandy beach and, having neither protection nor support, they flatten against the sand and dry to papery wisps. All vertebrate animals have skeletons and the character of their existence is inseparable from skeletons. Imagine a spirited horse without bones! In their relations to their environments and their achievements of speed, strength, and grace animals are greatly dependent upon an outer or an inner frame.

General Functions

The skeleton determines the form of an animal. Contrast the long leg bones of an ostrich and the lack of them in a snake; or the seven long vertebrae in the neck of a giraffe and the seven short ones in the neck of a man.

Bones are the living tools of the muscles. Watch the fingers striking piano keys, or the legs taking part in defense when a donkey kicks, and in offense when a cat springs upon a mouse.

The skeleton's oldest and most general function is protection. The shell is a·complete armor around a lobster; the boxlike cranium encases the human brain. The red marrow that produces the vital blood cells of vertebrates throughout adult life is housed within bones.

Skeletons are old in animal history. Even in early times the yielding protoplasm of the smallest animals was doubtless protected by shells and rodlets of hardened secretion as radiolarians are now (Fig. 9.1). Tons of fossil deposits that have been dredged from the sea bottoms testify to the abundance of such microscopic skeletons in primeval seas. Fossil animals of other groups show

135

that there were successive ages when skeletons were enormously large and heavy. Those of reptiles commonly weighed many tons. Even modern alligators have such heavy ones that they can scarcely lift their bodies from the ground.

During their evolution vertebrate skeletons have changed from ponderous burdens to light jointed bones, adapted to muscular control. Of all the land vertebrates, birds have the lightest skeletons, for their tubular bones contain air cavities connected with the lungs. The frigate bird, a famous flier, has a wing expanse of seven feet and weighs two pounds, but its skeleton weighs only four ounces, less than its feathers.

Types of Skeletons

Skeletons are either exoskeletons, on the outside of the body, or endoskeletons, within the body.

Exoskeletons of invertebrates are composed entirely of nonliving material, the secretion of cells usually deposited in layers (Fig. 9.2). The majority are light in weight, except the shells of mollusks that are often heavy. The muscles are attached on the inner surfaces of the shells (Fig. 9.5, crayfish).

Endoskeletons are composed of living cells with their products, such as the limy substance of bone. They are located between muscles and connective tissues, and the muscles are attached to their outer surfaces. Such skeletons are unique to the great group of chordates presently described.

SKELETONS OF INVERTEBRATES

In the vast assemblage of invertebrates there is an unending variety of skeletons that fit their owners to live in thousands of niches, in water, on land,

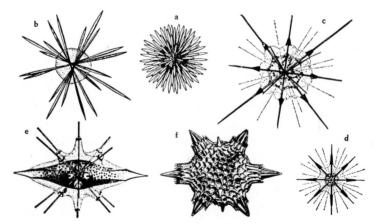

FIG. 9.1. Skeletons of representative radiolarians of crystal transparency, beauty and precision of pattern. A vast area of the ocean bottom is covered with ooze mainly composed of these skeletons that have dropped downward and accumulated through the ages. (Courtesy, Kudo: *Protozoology,* ed. 3. Springfield, Ill., C. C Thomas, 1947.)

or in the air. These skeletons are calcareous (limy), silicious (glassy), and chitinous (horny), or are combinations of these. Those of aquatic animals often have flotation devices, cavities that contain air or gas, fat, and oil droplets. In the larger groups of multicellular invertebrates there are three general types of skeletons.

Permanent Skeletons. Clams, snails, and other mollusks have but one skeleton throughout life enlarging it as their bodies grow. Although the molluscan shell is not called a skeleton it has the requirements of one. In clams the oldest part of the shell is the hinge region from which larger and larger concentric ridges show where new secretion has been added (Fig. 9.2). The swiftest mollusks are the squids whose skeletons are completely hidden by a fleshy mantle.

An exoskeleton may be a network of minute units, or a mosaic of closely fitted plates. As the animal grows, the units are enlarged or new ones added.

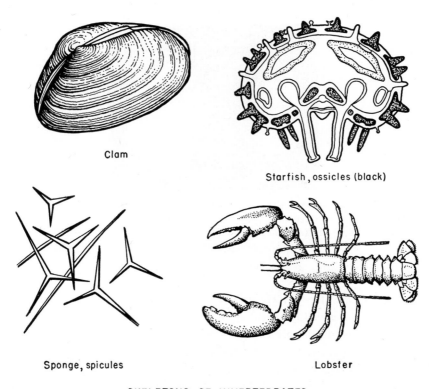

Clam

Starfish, ossicles (black)

Sponge, spicules

Lobster

SKELETONS OF INVERTEBRATES

Fig. 9.2. Skeletons of invertebrates. *Permanent:* clam with lines showing the additions to the shell throughout life; cut across the arm of a starfish showing the limy ossicles (shaded) embedded in the flesh of the body wall. Left lower: spicules of fresh-water sponge that form a net-like support in the body wall. *Temporary:* lobster whose skeleton is periodically replaced by a new one as long as the animal's growth continues.

These skeletal units are strikingly different, white limy ossicles in starfishes, glassy spicules in fantastic shapes and netted fibers in sponges.

Temporary Skeletons. Such skeletons are shed and replaced throughout the growing period of the animal. The peak achievements in invertebrate skeletons are the jointed ones of insects and other arthropods that are shed and replaced by larger ones as their owners grow (Fig. 9.2). A new shell is formed before the old one is shed and while the new cover is still soft and pliable it stretches enough to allow for another interval of growth (Fig. 9.3). Most insect skeletons are delicately wrought; those of moths and butterflies are covered with scales many of these lined with extraordinarily fine grooves. At the other extreme is that of the male Hercules beetle of tropical America, nearly five inches long, with heavy headgear that occupies a third the length of its body. Aquatic species are larger than the related land forms; crabs and lobsters have the heaviest skeletons of the arthropods. Yet when lobsters are submerged in

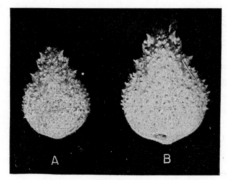

Fig. 9.3. Dorsal shells (carapace) of the same crab before and after molting. *A*, hard shell that was recently shed; *B*, larger new shell that stretched and is still soft. Crab, *Loxorhynchus grandis*, Pacific Coast. (Courtesy, MacGinitie and MacGinitie: *Natural History of Marine Animals*. New York, McGraw-Hill Book Co., Inc., 1949.)

their native sea water they are so buoyed up by it that the tips of their claws touch the rocks as lightly as if they were engaged in a ballet.

Joints. Joints are the places where adjacent parts of a skeleton join, often closely fitted together. In lobsters and other arthropods the outer covering or exoskeleton is continuous over them, yet it is so thin and pliable that the joint bends easily. Joints are highly developed in the skeletons of insects and vertebrates, two dominant groups of animals. Those of invertebrates began as creases in the epidermis and cuticle such as are so clearly visible in earthworms. As an insect breathes, its abdomen rhythmically lengthens and shortens at the telescopic joints. When air enters the body, the plates of the skeleton move apart, stretching the soft membrane between them (Fig. 9.4). Alternately, as the muscles of the abdomen contract and air leaves the body, the plates are drawn together with the edge of one overlapping the one behind it. Insects and other arthropods also have hinge joints. The leg of a lobster or an insect bends like a jackknife.

Changing Content of Skeletons

The content of skeletons is in part changeable, in part permanent. Their composition depends upon the material brought by the blood to the cells which produce the more rigid substance. What is brought depends upon the materials

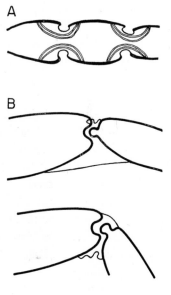

FIG. 9.4. Joints of the arthropod skeleton. *A*, telescopic joints in the abdomen of an insect when outstretched; pieces of skeleton held together by muscles and skin; *B*, insect's leg held straight and flexed showing the stretching and folding of the soft skin around the joints. (*A*, redrawn after Guyer: *Animal Biology.* New York, Harper & Bros., 1936. *B*, redrawn after Ross: *A Textbook of Entomology.* New York, John Wiley & Sons, 1948.)

in the animal's environment and the physiological pattern that the animal inherits.

Calcium, occurring in limestone, soil, and water, is continually passed in and out of animals, but during its sojourn in an animal's body it is mainly located in the skeleton. Striking exceptions are horny structures and the chitinous skeletons of insects. In its usual state, 16 per cent of a crab's shell is calcium; when it is "soft," such a shell is but one per cent calcium. This is the only time when the shell stretches.

The skeletons of primitive vertebrates are more or less cartilaginous; those of vertebrate embryos are at first composed of cartilage, later mainly replaced by bone. Cartilage is composed of connective tissue cells which produce a more or less resilient gel.

The connective tissue cells which produce bone form two different materials: minerals, chiefly calcium and phosphorus, and collagen, a protein. The collagen fibers are arranged spirally in the mineral matter, binding it like wires in concrete. The combination of the materials makes bone hard and resistant to strain. Bone can support a greater weight than granite without being crushed. Despite its great firmness, it is moderately flexible especially in young animals. The flexibility of the human skull at birth is well known; even in an adult the skull can stand some compression before it cracks. Bone may be deprived of either mineral matter or collagen and yet keep its shape. Soaking in dilute hydrochloric acid will remove the minerals; burning will remove the animal substance (mainly protein) (Fig. 9.10). The proportion of calcium to living matter varies with age, with the amount of vitamin D in the diet, and other factors. The body's calcium supply is regulated by the parathyroid glands that are located on either side of the thyroid gland (Fig. 15.1). Calcium also indirectly controls the coordinated activity of muscles by slowing down the transmission of nerve impulses to them. When there is an excess of impulses, the secretion of the parathyroids circulating in the blood extracts calcium from the supply in the bones. This, in turn, circulated in the blood, slows the activity of nerves and muscles. On the other hand, if the body becomes sluggish, the parathyroid secretion is diminished and less calcium is called forth from the bones. Again, the parathyroids may be too active and may rob the bones of their calcium and produce abnormal formations. Sometimes this is deposited as kidney stones.

Discoveries by Tracers. The behavior of calcium and phosphorus in the tissue of living bone has been observed by means of their isotopes used as tracer substances. The movements of radioactive calcium and phosphorus are detected by a sensitive instrument (Geiger counter) placed on the outside of the body (Chap. 2). Radioactive calcium has been demonstrated in the bones of mice 24 hours after its injection into the veins. Radioactive phosphorus was immediately deposited in the teeth, in the ends of bones, and in the ring of healing (callus) in a bone which had been fractured. Radioactive phosphorus in the form of a solution of sodium phosphate has also been given to human patients either by mouth or by injection into the veins and its movement in the body and its behavior in the bone followed by the Geiger counter. Such explorations are more and more frequently made in the treatment of broken and diseased bones.

Skeletons of Vertebrates and Their Ancestors

Notochord and Vertebral Column. Vertebrates are named from the chain of bones which composes the vertebral column, the oldest part of the skeleton and the support to which their development and dominance are supremely indebted (Fig. 9.6). "Having backbone" has long come to mean having strength and resolution. With a flexible, dorsal, median backbone, and the bilaterally symmetrical appendages which developed later, the vertebrates gained agility first in water and then on land. They moved about more, traveled in different ways and to different places, and made all manner of new relationships.

Long before any of this occurred, the ancestors of vertebrates had an internal axial support, the notochord, on the dorsal side of the body below the nerve cord and above the digestive tube (Fig. 9.5). Following their ancestors of millions of years past, every individual vertebrate, including man, has a complete notochord at some time during its embryonic life. In amphioxus the notochord persists through life; in the vertebrates it is replaced by cartilaginous or bony vertebrae. The presence of the notochord at some period of life in all vertebrates as well as in their nearer ancestors is the reason for the name of the phylum Chordata, the group to which they all belong. The more limited subphylum Vertebrata includes only the chordates that have vertebrae, lampreys, fishes, amphibians, reptiles, birds, and mammals, including man.

The notochord is a slender rod of turgid vacuolated cells held together so tightly within two sheaths that the whole structure is stiffened like a sausage and the substance itself resembles condensed jelly (Fig. 9.5). In mammals, it is soon replaced by bone and cartilage except possibly for a small part of the cartilaginous cushion (intervertebral disc) that persists between the vertebrae. In fishes, remains of it persist through adult life. The conical cavity at each end of a vertebra, familiar to us especially in salmon and tuna fish, was once filled with notochordal cells.

Vertebrae. A vertebra is a ring of cartilage, in sharks and other lower fishes, or of bone surrounding the nerve cord in higher vertebrates (Fig. 9.6). The

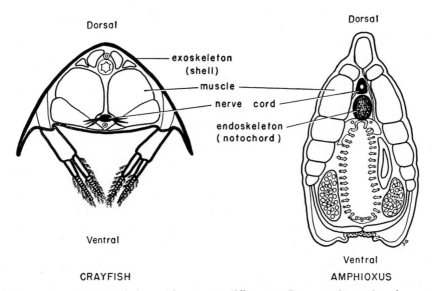

CRAYFISH   AMPHIOXUS

FIG. 9.5. A characteristic and important difference. Cross sections of an invertebrate (crayfish) with exoskeleton and ventral nerve cord; and a chordate (amphioxus) with endoskeleton and dorsal hollow nerve cord.

body or centrum occupies the space previously filled by notochordal cells and
is so shaped that it fits closely to its neighboring centra or to the intervertebral
discs. Dorsal to the centrum is the neural arch; fitted closely together the
neural arches form the bony canal in which the nerve cord is enclosed. Each
vertebra has particular areas, knobs, and edges, the attachment places of
ligaments and tendons of muscles that bind one vertebra to another, as well
as surfaces where the centra are pressed against the intervertebral discs. The
thoracic vertebrae have special hollows where the ribs articulate.

The joints between the vertebrae have only limited freedom of motion, yet

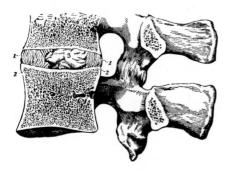

FIG. 9.6. A section through articulated
human vertebrae, showing one of the
intervertebral disks that separate the successive vertebrae; *1* and *2*, ends of circular fibers; *3*, central cushion of cartilage
(nucleus pulposus). (Courtesy, *Quain's
Elements of Anatomy*, ed. 11. New York,
Longmans, Green & Co., 1915.)

the backbone, like the spring from a curtain roll, can be bent backward, forward, or sideways and swung back into place (Fig. 9.7). A cat's back can
take a high curve in a split second, and that of a bucking bronco outdoes the
cat in curves; it lifts a cowboy and is just as fast. A snake coils and twists; a
kitten sleeps in a ball; an owl rotates its head until it looks directly behind
itself; and human acrobats are close competitors, yet the vertebrae stay in their
places.

Joints. In endoskeletons the muscles and ligaments are fastened to the outer
surfaces of the cartilages and bones. Some joints are immovable, such as those
in the cranium, little noticed except in very young infants in which they have
not grown together. Among the familiar types of movable joints are (Fig. 9.8):
(1) hinge joints, such as those that are worked hard in typewriting; (2) ball-
and-socket such as the hip joint in which the head of the femur fits into the
pelvic girdle, a joint that is highly important in tap dancing, as well as in
walking and sitting and rising; (3) rotating joints in which the radius of the
human forearm shifts on its axis across the ulna as when the hand turns a doorknob; and (4) pivotal joints that rock one upon another, such as the important "yes and no" joints, in action as the skull rocks upon the first vertebra
(atlas) when we nod "yes"; the atlas revolves upon the vertebra behind it
(axis) when we shake our heads "no."

In every typical free-moving joint the ends of the bones are held together
by sheets of tough connective tissue, the ligaments that enclose the joint in a

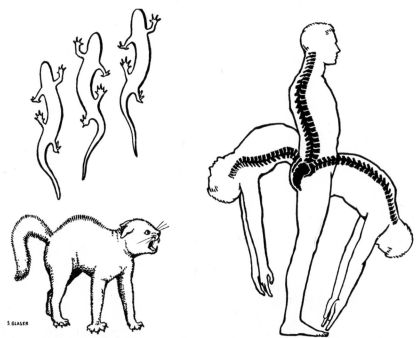

S. GLASER

FIG. 9.7. The flexibility of the vertebral column: in a walking salamander which swings from side to side like a fish; in a fighting cat that arches its back as easily as a bucking bronco. A human "backbone" bends forward, backward, and sidewise.

capsule (Fig. 9.8). The end of each bone is capped with cartilage and folds of thin synovial membrane project into the capsule of the joint from the sides. This membrane secretes the synovial fluid, a lubricator that is transparent and viscid like the white of egg. When the synovial membrane of the knee becomes inflamed, its excess secretion often accumulates as "water on the knee."

Long Bones. The humerus of the arm or femur of the leg may be taken as an example of the general structure of long bones (Fig. 9.9). The cellular structure of bone is described in Chapter 7.

The tubular plan of long bones makes them much stronger than rods of the same size and weight. Two arrangements of their bony tissue, the compact bone mostly surrounding the hollow shaft and the spongy (cancellous) bone at the ends, create strength and lightness at the same time. Spongy bone is a network of plates laid down in lines running in the directions which best meet the stress that falls upon the particular part, such as the weight borne by the head of the femur (Fig. 9.8). It contains spaces filled with red bone marrow in which the red and some of the white blood cells are formed (Chap. 7). An important layer of connective tissue, the periosteum, surrounds all bones. It

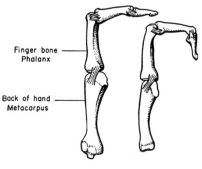

Finger bone
Phalanx

Back of hand
Metacarpus

Fingers bent
Typewriting   Clinging

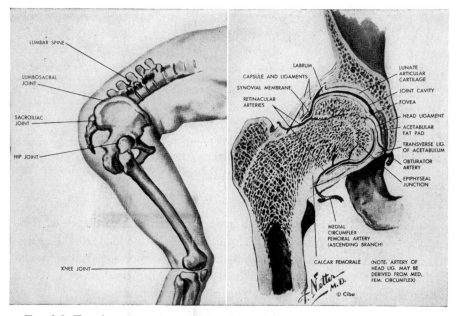

FIG. 9.8. Two important types of joints in the human body. *Top,* hinge joints: finger flexed as in striking typewriter, in clinging. *Bottom left,* ball and socket joint: the hip joint in which the head of the femur fits into a cup in the pelvic girdle. *Bottom right,* a section through the hip joint showing the capsule and the ligaments holding the head of the femur in place. The ligament that binds the head of the femur in place is the strongest in the body and rarely is torn even when the joint is dislocated. The section of the femur shows the smooth, very hard compact bone (whitish band) and outside it except at the joints the thin periostracum (black line) layer which is the growing zone of the bone. The network of bony tissue called spongy bone because of the many holes is well developed at the ends of long bones and its lines of strength here suggest the braces of a suspension bridge. It contains the red marrow in which red blood cells and granular leucocytes (white blood cells) originate. In life the center of the bone is occupied by the fatty marrow, here a black space. (Hip joint drawings courtesy, *Ciba Clinical Symposia,* Vol. 5, No. 2, 1953.)

receives abundant nourishment through a network of blood vessels and is the region that provides for increase in diameter in growing animals.

Arteries enter and veins leave the bones in an oblique direction and are

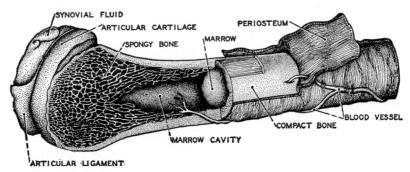

FIG. 9.9. Structure of a long bone. Periosteum is the growth area. (Courtesy, Rand: *Chordate Anatomy*. Philadelphia, The Blakiston Company, 1950.)

connected by capillaries within them. The abundance of blood vessels in bone emphasizes the fact that its cells are living, that metabolism goes on within them as elsewhere, and that in them food and oxygen are expended, and heat, energy, and waste are produced. Bone cells constantly take up organic and inorganic substances from the blood and release such substances into it.

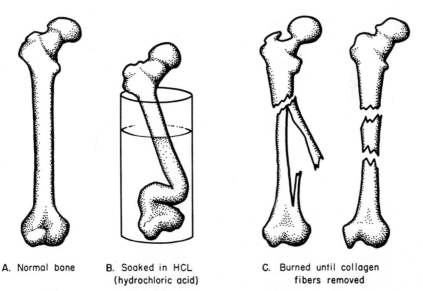

A. Normal bone   B. Soaked in HCL   C. Burned until collagen
                       (hydrochloric acid)   fibers removed

FIG. 9.10. *A,* normal bone. *B,* bone with calcium dissolved out after which it can be bent and twisted. *C,* bone burned until the organic matter, cells and fibers, are destroyed after which it is brittle. In a baby one year old the proportion of calcium to animal matter is about as 1:8; at eighty years it is commonly about 8:11.

The intimacy between bones and muscles is evident in the ridges and grooves on the surface of dry bones, for these are special attachment places of tendons. The latter are also attached to the large smooth areas of the pelvic bones and shoulder blades (Fig. 9.16).

Main Divisions of the Vertebrate Skeleton. All vertebrate skeletons consist of two basic divisions: the axial skeleton, composed of skull and vertebral column, and the appendicular skeleton, the shoulder and hip girdles and their appendages (Fig. 9.15). Their parts correspond in relative position and structure; they can be homologized more or less completely in all vertebrates.

The Vertebrate Plan

Early History. The lobe-fin fishes, probably ancestors of the land vertebrates, must have tugged their bodies across oozing mud from one pool to another, pulling with their front fins and pushing with the hind ones. Untold generations later, their successors also pulled and pushed their bodies but by limbs that bent at the joints and had small spreading bones at the ends that got a foothold upon the earth (Fig. 9.11). After many more generations, the limbs were held closer to the body and bent, the front ones backward and the hind ones forward. In all the four-limbed vertebrates that have succeeded them from early times into the present, the elbow, meeting place of the humerus with the radius and ulna, has pointed backward, and the knee, the

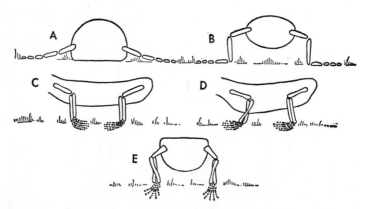

FIG. 9.11. Diagrams illustrating the evolution of the limbs of the ancestors of land vertebrates. *A,* front view of a probable early stage when the limbs projected side wise and the body rested on the ground, an era when land vertebrates tugged their bodies out of the water and through the muddy ooze. *B,* the body is lifted from the ground and the limbs are bent outward at the knee joints. *C,* side view, hypothetical condition; hind leg rotated so that the knee points forward; front leg rotated backward so that the elbow points backward. *D,* side view, condition in modern quadrupeds in which the radius crosses over the ulna when the forearm rotates forward. *E,* front view of stage shown in D. (After DeBeer. Courtesy, Walter and Sayles: *Biology of the Vertebrates,* ed. 3. New York, The Macmillan Co., 1949.)

meeting joint of the femur with the tibia and fibula, has pointed forward (Figs. 9.11, 9.15).

The Bridge. The plan of the vertebrate body is like the layout of a single-span bridge. The piers of the bridge are the front and hind limbs attached to their respective girdles and the arched span is the backbone. This metaphor drawn by D'Arcy Thompson has been developed effectively by W. K. Gregory in *The Bridge that Walks* with photographs of skeletons of fossil and present-day vertebrates that illustrate the theme (Fig. 9.12). In its long history the bridge plan of the vertebrate skeleton has admitted hundreds of variations without departing from its unique character and basic simplicity. It persists under many guises and ways of making a living, in burrowing ground moles, swimming muskrats, and climbing squirrels, in elephants that are sure-footed and ponderous, deer that are light and agile, cats that hunt their prey, and cattle that forage on grass.

Paired Appendages and Locomotion. Paired appendages attached to cartilaginous or bony girdles are typical of vertebrates. The basic pattern of these structures underlies great modifications, especially in amphibians and birds. In this pattern the pelvic or hip girdle is attached directly to the axial skeleton, the pectoral or shoulder girdle indirectly by muscles. Each girdle is formed of

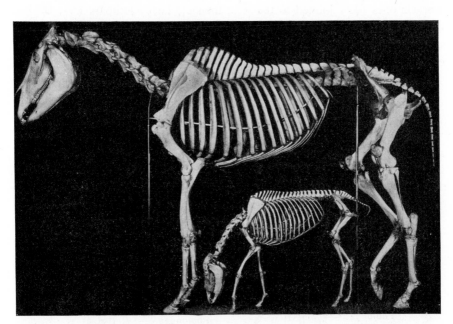

Fig. 9.12. Skeletons of a giant Percheron horse and a Shetland pony, the latter in grazing position. Both show the bridge-like plan of the vertebrate body, the front and hind limbs and their girdles taking the place of supporting piers, and the backbone that of a connecting span. The neck has been compared to the arm of a steam shovel; in the pony the steam shovel is in action. (Skeleton mounted by S. H. Chubb. Photograph, courtesy, American Museum of Natural History.)

three bones and the front and hind limbs likewise have three main bones (Fig. 9.13). The same number and arrangement of bones occur typically in the forefoot (or hand) as in the hind foot. Both are correlated with their uses in swimming, running, flying, climbing, and burrowing. The feet of horses have undergone striking modifications for running. In their wild state horses have grazed over wide ranges of grassland and escaped their enemies by speed. Their bodies are held relatively high by long slender legs. Through their evolutionary history their toes have been reduced to one, the third, on each foot and in readiness for flight they stand upon their hoofs, the nails of these single toes (Fig. 9.12, 9.14).

The Human Skeleton

The human skeleton has no bones which are not represented by similar ones in skeletons of other mammals. Nevertheless it has certain entirely unique features: a round head, a chin, a broad chest, a triply curved backbone, and most important, a bowl-shaped pelvis and an opposable thumb that fronts the fingers (Fig. 9.15).

Backbone. The 34 vertebrae of the human backbone are arranged like the stones in a tower with the smallest cervicals (7) at the top, next the stronger thoracic ones (12) jointed to the ribs, then the heavy lumbars (5). Beyond this broad base of the tower are the fused pelvic vertebrae (5) forming the sacrum which helps support the weight of the body and, finally, there is the coccyx, the fused vertebrae (5) which are the remnants of the tail.

A baby is born with a nearly straight backbone which gradually assumes its

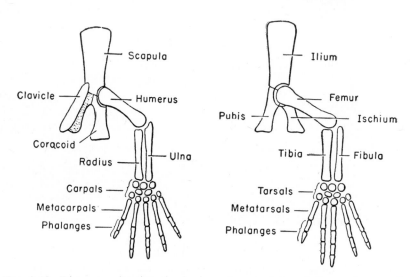

FIG. 9.13. Diagrams showing the basic patterns of the girdles and appendages of vertebrates and the similarity of arrangements in the fore and hind limbs. *A*, forelimb and pectoral girdle; *B*, hindlimb and pelvic girdle.

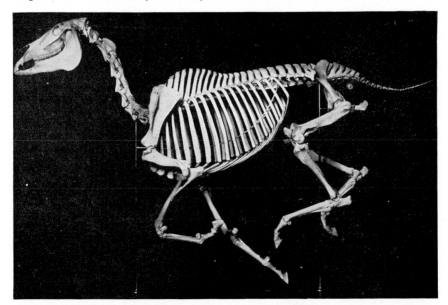

FIG. 9.14. Skeleton of the running horse, Sysonby, mounted after photographic studies from life. The versatility of the skeleton: the pillars of the bridge working as springs. (Skeleton mounted by S. H. Chubb. Photograph, courtesy, American Museum of Natural History.)

peculiarly human shape of three slight curves, two outward and one inward. In the thoracic and pelvic regions the outward curves create shallow bays filled respectively by the lungs and abdominal organs. The latter are suspended by mesenteries attached to the wall of the inward curve or small of the back. Thus there is a strain upon this part of the back even though the abdominal organs rest mainly upon the pelvic girdle. In the upright human body the weight of the organs comes only indirectly upon the front wall of the abdomen. In quadrupeds, the abdominal organs are strung more evenly along the back, rest directly on the ventral body wall and scarcely at all upon the pelvic girdle except in those that sit—cats, kangaroos, and others.

Ribs. Articulated to the thoracic vertebrae are the 12 pairs of ribs, 13 pairs in about 6 per cent of persons. These with the sternum or breastbone form a protecting basket for the heart and lungs. In the evolution of vertebrates the number of ribs has gradually decreased. There are many more in reptiles than in birds and more in lower than in higher mammals.

Pectoral and Pelvic Girdles, Arms and Legs. The human pectoral or shoulder girdle and the arms are carried about as passengers, important and active to be sure, but not burden-bearers like the hip girdle and legs. The human arms are legs freed from the former activities of legs and now engaged in every kind of business. The size, structure, and attachments of their bones allow for freedom of movement but not support.

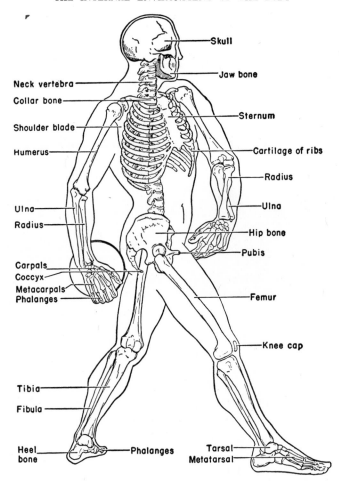

Neck vertebra

Collar bone

Shoulder blade

Humerus

Ulna

Radius

Carpals
Coccyx
Metacarpals
Phalanges

Tibia

Fibula

Heel
bone

Skull

Jaw bone

Sternum

Cartilage of ribs

Radius

Ulna

Hip bone

Pubis

Femur

Knee cap

Phalanges   Tarsal
                   Metatarsal

FIG. 9.15. The human skeleton. There are seven vertebrae in the human neck as there are in the neck of a mouse, giraffe and every other mammal. There are twelve vertebrae in the thorax, five in the small of the back (lumbar), five fused in the sacrum hidden by the hipbone, and four rudimentary ones forming the coccyx or tail. Comparison of right and left arms will show that (left) the radius is twisted around the ulna when the hand is rotated. In a frog's forelegs these bones are permanently crossed; in most mammals they are permanently straight. Power to rotate the forearm has provided man, monkeys, and other primates with facility in the use of their hands. (Courtesy, Etkin: *College Biology*. New York, Thomas Y. Crowell & Co., 1950.)

The broad thin shoulder blade (scapula) is anchored by muscles but not attached to the axial skeleton (Figs. 9.15, 9.16, 9.17). At the shoulder the scapula is joined by the collarbone (clavicle) extending to the breastbone (sternum). The head of the humerus of the upper arm fits into a relatively shallow cavity forming a ball-and-socket joint in the scapula that allows the free motion of throwing a ball. When an arm is lifted the pectoral girdle is

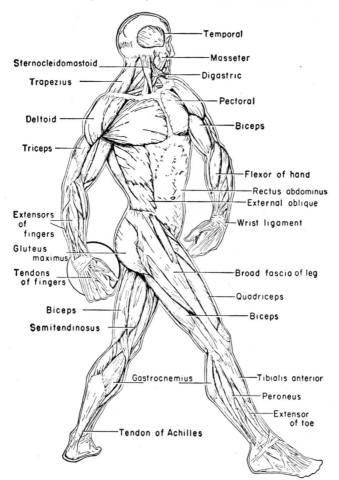

FIG. 9.16. Principal muscles of the human body. The names and uses of the muscles are given in Table 1. (Courtesy, Etkin: *College Biology*. New York, Thomas Y. Crowell & Co., 1950.)

lifted. Human clavicles stand out like slender bridges from shoulder to sternum, easily broken and dislocated. The whole shoulder girdle is turned and shifted in playing a piano, washing windows, driving a car. Clavicles are often reduced or lacking, as in cats and some other mammals that run and pounce, in horses that run, and in deer that leap.

The radius and ulna of the forearm, chiefly the ulna, articulate with the humerus at the elbow in a hinge joint. The upper end of the ulna is called the funny bone or crazy bone, because of the sharp pain which occurs when it is struck. This is due to the stimulation of the ulnar nerve which passes over a knob or condyle on the end of the humerus. At their opposite ends the bones of the forearm are jointed to the short wrist bones (carpals). Most of them are hinge-jointed and bound about by ligaments. The capacity of the hands to turn palms up and palms down and to twist a screw driver and turn a doorknob is due to the position of the radius on the thumb side. When the hand is held palm up, the radius and ulna are parallel; when it is turned palm down, the radius is twisted across the ulna (Fig. 9.15). In many vertebrates, excepting the primates, the radius and ulna are permanently crossed as in the frog, and the front foot cannot be rotated. When a cat is washing her face, her paw makes beautiful curves but never turns palm up.

Five metacarpals form the middle bridge between the wrist and the fingers (Fig. 9.15). The five phalanges, thumb and fingers, play the chief role in the remarkable activities of the hand. The thumb turned palmside to the fingers has taken great part in the development of art and science, actually in the whole of history. The power of the human hand is in its ability to do a large number of things moderately well, to scratch and dig in the soil, to write letters, and do hundreds of other things. A ground mole can scratch and dig in the soil with its front feet doing it extraordinarily well, but it cannot do anything else with them.

The pelvic girdle supports the trunk and, with the femurs firmly attached to it, takes the first impact of all the jolts of locomotion. It is a shallow bowl and in man bears the weight of the abdominal organs to a degree that is uniquely human. As in all other mammals, the pelvic ring of bones of the human female is the birth passage of the young.

Each side of the pelvic girdle is composed of three fused bones (ilium, pubis, and ischium). Where they meet a deep cavity receives the head of the femur in a ball-and-socket joint (Fig. 9.8), the hip joint, the most deeply set and strongly bound with ligaments of any joint in the body. As the shoulder girdle and arms are constructed for pliability, so the pelvic girdle and legs are built for strength. The neck of each femur is an arch that thins with age and becomes very easily broken.

In the leg the distal end of the femur articulates with the tibia and fibula at the knee, a critical joint which is protected by an extra bone, the kneecap (patella) (Fig. 9.15). The tibia and fibula are comparable to the bones of the forearm but are far more rigid. Their distal ends articulate with the ankle bones (tarsals), one of which forms the heel. These bones are bound so tightly by ligaments that they are not allowed much movement; on the inner side of the foot they are lifted up, and with the metatarsal bones take part in forming the arch or instep. Actually this is a double arch, one across the foot and the other running the length of it. The common flatfooted condition comes about when the ligaments lose firmness and allow the tarsals to separate and the metatarsals to drop down. Thus the foot loses its natural spring and lift.

The activities of human toes are slight as compared with those of the fingers. The first cause of their limitations is that the great toe cannot separate off from the other toes and face about with its sole side toward them. It cannot act like a thumb. Compared with the importance of toes in other mammals, that of the human toes is lessening.

Skull. The human skull is a group of bones (22) that forms the house of the brain. It holds most of the sense organs, the gateways to the brain, and the entrance way for food. The skull is divided into the cranium, holding the brain and the face with the eyes, nose, and ears arranged around the mouth. In man the cranium is large in proportion to the face; in a frog the cranium is relatively small and the face large. The uniquely human features of the skull are the rounded dome of the cranium and the chin (Fig. 9.15); the latter was not well developed in primitive man nor is it now in infants.

The 22 bones of the adult skull include a number that are fused together. In the newborn infant even the main immovable joints of the cranium have not closed and there are six spaces or fontanelles where the hard matter of the bone has not been formed. At birth the edges of these bones overlap as the baby's head is squeezed through the pelvic girdle. The skeleton of the human face is comparatively light in weight because it is so full of cavities. The prominent openings of eye sockets, nostrils, and mouth occupy a goodly area and there are also extensive cavities (sinuses) within certain bones (frontal, ethmoid, sphenoid, maxillary), all of which open by small passages into the nasal chambers. Painful inflammation of the lining of the sinuses commonly originates with colds and congestion in the nasal chambers and spreads through the passageways that open into them.

Teeth. Teeth are actually outgrowths of the integument or skin tissues and their ancestry goes back to the scalelike structures which develop about the mouths of sharks and other fishes. They are discussed with the intake of food and mechanical digestion, their main functions (Chap. 11).

Broken Bones and Dislocated Joints

These are common disorders of the skeleton (Fig. 9.17). Breaks or fractures are either simple, in which the skin is unbroken, or compound, if jagged, broken ends of bone protrude outside the flesh. With any fracture nerves and blood vessels are broken and there is pain and bleeding, the latter often within the flesh. In treating a break the bones are first put back into normal position. This is known as reduction. As a broken bone heals bone-forming cells, mostly from the newly formed fibrocartilage in which bone regenerates, gradually grow into the area surrounding the break. Limy salts characteristic of bone are deposited in an enlargement, a callus, that is later resorbed.

Sprains are due to the wrenching or twisting of ligaments that bind bones together at a joint. Severe ones may tear the ligaments and even the periosteum of the bone, but even moderate ones disturb nerves and blood vessels.

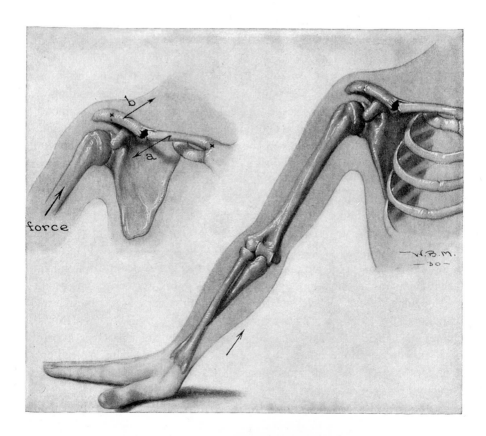

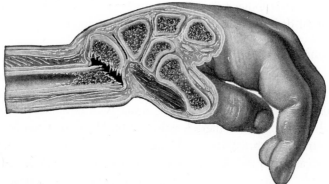

FIG. 9.17. Two common fractures. *Top,* break of the collar bone (clavicle), arrows showing the force of breakage. *Bottom,* section of a hand showing a break in the "wrist"; actually the end of the radius causes a displacement of the wrist and disturbance of the joint. (Courtesy, *Blakiston's New Gould Medical Dictionary.* Philadelphia, The Blakiston Company, 1949.)

10
Movement—Muscles

Partnerships of the Muscular System. The business of muscles is to pull; they cannot push. Voluntary muscles in the arms and legs pull from attachments to the skeleton; others such as most involuntary ones pull from fibrous attachments. They are specialists in contraction. Skeletons are the frameworks for the hundreds of bodily movements that we see in rabbits or butterflies, bird or man. The nervous system regulates and controls movement that the muscles accomplish with the skeleton as their essential tool (Fig. 10.1). The human brain is helpless to express itself without the contraction of muscles of the face, the eyes, hands, stomach; looking cheerful is a muscular exercise, looking cranky is another in which arms, legs, and face take part. Breathing and the circulation of the blood are completely dependent upon muscular action. When the thoracic muscles are paralyzed by poliomyelitis, breathing cannot go on without an iron lung to take the part of their contraction.

Compared with other tissues of the body, the activity of muscle demands a large amount of food, but it also liberates a great deal of energy and the major part of bodily heat. And heat is an important catalyst in chemical action, contributing greatly to the more rapid metabolism that is characteristic of warm-blooded animals.

Muscle constitutes a third to one-half the bulk of vertebrate animals as well as a goodly proportion of it in bees, lobsters, and many other invertebrates. Wherever they occur, muscles and skeleton contribute form as well as function to the body, the pillarlike legs of elephants, the supple foreshoulders of all the cat tribe. The greatest theme of sculpture has been the form and relationships and the power of muscles in such figures as the sitting greyhound, resting lion, flying Mercury, as well as those of kings, soldiers, and prophets. Actors on any stage turn the meaning of comedy or tragedy by tricks of their muscles. Without muscles television would be indeed a bleak monotony. All this is not to mention the muscular contractions that control the vocal cords whereby

155

FIG. 10.1. Kittens falling and preparing to land. The grace and flexibility of their muscles are unsurpassed. The nervous system controls the movements that the muscles accomplish with the skeleton as their tool. (Photograph by Ylla. Courtesy, Rapho-Guillumette Studio, New York, published in *Cats,* London, Harvill Press.)

the world is filled with cackle, bark, speech, and song. These and other characteristics of muscles are matters of great social and economic importance. Muscle is meat, almost the sole food of carnivorous animals and also of high value to man and other omnivorous ones.

Kinds of Muscle

There are two main types of muscle, distinguished by their activity and appearance under the microscope. Involuntary or smooth muscle, the older one in the history of muscle, is generally distributed in the invertebrates except arthropods, and occurs in the hollow organs of vertebrates such as the stomach, intestines, and arteries. The pupil of the eye becomes smaller when involuntary circular muscles contract and narrow the iris. Hairs stand up when their erector muscles contract from cold and other causes (Fig. 10.2).

Voluntary, skeletal, or striated muscles are the bulkier ones. Those of the body wall and arms and legs contribute largely to the form of the body (Figs. 9.16, 10.3).

Cardiac or heart muscle, often named as a third type, is intermediate in structure to striated muscle and in activity to smooth muscle.

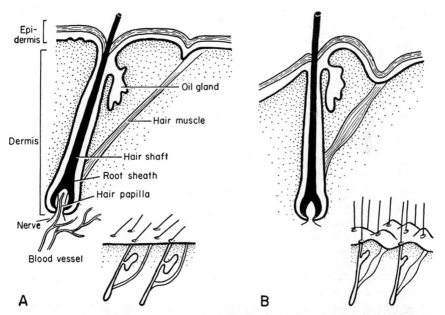

Epi-
dermis

Oil gland

Hair muscle

Dermis

Hair shaft

Root sheath

Hair papilla

Nerve

Blood vessel

A   B

FIG. 10.2. An involuntary muscle, the hair muscle. Diagrams of sections of skin showing the follicle or root of a hair with the muscle attached to the skin and the root sheath. *A,* hair naturally leans at an angle when the muscle is relaxed. The region about the hair is supplied with nerves associated with the muscle. *B,* under certain conditions, such as cold and nervous shock the nerves stimulate the hair muscles to contract pulling the hairs up straight and the skin into little hillocks, "goose flesh."

VOLUNTARY MUSCLE

Voluntary muscles are here presented before the simpler involuntary ones because they are the ones we most often see and eat. They are characteristic of animals with endoskeletons, that is, the backboned animals and their immediate ancestors.

General Structure and Arrangement. Each voluntary or skeletal muscle consists of bundles of slender cells. Each bundle is held together by very delicate connective tissue and the whole muscle is also sheathed by connective tissue, the white strands visible in roast beef and ham (Fig. 7.5). The older the animal, the thicker and tougher these are. Blood and lymph capillaries and nerves run throughout the muscle actually in touch with the muscle cells (Figs. 10.5, 10.6, 10.7).

Although the form of muscles differs with their functions, most of them are spindle shaped and the ends are drawn out to their points of attachment, the origin and insertion. The origin is usually on a firmly fixed part of the body; that of the biceps muscle which bends the arm is on the shoulder. Its insertion is on the radius of the forearm, the bone to be moved, and the at-

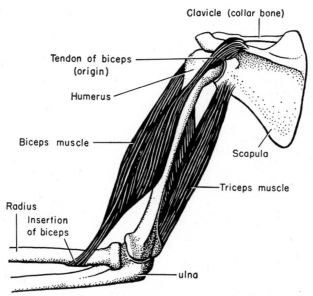

FIG. 10.3. Voluntary muscle. The biceps muscle takes the main part in lifting and bending the arm; the triceps acts in lowering and straightening the arm. These and other voluntary muscles work in pairs independently, e.g., as the biceps contracts, the triceps relaxes. The nicety of nervous control which is essential for such synchronous action occurs in many regions and at the same time. The shoulder joint adapted for flexibility should be compared with the hip joint adapted for support. (Redrawn from Haggard: *The Science of Health and Disease.* New York, Harper & Bros., 1927.)

tachment is by a tough and very flexible but inelastic tendon (Fig. 10.3). Like many muscles, the biceps and triceps of the arm work in opposition. The biceps muscle contracts and as the arm bends the triceps is stretched. The triceps contracts; the arm straightens, and the biceps is stretched.

The great advantage of tendons is in their strength, considering the small space they occupy. The cords on the back of the hand, each attached to a finger bone, are the tendons of muscles that straighten the fingers. All of these

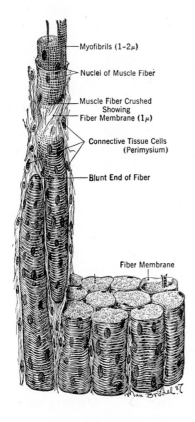

Myofibrils (1–2μ)

Nuclei of Muscle Fiber

Muscle Fiber Crushed Showing
Fiber Membrane (1μ)

Connective Tissue Cells (Perimysium)

Blunt End of Fiber

Fiber Membrane

FIG. 10.4. A group of skeletal or striated muscle cells commonly called fibers. Some of the fibers are cut off to show them in cross section. A skeletal muscle fiber is actually a sort of super-cell containing many nuclei and other cell elements, a highly specialized structure. (Courtesy, Gerard: *The Body Functions.* New York, John Wiley & Sons, 1941.)

muscles are located in the forearm and depend on the tendons to communicate their pull (Fig. 9.16); if the muscles were near the fingers the back of the hand would be a bulging pillow. By a similar arrangement in the leg, the calf muscle (gastrocnemius) lifts the heel by its tendon of Achilles (Fig. 9.16). Picture the tendon of Achilles omitted and the calf muscles moved to their immediate place of business at the heel!

Conditions of Muscular Activity. Muscles contain an enormous number of blood and lymph capillaries, the former apparently in contact with every muscle cell (Fig. 10.7). The glycogen stored in muscle cells is a readily oxidized, quickly available food. An extra amount of blood flows into muscles as soon

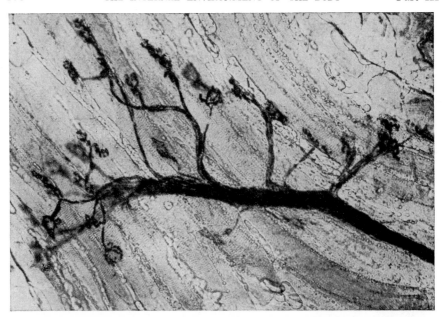

FIG. 10.5. Ending of a motor nerve cell fiber on a striated muscle cell, highly magnified. A change sweeps over the fiber of the nerve cell to the junction with the muscle fiber and there it acts upon the muscle stimulating it to contract. When a nerve cell acts upon muscle the ends of the nerve fiber produce a minute amount of chemical substance which stimulates the muscle to contract. This substance is a neurohumor, a chemical link between stimulation and activity. (Courtesy, General Biological Supply House, Inc., Chicago, Ill.)

as they go into action and, as they work, their great demand for oxygen is answered by deeper breathing.

Stimulation. Contraction is due to a rapid succession of stimuli coming into the muscle fibers from nerve cells (Fig. 10.5). If many fibers are stimulated the contraction is strong; if few are stimulated it is weak. The strength of the stimulation whether of one or several muscles depends originally upon stimuli received through the eyes, ears, nose, and other sense organs. Making a home run means that strong sensory stimuli, the sight of the opposing players, and applause of the spectators, have been translated into motor stimuli and have put millions of muscle cells into action. A muscle cell is stimulated, contracts, relaxes, and recovers. These steps are gone through with great rapidity and can be analyzed only because living muscle can be isolated and subjected to experiment and observation.

The contraction of muscle is completely dependent upon receiving messages via certain nerves. Muscles also send forth messages via certain other nerves. It is their ability to do this that makes it possible for us to know that our feet are on the floor.

Fatigue of Muscle. A muscle acts for a considerable period until it is fatigued. Fatigue is a loss of contractility, apparently from accumulation of the waste products of metabolism. Symptoms of muscle fatigue are easily produced. Hold your arm out straight; at first it is steady, then it trembles, and finally you cannot prevent its sinking down in exhaustion.

Tonus. This is the continuous partial contraction of muscle cells arising

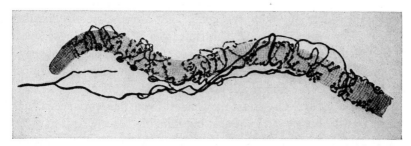

FIG. 10.6. Sensory nerve fibers with their end plates spread upon the surface of a fiber of an eye muscle. The sensory end plates can be stimulated by conditions within the muscle and changes sweep over the sensory nerve fibers as they do over the motor ones (Fig. 10.5). Muscles are supplied with both kinds of nerves. A muscle can receive a message and can also send one. (Courtesy, Maximow and Bloom: *Textbook of Histology,* ed. 6. Philadelphia, W. B. Saunders Co., 1952.)

from muscle sense of position. Sense of position is closely associated with environment and habit. An aviator may lose his "sense of right side up." A cat's feet feel for the floor or the ground surface to which they are accustomed (Fig. 10.1). Tonus of skeletal muscles of the legs and trunk occurs in sitting, standing, and walking. In general tonus does not require as much energy as ordinary contraction.

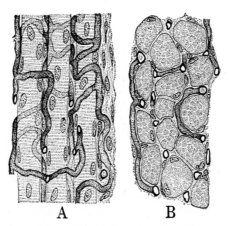

A   B

FIG. 10.7. Capillaries surrounding skeletal muscle fibers in a dog's tongue. *A,* longitudinal section; *B,* cross section. The abundance and intimacy of capillaries with the muscle cells reveal an elaborate provision for the exchange of oxygen and carbon dioxide and a rich supply of food. (Courtesy, Nonidez and Windle: *Textbook of Histology,* ed. 2. New York, McGraw-Hill Book Co., Inc., 1953.)

Tetanus. When a frog's muscle is stimulated by a single electric shock, it contracts and relaxes again within a tenth of a second. Usually muscles do not move so fast. This is because practically all contractions of voluntary muscles are tetanic, the results of rapidly repeated stimuli, which maintain their contraction. When you carry a box of eggs your arm holds them steadily, not by jerks. In human skeletal muscle tetanus results from stimuli entering the muscle cells at the rate of 40 to 60 per second. They are so close together that the resulting reactions blend into one. This shift from jerk to blend resembles that of moving pictures, the separate pictures are shifted so rapidly that they look continuous. Muscles may tremble and pictures will vibrate when the respective movements are not sure and rapid.

Production of Heat. Muscles are the greatest living heat-producers. Jumping rope increases the body's outgo of heat but thinking (except as it may involve the muscles) does not, much as it may seem to do so. The heat liberated by muscular action is an extremely important activator which hastens chemical reactions throughout the body. Even the fluffing out of feathers and fur provides extra heat because of the contraction of involuntary muscles in the skin. Honeybees can raise the temperature of their hives a few degrees by the muscular exercise of vibrating their wings.

Muscular Action. The energy for muscular action is freed by oxidation of food. Muscle cells hold a store of food, principally the carbohydrates, glycogen made from the glucose brought to them by the blood. How does the chemical energy in the food become the energy of motion in a particular kind of muscle? Although this is only partly known, a great many things have been learned about the minute structure of muscle and the chemical and physical changes which occur in it. A great deal has been discovered through observation and experiment on living muscle, commonly the calf muscle of the leg (gastrocnemius) removed from freshly killed frogs. Organic compounds, such as adenosine triphosphate, and glycogen, which muscle contains, are ready to break down and liberate energy whenever conditions allow it.

It was long ago discovered that during contraction muscles change their shape but not their size. In one of his excellent experiments the naturalist, Jan Swammerdam (1637–1680), placed a muscle in a container of water attached to a fine capillary tube in which the water line was visible. Then he watched the line while the muscle contracted and wrote, "I must confess that the drop of water sinks so little that I can scarcely observe it." A recent and significant observation of muscular activity is that it may take place in the entire absence of oxygen and without producing carbon dioxide. This means that contraction is not the usual oxidative process, but has not proved that contraction of muscle is independent of oxidation.

Chemical changes occur during muscular action and recovery. One unit of any muscular action consists of a latent period following stimulation, a contraction and relaxation phase and recovery, all together termed a muscle twitch. This is the reply to any one of the stimuli which come into muscle cells in rapid succession during muscular action.

Contraction is accompanied by the explosive breakdown of an unstable organic compound, phosphocreatine, into phosphate and creatine. The separation of the creatine and phosphate liberates the energy taking part in the contraction, plus some energy in heat.

Relaxation is also associated with a series of chemical changes. Through the action of an enzyme in the muscle, glycogen breaks down, ultimately into lactic acid. This energy takes part in reuniting phosphate and creatine into their previous state as the unstable organic compound, phosphocreatine. The muscle is then ready for another breakdown at the next contraction. The foregoing series of changes does not require oxygen and constitutes the nonoxidative or anaerobic phase of muscle action.

Anaerobic respiration of mammalian muscle is a chain of chemical reactions during which the muscle uses glucose, which it derives from its store of glycogen. These anaerobic reactions release the energy used by the muscle in doing work. The process results in the by-product of lactic acid. Part of this is eliminated by oxidation and the energy thus released rebuilds the remainder of it into glucose and glycogen. The muscle is then ready to do more work. It loses some of its store of glycogen with each contraction because the lactic acid that is burned in oxidation turns into carbon dioxide and water which are eliminated. Strenuous exercise may run up a debt of several quarts of oxygen. Lactic acid accumulates, diffuses into the blood, and makes it acid and this acidity is a demand for oxygen. Its increase in the blood, modified by the buffering salts, stimulates the respiratory center of the brain which sends out impulses that lead to vigorous breathing. Forced breathing continues until enough oxygen has accumulated to burn the lactic acid and reinstate the glucose. The blood is no longer unusually acid and ceases to stimulate forced breathing.

Recovery occurs following the changes in the relaxation phase of the muscle. One-fifth of the lactic acid previously produced in the anaerobic phase is now oxidized, and water, carbon dioxide, and energy are released. Of the energy thus freed part is heat and part becomes active in the resynthesis of the remaining four-fifths of the lactic acid in glycogen. These changes constitute the oxidative, the recovery or aerobic phase of the muscle action.

At first, it may seem as if there would be an advantage if oxygen came into the chemical changes earlier. Muscular action however actually starts more quickly because it does not. The blood is constantly bringing oxygen to the muscles, but they collect no supply above their momentary use. There is no extra oxygen to spend on a sudden action like snatching away one's hand when it touches a nettle or a hot iron. Although no supply of oxygen is ready, there is a reserve of an organic compound (phosphocreatine) ready to break down explosively and liberate energy at the instant the nervous impulses affect the muscle.

These chemical changes are a part of the intricate workings of muscle. They and others are going on in every animal motion that we see, the quick whirring of the hummingbird's wings, or the movements of the bagpiper who at the same time marches, blows into the bag, and fingers the keys for a Highland fling.

Involuntary Muscle

Smooth muscles contract and relax slowly, skeletal ones rapidly; these processes take several seconds in the former, less than one second in the latter. Smooth muscles may hold a certain degree of contraction for a long time without apparent fatigue and with great economy of energy. Smooth muscle cells are spindle-shaped, each with a single nucleus and minute contractile fibrils running lengthwise in the cell. None of them is cross-striped, hence the name smooth muscle.

They are never attached to bone and rarely have tendons (Fig. 10.8). In

FIG. 10.8. Integumental or skin muscles of a horse, by means of which the skin may be "shuddered" and flies dislodged especially on the neck and shoulders. Such muscles are practically absent on the flanks. (Redrawn from Walter and Sayles: *Biology of the Vertebrates*, ed. 3. New York, The Macmillan Co., 1949.)

the vertebrate body they occur mainly in the hollow organs of the body cavity, the stomach, intestines, the urinary bladder, the uterus, also in the blood vessels and the air passages of the lungs. In arteries the individual cells are curved in circular layers around the tube; in the intestine they form circular and also longitudinal layers. By the contraction and relaxation of circular layers the intestine executes its peristaltic waves of contraction and relaxation, bulges out in some places, squeezes in at others, shortens and lengthens much as an earthworm does with the rhythmic deliberations characteristic of smooth muscle.

In their control of skeletal muscle, nerve cells act through the long extensions of the cell body; in smooth muscle whole autonomic nerve cells may be present among the fibers. In addition to their stimulation by nerves, muscle cells are also stimulated directly by movements of one another as waves of contraction pass over them.

Smooth muscles are never bulky and conspicuous but their functions are dramatically important. Those of the uterus are responsible for birth. They hold blood in the vessels at a regulated capacity, thus largely maintaining blood pressure and the circulation of blood. Attacks of asthma are spasmodic contractions of smooth muscles that under normal nervous control regulate the amount of air in the bronchioles. Less serious but vivid in experience are the contractions in the walls of the stomach that cause hunger pains.

Muscles of Some Familiar Invertebrates

Smooth muscles are located in the viscera and the body wall of many invertebrates. Clams, mussels, and oysters can hold their shells closed for long periods, some of them for days at a time. The shells of all bivalves are hinged, and in the hinge is an elastic band which continually resists the closing of the shells. This resistance is met by the tonic contraction of adductor muscles attached at either end to the inner surface of the shells. The large adductor muscles of the scallop (Pecten) are familiar as fried scallops. Experimental stimulation of these muscles indicates that they contain certain rapidly contracting muscle cells along with a majority of slowly contracting ones. This combination is ideal for the lively habits of scallops which, by clapping their shells together and rapidly expelling the water between them, are able to skip out for short distances through the water by a kind of jet propulsion. Involuntary muscles with a very different function take part in the "blushing" of the squid. When these handsome relatives of the devilfishes are excited, glimmering flashes of pink and red shift over their bodies due to the movements of pigment (in chromatophores) controlled by muscles.

The movements of the common earthworm are an easily observed example of peristalsis, i.e., successive waves of contraction of the rings of smooth muscle in the body wall. Close to these, layers of longitudinal muscles extend the length of the worm. When the long ones contract, the fluid-filled body of the worm shortens and bulges; when the circular muscles contract, they squeeze the body to slenderness and drive the fluids forward and backward forcing it to elongate.

Insects have the most complex muscular systems and most clearly striated muscle of all invertebrates. The number of distinct muscles is very large, varying in different insects, but there are often over 2,000. In a dissection, muscle is one of the most conspicuous tissues of the insect body. It is either colorless and transparent, or yellowish white, often soft, almost gelatinous, notwithstanding its efficiency.

Patterns of Vertebrate Locomotion

No other animals take such long journeys by sea and land as the vertebrates; eels swimming down streams and half across the Atlantic; birds flying from Alaska to the Argentine; and human populations moving to distant lands. All these great travelers are aided by their bilateral symmetry, their light internal skeletons, and their muscles.

In fishes the muscles of the body wall are usually divided into segments (myomeres). They carry on the main work of locomotion; fins do not do the heavy work. Fishes move by a sidewise undulation, a wavy motion with muscles contracting first along one side of the body, then along the other (Fig. 10.9). They push their bodies with their tails giving the main drive. Spotted

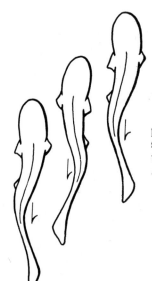

Fig. 10.9. A fish swims by undulating movements and pushes its body forward by pressing against the water, successive waves of curvature traveling backward along the trunk and tail. (Redrawn from Romer: *The Vertebrate Body*. Philadelphia, W. B. Saunders Co., 1949.)

newts (Triturus) spend one period of their lives in water and another on land, but they move with the wavy swing of the fishes all their lives (Fig. 34.2).

Land vertebrates have a different problem; they cannot push against the air with their bodies for air is too yielding; they must push the ground or its counterpart. Their movement on four legs from one place to another is the great achievement of their voluntary muscles and partner bones and nerves (Fig. 10.10). Man's movement on two legs is still more difficult and more significant in that it has left the muscles of his hands and arms free to use tools. Standing on two legs is a continued balance which requires that a large number of muscles be kept in sustained contraction in reply to impulses that recur because of the stimulation of the sensory receptors of position (proprioceptors). In contrast to the healthy resilience of upright posture is the complete limpness of muscles that follows poliomyelitis. The muscles are still normal but the motor nerve cell bodies in the spinal cord have been attacked by the virus. Walking on two legs involves holding the body and head upright and shifting the entire weight to the hind limbs, thus freeing the front ones. With the start of walking the body falls forward, then one leg, say the left one, is flexed and thrust forward to catch the falling body. At the same time the calf muscle of the right leg contracts and lifts the heel. The left foot is being placed on the ground and for an instant both feet are on the ground. The weight of the body is now shifted to the left leg and the right one is swung forward into

FIG. 10.10. The same pattern of movement of the arms and legs of a man, and the legs of a cat, an ancient inescapable habit.

a new position in front of the left. When the right foot is planted, the weight of the body is shifted to that leg, and the pull of the muscles now lifts the left heel. The left leg is then swung forward again in front of the right one. Thus walking is like the movements of a pendulum repeated several thousand times per day.

Infants begin their travels on all fours as quadrupeds continue to do through life. Brisk walkers swing their arms and when they do so the right arm and the left leg go forward at the same time in exactly the same pattern as in a walking cat and with the same muscles operating (Fig. 10.10). We cannot walk in any other way; neither can the cat. Inherited pattern of the movement of muscle is as inescapable as the inheritance of its structure.

11
Foods and Nutrition

Nature of Nutrition

Nutrition is a remarkable process by which the protoplasm of a cabbage becomes rabbit, that of a fish becomes cat, and the proteins of lamb are transformed into proteins of man. The processes of nutrition include: the physical and chemical breakup of foods called digestion; the absorption by cells of the foods simplified by digestion; and assimilation, by which the basic units of protein are interwoven into the particular pattern of proteins of the animal nourished, and the simplified carbohydrates and fats stored to be available for energy. All cells of the body and the chromosomes within them are nourished in this way. Human chromosomes doubtless contain substances that originated in beans and cattle, but they have lost their original characteristics and by assimilation have become the protein peculiar to the chromosomes of man.

Nature of Foods

Foods are the substances that are taken into the body and used in its metabolism, in building protoplasm for growth and repair, and in liberating energy to do work. Work includes all activity such as movement, responses of the sense organs, and secretion of glands. Animal food consists of plants and animals and their products, such as sugar and milk. The essential substances are proteins, carbohydrates, fats, vitamins, and very small amounts of certain minerals (Fig. 11.1). Water, necessary for all organisms, is essential in the process of nutrition.

Proteins. Since protein is constantly being broken down in the body, more of it must be furnished for repair as well as for growth. When there is no protein in the food, the body burns its own protein. This happens in starvation. Sixteen per cent of protein is nitrogen. The body must be kept in a nitrogen balance, that is, as much nitrogen should be taken in as is excreted, and sometimes more, as during pregnancy, during growth, and after injury or illness. Proteins are abundant in meat (muscle), cheese, eggs, peas, and beans. Their

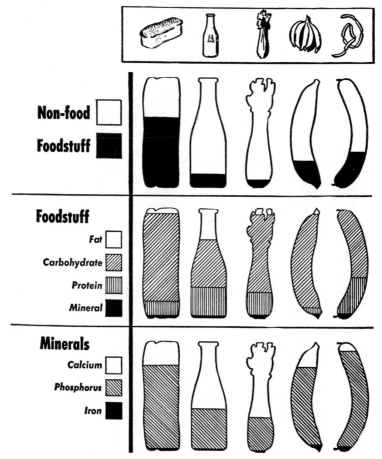

FIG. 11.1. Fats, carbohydrates, proteins, and minerals are contained in most food but in different proportions. (Reprinted from *Food for Life* edited by R. W. Gerard, by permission of The University of Chicago Press. Copyright 1952.)

basic elements are carbon, hydrogen, oxygen, nitrogen, sulfur, and phosphorus. The protein molecule is made up of amino acids of which at least ten are essential to life. The simplest one known is glycine ($H_5C_2O_2N$). All growth and repair of the body is dependent upon proteins, but they must be thoroughly digested into amino acids before they can be used. Fish protein does not repair the tissues of cats or increase the growth of kittens until it is thoroughly disorganized from its previous character. The body stores no protein. But after the removal of its amino group (NH_2) the remainder of an amino acid may be converted into glucose and used as food or changed to glycogen and stored in cells as starch is stored in a potato.

Carbohydrates. The familiar carbohydrates are starches and sugars. They are made up of the elements carbon, hydrogen, and oxygen, with the hydrogen and oxygen usually in the same proportion to oxygen as in water (H_2O). Carbohydrates furnish a large share of the energy required for the regular needs of living; they provide the energy for such routine processes as respiration, circulation, digestion, and excretion—the metabolism of the body. Fats also provide energy but they are chemically less quickly accessible for use. During digestion carbohydrates are broken down into glucose, a simple sugar ($C_6H_{12}O_6$) which is distributed in the blood to the liver, muscles, and other tissues throughout the body. It is converted into glycogen, commonly called animal starch. This is readily reconverted to glucose for immediate use anywhere in the body. Human blood usually contains about 0.1 per cent glucose ready for instant use.

Fats. Fat accumulates as pure fat, not mixed with water like protein and carbohydrate, and when oxidized has a high heat output. Fat is a long-range supply not ready for quick use like glycogen. Thus, the fat boy gets just as hungry as the thin one.

Fats (or lipids) are simplified by hydrolysis, that is, by chemically splitting up and taking in water, into glycerol (or glycerin) and fatty acids. The true fats, liquid and solid, are combinations of glycerin and fatty acids; oleic acid in butter ($C_{18}H_{34}O_2$) is an example. They all contain carbon and hydrogen, with less oxygen than carbohydrates. All fats are greasy and are soluble in organic liquids such as ether or benzene, rarely in water. Certain of them, such as cod-liver oil, are liquid in ordinary temperatures; others, such as lard and tallow, are solid. The wax produced in the human ear and beeswax are substances very like the fats. The sterols are complex waxlike compounds of a different chemical nature. Cholesterol in the bile and calciferol (vitamin D_2) are such sterols; the male and female sex hormones and certain cancer-producing compounds also belong to the steroid group. Compound fats such as lecithin contain nitrogen and phosphorus in addition to the elements regularly contained in fats. Lecithin occurs in almost all living cells; it is a major item in the yolk of eggs.

Vitamins. Vitamins are compounds that are present in foods in small quantities. They play an important part in human nutrition and probably in that of all plants and animals. Vitamins are highly specific; for example, vitamin A affects the cornea of the eye; others affect the hardening of bone (Fig. 11.3). Some are soluble in fats, others in water; certain ones are destroyed by heat, others are not. Human diet is apt to be deficient, especially in vitamin A, folic acid, riboflavin, ascorbic acid, calciferol, and thiamine (Table 11.1). In nature most of the vitamins are produced by plants. They are abundant in grasses, and cats frequently bite off grass blades, apparently satisfying some kind of hunger. Cats and other carnivores secure vitamins as they lick their fur and by eating the fur and feathers of their prey. The old name "limey" for a British sailor is indirectly connected with vitamins. In the days of sailing ships and

Table 11.1

A LIST OF IMPORTANT VITAMINS AND THEIR CHARACTERISTICS

Selected from the 40 or more known vitamins or vitaminlike substances. Investigations of vitamins are still in progress and new discoveries and revisions are constantly being made.

Name	Important Sources	Physiological Functions	Chief Results of Deficiency
A Group (fat soluble)	Plant form (carotene) in green leaves, carrots, tomatoes; animal form in liver, milk, egg yolk; both forms in eggs, milk and butter	Maintain health of mucous membranes and other epithelial tissues Needed to regenerate visual purple in retina of eye	Dry cornea of eye (xerophthalmia), no tear secretion Night blindness
B Group (water soluble) Thiamine	Whole grains of wheat, rice, other cereals, beans, peas, green vegetables, egg yolk, and lean meat Made synthetically	Needed for carbohydrate metabolism Stimulates root growth in plants	Beriberi, a disease of the nervous system; polyneuritis a nervous disability in birds, stops growth
Riboflavin	Green leaves, fruit, milk, eggs, liver	Essential for growth; concerned with body's use of food	Nervous disorders, stunted growth in cattle and poultry; scaly skin
Nicotinic acid or niacin	Green leaves, wheat germ, lean meat, eggs, milk, yeast. Made synthetically	Essential to normal functions of cells	Pellagra, a severe nervous disease in man and monkeys
Folic acid	Green vegetables, eggs, yeast, liver	Essential for growth and formation of blood cells	Anemia in man. Slow growth and anemia in chicks and rats
B_{12}	Egg yolk, fermentations of Streptomyces (source similar to that of penicillin), milk, fish, liver, meat	Essential for blood cell formation by bone marrow	Pernicious anemia, caused by a change in gastric secretion so that B_{12} is not absorbed from the digestive tract
C or ascorbic acid	Citrus fruits, tomatoes; oil of fish livers Can be made synthetically	Maintains the health of capillary walls	Scurvy, bleeding in mucous membranes, under skin, and into joints
D or antirachitic	Fish liver oils; exposure of skin to ultraviolet radiation	Regulates metabolism of calcium and phosphorus; needed for normal growth and mineral content of bones	Rickets in young, bones and teeth soft and often deformed; severe bowlegs
E or antisterility	Green leaves, wheat germ, and cottonseed oils	Essential to rapid cell division and growth in embryo	Sterility in poultry and rats, death of embryos
K or antihemorrhagic	Green leaves, spinach, cabbage, also in certain bacteria of the intestinal flora	Essential to production of prothrombin in liver, necessary for clotting of blood	Bleeding

voyages that took a year or more, the great dread of sailors was scurvy, a disease caused by the long steady diet of dried and salted foods lacking in vitamins. When it was discovered that eating limes would prevent scurvy, no ship went to sea without them. Sailors ate limes and unknowingly treated themselves to vitamin C (Table 11.1).

Vitamin research really began when it was discovered that animals needed vitamins and could be used as subjects in experimentation with deficiency diseases. The first clearcut results (Eijkman, 1893) were obtained upon chickens. When they were fed on polished rice, the chickens developed a disease similar to beriberi, common among human rice-eating populations (Fig. 11.2). As soon as they were fed the previously cast off rice polishings they recovered from the disease. As often happens, the wide significance of these results was not recognized until some time later. By 1915, however, it was fully realized that in addition to the regular foods, more than one vitamin was essential for health. The discovery of vitamin A came about through attempts (1913–1915) to use pure fats in the diets of experimental animals. It was observed that for no apparent reason butterfat was far superior to other fats, such as lard. When young rats were fed diets containing only lard, they were stunted and had a scaly, infected condition of the eyes known as xerophthalmia (Fig. 11.3). In contrast to this, when butter was substituted for lard in the diet, the rats grew and remained healthy. Oleomargarine made from vegetable oils has a food value identical with that of butter now that sufficient vitamin A is added.

Minerals. Minerals required by the body are usually obtained with the food or drinking water. Several such substances are essential to plants and animals, but in minute quantities. These are called micronutrients and trace elements, the latter not to be confused with radioactive tracer substances (Table 11.2). Experimental diets given to animals have revealed most that is known about the use of micronutrients.

Types of Nutrition

There are three principal types of diet: herbivorous, carnivorous, and omnivorous. *Herbivorous animals* feed on vegetation. They include grazing cattle, leaf-eating insects such as Japanese beetles, seed-eating birds, and rodents.

Carnivorous animals are flesh-eaters. Among the most voracious are the freshwater protozoans *Didinium nasutum*. When they are placed among a population of paramecia, each one immediately attaches its trunklike proboscis onto a paramecium which is speedily "swallowed" (Fig. 11.4). An individual Didinium may devour paramecia until its own body splits open. Among other carnivores no tiger can be more bloodthirsty than female mosquitoes and blood-sucking leeches. Most fishes are typical carnivores; so are snakes, owls, and hawks. The order Carnivora is a group of mammals that includes cats, tigers, dogs, wolves, raccoons, and seals but the animals of this group have no monopoly on the carnivorous diet.

Omnivorous animals feed on both vegetable and animal matter, dead or alive. They include such scavengers as lobsters, domestic fowls, and man. The

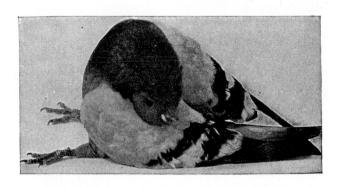

A

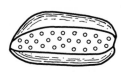

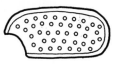

Rice grain in husk   Showing germ   "Polished rice"

B

FIG. 11.2. *A*, Pigeons: *top*, suffering from polyneuritis (beriberi) developed as a result of a diet of polished rice, lacking thiamine (of the vitamin B complex); *bottom*, the same bird after injection of thiamine resulting in a spectacular cure. *B*, Diagrams of rice grain (seed), in natural condition, and polished rice, with bran or husk and the germ removed as in the milling process. Thiamine is confined almost entirely to the germ. Milled grains contain little or no thiamine. In its absence an essential enzyme of the body fails to function and finally there is a poisoning of the nervous system known as polyneuritis. (*A*, after Morse. Courtesy, Heilbrunn: *Outline of General Physiology*, ed. 3. Philadelphia, W. B. Saunders Co., 1952.)

FIG. 11.3. *Left*, Dog with vitamin A deficiency causing xerophthalmia, a dryness of the eyeballs. *Right*, Same dog after treatment with cod liver oil for 10 days. From early times it has been known that night-blindness and xerophthalmia are associated with sparsity of fat in the diet. In man the most sensitive test for lack of vitamin A is loss of adaptation to darkness. The visual purple in the retina of the eye is a derivative of vitamin A. (After Steenbock, Nelson, and Hart. Courtesy, Bogert: *Nutrition and Physical Fitness,* ed. 3. Philadelphia, W. B. Saunders Co., 1941.)

Table 11.2

MINERALS AND/OR TRACE ELEMENTS* REQUIRED BY THE BODY OF MAN AND OTHER MAMMALS

Name	Location and/or Chief Functions	Effects Caused by Deficiency
Calcium	In bones, blood, teeth, nerves Stimulates milk production	Rickets, nervous irritability
Chlorine	Activates enzymes, such as gastric juice Regulates osmotic pressure	Loss of weight, loss of water, digestive disturbances
Fluorine	In enamel of teeth	Decay of teeth
Iodine	In thyroxin, a secretion of thyroid gland	Low basal metabolism, nervous disturbances
Iron	In hemoglobin of the blood	Decreased hemoglobin
Magnesium	In bones, nerves, muscles, especially of the heart	Retarded growth, rapid or irregular heartbeat, nervousness
Phosphorus	In bones, blood, teeth, muscles. Metabolism of carbohydrates and proteins; activates enzymes	Poor development of bones and teeth, rickets, retarded growth
Potassium	Important in muscle action, normal growth, osmotic pressure	Poor muscular control, irregular heartbeat
Silicon	In hair	
Sodium	Important in regulation of osmotic pressure	Loss of weight, nervous disorders
Sulfur	In proteins of the body	Retarded growth

* Authorities differ as to whether some of these substances are in small enough amounts to be classed as trace elements.

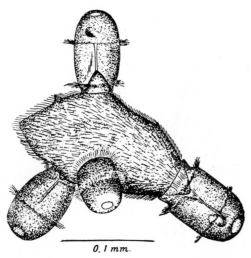

0. 1 mm.

FIG. 11.4. *Didinium nasutum,* a microscopic animal, nevertheless a fierce carnivore. A large paramecium is attacked by four small Didinia. The paramecium
is torn in pieces and each attacker gets a piece. Or, one Didinium gets the whole
paramecium and forces the others off while it swallows the victim. (Courtesy,
Mast, "Reactions of *Didinium nasutum*," *Biological Bulletin* **16**:100, 1909.)

human diet includes living plants, living animals, oysters and others; freshly
killed animals; and decayed plant and animal tissues. In primitive cultures the
latter are inexpensive foods; in more highly cultured circles, decayed foods,
among them "high cheese" and mellowed venison are expensive.

Food Intake by Plants and Animals

Plants absorb food in solution. Water and salts enter the plant through the
root hairs whose delicate surfaces must be constantly moist (Fig. 4.9). Roots
turn toward water and stems toward light, but plants hunt only in these ways.
Excepting parasites, most land animals and many aquatic ones go from one
place to another after food, a continual prowl if they prey on other animals,
sometimes a long wandering if they feed on plants. The majority of animals
eat solid foods, microscopic particles taken into the food vacuole of an ameba,
a whole sheep into the stomach of a great python snake. But before any food
is absorbed it must be in solution.

Feeding Devices. Contraction of protoplasm always figures in the intake of
solid food. The protoplasm of an ameba contracts about a diatom. The lashing
cilia of a paramecium or a rotifer create currents that bear processions of
microscopic food particles through their mouths and gullets (Fig. 11.5). Cilia
bring the food to the mouths of such aquatic animals as the sea anemones,
clams and oysters, and the swimming young of starfishes. Certain sizes and
shapes of particles are selected by the ciliary currents, often by means of

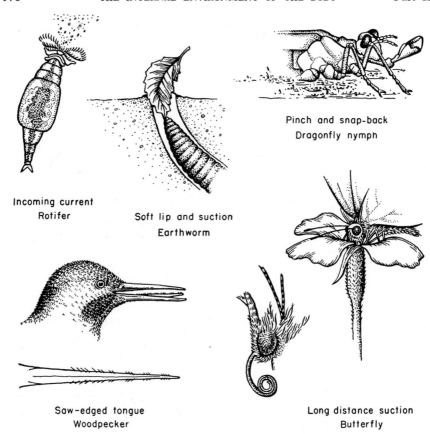

Pinch and snap-back
Dragonfly nymph

Incoming current
Rotifer

Soft lip and suction
Earthworm

Saw-edged tongue
Woodpecker

Long distance suction
Butterfly

FIG. 11.5. Animals gather food into their mouths by many devices. Circlets of cilia create currents of water on which particles ride toward the mouth; earthworm, a soft lip and ring of muscle grip the leaf and the suction of the pharynx pulls it in; dragonfly nymph with underlip outstretched to grasp its prey; woodpecker hammers its bill into the wood and saws with its tongue; butterfly extends its proboscis to the nectar of the flower and sucks.

elaborate filters. Other animals grasp food within a ring of muscle located in their fleshy lips, sucking it in as earthworms grip a wisp of leaves, and as infant mammals suck milk from a nipple. Most of the vertebrates seize their food with the aid of a beak or various kinds of teeth. Dogs lunge forward, clutch meat with their teeth, and hold it against the ridges on the hard palate.

With each lap of its tongue a cat gathers up milk and throws it well back into the gateway of its throat or, with strong strokes of its tongue, rasps the flesh from a bone. With strokes like these but rougher and stronger lions clean up the carcass of a zebra. A giraffe wraps its tongue around high-hanging leaves and pulls them down to its grasp; a cow does the same with a bunch of hay from the hayrack. Woodpeckers hunt over the bark of trees using their tongues like bayonets to pierce the grubs (Fig. 11.5). Thus, by thousands of devices, animals get their particular foods into their mouths, by pulling, pushing, cutting, and squeezing. Hunting and eating occupy most of the lifetime of animals. Compare the winning and eating of food by all human beings.

Essentials of Digestion

Digestion is a series of physical and chemical changes by which food is prepared for assimilation in protoplasm. Physically it is the breaking and mixing of food; chemically it is the process of changing large organic molecules into smaller ones through the action of hydrolyzing enzymes. Enzymes are not only essential to digestion but to all other chemical activities of a living organism. In all multicellular animals and in many protozoans digestion occurs in a cavity, a temporary one in the ameba, a sac in hydra, a tube in many invertebrates and in all vertebrates. Among the tools of digestion are beaks, teeth, muscles, and secretions.

Digestive Cavities and Their Accomplishments

Most of the multicellular animals contain relatively spacious digestive cavities (Fig. 11.6). In hydras, jellyfishes, corals, planarians, and others, it is a sac with but one opening. In the great majority of animals it is a tube, the alimentary canal, with extraordinary variations of structure and function. Some of them are adapted to other uses besides those concerned with food, such as the respiratory chamber in the intestine of the nymphs of dragonflies.

Successful developments in the alimentary canals of various animals are: holding capacity, means of movement and physical breakup of food, means of chemical breakup, extensive cell surface for absorption of digested food, and means of eliminating undigested waste. Animals have to take their food and drink when and where they find it and a capacious stomach to carry away as much as possible is useful. The stomach of a yellow perch may hold fishes of the catch of yesterday, of the day before, and of the day before that, each lot in a different stage of slow digestion. Cows graze steadily through the summer forenoon, swallowing grass into their storage stomachs and chewing it over at their leisure as they rest under the trees in the afternoon (Fig. 11.14). An arrangement like this might be a happy one for commuters who must rush through breakfast and catch the train. The holding capacity of stomachs is a social asset to termites, honey ants, and several other animals. The social and political prominence of many persons has been frequently due to the elastic capacity of their stomachs, and just as frequently they have come to grief because of it. Within colonies of certain species of honey ants, the repletes, continually overfed with honeydew, are useful to the community as living storage tanks of food and drink. From time to time a hungry worker taps the head of a replete which promptly spits a drop of honeydew into the waiting mouth of the worker.

Digestive Cavities (black)
Adequate digestive area developed within limited size of body

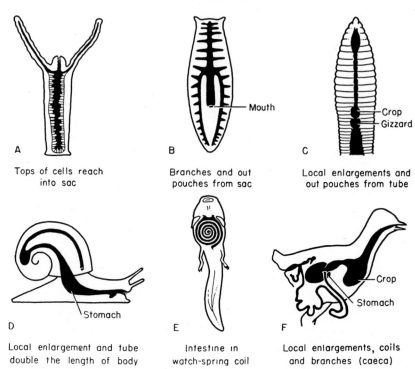

FIG. 11.6. Diagrams of digestive cavities (black). They are examples of relatively large capacity and area for secretory and absorptive cells contained within limited body size: *A,* Hydra, a sac into which the ends of secretory cells are extended; *B,* planarian, a sac with outpouchings that reach out through the body and partly take the place of circulating blood; *C,* earthworm, local enlargements, a common device for greater capacity; *D,* snail, lengthening and doubling-back of the digestive tube, mainly in mollusks; *E,* tadpole, the intestine, a watchspring coil; *F,* bird, enlargements (crop, stomach, gizzard), coils and branches (caeca). The foregoing are the chief patterns of the alimentary tract in multicellular animals; no account has been taken of accessory glands, such as the liver and pancreas.

There are various ways of breaking up food physically and chemically, especially the former: some of these are briefly mentioned or figured in this chapter.

Human Digestion

In the Mouth. The mouth cavity is the vestibule of the digestive system, the reception place of the food (Fig. 11.7). The teeth break it into pieces; the smaller the bits, the more quickly digestive enzymes can diffuse through them. In the meantime the alkaline saliva floods the mouth and pours over the food, a shifting mass because it is held on the tongue, a gymnast that continually ripples and tilts and explores every newcomer. No dry food is tasted until it is well moistened since the sense organs of taste on the surface of the tongue are stimulated only by substances in solution (Fig. 17.3). Saliva enters the mouth more or less continually, except under nervous tensions—when a song is to be sung and "the mouth goes dry." Saliva and mucus keep the mouth well lubricated (Fig. 11.8). In a few mammals, including man, saliva contains ptyalin (salivary amylase), a hydrolyzing enzyme, and a slippery substance,

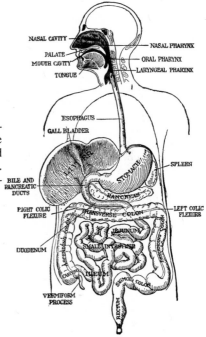

FIG. 11.7. Diagram of the human alimentary canal with the liver and pancreas. The same devices for adequate area in limited space as shown in Fig. 11.6. (After Morris. Courtesy, Rand: *The Chordates.* Philadelphia, The Blakiston Co., 1950.)

mucus, both secreted by the cells of the salivary glands. Ptyalin splits the large molecules of cooked starches into the smaller ones of sugar. In most mammals, however, there is no chemical digestion in the mouth.

Function of the Teeth. Because teeth tell what an animal eats, they also tell where it lives. The most specialized teeth belong to the mammals. According to their function, they are divided into incisors for cutting and chiseling, canines for grasping and tearing, premolars or grinders, and molars or crushers. Squirrels, mice, and other rodents chisel with incisors and crush nuts with molars. In horses, cattle, and other herbivorous animals except the rodents, the front teeth, especially the canines, are reduced or absent and the molars are well developed. In cats, dogs, and other carnivores the upper and lower premolars slide on one another like scissors (Fig. 11.9). A cat grasps meat with its canines, and tears the flesh with its premolars, hardly using the weak molars at all.

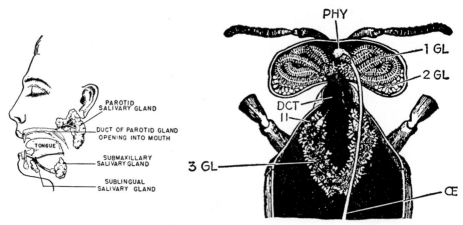

FIG. 11.8. Salivary glands. *Left,* In man the salivary glands are under the control of the autonomic (involuntary) nervous system. The parotid unit is stimulated indirectly by dry food and by acids. Substances in solution stimulate the taste buds of the tongue, nervous impulses are sent to salivary centers in the hind part of the brain, and are relayed by nerves to the salivary glands. *Right,* In the honeybee the salivary glands are relatively enormous. There are two pairs packed between the air sacs in the head and around pharynx (PHY) and the brain (pharyngeal and cephalic) (1GL, 2GL), and another pair (thoracic) (3GL) extends into the thorax and about the esophagus (OE). In bees the uses of saliva are highly social: in royal jelly food for the young queen; mixed with honey; mixed with the wax for the comb, and other materials. (*Left,* Courtesy, Mac-Dougall and Hegner: *Biology.* New York, McGraw-Hill Book Co., 1943. *Right,* Courtesy, Snodgrass: *U. S. Bureau Entomology Technical Series Bull. No. 18.*)

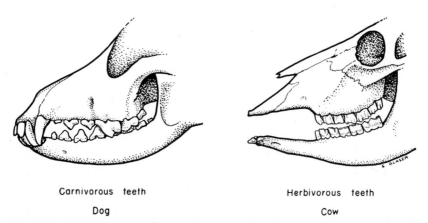

FIG. 11.9. Carnivorous teeth of a dog and herbivorous teeth of a cow. Carnivores have few cheek teeth and those shear like scissors. Dogs grip their food with their stabbing upper canines and gulp it hurriedly. Herbivorous mammals have full sets of cheek teeth with high crowns resistant to grinding. Cattle have no canines and no upper incisors but clinch grass between their lower incisors and a horny pad on the upper jaw.

As to teeth, at least, the human mouth is a middle-of-the-road type. Human teeth like pigs' teeth are generalized and adapted to mixed diets. Although the main kinds of teeth are moderately represented, none could be safely used to nibble a cupboard door. There are 20 human milk or baby teeth, which usually develop before three years of age; and ordinarily 32 teeth in the so-called permanent set which begins to appear at about six years and finishes at twenty-five (Fig. 11.10). Actually we have one-and-a-half complete sets of teeth in a lifetime, the first set and a partial second one, since the molars of the first are not shed like all the other milk teeth.

The jaws of modern man are shorter than those of his early ancestors who

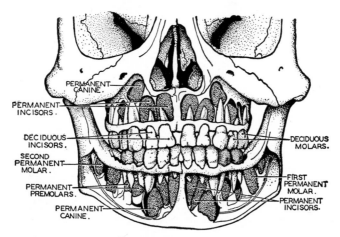

FIG. 11.10. Human teeth, one and a half natural sets in a lifetime. The teeth of a five-year-old child with portions of the jaws cut away to expose the roots of the milk teeth and the partially developed permanent teeth. (Courtesy, Rand: *The Chordates.* Philadelphia, The Blakiston Co., 1950.)

still had a fourth molar, now uncommon. Even the third molar or wisdom tooth comes late and with difficulty and is little more than a nuisance. As a result of the modern shortened jaws, the wisdom teeth often do not have enough room, are crooked and out of position.

Swallowing. When food is about to be swallowed, the tongue is moved backward and pressed up against the hard palate (Fig. 11.11). One swallows quickly and momentarily stops breathing. In that instant the food, now almost at the crossways in the pharynx, moves obliquely toward the esophagus. It might go into the nose, back into the mouth, or into the windpipe were it not so well prevented. But the soft palate is automatically pulled up, closing the way to the nose, and the base of the tongue shuts off the mouth. At the same time, the voice box, or larynx is pulled upward against its cover, the epiglottis, and this shuts off the road down the windpipe. On the instant that all the ways are closed, the throat muscles contract and the food is shot

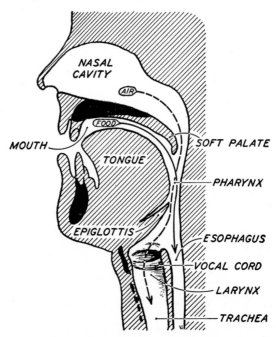

FIG. 11.11. The passageways for air and food, showing the cross ways in the pharynx that must be taken separately by each. When air has the road the trachea (windpipe) is open and the esophagus is closed. When food has the road, the epiglottis covers the trachea and the esophagus is open. (Reprinted from *The Machinery of the Human Body* by Carlson and Johnson, by permission of The University of Chicago Press. Copyright 1948.)

into the esophagus, always slippery with mucus. There circular muscles grip it and urge it along the short passage to the stomach (Fig. 11.12). In the upper part of the mammalian esophagus the rapid contractions of striated muscles extend all the way to the stomach, an arrangement well adapted to the amazing rapidity with which animals swallow their food, a long established

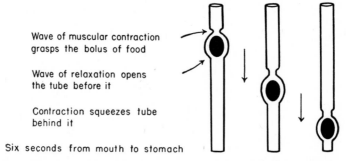

Wave of muscular contraction grasps the bolus of food

Wave of relaxation opens the tube before it

Contraction squeezes tube behind it

Six seconds from mouth to stomach

FIG. 11.12. It takes about 6 seconds for a bolus of solid food to pass from the mouth to the stomach. A wave of contraction follows a bolus of food; a wave of relaxation opens the way in front of it.

eat and watch and run habit. But no matter how we try to hurry it, the human esophagus never speeds up like that of a dog; on the contrary like an elevator, it takes its own time. At many a modern table the primitive habit of eat and watch and run continues.

The human esophagus is strictly a passageway. Usually we swallow downward, but it is quite possible to swallow upward while standing on one's head. Any acrobat can demonstrate this and every day horses and cows drink upward at a sharp angle. Even if its esophagus rises perpendicularly to the milk, this does not hinder a drinking weasel (Fig. 11.13).

FIG. 11.13. Weasel drinking milk with its esophagus at right angles to the milk. (Courtesy, American Museum of Natural History, New York.)

In other animals the esophagus may be distended into a sac which holds the extra food and acts as a waiting-room for gastric digestion. Cattle and other ruminants have such temporary storage sacs: the largest one is the rumen which in an average-sized steer has a capacity of about 30 gallons; the others are the reticulum and omasum. In the market the lining of the reticulum is known as honey-comb tripe (Fig. 11.14). After a period of eating and swallowing into the rumen, cattle, sheep, deer, and other ruminants lie down to chew their cuds. At that time contractions of the esophagus go into reverse and bring one bolus after another of the slightly fermented grass to the mouth where it is chewed and again swallowed, this time permanently.

The crops of birds, especially of domestic fowl, are lateral enlargements of the esophagus. The chicken that goes to roost with a full crop sleeps on while

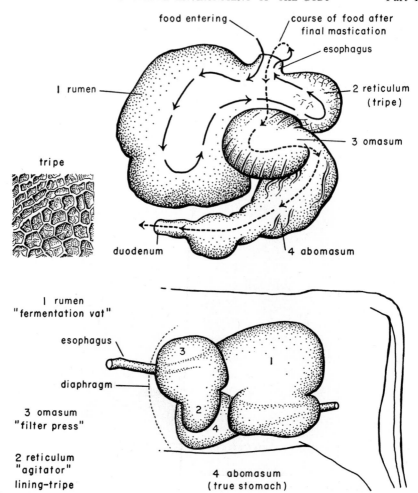

FIG. 11.14. The pouches and stomach of a cow, a cud chewer or ruminant. Three pouches, all enlargements of the esophagus, compose the rumen (capacity 120 or more liquid quarts), the reticulum, and the omasum; the true stomach is called the abomasum. In the upper figure the course of the food after its first swallowing is shown by long dashes and arrows. The second swallowing, after the cud has been chewed, is indicated by short dashes and arrows. In the *lower figure* the pouches and stomach are in their natural position.

its crop automatically delivers the corn and grass to the glandular and grinding sections of its stomach (Fig. 36.15).

Function of the Stomach. The human stomach is a J-shaped enlargement of the digestive tube with a muscular wall and a glandular lining. Its anterior end closes by the contraction of a ring of muscle (cardiac valve) and its posterior end by another ring (pyloric valve). Its muscular movements are controlled by the nerves of the autonomic system; the vagus nerve, partly parasympathetic, stimulates contractions, and the sympathetic nerve inhibits them (Figs. 11.15, 11.16). While food is in the stomach it is stirred and pressed by the contractions of the walls, and digestion of protein and some fats is begun by the gastric juice. Nerves from the taste organs in the tongue are associated with the vagus nerve, branches of which spread through the stomach wall and carry impulses that start the secretion of the gastric juice while food is still in the mouth.

Glands in the wall of the stomach produce the gastric juice containing mucin, hydrochloric acid, and three digestive enzymes or ferments, pepsin, rennin, and gastric lipase, of which pepsin is the most important. The estimated 35,000,000 gastric glands formed by inpocketings of the stomach lining

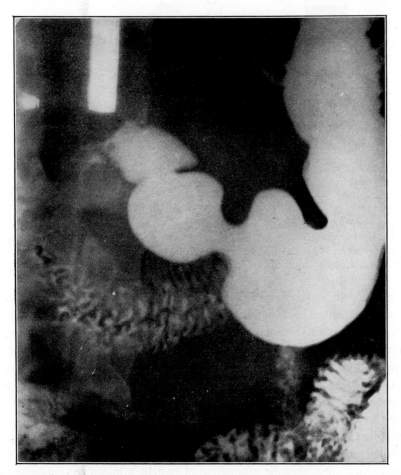

FIG. 11.15. An x-ray photograph of the waves of contraction of the human stomach. Such contractions work upon food and in the early stages of an empty stomach cause hunger pangs. The stomach is here made visible by barium salts recently swallowed in milk. Bits of intestine are similarly visible in the lower part of the illustration. (Courtesy, Gerard: *The Body Functions.* New York, John Wiley and Sons, 1941.)

show how the surface of an organ can be enormously increased without enlarging the organ.

Of the various components of the gastric juice, mucin secreted by mucous cells makes a slippery protective layer over the lining of the stomach, and the hydrochloric acid kills bacteria and provides an acid medium without which the gastric enzymes will not work. Enzymes work best in a particular acidity or alkalinity, and if this changes, their action is hampered or stopped. The

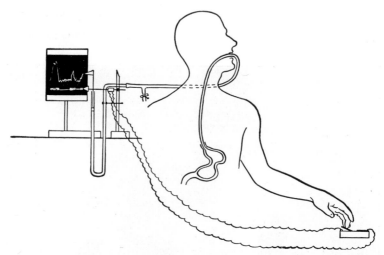

FIG. 11.16. Arrangement for recording stomach contractions on a kymograph, the revolving drum that carries a strip of smoked paper. The writing finger, at the top, makes the sharp lifts that record contraction. The other finger records the repeated pressures caused by breathing. (Courtesy, Gerard: *The Body Functions*. New York, J. Wiley and Sons, 1941.)

enzyme, pepsin, reduces protein only to the stage of proteoses and peptones; probably no amino acids are formed, and there is relatively little absorption from the stomach (Table 11.3). The action on proteins is a preliminary hydrolysis, a splitting and absorption of water that expose the products to the enzyme action that occurs after they enter the intestine. The enzyme, rennin, is an aid to pepsin in that it coagulates milk and produces the soluble milk protein, casinogen, upon which pepsin can act. Lipase is an enzyme that acts on the finely emulsified fats of cream and egg yolk. The production of gastric juice is first stimulated by food in the mouth, but when it reaches the stomach, the flow is greatly increased. Experiments on animals have shown that partly digested food stimulates the production of gastrin, a hormone said to be produced by cells of the lining of the pyloric end of the stomach and discharged into the blood stream whenever such food comes in contact with these cells. If an extract of pyloric lining is injected into an animal, its gastric glands begin to secrete within a short time. In cross-circulation experiments a blood

Table 11.3

THE MAIN ACTIONS OF CHEMICAL DIGESTION

Location of the Process	Source of the Secretion	Digestive Enzymes Present	Substances Acted Upon	Products
Mouth	Salivary glands	Ptyalin (salivary amylase)	Cooked starch	Double sugars
Stomach	Gastric glands	Pepsin	Proteins	Proteoses and peptones
		Rennin	Milk proteins	Curdled proteins (intermediate stage between protein and amino acids)
		Gastric lipase	Finely emulsified fats	Simpler fats
Small intestine	Pancreas	1. Trypsino-gen* (converted into trypsin acts upon peptones)	Proteins or peptones	Peptones and amino acids
		2. Steapsin (pancreatic lipase)	Fats	Fatty acids and glycerol
		3. Amylopsin (pancreatic amylase)	Starches, intact or partly digested	Simple sugars
	Intestinal glands	Erepsin	Peptones	Amino acids
		Lactase	Lactose (milk sugar)	Simple sugars (glucose)
		Maltase	Malt sugar	Simple sugars (glucose)
		Sucrase	Sucrose	Simple sugars (glucose)
		Enterokinase*	Trypsinogen* (inactive)	Trypsin* (active)
			Peptones	Amino acids
		Lipase	Fats	Fatty acids and glycerol

* Trypsinogen is an inactive enzyme produced by the pancreas. It passes into the intestine in the pancreatic juice, is there acted upon by enterokinase produced in the intestinal wall, and becomes the active enzyme trypsin.

vessel of one dog is connected by a rubber tube with the blood vessel of another. After food given the first dog has arrived at the pylorus, the gastric glands of the second dog begin to secrete gastric juice although that dog has been given no food. This shows clearly that they are stimulated by a hormone carried by the blood from one dog to the other.

The time that food remains in the stomach depends mostly upon its consistency. Fluids (alcohol is absorbed directly into the blood) leave almost immediately, and solids last; carbohydrates, proteins, and fats leave the stomach in that order. An ordinary mixed meal remains in the human stomach from three to four hours.

OBSERVATIONS AND EXPERIMENTS. The famous experiment which first showed that food undergoes chemical changes during digestion was performed by a pioneer in experimental zoology, René Réaumur (1683–1757). It proves first of all that an inquiring mind can discover something with simple equipment. Réaumur placed bits of meat in small, perforated metal tubes fastened to threads and fed them to his falcon and some other pet animals. When he recovered them from the stomachs, he found the meat partially dissolved. Soon after that he fed bits of sponge to a chicken and later pulled them forth drenched with gastric juice. He next discovered that meat would be dissolved if dropped into an open dish of gastric juice. Years later the Russian physiologist, Pavlov (1849–1936), discovered that the gastric glands were stimulated not only when a dog took food into its mouth, but when it smelled food, or heard a bell which it associated with food.

Experiments with balloons have shown that hunger pangs are due to the futile contractions of an empty stomach. The subject of such experiments swallows a soft balloon which is then partially inflated and attached by a tube to an apparatus which records the changes of pressure on the balloon. Every time the stomach contracts it squeezes the balloon, causing a lift in the writing point of the kymograph. At the same time the subject, who does not see the record, presses a button because he feels a hunger pang (Fig. 11.16). As the experiment proceeds, the signal of the hunger pang and the record of a squeeze on the balloon occur regularly at the same time. Contractions during hunger do not seem to be different from ordinary ones except that they are stronger. In moderate hunger the pangs are felt for a time and then cease, like a recovery from frustration. Observations and photographs of the movements of the stomach are made by x-ray after a meal containing some harmless substance, usually barium sulfate, that appears opaque in the photographs (Fig. 11.15).

Function of the Small Intestine. Food comes into the intestine in jets of fluid projected through the relaxed circular muscle that forms the pyloric valve. In doing so, it is shifted from the highly acid environment of the stomach into an alkaline environment in which different digestive enzymes can work. The small intestine is the most important region of the digestive tract, the one where food is treated by the versatile pancreatic and intestinal juices (Fig. 11.17). It is lined with millions of motile villi through which almost all absorption of food occurs (Fig. 11.19). The intestinal tract consists of the small intestine, much longer (human, about 20 feet) if not as large around as the large intestine. The first part of the small intestine is the important region into which the ducts of the liver and pancreas open. This U-shaped bend is the duodenum, an old-time name meaning 12, given it because in man it is about the length of 12 fingers. Except in the duodenal region, the intestines are loosely attached to the dorsal body wall by mesentery (Fig. 11.18).

Function of the Liver and the Gall Bladder. Among its many other activities, the liver secretes the bile, vitally important in digestion although it contains

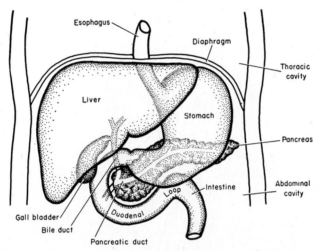

Esophagus
Diaphragm
Thoracic cavity
Liver
Stomach
Pancreas
Intestine
Abdominal cavity
Loop
Gall bladder
Duodenal
Bile duct
Pancreatic duct

FIG. 11.17. Diagram showing the human liver and stomach beneath the diaphragm, and ducts from the liver, gall bladder and pancreas leading through one opening into the intestine.

no enzymes. All the blood in the body passes through the liver several times per hour; thus it maintains a content of about one-fifth of the body's total blood supply.

Microscopic bile capillaries so permeate the liver that they are in contact with every cell. These capillaries join to make the larger hepatic ducts, which in turn form the main bile duct to the duodenum. The gall bladder, a temporary storage place for bile and part of a remarkable mechanism, branches from the main duct. As it is produced bile passes into the bile duct, but is ordinarily kept from passing into the intestine by the continued contraction of a band of muscle that encircles the opening of the bile duct into the intestine. When the duct is filled, the bile is forced back into the gall bladder where it is stored until required, in the meantime becoming more concentrated by loss of water through the bladder wall. With the entrance of food into the duodenum, the gall bladder contracts and discharges bile down the duct whose circular (sphincter) muscle then relaxes, allowing the bile to flow into the intestine. Although the gall bladder is controlled by the parasympathetic part of the vagus nerves, experiments have proved that it will contract after the nerves are cut away. They have also shown that its contraction is stimulated by a hormone, cholecystokinin, secreted by the lining of the duodenum. Products of the digestion of fats in the intestine seem to stimulate the production of this hormone much more than those of proteins and carbohydrates. Bile contains organic salts. Some of these are absorbed by the lining of the intestine, taken up by the blood and returned to the liver. These bile salts and secretin, a hormone from the intestine, both

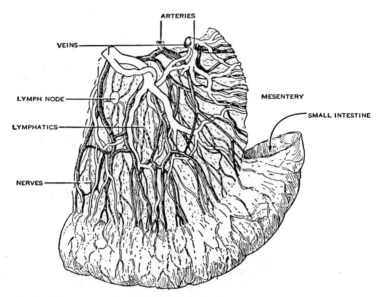

FIG. 11.18. The mesentery formed by a double layer of the peritoneum supports the intestine; between its layers are the blood vessels, nerves and lymphatics that supply the intestine. (Courtesy, Haggard: *Science of Health and Disease*. New York, Harper & Bros., 1927.)

stimulate further bile-making in the liver. As digestion in the intestine is completed, the production of secretin and cholecystokinin is reduced. With this reduction the sphincter muscle at the exit end of the bile duct tightens. This prevents the escape of bile which once more fills the bile duct and backs into the gall bladder.

A gall bladder may be regularly present in one species of animal and regularly absent in another nearly related one with a similar diet. It is lacking in the white rat, horse, pocket gopher, and pigeon, but present in the Norway rat, mouse, cow, striped gopher, chicken and duck, also in cats and dogs. Experimental study of these animals has shown that the ones without gall bladders have a relatively larger production of bile than the others. The human gall bladder is often removed because of inflammation and the formation of gallstones by accumulations largely of cholesterol, the fatlike substance that the liver absorbs from the blood. Its removal does not necessarily cause any digestive difficulties.

FUNCTIONS OF BILE. Bile produces no digestive enzyme but it performs several functions in the intestine. It supplies organic salts (bile salts) which are the emulsifying salts of fats. Bile salts serve as specific activators of pancreatic lipase.

Important as bile is for the more efficient digestion of fats, it is still more important for their absorption. If bile is prevented from entering the intestine, a large proportion of the fatty acids passes out with the waste products instead of being properly absorbed. This effect of the absence of the bile salts has only recently been discovered. Bile salts unite with the fatty acids and form compounds that pass into the lining cells of the intestine. Here the bile salts are separated from the compounds, enter the blood capillaries, and are carried to the liver where they are picked up by the liver cells and once more go into the bile. The fatty acids that were freed from the bile salts combine with glycerin (absorbed by the lining cells) to form neutral fat. The greater part of this fat passes into the microscopic lymphatic vessels, the lacteals, in the centers of the intestinal villi (Figs. 11.19, 11.20). It eventually enters the blood by way of the lymph.

Bile salts make possible the absorption of the antihemorrhagic vitamin K, which occurs in spinach, cabbage, and other green foods (Table 11.1). In the treatment of obstructive jaundice, when the bile ducts may be clogged by gallstones and no bile enters the intestine, the usual tendency toward bleeding is countered by doses of bile salts. Chickens develop a hemorrhagic disease if they do not get any grass or other green foods.

Functions of the Pancreas. The pancreas lies between the stomach and duodenum (Fig. 11.17). It is an irregularly shaped gland composed of groups of lobules that make the surface look bubbly. In each lobule the cells are arranged around a minute drainage tubule. These tubules unite with one another and finally form the main pancreatic duct. This carries the secretion to the intestine, emptying into it through a common opening with the bile duct. Scattered through the pancreas are the entirely different glands called the islands of Langerhans. Their hormone, insulin, is secreted directly into the blood and is necessary for the utilization of sugar in the body, the safeguard against sugar diabetes (diabetes mellitus).

The pancreatic juice is a clear alkaline fluid secreted on an average of about a liter (1.05 liquid quarts) per day. Its principal enzymes are: trypsinogen, which, when converted into trypsin, carries the digestion of proteins a step beyond that occurring in the stomach; amylopsin (pancreatic amylase) which completes the digestion of starch begun in the mouth, and steapsin (pancreatic lipase) which splits fats into fatty acids and glycerol. Pancreatic secretion collected directly from the ducts has very little power to digest

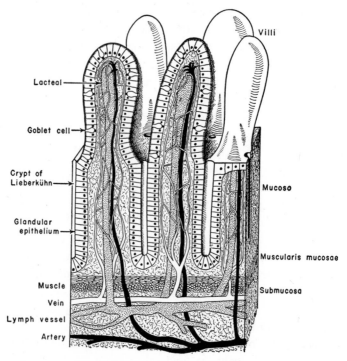

Villi

Lacteal

Goblet cell

Crypt of
Lieberkühn

Mucosa

Glandular
epithelium

Muscularis mucosae

Muscle

Submucosa

Vein

Lymph vessel

Artery

Fig. 11.19. Diagrammatic view of a minute portion of the lining of the small intestine showing the villi that are constantly dipped into the digesting food; two of them are cut open to expose the blood and lymph vessels into which digested food is absorbed. The continual springing up and down of the villi keeps the food in motion. (Courtesy, Villee: *Biology. The Human Approach*, ed. 2. Philadelphia, W. B. Saunders Co., 1954.)

proteins. On the other hand, when it is mixed with intestinal juice containing the enzyme enterokinase secreted by the glands in the lining of the intestine, it immediately becomes potent.

As soon as food comes into the intestine, pancreatic juice begins to flow into it. The reason for this was a puzzle for many years. The nerves leading to the pancreas were cut but, in animals thus treated, the flow went on as before. In 1903, the British physiologists Bayliss and Starling discovered that the mysterious messenger was a fluid, the hormone, secretin. The partly digested food from the stomach stimulates glands in the intestinal wall to produce secretin. This is picked up by the blood, carried to the pancreas, and immediately stimulates that gland to produce its digestive secretion.

The Completion of Digestion. The walls of the small intestine contain minute glands which secrete additional enzymes that complete the digestion of proteins and carbohydrates and fats (Table 11.3). Peptidases (erepsin and others) complete the breakdown of protein into amino acids that can be absorbed into cells everywhere. Sucrase, maltase, and lactase are enzymes that act upon cane sugar, malt sugar, and milk sugar, respectively, turning them into simpler sugars, such as glucose, which can be absorbed by cells of the body. The intestinal glands also secrete enterokinase which changes inactive trypsinogen into active trypsin that simplifies proteins. An intestinal lipase acts on fats. Glands in the intestinal wall also secrete a large amount of mucus that lubricates the passage of the food.

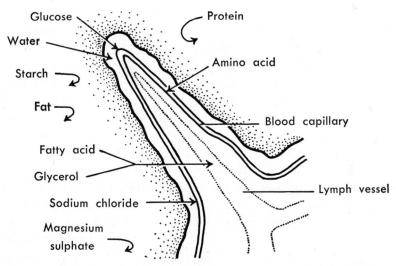

FIG. 11.20. The surroundings of a villus, one among millions, and names of some substances absorbed. Large particles cannot penetrate the wall of the villus; most others enter it and the blood capillary along with certain minerals. Fats enter the lymph vessel and later pass into the blood.

Absorption of Food

Absorption of food occurs almost entirely in the walls of the small intestine. Only then is it actually inside the body. This wall has in superlative degree three essentials for the absorption of food: means for keeping the food in constant agitation, a great area of semipermeable membrane, and blood and lymph to pick up and transport the absorbed food (Figs. 11.19, 11.20). The walls of the small intestine contract peristaltically, pushing the content of the food through the lumen. They also constrict rhythmically, sharply squeezing the tube into segments like a chain of sausages and repeating the process again and again, twenty times per minute or more (visible by x-ray), each time pressing the food against the absorptive wall.

Especially in the duodenum the lining is thrown into circular folds and its entire surface, folds and all, is covered with millions of villi all in more or less continual, slightly tremulous motion. The shortening, lengthening, and bending of the villi keep the digested food agitated and moving against the cells which are absorbing it. Between the villi are the microscopic openings of the intestinal glands. Each villus is covered with epithelial cells into which the food is absorbed (Fig. 11.19). In the core of each one is an arteriole and a venule with their connecting capillaries; the blood in these vessels picks up the digested food (except the bulk of the fat) and transports it to the liver. Also in the core is a minute lymph vessel, a lacteal, that ends blindly at the tip, but at the other end is continuous with larger lymph vessels. Lymph vessels from all over the body finally coalesce and form the thoracic ducts which flow into large veins. Thus the fat, now a milky white emulsion, ultimately reaches the blood.

There is no adequate theory to account for the assimilation of the vital proteins in the various tissues from the collection of amino acids that is assembled in the blood stream. It is known, however, that there is a rigid selection and that a given cell, perhaps a muscle or nerve cell, always assimilates particular amino acids. The changes of proteins and amino acids within the cells have been revealed by tracing the paths of compounds containing "labeled" isotopes of hydrogen, carbon, or nitrogen during metabolism.

Function of the Large Intestine (colon and rectum). Reabsorption of water is the principal function of the large intestine in all mammals. It produces no digestive enzymes and little or no food is absorbed in it, but it secretes a large amount of mucus which acts as a lubricant. The indigestible matter is gradually admitted from the small intestine with considerable water and some unabsorbed secretions. An enormous population of bacteria is always present. In no part of the alimentary canal are all bacteria destroyed.

At the junction of the small and large intestine there is a sac or caecum, large in birds and other herbivorous animals and small or missing in carnivores (Fig. 11.6). In many mammals, especially in monkeys and man, there is a blind sac at the end of the caecum, the vestigial appendix (Fig. 11.7). In the primitive monotremes, e.g., the duckbill platypus of Australia, the rectum opens into the cloaca as it does in the frog, but in all other mammals it has a separate external opening.

12

Circulation and Transportation— Body Fluids

However dry the atmosphere may be outside, the climate inside an animal is as wet as a rain forest. In the majority of many-celled animals the creation of such an adequate internal environment is due to circulating fluids, primarily the blood. It provides for the needs of cells no matter where they are located; those in the roots of the hairs receive oxygen as freely as those in the lungs; waste products are cleared from the bones as well as from the kidneys.

Water and Body Fluids

Water composes the largest part of all body fluids. In lower animals the internal fluid is known as body fluid, in higher ones, as blood with its auxiliaries, tissue fluid and lymph. The high water content of their bodies has made it possible for animals to travel long distances over parched lands. Even in the desert a lizard is a colony of wet cells watered by streams of blood, an oasis in the sands.

Balancing their water content, to keep the right amount of it in and out and to make up for what is lost, is a universal problem of plants and animals. Evaporation is prevented by thick skins, shells, and scales; undue loss from excretion is prevented by controls of the sweat glands and kidneys; and loss from various causes throughout the body is offset by shifts in the osmotic pressure of membranes. Wherever animals live, in fresh water, salt water, or on land, their body fluids are similar; all are salty. In marine invertebrates, whether jellyfishes or horseshoe crabs, the body fluids are practically filtered sea water. Even in fresh water and land animals, the saltiness of the body fluids tells of their origin in ancient ancestors that lived in the sea.

195

Human Blood

General Composition. Blood is composed of fluid and cells. It is as much a tissue as bone; in blood the substance between the cells is fluid; in bone it is solid. When a tube is filled with blood and whirled in a centrifuge, the cells are thrown down to the bottom of the tube. The blood is thus separated into a mass of cells constituting about 45 per cent of the whole blood, and a clear pale yellowish fluid, the plasma, composing the other 55 per cent (Fig. 12.1).

Plasma and lymph and tissue fluid are fluids which come and go, join together, are separated, and join again, over and over, continually sharing

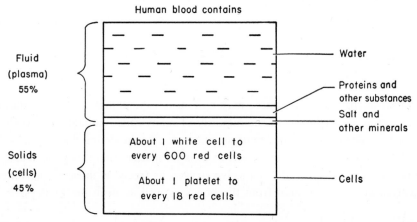

FIG. 12.1. Fluid and solids of human blood. (Redrawn and modified from *Public Affairs Pamphlet No. 145.* New York, Public Affairs Committee, Inc., 1948.)

their contents (Fig. 12.2). Plasma is complex because via the tissue fluid it receives contributions of every kind from all cells of the body (Table 12.1). When blood is under sufficient pressure in the capillaries, the excess fluid seeps through the walls and becomes the only fluid that is in actual direct contact with cells. When there is greater pressure on the tissue fluid outside than on the blood inside the capillaries, the excess fluid goes back into the capillaries or the lymph vessels from whence it is ultimately returned to the blood. Thus these fluids continually pass to and fro; taking food and other substances to the cells; removing their useful secretions and waste products; distributing the heat of their oxidations; keeping them wet; providing them with necessary salts, acids, and gases; and guiding their behavior by hormones. The life of all cells is dependent on the continuity of this environment, and its delicately balanced content must not change unless it is altered specifically and in a way useful to the whole animal. If the plasma does not contain enough salt the osmotic pressure rises and water enters the blood corpuscles until they burst; if it contains too much salt they shrivel. Or, the salt content of the plasma may be right but the proportion of other constituents may be wrong. Without oxygen cells cannot liberate their energy and they die; without sugar they starve. In a solution that contains potassium but no calcium, muscle tissue twitches; with too much calcium it becomes inert.

Plasma, Its Content and Functions. Plasma maintains a content of about 90 per cent water that is constantly lost and replaced. Water is lost from the lungs in amounts varying with the temperature and humidity of the air and the rate and depth of breathing, from the kidneys in urine, and from the

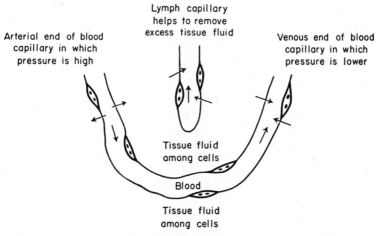

Fig. 12.2. Diagram of the balancing of body fluids. When pressure in the blood capillary is high fluid passes out of the blood through the capillary wall, is dispersed among the cells, and becomes tissue fluid. When the pressure upon the tissue fluid becomes high, the latter may enter the lymph capillary becoming lymph or it may return to the blood capillaries to merge with the blood plasma. Normally there is a constant balancing easily disturbed by slight chemical changes.

sweat glands in sweat. It is increased mainly by eating and drinking. There is a more or less constant demand for water, since in animals there is no special storage of water, as there is of fat. There are some exceptions to this. Camels, like cattle, swallow their food into a pouch, to be recalled later for leisurely chewing. They are also provided with water stored in water pockets opening off the pouch. The great mass of fat in the hump also provides water as well as energy.

ORGANIC SUBSTANCES. About 7 to 9 per cent of the plasma of human blood consists of proteins. These take part in keeping the volume of blood constant in the vessels, in giving thickness or viscosity to the blood, in holding back too great seepage from the vessels, and in maintaining normal blood pressure. Fibrinogen is unique among the proteins in its essential role in the coagulation of blood. Serum globulin is associated with the development of substances that create immunity to disease. Amino acids, the building stones of protein, are the materials for building and repairing tissues.

BLOOD SUGAR. Glucose, the fuel necessary for most cell metabolism, must always be available in proper amounts. It is never excreted by the kidney until the amount in the plasma is excessive, as it is in diabetic conditions when the insulin from the pancreas fails to provide for its complete use in the body. Uncomfortable and serious conditions follow if blood sugar falls to half its normal amount. This drop occurs only in certain illnesses, because normally the glycogen stored in large amounts in the liver is converted into glucose as need arises. Among other organic substances in the plasma are urea, uric acid, and fats absorbed through the walls of the intestine.

INORGANIC SUBSTANCES. Sodium chloride (table salt), the commonest salt in the blood plasma, is continuously taken in with the usual diet and lost in urine, in sweat, and the lachrymal fluid which keeps the eyes moist and is known to everybody as tears. Salt hunger is persistent in all animals, especially those that live on plant diets, usually low in salt. Much was heard about the salt hunger of East Indians at the time of their rebellion under Gandhi's leadership against the British salt tax. Wild animals will take great risks in order to reach a saltlick.

Calcium is also an essential substance for metabolism, for deposition in bones, and coagulation of blood. The control of the amount of calcium in

Table 12.1

IMPORTANT CONSTITUENTS OF HUMAN BLOOD PLASMA

Constituents		Role	Fate
Water (90 per cent of plasma)		Water necessary for life of all cells Transports all substances First importance in maintaining blood pressure and the constancy of other components	Excreted by kidneys, lungs, sweat glands
Proteins (7 per cent of plasma)	Fibrinogen Albumin and globulin	Major role in clotting of blood Associated with stickiness or viscosity of blood	Some used when blood coagulates Albumin sometimes excreted by kidneys, not normal
		Globulin concerned with differences of blood groups	
Nonprotein nitrogenous substances	Urea Uric acid Creatin	Waste substances in transport to excretory organs	Excreted by kidneys

Table 12.1 (Cont'd)

Constituents		Role	Fate
	Amino acids	Food in transport to cells	Building materials of new protein Some excreted by kidneys
Nonnitrogenous substances	Phosphatides (fatty compounds)	Food in transport Important to cells in coagulation of blood	
	Sugar (glucose)	Food in transport to cells	Burned to carbon dioxide and water; energy released Stored in liver, muscles, some excreted
	Fat	Food in transport	Burned to carbon dioxide and water, excess stored
	Cholesterol	Quantities in nervous tissue and adrenal glands	Part excreted in bile
	Lactates (products of sugar breakdown)	Associated with contraction of muscles	Burned to carbon dioxide and water; some reconverted to glycogen
Salts (0.9 per cent of plasma)	Compounds of sodium, potassium, calcium, magnesium, and iron	Changes in concentration of various salts result in profound changes in activity of cells Calcium acts in coagulation of blood Iodine important to thyroid gland	If in excess they are excreted
Special substances	Enzymes Hormones	Regulation and coordination of activity of cells, tissues, and organs	If in excess hormones appear in urine
	Antibodies	Act on bacteria and foreign proteins	May appear in excretions
Gases	Oxygen	Oxidation Carried mainly in loose combination with hemoglobin in red blood cells	Burned in oxidation
	Carbon dioxide	Produced by oxidation in cells Carried in plasma mainly as sodium bicarbonate	Exhaled
	Nitrogen	An inert gas dissolved in plasma	Diffuses into lungs and exhaled

the blood depends upon the proper amount of a hormone produced by the parathyroid glands (Chap. 15). Potassium acts in opposition to calcium and it is the balance between the two rather than the exact amount of either one that is essential. In blood plasma there are about 20 milligrams of potassium per 100 cubic millimeters of plasma but over 800 milligrams of sodium; in muscle cells this proportion is reversed. If blood potassium rises a little, muscle is stimulated; if it rises too much, the muscle is paralyzed. Its amount is regulated partly by a hormone from the cortex of the adrenal gland.

Nervous Control of Body Heat. The main control of body temperature is in the hypothalamus, an ancient part of the floor of the brain. When this is destroyed, the muscles are paralyzed and their ability to liberate heat is lost; when it is stimulated, the muscles are activated and the body temperature rises (Fig. 12.3).

HUMAN BLOOD CELLS

This description of blood cells is based chiefly upon human blood with references to other vertebrates (Fig. 12.4).

There are two main kinds of blood cells, red and white ones (Fig. 12.5). Erythrocytes, red cells or corpuscles are those whose cytoplasm is permeated with nonliving hemoglobin. Mammalian red cells lose their nuclei as they

FIG. 12.3. Nervous control of body heat. Rabbit with left ear in normal condition; the blood vessels are kept in a state of partial constriction by vasoconstrictor nerves. The vasoconstrictor nerves to the right ear have been cut; the vessels are dilated and the ear is unnaturally hot. (From Best and Taylor: *The Living Body,* ed. 3. Copyrighted by Henry Holt and Co. Reprinted with their permission.)

become mature; in all other vertebrates they are retained. Leucocytes or white cells are of several kinds; none of them has hemoglobin; all have nuclei. In mammals blood also contains colorless bodies called platelets.

Red Cells. The red cells (erythrocytes) of mammals (except camel, llama) are biconcave discs (Fig. 12.4). It is estimated that 3000 human red cells set in a line would make a row less than an inch long. The number in a cubic millimeter of blood is calculated as four and a half million for women and five million or more for men. It varies slightly during a 24-hour period, being lowest in the early morning, and increasing through the day. In a healthy person it is increased during exercise, at high altitudes, and with a rise in the temperature of the environment.

In microscopic preparations and within the living capillaries red cells often

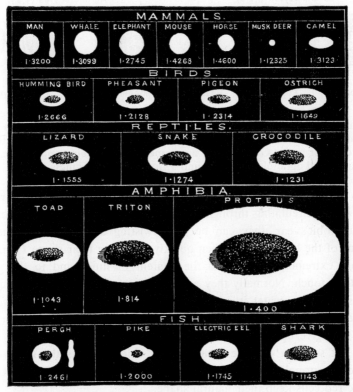

Fig. 12.4. Relative sizes of red blood cells, all microscopic, of representative vertebrates. The size of the red cells varies much in different classes of vertebrates; that of the white blood cells, not shown here, is more uniform. Their extremely minute size, coupled with relatively large surface exposure, is a key to the efficiency of the mammalian red blood cells in their intake and outgo of oxygen. The absence of nuclei in all mature mammalian red cells allows extra room for oxygen. (Courtesy, Guyer: *Animal Biology,* ed. 3. New York, Harper & Bros., 1941.)

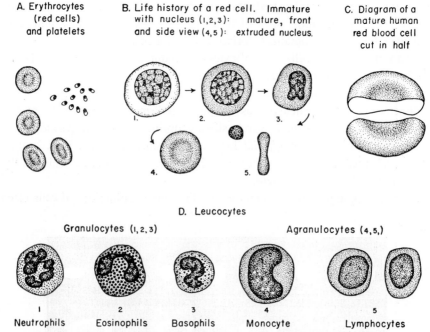

A. Erythrocytes (red cells) and platelets

B. Life history of a red cell. Immature with nucleus (1,2,3): mature, front and side view (4,5): extruded nucleus.

C. Diagram of a mature human red blood cell cut in half

D. Leucocytes

Granulocytes (1,2,3)   Agranulocytes (4,5,)

| 1 | 2 | 3 | 4 | 5 |
| Neutrophils | Eosinophils | Basophils | Monocyte | Lymphocytes |

FIG. 12.5. Types of human blood cells in stained preparations. The cells and their parts are different chemically and take different stains. Leucocytes *D 1, 2,* and *3* are named for their reaction to dyes, e.g., *2,* an eosinophil, takes the pink-orange color of eosin. Granulocytes are named for the grainy appearance of their protoplasm, and agranulocytes, *D 4* and *5,* for lack of graininess.

pile up in rolls, the rouleaux formation. Red cells are pliable and resilient, and in blood circulating through the capillaries in the web of a frog's foot or in a rabbit's ear, they can be seen twisting and turning at the sharp junctions of the branches and then quickly regaining their shape (Fig. 12.6). They are extremely sensitive to the content of fluids and to the surfaces which they touch. Normally they are in a state of osmotic equilibrium with the plasma. When water is added to the plasma, they absorb it, swell, and lose their hemoglobin; when water evaporates from the plasma or salt is added, they give up water, shrink, and appear spiny (or crenated). Physiological salt solution (0.9 per cent sodium chloride) has the same osmotic pressure as normal human plasma, which accounts for the fact that in this fluid the red cells keep their natural shape.

FUNCTIONS. Red cells function first as carriers of oxygen to cells; they also carry carbon dioxide in much smaller amounts from the cells to the lungs or to the gills of aquatic animals. Their color and power to carry oxygen is due to hemoglobin which composes about a third of the content of each cell. Hemoglobin is the combination of a pigment containing iron and a protein, and is related to other blood pigments such as the bluish hemocyanin of clam blood that creates the blue-gray tinge of clam broth. Hematin, the most important pigment in the higher animals, is a near relative of the pigment of chlorophyll, the substance in plants which can utilize energy from the sun.

In the lungs and in the gills of aquatic animals where oxygen pressure is high, hemoglobin combines with oxygen and forms oxyhemoglobin, an unstable combination which colors the blood bright red (Chap. 13). In the

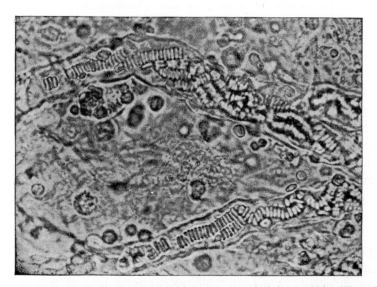

FIG. 12.6. Photograph of blood vessels in ear of living rabbit. The picture is taken through glass pressed against the skin with the camera focused into the vessels. The red cells are moving through the capillaries in rolls (rouleaux), the number of these probably increased by the pressure of the glass. The extreme thinness of the capillary wall is an evidence of the ease with which certain cells pass through it. (Courtesy, Bremer and Weatherford: *Textbook of Histology,* ed. 6. Philadelphia, The Blakiston Co., 1944.)

tissues of the body the oxygen pressure is low and the oxygen separates from the oxyhemoglobin leaving reduced hemoglobin which darkens the blood, usually in the veins. Hemoglobin also takes part in transporting very small amounts of carbon dioxide from the tissues to the lungs or gills.

With the aid of isotopes the life span of human red cells has been shown to be about 120 days. They wear out and fragments of them are eaten by macrophages (phagocytic cells) in many parts of the body, especially in the spleen, bone marrow, and liver. In a healthy human adult about one million red cells are thus destroyed per second and a comparable number of new ones are added per day as the blood passes through the red marrow of the bones.

BLOOD COUNTS. By diluting a small, measured quantity of blood and spreading it upon a special ruled slide, the different kinds of blood cells can be counted and their proportionate numbers determined. This is a routine examination in many doctors' offices and hospitals.

IRREGULARITIES IN NUMBERS OF RED CELLS. Polycythemia, an increased number of red cells, accompanies conditions in which the body fluids are decreased. Rarely there may be an overproduction of red cells in the red marrow.

ANEMIA. In anemia the amount of hemoglobin is below normal; either there is too little in the red cells or there are too few of them. There are many causes and types of anemias.

Anemias are caused by malnutrition, excessive blood loss, or destruction of cells due to: (1) lack of iron in the diet resulting in sparsity of hemoglobin in red cells; (2) hemorrhages from wounds, ulcers, etc; (3) defects in the cells or poisons (hemolytic anemias); (4) an inherited condition, the Rh factor (Chap. 20).

Anemias are caused by defective formation of cells because of failure of red cells to develop to maturity as in pernicious anemia; or damage to red bone marrow due to certain chemical poisons, e.g., radium salts.

The effects of various articles of diet, especially liver, on the regeneration of hemoglobin was first noted by Dr. G. H. Whipple at the University of Rochester. In 1926 Dr. G. R. Minot and Dr. W. P. Murphy at Harvard University suggested that liver might be of value in treating pernicious anemia. Although this has not proved to be a cure, it has become a treatment which has kept thousands of persons living efficiently as long as it is continued. It is now known that the liver discharges into the blood a substance (vitamin B_{12}) essential for the blood cell-making function of the bone marrow, and that pernicious anemia is caused by lack of this antianemic substance (Table 11.1). It is originally produced by the reaction of a specific secretion of the stomach upon some substance in meat. The secretion by the stomach being the inside product, it is called the intrinsic factor in contrast to the substance in meat, an outside or extrinsic factor. Together these result in the antianemic material which is stored in the liver, whence it is taken up by the blood. It is this that eventually reaches the red marrow of the bones and stimulates the development of the red cells (Fig. 12.7).

White Cells. White cells (leucocytes) look white only when several are banked together, otherwise they are colorless. They never contain hemoglobin, are always nucleated, are more resistant to change than red cells and exist in smaller numbers, in human blood—one to about 600 reds. They are older in animal history than the red cells. Colorless nucleated cells occur in the body fluids of planarians, annelids (earthworms, clamworms), insects, and other arthropods. In mammals, some of them originate in the red bone marrow and others in the lymphatic tissues (Fig. 12.8). In circulating blood their number varies with the physiological changes in the body during the

24-hour day and in different parts of the circulatory system. Some white cells are phagocytic. Motion pictures show them consuming bacteria, overstuffing themselves with anything alien or broken that they can manage; even the human appetite cannot be so overreaching. Many white cells destroy themselves by their consumption of bacteria and others wander through the walls of the intestine and are swept out of the body.

MAIN TYPES. In structure there are two main types of white cells: granulocytes, those with specific granules in the cytoplasm and nuclei with lobes;

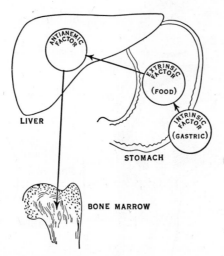

FIG. 12.7. Diagram of the general location of the substances responsible for the development of the red blood cells in the red marrow of bone. The intrinsic factor is a specific secretion of the stomach; the extrinsic factor is a substance in meat. Together these pass to the liver via the blood, are stored there, and in combination are gradually given off via the blood to the red marrow of the bones. (From Best and Taylor: *The Living Body*, ed. 3. Copyrighted by Henry Holt and Co. Reprinted with their permission.)

and nongranulocytes, those without specific granules in the cytoplasm and with unlobed nuclei (Table 12.2, Fig. 12.5). White cells are very sensitive in their reactions to chemical conditions both in the blood and outside the body when they are treated with stains. They are classified according to their reactions to the latter.

Granulocytes are of three types, whose names end in *phil* indicating their love or affinity for the respective stains, eosinophils (the stain, eosin), basophils (basic stains), and neutrophils (neutral stains). The group of nongranulocytes contains the monocytes and the lymphocytes (Table 12.2 and Fig. 12.5).

FUNCTIONS. The neutrophils, lymphocytes, and monocytes, together with the phagocytic cells of the connective tissue constitute one of the body's most important defenses against poisons and invading organisms. All leucocytes

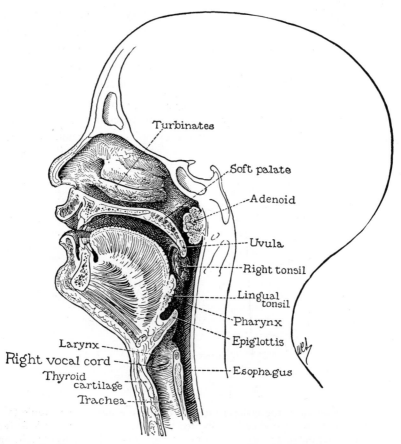

FIG. 12.8. The upper respiratory tract of a child showing half of the ring of lymphatic tissue, the right tonsil, the adenoid, and lingual tonsil, at the back of the throat. All of these are relatively large in children. In mammals some white cells originate in red bone marrow and others in lymphatic tissue. (Courtesy, Clendening: *The Human Body*. New York, Alfred A. Knopf, Inc., 1930.)

are to some extent motile and move about in other tissues as well as in the blood, the neutrophils most actively of them all. They are easily observed alive in microscopic preparations and when properly warmed, behave like so many active amebas. Neutrophils, lymphocytes, and monocytes wander among the cells of the body, rapidly working their way in and out through capillary walls with scarcely any place barred to them (Fig. 12.9). When on its way through a capillary wall, a neutrophil wedges itself between the cells and quickly pushes them apart. Whenever neutrophils reach a place where bacteria are present they at once proceed to engulf them, living up to their name of phagocytes (cell eaters). Within the leucocytes the living bacteria are killed by digestive fluids as live oysters are killed in the human stomach.

Table 12.2

BLOOD CELLS

(Refer to Figure 12.5)

Kinds and Amounts of Cells	Role	Origin	Fate
Red blood cells or erythrocytes 4,500,000 to 5,000,000 per cubic millimeter	Transport oxygen and small amount of carbon dioxide	Red marrow of bone	Filtered out mainly in spleen and liver. Life span figured from tracer experiments to be about 120 days
White blood cells or leucocytes 1. Granulocytes, with granular cytoplasm a. Neutrophils so named because they take neutral stains—60 to 70% of leucocytes	Marked motility outside blood vessels and destroy bacteria except tubercular ones	Bone marrow, ribs, long bones	May be filtered out in spleen and live in spleen and liver
b. Eosinophils Take acid stains e.g., eosin —2 to 4% of leucocytes	Migrate into tissue spaces of digestive and respiratory tracts. Numbers increase in disease caused by parasites and allergic conditions	Red marrow of bone	Filtered from circulating blood by spleen and liver. Others may perish outside the blood vessels
c. Basophils Take basic stains 0.5 to 1.5% of leucocytes	Function unknown No phagocytosis and motility feeble	Red marrow of bone	Uncertain
2. Nongranulocytes a. Monocytes 5 to 10% of leucocytes	Phagocytes within (?) and without the blood stream	Uncertain	Most of them degenerate within the blood stream
b. Lymphocytes 20 to 30% of leucocytes	Not phagocytic; occur in blood and lymph vessels, in tissue fluid and probably function differently in each place	Lymphatic tissue and glands	Degenerate outside the blood stream
Platelets estimated over 200,000 per cubic millimeter	Seem to be essential in clotting of blood		

Although the lymphocytes are the greatest wanderers of all blood cells, little is known about their function. They work their way out through the walls of blood vessels, lymph vessels, and the lining of the alimentary canal. The tonsils and the appendix are loaded with them (Fig. 12.8). Great migrations of lymphocytes accompany certain types of inflammation.

VARIATIONS IN THE NUMBERS. Certain normal physiological conditions, among them muscular exercise and pregnancy, cause an increase of leucocytes. Quick shifts in temperature and in states of mind may result in their immediate increase in the blood as if they had suddenly moved from the sides of the blood vessels out into the currents (Fig. 12.10). There are also daily rhythms with an afternoon rise. In order to determine what type of cell has increased, it is necessary to make differential counts. Stained preparations

FIG. 12.9. Drawings of a leucocyte (neutrophil) at one-half-minute intervals to show its movement and ability to consume bacteria, represented by dots. Myriads of such cells are continually moving about in the body. (From Best and Taylor: *The Living Body,* ed. 3. Copyrighted by Henry Holt and Co. Reprinted with their permission.)

of blood are examined and since different types of leucocytes stain differently, it is easy to distinguish them. Several hundred leucocytes are counted and the various types are recorded separately. The percentage of each type is then calculated.

Blood Platelets. The blood platelets are about one-quarter the size of the red cells. They have no nuclei, seem to be fragments of certain giant cells of the red bone marrow, and are usually clumped together. They play an important part in the coagulation of blood, but beyond that their function is unknown (Fig. 12.11, and Table 12.2).

Human Blood Groups. Whenever foreign proteins such as those of bacteria are taken into the blood stream of an animal, the cells of the body produce antibodies, counteracting substances that immunize foreign matters. Antibodies are produced abundantly by the cells of the blood. The foreign proteins that stimulate the production of antibodies are called antigens. "No smoke without a fire" might be changed to "no antibody without an antigen."

Whenever one or another kind of antigen and antibody are brought together, a characteristic reaction occurs. If the antigen is a poison, the antibody that neutralizes it is called an antitoxin. Foreign cells, such as bacteria or alien blood cells, may get into the human blood stream by injection. Although

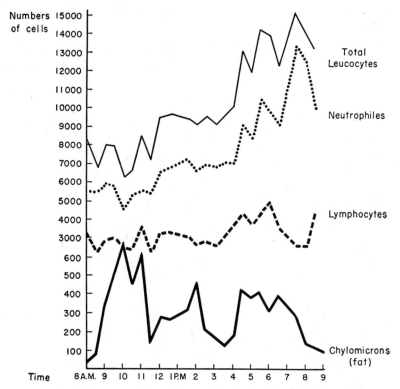

FIG. 12.10. Increased number of leucocytes in the blood due to emotional disturbance in afternoon after receiving a letter from fiancé. Curves showing total number of white blood cells, of neutrophils, of lymphocytes, and of fat particles (chylomicrons), the last not concerned in the disturbance. (Data, courtesy Smith: "The Absence of Digestive Leucocytosis," *Folia Haematologica,* Leipzig, 1932.)

human blood, it may be the wrong type. In this case the red cells carry an antigen (agglutinogen) which reacts with an antibody (agglutinin) already present and the blood cells are agglutinated, i.e., stuck together in clumps (Table 12.3).

In 1900 Karl Landsteiner, experimenting in a medical laboratory in Vienna, discovered that when the blood cells of some persons were mixed with the blood plasma of others, the cells remained separate in some cases and clumped together in others. This was the beginning of the discovery of blood groups which made possible the transfusion of blood from the blood vessels of one person to those of another. Before this, the unexplained and sometimes fatal results of transfusion made it a last resort. The clumping of the red cells of incompatible bloods plugged up the blood capillaries and ultimately caused death. The bloods of donor and patient, therefore, must be compatible. Tests have shown that two kinds of antigens (agglutinogens), called *A* and *B*, occur in the red cells of different persons and that the plasma of the blood contains two kinds of antibodies (agglutinins), *a* and *b*. There are four main blood groups among human beings: Group O with antibodies a and b but no antigens is a universal donor; Group A, antibody b and antigen A; Group B, antibody a and antigen B; and group AB, antigens A and B but no antibodies in the plasma is a universal recipient (Table 12.3). Many more groups have been described; this is a much simplified statement of complex reactions. The characteristics of blood groups are inherited and remain constant throughout life.

Table 12.3

RESULTS OF MIXING RED CELLS AND PLASMA OF HUMAN BLOOD GROUPS

			Blood Group			
			O	A	B	AB
			Antigen in Red Cells			
			None	A	B	AB
Blood Group	O	a,b	−	+	+	+
	A	b	−	−	+	+
	B	a	−	+	−	+
	AB	None	−	−	−	−

−Compatible; no agglutination
+Not compatible agglutinates

TRANSFUSION OF BLOOD

When more than 40 per cent of the blood is lost within a short period, the body cannot make up the loss. In such a case a transfusion is made, that is an injection into a vein of whole blood, plasma, or serum from another person in an effort to restore volume. Great care must be taken to choose compatible blood to inject into the recipient. Wrong types of blood cells block the capillaries and later disintegrate; the pigment finally fills the tubules of the kidney, ultimately causing death. Blood types are inherited according to Mendelian laws (Chap. 20), and as a child of a blue-eyed and brown-eyed parent may have either blue or brown eyes, so it is impossible to predict the exact blood characteristics of a child from those of its parents.

Transfusions of whole blood are the only adequate treatment when loss of blood is excessive. The need is usually immediate because cells are necessary to take oxygen to the tissues. The question has always been how to have the blood ready for the emergency. In August 1944, refrigerated whole blood was sent to the European and Pacific battlegrounds. The great impetus for the use of whole blood that has continued in peacetime came with the discovery of a special solution that would preserve whole blood at least 28 days. The solution is known as ACD because it contains acid citrate which lengthens the life of the cells, citrate of sodium that prevents coagulation, and dextrose that provides nourishment. Great strides have also been made in the preparation and use of dried plasma. To prepare this, whole blood is centrifuged as in a cream separator, thus dividing the cells from the plasma, which is then frozen and dried. When the plasma is distributed, it is mixed with sterile water just before using. Another important preparation, developed by Dr. Edwin J. Cohn and his associates at Harvard University, was also used during the war. This preparation included the isolation of the serum albumin which constitutes about half of all the protein in plasma but occupies a very small amount of space. Serum albumin was found to be mainly responsible for holding the balance of pressure between the capillaries and surrounding tissues, and thus it counteracts effects of shock, such as failure of the circulation. In severe shock in which there is a marked loss of blood-volume the effects on the body are serious and complex. Capillaries are damaged and plasma and blood cells escape into the tissues; circulation is slow and inefficient.

CLOTTING OF BLOOD

The clotting process is a series of changes in the proteins and platelets of the blood due to new conditions which arise when the organization of the plasma is disturbed by a rough, jagged surface or by breaks in the blood

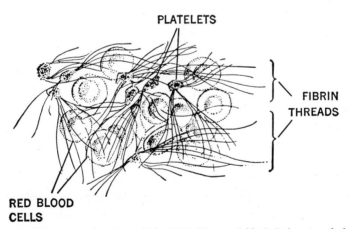

FIG. 12.11. Fragment of a clot of blood highly magnified. It is a tangled mesh of delicate filaments among which blood cells and platelets are entrapped. The filaments are composed of fibrin produced during the clotting process, and appear to radiate from groups of platelets. (From Best and Taylor: *The Living Body*, ed. 3. Copyrighted by Henry Holt and Co. Reprinted with their permission.)

vessels. The changes are climaxed by the formation of gel fibrin, the strands of which hold the cell mass together in the clot (Fig. 12.11).

Some of the substances that take part in forming fibrin, such as calcium, prothrombin, and fibrinogen are present in circulating blood; the others, thrombokinase and thrombin are formed during the clotting process. At the beginning of this process the exceedingly delicate platelets are injured and in most cases the cells of the blood and the vessel walls as well. The substance liberated by the decomposing platelets and broken cells is thrombokinase, an enzymelike clot-hastener. The newly formed thrombokinase unites with the calcium and prothrombin already in the blood and produces thrombin. This second newly formed substance unites with fibrinogen, also already in the blood and produces the fibrin whose strands hold together the cell mass called the clot. The process may be summarized as follows:

Thrombokinase + calcium + prothrombin = thrombin
Thrombin + fibrinogen = fibrin
Fibrin + cell mass = clot

The existence of prothrombin in healthy circulating blood depends in turn upon the presence of the antihemorrhagic vitamin K (Table 11.1). This is taken in with food and with the aid of bile is absorbed in the intestine, then goes to the liver where it takes part in the formation of prothrombin. If vitamin K is missing, the formation of prothrombin is prevented, clotting does not take place, and bleeding results.

Abnormal Blood Clotting

Hemophilia is an inherited defect in blood clotting. Persons who suffer from it are known as bleeders (Chap. 20).

Thrombosis is coagulation of the blood in any part of the circulatory system. A coronary thrombosis is the stoppage of a coronary artery by a blood clot; the coronary arteries originate near the base of the aorta and supply the walls of the heart. Occasionally a fragment of a clot, called an embolus, breaks off, is carried free in the circulation, and becomes lodged in the brain or heart. In the brain a clot results in loss of memory, speech, and paralysis of various parts of the body.

The Lymphatic System

Lymph originates from plasma that, except for its proteins, filters through the walls of blood vessels. Outside them it becomes tissue fluid occupying any spaces there may be among the tissues. As it fills these spaces and as the pressure in them rises, it filters through the walls of the lymph vessels and becomes lymph. Lymph capillaries end blindly. The ready entrance of tissue fluid into lymph capillaries is due to their extreme thinness and delicacy. When the pressure becomes high in lymph capillaries and tissue spaces, the fluid filters into the blood capillaries and joins the plasma.

Lymph flows in only one general direction, toward the heart. In its course it runs through larger and larger vessels finally converging in the left thoracic duct that empties into a large vein in the left shoulder—in man, at the junction of the left jugular and subclavian veins (Fig. 12.12). Thus, lymph continually filters out of the blood and then returns to it by a large inflow, as well as by a refiltering through capillary walls. Blood flows away from the heart through arteries and capillaries, but its fluid content returns not only as blood through capillaries and veins, but as lymph through the lymph vessels.

Lymph vessels are provided with efficient bacteria traps in the many lymph nodes that are located along the vessels (Figs. 12.13, 12.14). Each of them is a labyrinth of lymphatic tissue in which lymphocytes are produced. In its regular course lymph flows slowly through these mazes populated with phagocytes which attack and engulf such bacteria and foreign particles as may be passing by. Dense lymphatic tissue is abundant about the throat (e.g., the tonsils) and respiratory passages, and in the intestinal wall, places where bacteria abound. In an infected thumb the lymph vessels become inflamed and hinder the circulation of the blood so that red streaks extend up the inner side of the arm to the elbow where there are good chances that the poisons may be caught in the lymphatic tissue, kept out of the general circulation, and ultimately destroyed.

Lymph moves slowly through the vessels pushed along by the volume

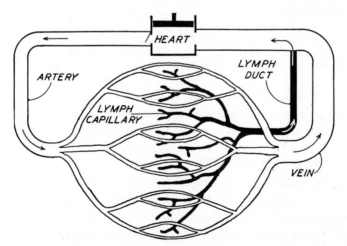

Fig. 12.12. The relationship between the blood and lymph circulations (the latter in black). Arrows indicate the flow of blood to and from the heart, and the flow of lymph always toward the heart and finally emptying into the blood, in man mainly at the junction of left jugular and subclavian veins. (Reprinted from *The Machinery of the Human Body* by Carlson and Johnson, by permission of The University of Chicago Press. Copyright 1948.)

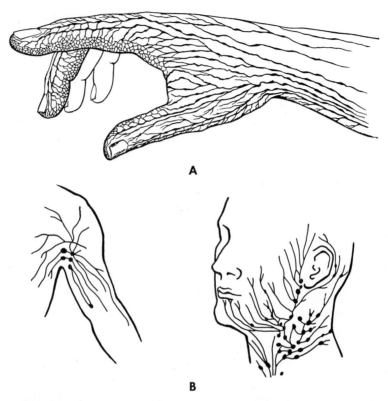

A

B

Fig. 12.13. *A*, The superficial lymph vessels of the thumb and finger. A small part of the great network in which a balance of fluid is maintained with that in the blood vessels and other tissues. *B*, Superficial lymph nodes in axil of arm and throat region; both are incomplete but they suggest the prevalence of lymph nodes. (Redrawn after Brash, ed.: *Cunningham's Textbook of Anatomy*, ed. 9. New York, Oxford University Press, 1951.)

behind it, by breathing movements, and the contractions of muscles; valves keep it from going backward just as valves do in many of the veins. In mammals there are no lymph hearts as there are in frogs.

Blood Circulation in Mammals

The blood vessels form a complete series of intercommunicating tubes. The heart is an enlarged and sharply bent part of a tube protected by the pericardial sac. The tubular shape of the heart can be seen clearly in the development of the human embryo and other higher vertebrates, and in adult fishes (Fig. 33.12). In fishes the heart is continuous at one end with the arteries that carry blood away from it and at the other with veins that return blood to it. Connecting the larger vessels are the microscopic capillaries usually between arteries and veins, but in the hepatic portal system between veins and veins.

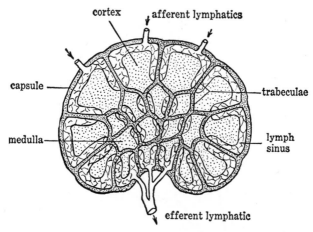

cortex   afferent lymphatics

capsule

trabeculae

medulla

lymph sinus

efferent lymphatic

FIG. 12.14. Diagram of a lymph node sectioned to show its internal structure, the pocket endings of the vessels, and the valves within them that prevent backward flow. The lymph spaces are shown with their usual contents of lymphocytes (black). Such nodes are situated at strategic points on the lymph vessels and act as filters removing bacteria otherwise entering the lymph. (Courtesy, Nonidez and Windle: *Textbook of Histology*, ed. 2. New York, McGraw-Hill Book Co., Inc., 1953.)

Main Circuits. Circulating blood goes through two main circuits, the pulmonary route from the heart to the lungs and back to the heart, and the systemic route from the heart over a long course through the body and back to the heart (Figs. 12.15, 12.16). It is calculated that in man the complete double circuit of the blood takes about 23 seconds.

Two factors are of great importance in the movement of blood. The first is the pumping of the heart and the second, the resistance that the blood encounters along the sides of the vessels and at the forking of their manifold branches. Blood that is pumped from the right ventricle into the pulmonary artery to the lungs and back to the left auricle meets with little resistance in this short circuit as compared with that in the long route through the aorta and over most of the body. With the contraction of the left auricle, blood flows into the left ventricle, the main pumping chamber of the heart (Fig. 12.17). The contraction of this chamber forces the blood past the semilunar valves into the aorta. From there it begins the great systemic circuit through several arteries: to the head through the carotids, to the arms through the subclavians, and to the viscera, trunk, and legs through the dorsal aorta.

Two special parts of this circuit are of most vital importance. The first is the circulation in the walls of the heart. Although the chambers of the heart are continually receiving blood, the action of the muscle in its walls depends upon the coronary arteries from the aorta for an income of blood, and upon the coronary veins emptying into the right auricle for its outgo. Any reduction of blood to these muscles cripples the heartbeat and a complete block of

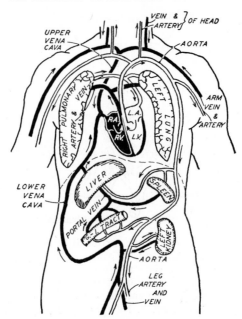

FIG. 12.15. Scheme of the main circulation of the human blood. The vessels carrying well oxygenated blood are in outline; those containing blood poor in oxygen are in heavy black. The vena cava and the aorta actually course along the mid dorsal line of the body but have been pulled aside for labeling. Stomach and right kidney are omitted for space. (Reprinted from *The Machinery of the Human Body* by Carlson and Johnson, by permission of The University of Chicago Press. Copyright 1948.)

blood in them stops it. The second important part of the circuit is to the liver. This important organ receives both arterial and venous blood; the latter represented by the hepatic-portal vein is the unique feature (Fig. 12.15). It carries food-laden blood from the small intestine and blood from the spleen and pancreas directly to the liver and there breaks up into the hepatic-portal system of innumerable capillaries that eventually converge into the hepatic veins. These carry blood into the postcaval vein and on to the right auricle.

In the systemic as in the pulmonary circuit the flow is from larger to smaller arteries on into the capillaries; thence it goes into larger and larger veins and on until it empties into the heart.

Whatever the region of the body, blood stays longest in the capillaries and is there constantly engaged in exchanges with the surrounding cells and fluids (Fig. 12.18). In the capillaries it distributes the supplies for metabolism, foods and oxygen, and receives the products of metabolism, carbon dioxide and nitrogenous by-products. These are but the high points in the complex capillary cell and tissue fluid exchange.

The complexity of the internal aquatic environment of the body results from the liquid that penetrates through capillary walls. This has never been so

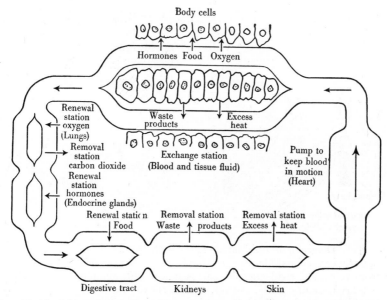

Fig. 12.16. Diagram illustrating how a suitable environment within the body is maintained by the circulation of the blood. (Courtesy, Woodruff and Baitsell: *Foundations of Biology*, ed. 7. New York, The Macmillan Co., 1950.)

well demonstrated as by experiments with isotopes made at the Carnegie Institution of Washington and reported by Dr. G. W. Corner as follows:

The use of substances such as heavy water and radio-active salts, differs little from ordinary water and salts in their physiological activities but are easily identified as they travel through the body by their weight or radioactivity respectively. In man, 78 per cent of the blood-plasma sodium and 105 per cent of the plasma water is exchanged per minute with extravascular sodium and water. An amount of water equal to a man's entire weight passes out of his blood capillaries, and is replaced by an approximately equal amount, every 20 minutes. The capillary part of human blood circulation, seen in the light of these facts, is a system of fine tubules with permeable walls through which floods of water bearing salts and other metabolic substances are pouring at every moment throughout life.*

Control of the Heartbeat. The heartbeat is under two nervous directives: a control by the neuromuscular mechanism and a control by the central nervous system. The neuromuscular control is the one that may act for some time after the heart of a frog or a mammal is completely separated from the body. Thus the neuromuscular control can act without the central nervous control, but the latter cannot act without the neuromuscular control.

Neuromuscular Mechanism. Figure 12.19 shows the important features of the mechanism. The sinuauricular and auriculoventricular nodes are networks of atypical muscle cells (Purkinje cells), just visible to the naked eye,

* From *Annual Report of the Director of the Department of Embryology*. Carnegie Institution of Washington, 1948–49, p. 129.

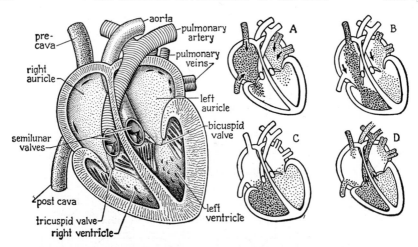

FIG. 12.17. Diagram of the human heart with the front wall removed. Heavy stipple, poorly oxygenated blood; light stipple, richly oxygenated blood. *A,* Auricles filling from veins, i.e., right, precava and postcava; left, pulmonary veins. *B,* Blood entering relaxed ventricles. *C,* Auricles contracting, ventricles relaxed and filling. *D,* Ventricles contracting, blood forced into aorta and pulmonary arteries. (Courtesy, Storer: *General Zoology,* ed. 2. New York, McGraw-Hill Book Co., Inc., 1951.)

that conduct the heartbeat. The sinuauricular node, or pacemaker, is named from its origin from the edge of the sinus chamber present in mammalian embryos and adults of lower vertebrates (see frog heart); the similar auriculoventricular node is named from its position between these chambers. Muscle fibers from the sinus node spread through the walls of the auricles but are not shown in the diagram because of the thinness of the walls. Muscle fibers from the auriculoventricular node extend through the septum between the ventricles (auriculoventricular bundle) and spread throughout the walls of the ventricles. The auriculoventricular bundle of muscle and nerve-cell fibers is the functional bridge between the auricles and ventricles.

THE PACEMAKER OF THE HEART. The neuromuscular mechanism is responsible for the conduction of the rhythmic contractions of the muscle of the heart. The pacemaker is the dynamic center of the heart's action. In some way not well understood, rhythmic stimuli develop from it and spread in waves of contractions through the walls of the auricles. From there waves of contractions spread through the auriculoventricular bundle of fibers in the septum and thence throughout the ventricular walls. If this bundle is cut experimentally or damaged by disease, the ventricles either stop beating or beat independently of the beat in the auricles.

CENTRAL NERVOUS CONTROL. The heart is profoundly a part of the body as a whole. It can beat temporarily when separated from the body, but the way it normally beats, weak or strong, slow or fast, is affected by conditions

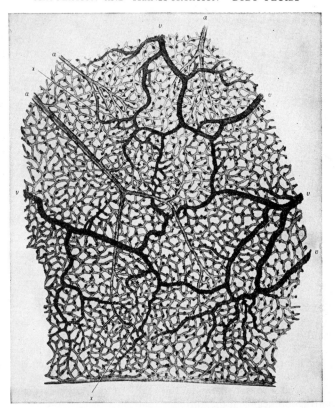

FIG. 12.18. Network of blood vessels in the web of a frog's foot, darker ones with venous and paler with arterial blood; *a*, arterioles; *v*, venules; *x*, a direct connection between arteriole and venule. Many pigmented cells are scattered along the capillaries. A view of the circulating blood in such a network can be easily obtained by extending the moist web of a lightly anesthetized frog on the stage of the microscope. (Courtesy, Maximow and Bloom: *Textbook of Histology,* ed. 6. Philadelphia, W. B. Saunders Co., 1952.)

in parts or the whole of the body. Cold or heat, food or lack of food, work or rest, and turns of mind, such as mirth, fear, and worry are all significant influences, and worry is the most devastating in its effects. Sensory nerve fibers in the arteries, especially in the arch of the aorta, also contribute to the rate of the heartbeat.

Stimulation of the paired inhibitor nerves (parasympathetic branches of the vagus) slows the heartbeat. The impulses come from the vagus centers in the medulla and pass over the nerve fibers into the walls of the heart, in and near the pacemaker nodes (Fig. 12.19). Stimulation of the paired accelerator nerves (sympathetic) quickens the heartbeat. Both nerves produce hormone-like substances. Acetylcholine from the vagus nerves slows the action of heart muscle and an adrenalinlike substance from the accelerator nerves quickens it. The inhibitor and the accelerator nerves have been called the reins and the whip of the heart, the inhibitor (parasympathetic) curbing its speed, the accelerator (sympathetic) whipping it up.

Blood Pressure. Every aspect of blood pressure depends upon the pumping of the heart that works against the friction of the blood vessels, and gravity. The nearer the blood is to the pump, the greater the pressure upon it. Farther away from the pump with more and smaller vessels, the friction increases and

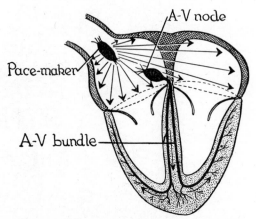

Fig. 12.19. The neuromuscular mechanism that establishes the rhythm of the heartbeat. Diagram of a frontal section of the heart. During each beat a wave of contraction begins in the peculiar muscle fibers in the pace-maker (sino-auricular node) and spreads through them in the walls of the auricle (arrows); another wave of contraction begins at the auriculo-ventricular node (A-V), spreads through the A-V bundle of muscle and on throughout the walls of the ventricles. If either of the nodes is damaged, the auricles continue to beat normally but the ventricles stop beating or beat irregularly. (Courtesy, Gerard: *The Body Functions.* New York, J. Wiley and Sons, 1941.)

the energy of pressure is expended in overcoming it. In the capillaries the friction is enormous and the drop in pressure correspondingly great. In the veins no pressure is regained until just before the blood enters the heart.

PRESSURE IN THE VESSELS, ARTERIES. In the arteries blood travels by spurts since the pressure upon it increases each time the heart contracts (systolic pressure) and decreases each time it relaxes (diastolic pressure). The pulse is an expression of the uneven pressure upon blood in the arteries (Fig. 12.20). It is a wave of the muscular contractions that begins in the left ventricle and spreads throughout the arteries. The contraction of the left ventricle sends a spurt of blood into the aorta that swells out the walls. The spurt of blood is immediately squeezed forward by the rings of muscle behind it and by the action of the elastic tissue in the arteries. By this time the ventricle has contracted again and another lump has started along the aorta. Thousands of these little lumps are constantly moving in processions over the arteries. The rate at which they move past a certain spot is the pulse,

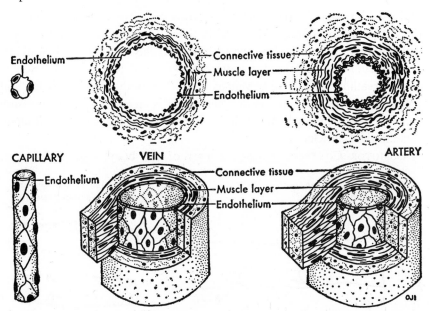

Fig. 12.20. Three types of blood vessels. In the muscle layer of an artery the contraction of the heart is actually continued (pulse); in the thinner muscle layer of a vein it is not. In the cavity of an artery blood is under more pressure than in the larger cavity of a vein of the same size. The walls of capillaries, but one cell thick, make the income and outgo of substances easy. (Courtesy, Hegner and Stiles: *College Zoology*, ed. 6. New York, The Macmillan Co., 1951.)

usually taken on the radial artery at the wrist; its rate is identical with the heartbeat, in adults about 70 times per minute.

CAPILLARIES. When blood enters the capillaries, it encounters a network whose combined caliber is greater than that of the artery from which it came, thus bringing it under less pressure. It drags along their walls and runs against the forkings of their branches. Its energy of motion is continually dissipated in the heat of friction (Chap. 2). At the arterial end where pressure is higher, water is pushed out of the capillaries into the tissue fluid; at the venous end where pressure is lower, water from the tissue fluid is taken back into the capillaries. Thus the water content of the plasma is kept constant and that in the tissue fluid is continually refreshed.

VEINS. Nearer the surface of the body than arteries, veins are thin-walled, extensible, and the larger ones are provided with valves that prevent backward flow (Fig. 12.21). Blood is pushed through the veins by the pressure of more blood coming from the capillaries, by the movements of skeletal muscles, and by the motions of the body in breathing. Most veins are surrounded by skeletal muscles; when they contract the veins are collapsed; when they relax, the veins refill and the blood continues flowing toward the heart. This "milking" motion helps the venous flow of blood just as it does the flow of lymph. It is especially important in returning blood from the legs against the pull of gravity. If a person stands still for some time, the blood in the veins is not circulated properly and the feet and legs swell. If the same person is walking, the contractions of muscles force the blood onward and no such swelling results. Breathing greatly aids venous flow. When the chest muscles and diaphragm contract, the space in the chest cavity is increased, and the pressure within it is lowered to such an extent that air enters the lungs freely and blood enters the right auricle.

VASOMOTOR CONTROL. When one part of the body, e.g., the skeletal

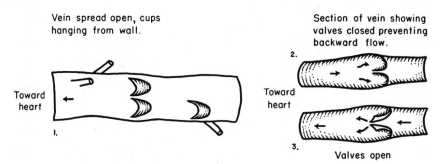

FIG. 12.21. The valves of the veins which prevent a backward flow of blood. They were used by William Harvey (1578–1657) in his argument that the blood continually circulates through the body in one direction.

muscles, the brain, the stomach, is especially active, it receives an extra amount of blood. The walls of arterioles contain smooth muscle innervated by two sets of nerves. An increase in the number of impulses in one set of these nerves (vasoconstrictors) causes the muscles in the walls of the arterioles to contract, decreasing the size of the vessels, and lessening the blood supply. An increase in the impulses in the other set (vasodilators) causes the muscles to relax and increases the size of the arterioles and the consequent flow of blood within them. Ordinarily, these muscles are partially contracted, due to a balance of the impulses in both sets of nerves.

CHEMICAL CONTROL. Arterioles are also affected by carbon dioxide and epinephrine. When muscles are very active, e.g., as in running or sawing wood, their highly increased output of carbon dioxide acts on the smooth muscle of the arterioles, causing them to relax. Arterioles are enlarged and the blood supply to the hard-working muscles is increased. Epinephrine relaxes the muscles in the walls of arterioles in skeletal muscles, but contracts those in the internal organs such as the stomach and intestine.

WILLIAM HARVEY AND THE CIRCULATION OF BLOOD

For upwards of 2000 years human blood was believed to ebb and flow in the vessels like the tides of the sea. Capillaries were unknown, because of the lack of microscopes, and arteries seemed to be always empty except for air. In 1628 William Harvey, an English physician, showed that the blood moves "as it were, in a circle." If we consider the quantity of blood that is thrown out by the heart every minute (approximately two ounces times 72 beats), he said, "where can it go unless it circulates?" This argument was set forth in Harvey's great work, *De Motu Cordis* (*On the Motion of the Heart*) published in 1628, eight years after the Pilgrims landed in New England. This small book opened the door to modern medical treatment. It is a record of observations and experiments made by an adventurous and reasoning person.

13

The Release of Energy—

Respiration

The respiration of living organisms depends upon gases that originate mainly in the atmosphere. Whether they are in the atmosphere or dissolved in water, the conditions that govern these gases deeply affect the lives of plants and animals.

Air. The earth is completely surrounded by the atmosphere, a covering of mixed gases and water vapor. It is about 100 miles deep and is held to the earth by gravity. In dry air the mixture of gases is mainly nitrogen, approximately 78 per cent, and oxygen, 21 per cent (Fig. 13.1). The other one per cent is carbon dioxide with minute amounts of hydrogen, helium, argon, and some other rare gases. When water vapor is abundant, the air is humid. In dry air the proportions of gases do not change at different atmospheric levels, but the total amount of gases does. At low levels molecules bombard one another at close quarters. With lessened pressure the gases expand and the molecules are not even near neighbors. At greater and greater heights there is less and less gas in the air.

Atmosphere is piled up on the surface of the earth like hay in a stack (Fig. 5.16). The hay at the bottom bears the pressure of all that is above it. This pressure is evenly distributed within and without in all directions. The distribution prevents the existence of weight in its ordinary sense although atmospheric pressure is usually expressed in terms of weight. It is calculated as the weight of a column of air one inch square and reaching from sea level to the upper limit of the atmosphere. At sea level it is 14.7 pounds per square inch. The pressure upon the air drives it into the lungs and acts as the first step in inhaling. At 18,000 feet it is not strong enough to force the oxygen from the lungs into the blood, the next necessary step. The effects of oxygen-lack in the body have long been known as mountain sickness, the weakness,

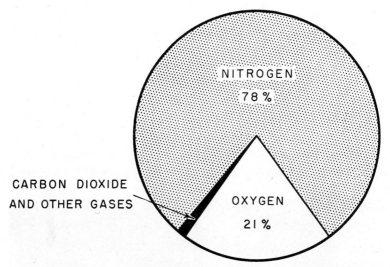

CARBON DIOXIDE
AND OTHER GASES

Fɪɢ. 13.1. Proportions of gases in a relatively dry atmosphere at sea level. Actually the average atmosphere contains a variable amount of water vapor, usually one to five per cent, which slightly changes the proportions given here.

dizziness and unconsciousness that have overcome many mountain climbers. At the top of Mount Everest 29,002 feet, the highest mountain in the world, the air pressure is only 4.4 pounds.

The commonest way to adjust to high altitudes, especially in airplanes, is to increase the oxygen content of the air by breathing through a mask connected with an oxygen tank. Beyond 38,000 feet even breathing pure oxygen is not enough because the atmospheric pressure is too low to drive any gas into the blood. At this height it is necessary to have a hermetically sealed plane, a pressure cabin, which confines the higher pressure caught in it at lower levels. Those who have lived in low countries and later moved to high mountains (14,000 feet or more) usually find that they are weak and short-breathed. The red blood cells of the newcomers are too few. The usual immediate reaction is in the spleen which contracts and forces its store of red cells into the circulation, creating a sudden increase in the number of blood cells in the peripheral blood. This is followed by further increases due to the formation of blood cells in the red bone marrow.

Of the other atmospheric gases only carbon dioxide is directly active in respiration. A very minute amount of it in the blood is necessary to stimulate the mechanism of breathing; more than that is a poison and is normally eliminated.

Nitrogen forms the great bulk of air, takes no part in respiration but is of necessity inhaled and exhaled in breathing and is regularly present in the blood as a dissolved inactive gas. When pressure on the body is suddenly lifted nitrogen comes out of solution and forms bubbles in the blood, in the joints and lungs, and under the skin (Fig. 13.2). The condition is well known to divers as the bends or the caisson disease. It can be prevented by bringing them to the surface in a series of decompression chambers, so that the adjustment of the nitrogen content of their body fluids to ground level pressure is gradual and harmless.

Water. Wherever water comes in contact with air it absorbs gases that become dissolved in it. Thus air and water are continually being mixed at the surfaces of all bodies of water. In lakes and seas the aerated water is rolled under by the winds and distributed by currents to considerable depths. Green plants, included in the microscopic plankton, contribute to the dissolved oxy-

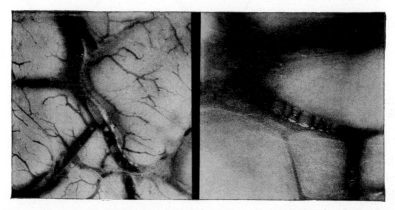

Fig. 13.2. Bubbles of nitrogen in the veins of animals subjected to very low atmospheric pressure. This is aeroembolism, produced by rapid decrease of pressure such as occurs in aircraft flights to high altitudes and is marked by the formation of nitrogen bubbles in the fluids and tissues of the body, especially in fat. (Courtesy, Armstrong: *Principles of Aviation Medicine,* ed. 2. Baltimore, Williams and Wilkins Co., 1943.)

gen. The respiratory gases are present in water as in air. Though there is much less of it, dissolved oxygen takes the same important part in aquatic respirations; so do small amounts of carbon dioxide. Nitrogen in water is an inactive passenger as it is in air. Although water is a combination of hydrogen and oxygen (H_2O), this oxygen is chemically locked and living organisms cannot utilize it for respiration.

Respiration Liberates Energy. From mankind to the simplest animals and plants all direct or aerobic (with air) respiration depends upon free oxygen. The more complex the animal, whether race horse or hummingbird, and the greater its activity, the more constant is its dependence upon respiration.

Respiration is above all the process by which plants and animals, with oxygen as the key, release the energy locked up in food. The oxidation of food is a biochemical process in which oxygen unites with carbon and hydrogen, forms carbon dioxide and water, and sets free the energy that once came from the sun. Everybody sees the oxidation of dead cells in a burning cigarette, with the energy escaping in light and heat. In chemical terms it is expressed as:

$$C_6H_{12}O_6 \quad + \quad 6O_2 \quad \rightarrow \quad 6CO_2 \quad + \quad 6H_2O \quad + \quad energy$$

carbohydrate + oxygen yields carbon + water + energy
dioxide

Respiration may also occur without air, that is, anaerobically. When atmospheric oxygen is absent, oxidation is incomplete; only part of the energy is released and certain intermediate compounds are formed. Anaerobic respiration is a phase of the ordinary respiratory process rather than an entirely different kind. It occurs in certain bacteria and in yeast cells. It is well known and important in mammalian muscle. The ability of muscles to work for a short time without oxygen is one of their most important characteristics (Chap. 10). This doubtless always occurs in athletic contests and in horse races.

Arrangements for Respiration

The simplest respiratory arrangements are in aquatic animals, usually small ones (Fig. 13.3). The covering of these animals is thin and outspread. The

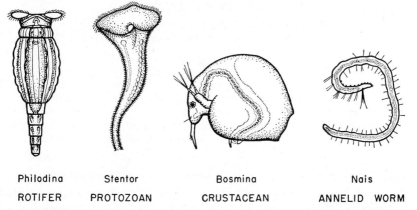

| Philodina | Stentor | Bosmina | Nais |
| ROTIFER | PROTOZOAN | CRUSTACEAN | ANNELID WORM |

FIG. 13.3. Minute aquatic animals whose size and relatively large exposure of thin membranes allow adequate diffusion and exchange of respiratory gases.

bodies of protozoans, planarians, rotifers, and minute worms are thread-shaped, branched, and star-pointed, with crevices and outriggers that welcome oxygen. In all of them respiration is direct. Gases diffuse directly from water into the cells and vice versa. Although they are much larger animals, sponges and jellyfishes also depend upon direct respiration. They are able to do this because they are extremely water-saturated, and their bodies are interlaced by passageways through which circulating water distributes gases directly to and from the cells.

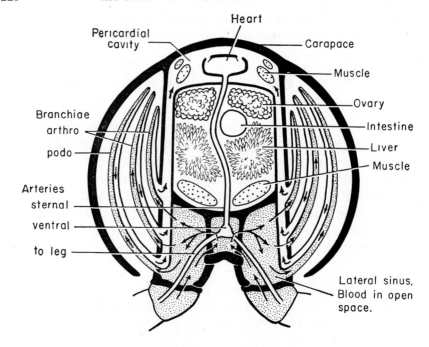

FEMALE CRAYFISH

Cross section of the body through the heart;
arrows indicate the course of blood flow.

A

Fig. 13.4. Respiratory organs of invertebrates. *A,* Blood gills of crayfish visible in a cross section through the thorax. After its passage from the heart and through various arteries the blood flows free in the tissues, through the sternal sinus, thence throughout the vessels of the gills and back to the heart. (After Storer: *General Zoology,* ed. 2. New York, McGraw-Hill Book Co., Inc., 1951.)

Gills. Gills are the characteristic respiratory organs of aquatic animals. The majority of them are outgrowths of the body wall that contain circulating blood (Fig. 13.5). Those of immature aquatic insects contain air tubes (Fig. 13.4B). Blood gills are most commonly near the head, associated with the pharynx as in fishes. Experiments on the larvae of Salamandra showed the responsiveness of the gills to their environment. When these larvae were kept in highly oxygenated water, their gills grew very slowly, while in control animals kept in water poor in oxygen the gills grew very large, as if striving to satisfy the body's demand for oxygen (Fig. 13.5). In spite of this attempt at compensation the metabolism was reduced and the growth of the body was slowed.

The gills of fishes are in the sides, apparently of the mouth cavity, actually of the pharynx. When a fish breathes it opens its mouth and the fleshy skin

FIG. 13.4. Respiratory organs of invertebrates (*continued*). Tracheal gills of the aquatic stage of a mayfly (Epeorus). The tracheae contain gases but ordinarily no fluid. The leaf-like gills extend from the abdomen; their movements are quickened whenever oxygen is sparse. The tracheae are visible as a tracery of dark lines upon each gill and in the body. Total length of insect, one inch.

B

folds (oral valves) are bent backward allowing the water to pour in (Fig. 13.6). The water at once expands the cavity and presses the folds together. The esophagus is contracted so that little or no water is swallowed and for a moment it is also prevented from moving out through the slits at the sides of the mouth (pharynx) by the closure of the opercula (Figs. 13.6, 13.7). The floor of the mouth is then raised, the opercula are lifted, and the water escapes through the gill slits. As it does so it washes the slender filaments of the gills (attached to the gill arches) that contain the circulating blood. This is the moment when the exchange of gases takes place. As soon as the water passes out of the mouth (pharynx), the opercula close and another breathing action begins. Each time that water passes over the gills, food contained in it is caught on the strainers called gill rakers (Fig. 13.7). Fishes do not necessarily close their mouths when breathing, but simply open them wider when they inhale water.

Gills are significant only in connection with the circulation (Fig. 13.6). The two main chambers of the heart of fishes lie below the pharynx. Venous blood passes from the general circulation into the sinus venosus, thence into the auricle, and on into the muscular ventricle which forces it forward via the bulbus arteriosus into the ventral aorta, and then into four pairs of afferent branchial (or gill) arteries. Branches from each of these enter the gill filaments where they divide still further into capillaries (Fig. 13.6). These are the scene of the exchange of gases between the water and blood. The blood comes to the gills with its oxygen low and its carbon dioxide high; it leaves the gills by the efferent branchial arteries with these qualities reversed. It flows over the body, entering the great dorsal aorta first, then goes through many branches distributing oxygen and receiving carbon dioxide. Finally it reaches the heart and again takes the direct route to the gills.

It is important to note that the mouth (pharynx) of fishes is a single road

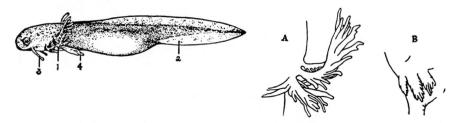

FIG. 13.5. Respiratory organs of vertebrates. *Left,* Larva of spotted salamander (Amblystoma) with blood gills. *1,* gills; *2,* fin; *3,* balancers; *4,* legs. *Right,* Blood gills of salamander larvae showing responses to differences in the amounts of dissolved oxygen in the water: *A,* after living in water poor in oxygen; *B,* control animal, after an equal time in water rich in oxygen. (After Drastich. Courtesy, Krogh: *The Comparative Physiology of Respiratory Mechanisms.* Philadelphia, University of Pennsylvania Press, 1941.)

for breathing and swallowing. This is true from frogs to man except that the air route from the nose crosses the food route from the mouth (Fig. 13.8). The crossing is awkward. Crumbs go down the windpipe when it is not quickly covered. This happens often enough to give everybody experiences in that variety of choking.

Lungs. More difficulties are involved in absorbing oxygen from air than from water. Since living organisms are largely composed of water their thin membranes are soon dried and useless if exposed to air. Except for this, air breathing has great advantages, because air is richer in oxygen than water, holding about 20 times more. This is a boon for greater activity and a higher rate of metabolism, expressed especially by birds and mammals.

Lungs are the tools by which air-breathers have so successfully tapped the oxygen supply. They have progressed toward greater efficiency by increase of area, by greater diffusion of gases, and by efficient ventilation of the cavity of the sac. The increased diffusion area has come with the enlargement of the

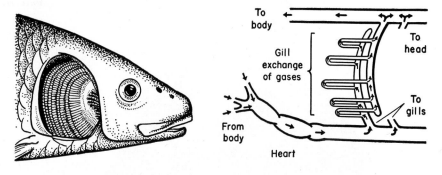

A Operculum removed
exposing gills

B Circulation through heart and gills

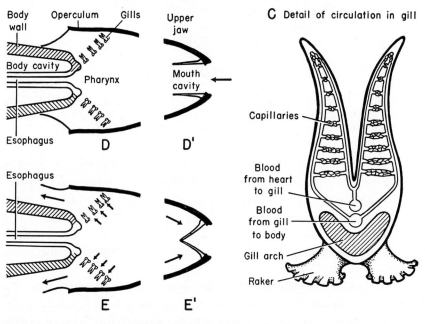

D,E Horizontal section
from right to left

D',E' Vertical section
dorsal to ventral

D,D' Intake of water

E,E' Outgo of water

FIG. 13.6. Diagrams to show how a fish inhales and exhales water, i.e., breathes and where the exchange of oxygen and carbon dioxide between water and blood, i.e., external respiration mainly occurs. *A, B, C;* The structures are typical ones of a bony fish. *D, D¹;* As the valves on the upper and lower jaws open, water flows in and fills the cavities of mouth and pharynx; it passes between the gills and floods over them but momentarily cannot escape because the operculum and its membrane stop the rear passage on each side. This is the moment of the exchange of oxygen and carbon dioxide between the water and blood, possible because the blood is circulating through the capillaries in the hundreds of gill filaments. *E, E¹;* The valves of the mouth are closed; the opercula press inward and the water lifts the rear membranes which opens the back passages for its escape. With these movements completed, the fish has taken a full breath of water and is ready for another.

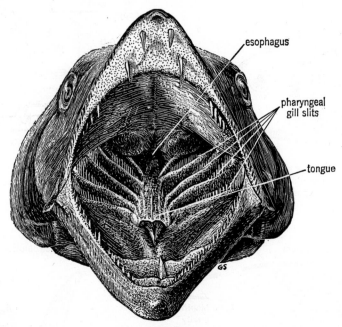

FIG. 13.7. View into the open mouth of a fish (barracuda) showing the gill slits and arches in the walls of the pharynx. (Courtesy, Weichert: *Anatomy of Chordates.* New York, McGraw-Hill Book Co., Inc., 1951.)

lung and the extension of its inner layer by partitions. In frogs the partitions form alcoves, in toads open rooms, and in mammals the respiratory space is completely divided up into minute cavities, the alveoli (Figs. 13.9, 13.10). In each of these successive arrangements more area for blood capillaries is secured. Increase in the numbers of blood capillaries parallels greater diffusion of gases. Nerves, connective tissue, and lymphatic capillaries are also present in highly developed lungs.

The ventilation mechanism differs in various classes of vertebrates. With tightly closed mouths frogs take air through the nostrils and into the mouth, and by contracting the throat, press it into the open glottis, actually swallowing air into their lungs. Reptiles enlarge the body cavity by pulling the partially folded ribs forward. Air is then drawn through the nostrils, windpipe, and into the lungs because of the reduction of pressure in the body cavity around them. In birds the mechanism is complicated and, for the full action of the lungs, depends largely upon the movements produced particularly while flying. The main body of the bird's lungs is small but the extensions of the lungs in air sacs are relatively large (Chap. 36). The upper surface of the lungs adheres to the ribs; indentations of the latter show clearly when the lungs are pulled away. A special membrane ventral to the lungs is also attached to the ribs. In quiet breathing intercostal and abdominal muscles

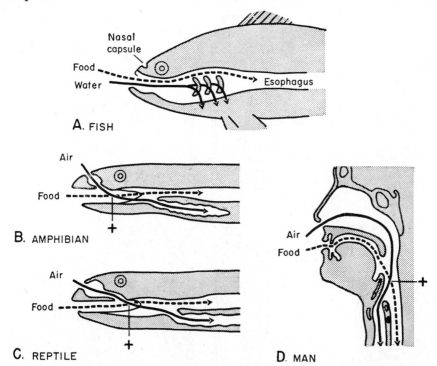

Fig. 13.8. Diagrams of breathing and swallowing routes in aquatic and terrestrial vertebrates. Fishes inhale through the mouth. The routes of water and food are parallel and entirely separate from the olfactory cavities. Beginning with amphibians the routes of breathing and swallowing cross as they do in all other air breathing vertebrates. The precise timing of nervous and muscular action keeps the crossing clear for air or food. If both meet at the open trachea, choking results.

enlarge and contract the body cavity, drawing air in and out of the air sacs, and through the lungs. During flight the pectoral muscles (white breast meat) provide ventilation by moving the sternum (breastbone) toward and away from the vertebral column.

Tracheae of Insects. These airtubes extend throughout the body from openings in the body wall and are the main distributors of oxygen (Chap. 30).

Human Respiration

Lungs. The human lungs begin as an outgrowth of the floor of the future pharynx and develop a single trachea or windpipe which forks into two bronchial tubes (Fig. 13.10). Within each lung the bronchial tubes rebranch many times and finally divide into minute bronchioles. Each bronchiole continues into a small cluster of air sacs out of which minute alcoves or alveoli open and create still further area for diffusion of gases between air and blood (Fig. 13.11). The bronchioles are encircled with smooth muscle innervated

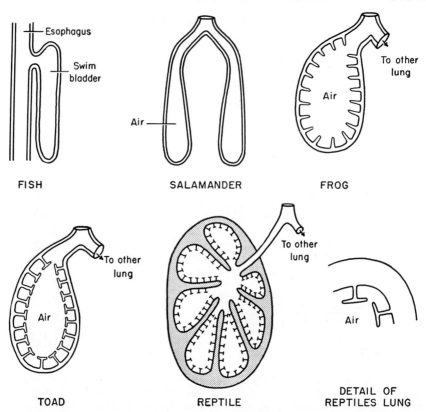

FIG. 13.9. The evolution of lungs shows a great increase in the area of lining exposed to air, and the close association of air and blood, the latter circulating in capillaries between the lining and the covering of the lungs. The great development of the lining is emphasized in this figure. The lining is the membrane through which oxygen and carbon dioxide pass to and from the blood, i.e., where external respiration occurs.

by branches of the vagus nerves. These control the size of the passageways through the bronchioles, many of which are closed in ordinary shallow breathing. In the disease of asthma large numbers of them are closed spasmodically. The capillary-covered alveoli are the real functional structures of the lung, the part of it in which the major exchange of gases takes place (Fig. 13.10). It is estimated that there are millions of these in human lungs and that four to five quarts of blood pass through the lungs per minute during rest, and at least 20 times that during violent exercise.

Passage of Air to and from the Lungs. Air is normally inhaled through the nostrils into the nasal chambers. There it is broken into eddying currents as it comes in touch with the warm, ciliated, mucous epithelium that covers the turbinate bones that hang down like curtains into the nasal chambers (Fig. 13.12). This combination of structures constitutes an air conditioner, heater,

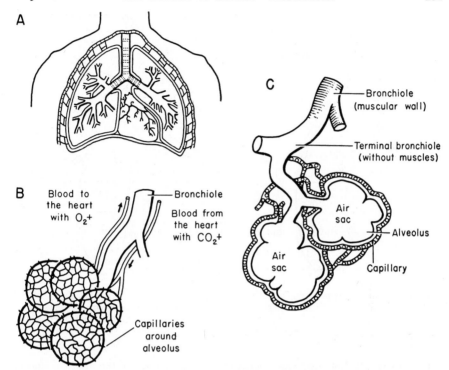

FIG. 13.10. *A,* The human lungs, each enclosed in a double walled sac and attached to the body only by the bronchial tubes and trachea. The two lines around the lungs represent their outer membrane and the lining of the thoracic cavity (pleura). *B,* Diagram of five alveoli with their blood supply. *C,* Lung tissue consists of an enormous number of bronchioles leading to microscopic air sacs with their alveoli closely surrounded by capillaries. Two air sacs are shown as cut in section and greatly magnified. Air is separated from the blood only by the extremely thin walls of the blood capillaries and of the alveoli of the lungs. It is estimated that there are 750,000,000 alveoli in the human lungs.

humidifier, and filter. With a "cold in the head," when the mucous cells are inflamed, they greatly overdo the humidifying. Worse yet, the lining swells to such an extent that for the time being it stops up the nasal passages entirely. Minute particles of anything of any description that may be in the air are caught against the moist walls of the nasal passages. That is the reason that we smell so many things. The nose is the most democratic and hospitable of our body structures.

It is easy to see why the nasal cavities and pharynx become infected and how they infect adjoining cavities in the head (Fig. 13.12). Several hollow, mucous-membrane lined cavities open out of the nasal ones, the frontal sinus on each side above the eye, and a maxillary sinus on each side of the upper jaw. The Eustachian tubes leading to the right and left middle ears open into the nasopharynx just above the soft palate. The nearby tonsils and adenoids,

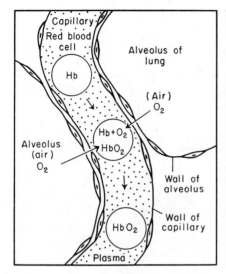 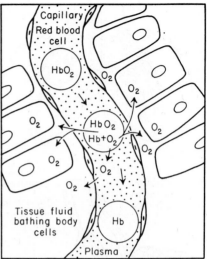

A. In the lung. Oxygen (O_2) diffuses from air in the lung. and combines with hemoglobin (Hb) in the red blood cells to make oxyhemoglobin (Hb O_2).

B. In other parts of the body. Oxygen separates from the loosely bound oxyhemoglobin and diffuses into the tissue fluid and cells.

FIG. 13.11. *A*, the exchange between air and blood in the lungs (external respiration); and *B*, between the blood and cells of the body (internal respiration). The rate and direction of the diffusion of a gas is determined by its pressure. When oxygen is abundant in the lungs its pressure is high and it diffuses into the blood. Carbon dioxide diffuses out of tissues, e.g., muscle, to blood, and then to lungs because it passes from higher to lower pressures. Carbon dioxide is carried by the blood in two ways; in loose combination with hemoglobin (CO_2Hb); and combined with water as carbonic acid ($CO_2 + H_2O$). Most of the carbonic acid is converted into bicarbonates through neutralization by sodium or potassium ions released when oxyhemoglobin is changed to hemoglobin. The process of converting carbonic acid back into carbon dioxide to diffuse out in the lung capillaries is speeded up by a special enzyme, carbonic anhydrase.

often large in children, are masses of lymphatic tissue in which bacteria sometimes accumulate.

Whether air enters through the nose or mouth it must pass through the pharynx in order to reach the open trachea with its lifted cover, the epiglottis (Fig. 13.12). In mammals, the pharynx is merely a place where the paths of air and food cross in an awkward fashion. It is a place where indecision is quickly punished. Either air enters it and goes straightway into an open trachea, or food enters it, passes a closed trachea, and goes into the esophagus. If both enter simultaneously, neither arrives and choking follows. A choke is a forced expiration, an attempt to dislodge the crumbs that have "gone down the wrong way." In ordinary breathing air passes quietly into the open trachea through the larynx and enters the bronchial tubes.

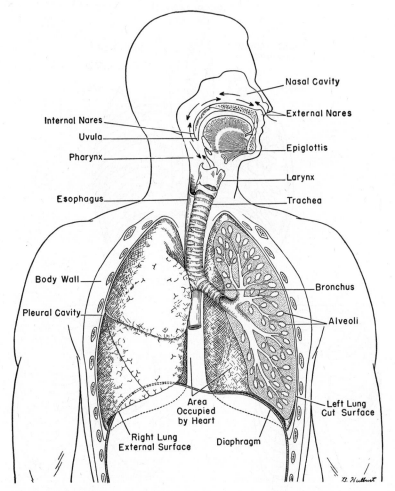

FIG. 13.12. Human respiratory system. (Courtesy, Villee: *Biology. The Human Approach,* ed. 2. Philadelphia, W. B. Saunders Co., 1954.)

MECHANISM OF BREATHING

Inspiration. Lungs expand because the chest cavity pulls upon them from all sides. Nerve impulses from the respiratory center in the medulla stimulate the intercostal muscles to contract, which means lifting the ribs (Fig. 13.13). The ribs then move outward as they are lifted, like the handle of a pail, and thus they increase the spread of the chest. The breastbone also moves up carrying the front ends of the ribs with it, and increasing the chest cavity from front to back. At the same time impulses from the respiratory center are relayed over the phrenic nerves to the diaphragm and make it contract, deepening the chest cavity. Instead of a low dome pressing up into the thoracic cavity, the

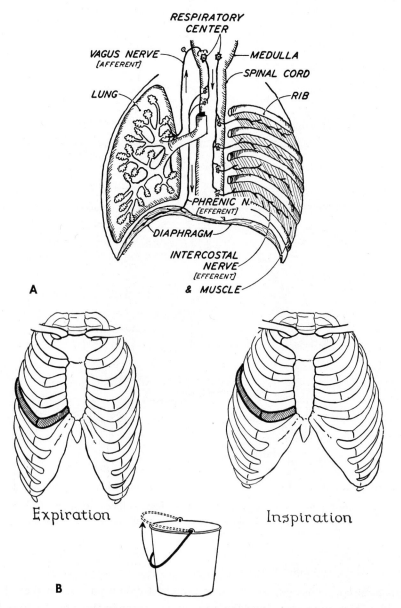

FIG. 13.13. *A*, Some of the nerves connected with human breathing. All of the structures shown are symmetrical on both sides. The intercostal muscles move the ribs out and up. Volleys of impulses are discharged rhythmically from the paired clusters of nerve cells in the respiratory center in the medulla or brain stem. These pass through the spinal cord to the intercostal muscles, and through the vagus and phrenic nerves to the lungs and diaphragm. *B*, Intercostal muscles lift the ribs out and up as the handle of a pail is lifted. (*A*, reprinted from *The Machinery of the Human Body* by Carlson and Johnson, by permission of The University of Chicago Press. Copyright 1948. *B*, courtesy, Gerard: *The Body Functions.* New York, John Wiley and Sons, 1941.)

contraction of the diaphragm creates a flat floor. The floor now presses on the organs beneath, the muscles of the abdominal wall relax and the abdomen bulges.

The chest expands because the muscles contract. But why do the lungs follow its expanding walls? In the first place lungs are free to move, since they are attached only by the bronchial tubes and the partition between them. Thus they can slide easily on the lining (pleura) of the lung cavity. In addition, there are many elastic fibers in the lung, all of them stretched and trying to shorten just as they do in the arteries. Thus their action keeps the lungs in a state of trying to pull away from the walls about them. But they meet the strong opposition of the low pressure in the space between the lungs and chest wall. Within the lungs the pressure is near that of the atmosphere, slightly below at the beginning of inspiration, the reason that air enters them. On the other hand, in the space outside the lungs, there is no air, only a little fluid and a suction or negative pressure. This exerts a pull on the lungs that is stronger than they can resist. It is why they cling to the thoracic wall as long as that is intact. When it is perforated by accident, or in the treatment of tuberculosis to give one lung a rest that lung instantly collapses. This is the rather well-known state of pneumothorax.

Expiration. Often called breathing out, expiration is a purely passive relaxation of muscles; the ribs are dropped; the dome of the diaphragm once more presses upward against the lung cavity. Ordinary quiet breathing is an inspiration and expiration repeated about 16 times per minute, the number differing slightly in different individuals.

Chemical Control. As carbon dioxide increases in arterial blood, it acts upon the respiratory center of the medulla and indirectly on the chemoreceptors of the carotid body, which are thus stimulated to discharge impulses that quicken respiration. In contrast, a decrease in carbon dioxide affecting the respiratory center diminishes or stops breathing. And the content of these gases in the blood depends upon the proportions of oxygen or carbon dioxide in the lungs.

Nervous Control. You can hold your breath but not your heartbeat, and you cannot even hold your breath for long. But the fact that you can hold your breath at all shows that messages come from the higher centers of the brain and act upon the respiratory center in the medulla (Fig. 13.13). The failure to continue holding the breath means that the chemical control by accumulated carbon dioxide has gotten the upper hand of any nervous control. Branches of the truly named vagus (wandering) nerves help control ordinary breathing. During inspiration their receptor endings in the pleura are stretched and the messages from them to the medulla are more frequent. The expansion of the chest finally causes the respiratory center to stop sending the impulses which stimulate inspiration. As soon as this occurs, another group of receptors also belonging to the vagus nerve is affected by the collapse of the lungs and starts stimuli and stimulate a new inspiration.

VOLUME OF AIR IN THE LUNGS

The amount of air which can be taken into or forced out of the lungs is easily measured by a spirometer. A person at rest, breathing about 16 times per minute, regularly inspires and expires about one pint of air. By great effort, three pints more can be expelled in addition to the pint of the regular inspiration. Even after such a forced expiration there is still about a pint left in the lungs. There is, therefore, a reserve supply of over five pints of air with which the fresh pint in the regular inspiration is mixed. It must not be concluded that all the oxygen of inspired air is extracted with each breath; expired air contains about three-fourths of its previous content of oxygen. Air is breathed over and over again. Note the possibilities in the next crowded bus!

VOICE

Voice is due to the expulsion of air across the vocal cords, folds of the lining of the larynx which contains bands of dense elastic tissue and muscle. Although called vocal cords, they are not cords and do not resemble them. The upper folds are called the false vocal cords and the lower ones the true vocal cords. The larynx, characteristic of higher vertebrates, is located just below the glottis or opening of the trachea (Fig. 13.14).

Electronic devices have proven that the deep sea is far from noiseless; fishes have no larynx but they make grunts and kindred sounds with their swim bladders; whales and their kin, being all good air-breathers, have an equipment for voice. The really vociferous vertebrates are the birds and mammals. In

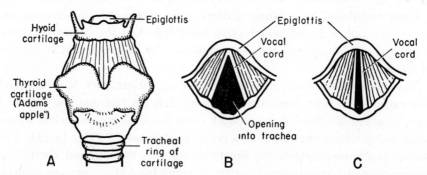

FIG. 13.14. The human larynx. *A*, Front view from above, looking into the throat; *B*, with vocal cords swung away from one another when at rest; *C*, cords swung near together during speech. Loudness depends on the pressure with which air is exhaled between them. Pitch depends partly upon the tightness of the contraction of the cords. Quality of voice depends upon many factors. (Redrawn after Brash, ed.: *Cunningham's Textbook of Anatomy*, ed. 9. New York, Oxford University Press, 1951.)

birds, a kind of historical larynx is present in the typical position, but without vocal cords. Another and different kind of voice box, the syrinx, is located at the junction of the bronchi. The whole bird chorus depends upon the syrinx, such a range of sounds as those of parrots and thrushes, crows and robins.

Characteristic features of the mammalian larynx are its cartilaginous cover, the epiglottis, which is quickly pulled down in swallowing, and the strongly developed vocal cords (Fig. 13.14). The framework of the larynx is a group of cartilages held together by muscle; the odd-shaped thyroid cartilage that protrudes from the front of the neck is especially large in human males, and known as Adam's apple. The contractions of muscles between the cartilages change the shape of the larynx and vary the size of the opening between the vocal cords. The pitch of the voice is determined by the length of the cords; low with longer cords and high with shorter ones. Pitch can be modified voluntarily. By persistent effort, a voice can be pulled away from the front teeth where it sounds like an alarm clock, and placed properly in the larynx where its tones may become clear and mellow.

SPECIAL WAYS OF BREATHING

Coughing is a quick inspiration followed by contraction of abdominal muscles, causing an increase of pressure in the thorax. The throat contracts and the glottis is closed. After a certain amount of pressure gathers in the lungs, the air escapes with a rush, pushing open the glottis and carrying with it crumbs or other extraneous material. Coughing is generally a reflex act resulting from stimuli in the mouth and throat. Psychic coughing is stimulated by hearing someone else cough.

A sneeze is a violent expiration with the air thrown into the nose and against the hard palate.

Hiccoughs (hiccups) are due to the spasmodic contraction of the diaphragm and a sudden inspiration cut short by the snaplike closure of the glottis. They are often stimulated by very hot fluid taken into an empty stomach.

Sighing is a prolonged inspiration followed by a deep expiration, often with fading voice.

Yawning is similar to sighing but is accompanied by stretching of the lower jaw, sometimes of legs and arms.

Snoring is an accompaniment to deep breathing through the mouth. The treble is the vibration of the soft palate.

Dyspnea is labored breathing due to choking, reduced absorptive surface of lungs as in pneumonia, or lack of oxygen in the air.

Purring is probably caused by vibration of air drawn across the false vocal cords by a comfortable cat, a social expression that corresponds in satisfaction to human humming.

14

The By-Products
of Metabolism—Excretion

Excretion keeps a balanced content in the internal environment of the body. This content is continually tipped between income, expenditure, and remainder, between too little and too much. Food and water furnish the income; activity with respiration is the expenditure; excretion removes the remainder. Altogether this is metabolism, the continual buildup and breakdown that liberates energy and leaves an ordinarily useless remainder.

Residues must be thrown out of the body because they are in the way and even poisonous. The excretory organs carry on these processes; they are the regulators of body content, keeping water, gases, salts, and other substances from increasing beyond an essential standard. Excretion maintains a chemical balance in the internal environment of the body; it includes separation, collection, and elimination of undesirable substances. The excretory organs of vertebrates are the gills, lungs, liver, and the kidneys, also called renal organs (L., *ren,* kidney), and in lower animals nephridia (Gr., *nephros,* kidney). The responsibility for maintaining the delicate, complex adjustments of the blood rests mainly with the liver and kidneys, the latter being the chief excretory organs.

All living cells give off by-products of the chemical reactions that take place within them. Since every cell surface is capable of excretion, this occurs whether the animal has kidneys and other excretory organs, or no excretory organs, as in hydra (Fig. 14.1). Except for the contractile vacuoles the structural arrangements of excretory organs are basically similar and the chemicals excreted are the same. The oxidation of carbon frees energy and creates an end product of carbon dioxide; most, but not all, of this is excreted in the gills or lungs. Almost all excreted hydrogen is in the form of water. Nitrogen from the breakdown of proteins is usually eliminated as ammonia, urea, and uric acid. Besides these there are other substances in very small amounts.

The Simple Excretory Organs and Their Functions

Vacuoles. In most protozoans there is no hint of a special excretory organ. In fresh-water amebas, paramecia and others, the water constantly entering the animal collects in contractile vacuoles along with the metabolic waste products (Fig. 14.1). A vacuole is in no sense empty. It fills until the surrounding protoplasm will stretch no more then suddenly contracts and dumps the contents outside. Through the lower power of the microscope the vacuole, as it were, winks at the observer. A contractile vacuole is primarily a water-regulator that disposes of extra water diffusing into an animal because its

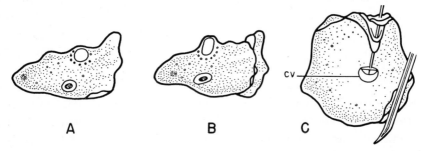

A   B   C

Fig. 14.1. The simpler excretory organs. The contractile vacuole of *Amoeba verrucosa*. *A,* Vacuole that has reached full size and is near the surface of the body. *B,* The vacuole, about to empty, is pressed against the outer covering which stretches momentarily and forms a cone before it breaks. *C,* A living ameba is held in place by a minute rod. A slightly blunt microneedle is inserted into the animal and pushed against the contractile vacuole indenting it like a transparent rubber ball pushed in from one side. This and other experiments have shown that a contractile vacuole is enclosed by a transient but definite membrane. (Redrawn after Howland: "Experiments on the contractile vacuole of *Amoeba verrucosa*." J. Exp. Zool. **40:**251–270, 1924.)

protoplasm is saltier than the water outside. Fresh-water fishes would have the same trouble if they did not have means of preventing it. Marine amebas do not have vacuoles, and when fresh-water species are kept in salt water their vacuoles disappear or work very slowly since the salt content of protoplasm and sea water nearly balance.

Association of Kidneys and Blood. Except for the vacuoles all excretory organs are tubes, always intimately associated with blood or other body fluid. In lower animals the kidney is called a nephridium and many words associated with this term are used in connection with all kidneys, such as nephritis, a disease of the kidney.

Fresh-water planarians have no circulating blood to transport waste and the excretory system is a series of minute tubes whose closed ends, the flame cells, are surrounded by the body fluid. These flame cells are so named because a tuft of flagella in the funnel-shaped hollow of the cell flickers like a flame. Actually the flagella constantly wave fluid into the tubes, ultimately to pass out of the body through numerous fine pores. Planarians that live in fresh water have well-developed flame cells; whereas in those living in brackish water, the entire excretory system is reduced. As with marine amebas, the osmotic pressure of salt in the surrounding water and that of the protoplasm are balanced.

The kidneys (nephridia) of earthworms repeat the essentials of kidney form and function, tubules closely associated with blood and body fluid, each one a guardian of the content of the blood. There are two kidneys in nearly every segment of the earthworm (Fig. 14.2). Their inner ends are immersed in the watery coelomic fluid; their outer ends open on the body surface; the tubules themselves are entwined with blood capillaries. The inner end of each nephridium is a funnel formed by ciliated cells arranged in beautiful symmetry like the ribs of a palm-leaf fan, coming together at the mouth of the tubule which receives fluid from the body cavity. The funnels draw in fluid and thus keep down any excess of incoming water.

The kidneys of crayfishes and lobsters are hardly recognizable as such either in shape or position, but they actually are tubular and are guardians of the content of the blood (Fig. 14.2). In lobsters they are the paired green glands, one on each side of the head near the eye. Each one is a two-lobed, saclike tube whose inner end opens into a body cavity (hemocoel). The outer opening is a hole easily seen on the basal segment of the antenna. Excretory systems usually include pairs of kidneys located well forward in the body like those of lobsters and crayfishes. This does not occur in adult vertebrates but as an embryo every vertebrate animal goes through a stage when it has "head kidneys" (Fig. 14.3).

Kidneys of Vertebrates

Likeness of Structure and Function. The vertebrate kidney is an assemblage of excretory tubules, always in a dorsal location and composed of many units, each one basically similar to a kidney of an earthworm. In the kidneys of the most primitive fishes, there are only a few of these units in one kidney; one human kidney, however, contains at least one million of such tubules. During their evolution the various types of kidneys of vertebrates that have appeared are: those connected with coelomic fluid, that is, coelomic blood, free in the main cavities, (pronephros); with coelomic fluid and circulating blood, (mesonephros); and solely with circulating blood (metanephros), the kidneys of adult reptiles, birds, and mammals.

Historical Succession of Kidneys—Pronephros, Mesonephros, Metanephros. The first or pronephric kidneys are near the anterior end of the animal and consist of a few tubules. The inner ends of these are ciliated funnels immersed

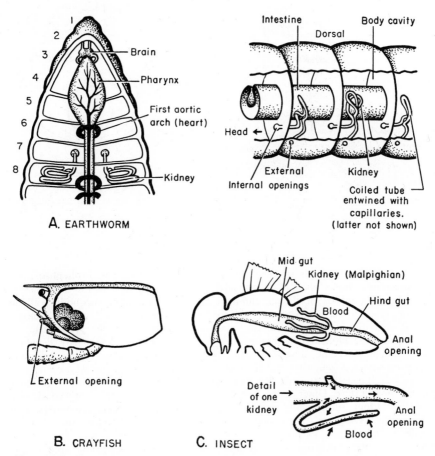

A. EARTHWORM

B. CRAYFISH   C. INSECT

FIG. 14.2. Examples of the tubular structure of excretory organs and their characteristic association with body fluids. *A, left,* Earthworm: body cavity and first pair of kidneys seen from the dorsal side; there is one pair in each of the one hundred or more segments behind this. *Right,* Body cavity of earthworm seen from the side showing one of each pair of kidneys; the inner end opens into the body fluid; the coiled tube is entwined with blood capillaries. *B,* Left kidney of the single pair of kidneys in the crayfish seen from the side after the shell and gills are removed. It appears as two bodies, one including the bladder and another called the "green gland." The gland consists of a labyrinth of excretory tubules connecting through a canal with the urinary bladder which has an external opening just below the eye. Blood capillaries are entwined about the tubules. The entire crustacean kidney has been compared to one unit of the vertebrate kidney. *C,* Simplified diagram of an insect's body cavity and organs. The kidneys (Malpighian tubes) open into the gut and extend into the body cavity where they are continually bathed by the blood. (*A* redrawn from Strausbaugh and Weimer: *General Biology.* New York, J. Wiley and Sons, 1944.)

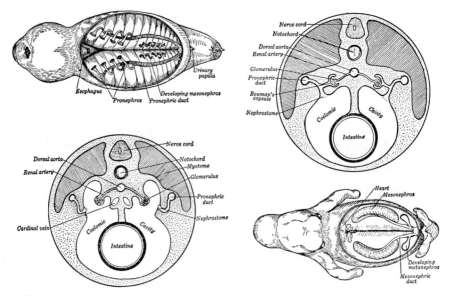

FIG. 14.3. The kidneys of vertebrates, a succession of types, pronephros, mesonephros, metanephros, all of them paired tubes associated with the blood. *Upper
left,* The pronephros of the amphibian embryo shown after the body wall and
viscera are removed. Each pronephridium opens into the body cavity by a ciliated
funnel as in the earthworm but the other end connects with the pronephric duct
leading via the cloacal chamber to the external opening. The partly developed
mesonephros is visible, a similar series of tubules that join the pronephric duct.
The pronephros degenerates and is succeeded by the mesonephros whose important
advance is the association of the blood vessels of the glomerulus and the kidney
tubule. *Lower left,* Diagram of a cross section of the dogfish embryo showing
that the kidney tubules and the capillaries of the glomerulus are independent.
Upper right, Diagram of a cross section of an amphibian embryo in which the
capillaries of the glomerulus are in the clasping cup of the tubule. *Lower right,*
Embryo of man showing the beginnings of the metanephros, the final kidney.
(Courtesy, Little: *Structure of the Vertebrates.* New York, Long and Smith, 1932.)

in coelomic fluid; their outer ends are joined and form the pronephric ducts,
one on each side of the vertebrae extending backward to a single opening near
the anus (Fig. 14.3). Pronephric kidneys occur in the adults of only a few of
the most primitive fishes. They develop, however, and are present a short time,
often only as rudiments, in the embryo of every vertebrate including man.
They exist for a time as the functional kidneys of young tadpoles. The mesonephros is the kidney of the majority of adult fishes and of amphibians and, as
the follower of the pronephros, is present and functions for a time in the
embryos of reptiles, birds, and mammals.

Most kidney tubules end in a saclike enlargement, the renal capsule, that
holds a tangle of capillaries, the glomerulus (L., a little ball). The capsule and
capillaries together constitute a working unit of the kidney, called a renal or
Malpighian body (Fig. 14.3). In every such unit, water and other products

are filtered from the blood into the renal capsule and a dilute urine is formed. In primitive animals, a funnel of the tubule also opens into the coelomic fluid. Altogether each unit has a two-way access to the vital fluids and water content of the body and an equipment for the selective filtering of metabolic products and water.

Adult reptiles, birds, and mammals all have the metanephric type of kidney whose units are associated solely with the blood. These kidneys are provided with large supplies of blood and consist of large numbers of kidney units held together by connective tissue and the blood vessels. Externally they have no resemblance to tubes, actually each kidney contains, in different species, from a few dozen to about a million microscopic tubular units.

Human Urinary System

The human urinary system includes two kidneys, two long tubes, the ureters which carry urine from each kidney to the bladder, a reservoir for urine, and the urethra, a tube leading to the external opening (Fig. 14.4).

KIDNEYS

General Structure. The kidneys lie against the dorsal body wall beneath the peritoneal lining. Although they appear to be in the coelom or body cavity they are separated from it by the transparent layer of tissue which covers all the other organs. All mammalian kidneys are bean-shaped and very similar in structure. In the kidneys of rodents and carnivores the tubules all run toward one point making a single pyramid. In the human and other mammalian kidneys the tubules come to a focus in several pyramids (Figs. 14.4, 14.5). When split in half longitudinally the cut surface shows two parts: an outer finely rayed band, the cortex, and a central part or medulla. The cortex contains the renal bodies and the coiled parts of the tubule. The medulla contains the U-shaped part of it and the collecting ducts which deliver urine through pores in the tip of each pyramid. The urine flows through the minute openings of the collecting tubules into the pelvis and drains from the pelvis into the ureter. The ureter delivers it to the urinary bladder from whence it is discharged through the urethra.

Circulation of Blood. The kidneys are located on the high road of circulating blood. The renal arteries bring blood directly from the heart under high pressure, and the renal veins turn the great part of it into an easy road back to the heart. There are no renal portal veins such as those in the frog that bring blood from the hind legs to the kidneys (Fig. 34.18). In frogs, these help to combat the income of water through the skin by providing the blood with extra access to the kidneys where more water is filtered out, a process that helps to prevent drowning from inside. Mammals and other land vertebrates have waterproof skins and their kidneys are less important as water pumps.

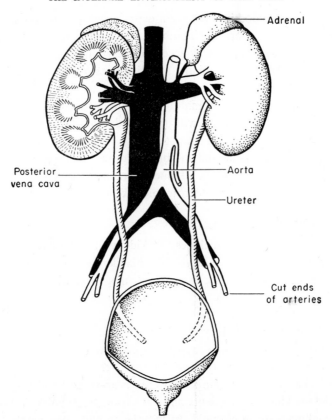

Fig. 14.4. Human urinary system, ventral view. The kidneys are seen connected with the great highways of the blood by the urinary arteries (white) and the urinary veins (dark); the ureters open obliquely on the dorsal side of the bladder. Half of the right kidney has been removed showing the pelvis, a cavity through which the urine is delivered to the ureter; the cortex contains the renal (or Malpighian) corpuscles, the functional units of the kidney; from them bundles of collecting tubes extend toward the pelvis and deliver urine through pores into each calyx. The adrenal glands adhere to the kidneys but have no direct connections with them.

All through their history the behavior of the kidneys has been modified by the necessity of keeping water in or out of the body in order to create an adequate internal environment. They have been highly important in the evolution of fresh- and salt-water and land vertebrates.

Branches of the renal artery enter each kidney and there unite finally into an arcuate artery that gives rise to the afferent arteries, one entering each glomerulus. These divide into the capillaries of the glomerulus lying in the renal capsule (Fig. 14.5). These capillaries join to form an efferent artery of smaller diameter than the afferent one. After leaving the glomerulus the efferent artery breaks into arterioles and capillaries that lace the walls of the

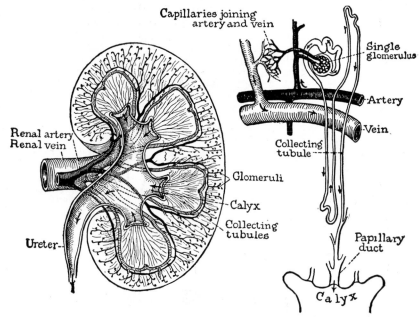

FIG. 14.5. Finer structure of a mammalian kidney. *Left,* Cut surface showing the veins and the arteries (black) with their many branches in the cortex and the collecting tubes that converge and open into the calyx. *Right,* One functional unit of a kidney showing a glomerulus such as those represented by dots in the cortex in Figure 14.4. The afferent artery to the glomerulus is actually larger than the efferent one. (Courtesy, Clendening: *The Human Body.* New York, Alfred A. Knopf, Inc., 1930.)

tubules, then come together to make minute veins that empty into the arcuate vein. This and its branches finally join to make the renal veins that open into the vena cava which carries blood directly to the heart.

Units of the Kidney and Their Work. Each tubule with its accompanying capillaries is one of about one million working units in each human kidney (Fig. 14.6). In outlining the function of the kidney the parts named in the preceding paragraphs will be mentioned again.

Each unit begins near the outer surface of the kidney where it holds the glomerulus in a double-walled cup, the renal capsule. Both walls are very thin and slightly separated by a space that is continued into the kidney tubule. The plasma of the blood in the glomerulus is continually under pressure by the drive from the heart, plus additional pressure due to the fact that the afferent artery through which blood flows into the glomerulus is larger than the efferent one through which it flows out. Except for proteins and other large molecules the contents of the renal capsule are continuously filtered through its thin inner wall into the cavity that leads into the tubule. Reabsorption occurs farther on where capillaries surround the many loops of the tubule.

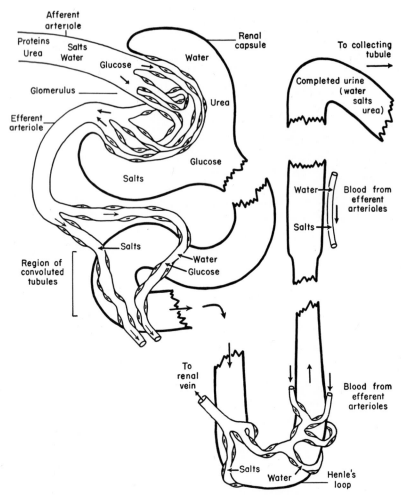

FIG. 14.6. Diagram of the general exchange of substances in the formation of urine. During filtration all the components of the blood plasma pass into the renal capsule except proteins. This includes water; urea; glucose; and various salts. During reabsorption urea is concentrated in the kidney tubule and water and glucose are reabsorbed in the blood. Salts may or may not be reabsorbed.

It is estimated that about 45 gallons of blood are filtered per 24 hours in the human kidneys. Of course this includes the same blood passing through the glomeruli many times. The first filtrate is a very different fluid from urine. It is probably like the watery urine of man's aquatic ancestors in which water came through the skin and flooded into the body and was then filtered out of the blood, creating the same kind of watery urine as that of present-day frogs.

Here, stimulated by a hormone released from the pars nervosa of the pituitary gland, about 99 per cent of all the sugar and the water is reabsorbed into the blood as it passes through these capillaries at comparatively low pressure

(Fig. 14.6). About one cubic centimeter per minute accounts for the three pints or thereabout of urine usually excreted from the kidneys per day. After reabsorption of the water, the concentration of urea and nitrogenous substances in the urine may be over a hundred times greater than in the blood plasma. Up to a certain amount, the cells in the walls of the tubules are evidently capable of taking up glucose and other useful constituents from the excreted fluid in the tubule and passing them back to the blood. The blood plasma and the filtrate in the tubule are always coming to a balance with one another in their content of water, sugar, salts, and urea.

Water-saving insects, reptiles, and birds dispose of their nitrogenous waste as semisolid uric acid. The kidneys of all land vertebrates take back by reabsorption much of the contents of the filtrate, the watery urine that is first made according to the ancient ancestral pattern and then brought up to the modern pattern. This is a roundabout way; it is also a physiological reminiscence.

Ureters and Bladder

Function. Urine is propelled through the ureters by peristaltic contractions and enters the bladder in jets at the rate of one to five per minute. As the bladder becomes distended it presses against the oblique openings of the ureters, preventing backflow into them. It also sets up afferent nerve impulses to the spinal cord. These in turn set up impulses from the cord which stimulate rhythmic contraction of muscles in the bladder, and eventually cause relaxation of the sphincter valve at its opening into the urethra. In very young animals this action is involuntary, but later it becomes a habit formed by voluntary behavior.

Conditions and Diseases Affecting the Work of the Kidneys

Nephritis. Various kinds of inflammation of the kidney tubules are called *nephritis*. Although the term is used commonly it gains real meaning with the knowledge that the nephric tubule is the essential working unit of all kidneys. The type of nephritis commonly known as Bright's disease was described by Richard Bright (1789–1858), a British physician, one of the great modern pathologists. He did not theorize or experiment but did the observing upon which theory and experiment are based. He was the first to connect with the kidney the symptoms of a disease known since the time of Hippocrates. Bright enjoyed life, his work, his travels, and the sketches that he made to illustrate the accounts of them.

Floating Kidney. A floating kidney is due to a shift in the position of the kidney either posteriorly, or tilted away from the dorsal wall. The kidneys of fishes, reptiles, and birds fit snugly along each side of the backbone; those of amphibians and mammals are attached loosely beneath the peritoneum.

Diabetes Mellitus. This is a condition in which sugar appears in the urine, and is commonly called *sugar diabetes*. It is due to a defect in the glands (called the isles of Langerhans) within the pancreas which secrete insulin. Because of this the body is unable to use or to store carbohydrates and the blood becomes loaded with sugar. So much sugar is filtered out of the glomerulus that the kidney tubules are unable to reabsorb and return it to the blood, consequently it passes out with the urine.

Diabetes Insipidus. A less common form of diabetes in which too much water is lost but no sugar is diabetes insipidus. The kidney tubules are unable to reabsorb the water filtered out of the blood in the glomerulus. Experiments upon animals have shown that the water-absorptive function of the kidney tubules is dependent upon pitressin, a hormone secreted by the pars nervosa of the pituitary gland (Chap. 15). The disease may be controlled by injections of pituitary extract just as was first done experimentally in treating the similar disease in rats and dogs.

Factors Influencing Urine Volume. The volume of blood is reduced if no water or other fluid is taken, or blood may be lost by hemorrhage. In any such case, the blood pressure is lowered in the kidneys; there is less filtration, and less urine. Conversely, the more fluid that is taken, the greater the pressure in the vessels, and the more urine produced.

Diuresis, or increased production of volume of urine, is caused by a variety of conditions and substances, such as nervous stimuli affecting the circulation, temperature affecting the circulation, and certain stimulants. A swim in cold water drives blood into deep vessels, increases the blood pressure in the kidney, and consequently the filtration of urine. Tea and coffee act as diuretics, especially if a person is not accustomed to them.

Other Organs that Eliminate Metabolic Wastes

Gills and Lungs. The respiratory organs remove most of the carbon dioxide brought to them by the blood. Molecules of it diffuse into the water through the thin membrane of the gills, and into the air within the lungs through their equally thin membranes. Water is carried from the lungs with the expired air; in man it usually amounts to about a cupful in 24 hours. Molecules of other substances are carried out with the breath; those of whiskey, gin, onions, and garlic are among the most vivid of the broadcasts.

Sweat Glands. These glands remove water, salts, traces of nitrogenous substances, and very little carbon dioxide. The amounts especially of water vary greatly with metabolic activity. It is common experience that the sweating incident to high temperature and exercise stimulates drinking of quarts of water.

Liver. The liver may be said to deal with the raw waste products of metabolism since it manufactures the urea from the nitrogenous waste released by all the cells and brought by the blood. Later the urea is released from the liver cells into the blood and carried to the kidney where it becomes the basis of urine in most animals.

Explorations of the Kidney

The knowledge of excretion and regulation has been and is still being built up, especially by experiment and observations upon animals (Fig. 14.7).

The malpighian body of the vertebrate kidneys and the Malpighian tubules of insects were named for Marcello Malpighi (1628–1694), an astute observer whose admiration of perfection in miniature structures was stimulated by those in the kidney.

Although the function of the renal or Bowman's capsule was not known in 1842, Sir William Bowman (1816–1892) had a theory that the renal capsule and glomerulus together might be a kind of filter. Proof of it came with experiment. In 1920 and later years, Dr. Alfred N. Richards performed experiments on frog's kidneys that dispelled any doubt that the capsule and specifically the glomerulus does act as a filter. He obtained a sample of the filtrate as it was being made in the kidneys of the living frog by inserting a fine glass pipette into the renal capsule and drawing out some of the fluid (Fig. 14.7). What he secured contained glucose and other constituents of plasma except the proteins, a real filtrate, essentially a deproteinized plasma.

Studies made by Dr. Homer W. Smith extending over several years (1916–

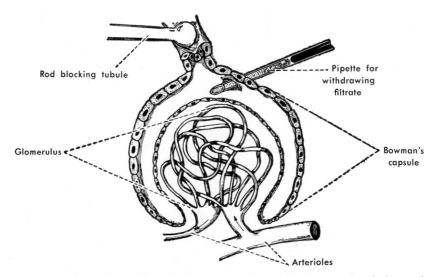

FIG. 14.7. Method used by A. N. Richards in obtaining a sample of glomerular filtrate in the frog's kidney. He inserted a very fine pipette into the individual capsules in the frog's kidney and analyzed what had passed across the membranes. (Courtesy, Gardiner: *General Biology*. New York, The Macmillan Co., 1952.)

1951) have dealt with the relation of the function of the kidneys to the kind of environment in which their owners live, and also with the evolution of the vertebrate kidney in relation to the surrounding fresh or salt water, or the dry land. His discussion of water regulation emphasizes the ecological significance of the kidney, the part it has taken in limiting or extending the distribution of animals.

15
Chemical Regulation—
Endocrine Glands

Chemical Coordination

The bodily activities of living organisms are so coordinated that every plant and animal acts as a unit. Their chemical coordination is carried on mainly by hormones, substances that are moved from one part of the body to another, like messages in letters (Fig. 15.1). Contrasting with this, their nervous coordination is achieved by cells with long processes over which changes (impulses) move rapidly from one end to the other, like messages over a telegraph wire. The relations of the endocrine and nervous systems are complex and intimate.

Hormones are usually concerned with gradual changes in the body: growth, whether to usual or to dwarf or giant size, whether to normal form and symmetry or misshapen; the rate of metabolism, whether oxidation is rapid and temperature high or vice versa; the reproductive functions, those of the sex cells and the structures connected with them, and of the animal as a whole. Together the nervous and endocrine systems carry on a cooperative enterprise, creating in the body an internal environment that is sensitive and adjustable to the world outside.

Nature and Importance of Hormones

Hormones are chemical compounds that activate, maintain, or depress the functions of particular parts or the whole of an organism; they are liberated directly into the blood often functioning far away from their point of origin. The name hormone (Gr., *hormon,* exciting) was first used in 1903 by the British physiologists, Bayliss and Starling, who applied it to a secretion of certain cells in the intestinal wall. Since then it has appeared that the action of some hormones is depressing, while some others under certain circumstances, excite activity and under others depress it.

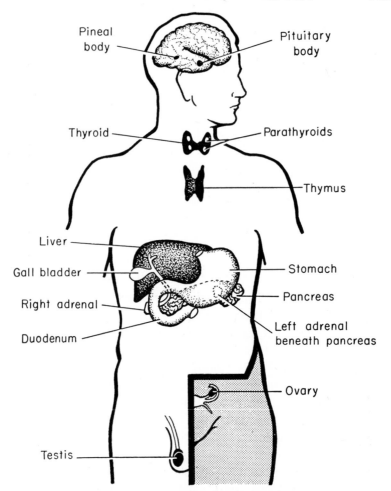

FIG. 15.1. Location of the human endocrine glands. The hypophysis cerebri of this drawing is commonly known as the pituitary gland. The functions of the pineal body, thymus and spleen are incompletely known but may be in some way associated with the endocrines. The total weight of the endocrine glands of the adult human body is about one quarter of a pound.

Hormones are carried wherever the blood goes but act only when they reach their particular targets. The relationships of endocrine glands are close, complex, and often essential to life. When an animal is exposed to cold, nervous stimuli cause one gland (the anterior lobe of the pituitary) to produce a secretion (thyrotrophin) that stimulates another gland (the thyroid) to yield its secretion (thyroxin). This in turn stimulates metabolism with accompanying liberation of heat and energy. This complicated process is covered in the common saying, "I got used to the cold."

One group of endocrine secretions consists of comparatively simple chemical substances (steroids); the other, of complex substances (proteins). They occur in the blood in remarkably minute quantities, and as drugs are extraordinarily powerful. The hormone of the thyroid gland is so potent that one grain of it in circulating human blood will raise the rate of metabolism in an adult by about one-third. Sparsity of only one of the hormones of the anterior pituitary in a child can make it a dwarf, and an oversupply of the same hormone can create a giant. In certain animals and human tribes these conditions have become hereditary; among dogs, the Great Danes are giants and toy Pomeranians are well-formed dwarfs. Much of individuality originates in hormones. They also aid and regulate embryonic development and growth.

Distribution of Hormone Production among Animals

Hormones take part in the control of essential activities in the lives of many invertebrates and of all vertebrates.

Invertebrates. Hormones have been clearly demonstrated in arthropods, especially crustaceans and insects. In each eyestalk of crayfishes and shrimps there is a minute endocrine gland, the sinus gland (Fig. 15.2). Results of experiments indicate that these glands secrete at least five hormones: three that regulate the pigment in the chromatophores (pigment cells) of the skin, one that stimulates the movement of pigment grains into a location in the cell characteristic of them when the eye is adapted to full light, and one that delays molting until a particular time.

The hormonal control of molting in insects has been definitely established.

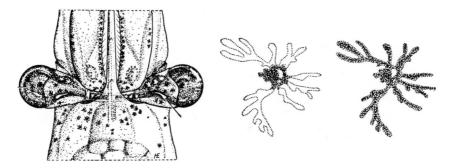

FIG. 15.2. *Left,* Part of the head of a shrimp (*Palaemonetes exilpes*), showing the position of the sinus glands in the eye stalks. They produce hormones which influence the movement of pigment in the cells of the retina when the eyes change from a dark to a light adapted state. *Right,* A diagram illustrating the dispersion and concentration of pigment in cells (chromatophores) when the skin changes from dark to pale color and the reverse; full color effect in a pigment cell occurs when pigment granules occupy the numerous branches of the cell; the least possible display of color in the same cell when the granules are crowded into the center. One cell may contain several kinds of pigment and the granules of each kind may be dispersed and concentrated independently. (*Left,* courtesy, Turner: *General Endocrinology.* Philadelphia, W. B. Saunders Co., 1948.)

It was first discovered in 1922 in the changes of the gypsy moth, Lymantria, from caterpillar to pupa to adult. Since then it has been shown in other insects, among them moths, butterflies, and beetles. When the cerebral ganglia of the brain were removed, the caterpillars failed to pupate even though they were sufficiently mature. However, they did pupate when the ganglia were removed from the head but transplanted into the abdomen. This implanting was effective only if done a few days before pupation would otherwise have begun. The secretions of minute glands, the corpora allata, closely associated with the brain, also take part in the regulation of rates of growth, as in the cockroach, and the changes of form such as from pupa to butterfly (Fig. 15.3). If these are removed from the early nymphal stage of a grasshopper, the nymphal period is shortened, molts are suppressed and adult differentiation begins prematurely. The hormone from the corpora allata, called the *juvenile hormone,* causes insects to remain youthful. There are other hormones, produced by groups of neurosecretory cells in the brain, that stimulate molting and pupation. It appears that some insects are capable of changing their form at any time but are kept from doing so by the hormones circulating in their blood.

Vertebrates. Endocrine secretions are important to vertebrate animals throughout their lives. They are effective not only in the animal in which they develop, but in the bodies of animals into which they may be injected. They may be taken from different species, even from different orders of animals. Extracts of pig thyroid are commonly used for human thyroid deficiency. The

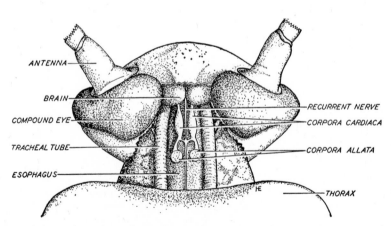

FIG. 15.3. A dissection of the head of a cockroach (*Periplaneta americana*) showing the paired endocrine glands, corpora allata and corpora cardiaca. The corpora allata secrete a hormone that prevents the insect from maturing precociously, i.e., before it has grown to its typical size. The glands can be removed surgically after which the insect becomes a dwarf adult; if extra glands are grafted into an insect it becomes an immature giant. (Courtesy, Turner: *General Endocrinology.* Philadelphia, W. B. Saunders Co., 1948.)

endocrine glands are located in relatively similar positions in all vertebrates (Fig. 15.1).

Endocrine Glands

Nomenclature. Endocrinology is a recent and very important study in which many investigators have joined. New discoveries have suggested new names until each gland and hormone has been christened and rechristened with several names. The International Commission on Anatomical Nomenclature is attempting to clarify this situation.

Study of the Endocrines—An Illustration of the Experimental Method. Endocrinology stands forth among biological subjects as a peculiarly striking example of the successful use of the experimental method of study. The only way to find out what a gland does is to show what occurs when it is removed, thus creating a deficiency of its hormone, or what happens if it is implanted into the body of a healthy animal, or its secretion or an extract is injected thus creating an excess of the hormone. Thousands of experiments have been done. In the pioneer days of endocrinology Charles Berthold made the first experimental demonstration of the chemical effects of one part of the vertebrate body upon another. In 1849 he removed the testes from young cocks and replanting them, found that the usual changes after castration did not occur. In 1855 Claude Bernard put forth the idea that organs liberate special substances into the tissue fluids and coined the phrase "internal secretion." Before these experiments were made, there was only a vague knowledge of chemical control. Although much is still to be learned about endocrines, many of their extraordinarily complex relationships have been clearly demonstrated.

Light has been thrown upon the body at work by experimental surgery upon living animals, especially by removing and transplanting glands. This has been done with great care for the comfort of the animals, and the results have proved highly important contributions to the intelligent treatment of human diseases. That those who have "sugar diabetes" can live out their lives so successfully is wholly due to experiments upon the pancreas of living animals. Goiter, a serious disease of the thyroid gland, has been eliminated in many regions thanks to the results first gained from the experimental treatment of the goiter of fishes (Fig. 15 4). Other experiments include the culture of gland cells outside the body under conditions which allow them to grow and to be examined alive under the microscope.

THYROID GLAND

Form and General Activity. From the lower fishes to man, all vertebrates have a thyroid gland. The human thyroid consists of a pair of lobes, one on each side of the trachea joined by a band that crosses the trachea just below the larynx (Fig. 15.1). It is supplied with many blood and lymph vessels, the

FIG. 15.4. Brook trout (*Salvelinus fontinalis*) with swollen gills and an external goiter, a disease at one time prevalent among carnivorous fishes raised in hatcheries. The disease was finally prevented by food and water containing iodine, largely through the suggestions of Dr. David Marine (1910). This treatment has also been applied with success to certain types of human goiter. (Courtesy, Marine and Lenhart, *J. Exp. Med.* **12**:311–335, 1910.)

former broken into capillaries which surround the follicles that compose the bulk of the gland (Fig. 15.5). The follicles are held together by loose connective tissue. The wall of each one is formed by a single layer of epithelial cells that produce the jellylike colloidal secretion. The activity of the thyroid depends upon the diet, temperature, and conditions of special physiological stress, and is primarily under the control of the pars anterior of the pituitary gland. Sea food with its high content of iodine reduces thyroid activity, and heavy meats, fats, and proteins increase it. It also responds to conditions of the body such as activity of the reproductive organs and to climatic changes.

The varying states of the thyroid, its diseases, and the results of experiments all show its close relation to the general metabolism of the body. High activity of the body, rapid oxidation, and quickened heartbeat all go with an overactive thyroid. The secretion thyroxin ($C_{15}H_{11}O_4NI_4$) has been isolated and synthesized. The adult human body contains a little less iodine than there would be in ten drops of a medical solution of it. There is iodine in the skeleton, muscle, and liver, but the small thyroid gland itself contains about one-fifth of the total iodine content of the body.

Diseases of Deficient Thyroids. Too little thyroid secretion is due to injury or underdevelopment of the gland, to some defect in pituitary control, to accident or disease, and commonly to lack of iodine in the food. However, iodine should not be taken without expert advice, nor should "iodized salt" be put into general use. The latter has nearly disappeared from the markets.

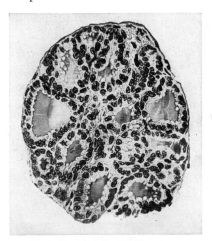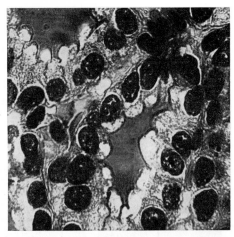

FIG. 15.5. Sections of active thyroid glands of the salamander (*Triturus viridescens*). Thyroid glands are composed of vesicles or follicles lined by a single layer of secretory cells. The cavities of the follicles contain the hormone produced by those cells. This is absorbed into the blood through the walls of the blood vessels between the follicles where there is connective tissue, fat and nerve cells. *Left*, Section of a whole gland under low power. It is about half the size of an apple seed. The white tips of the secretory cells are bulging with secretion. The nuclei appear black. *Right*, Section of a gland under high power. The white tips of cells full of thyroid secretion project into that which (dark) is stored ready to be absorbed by the blood.

GOITER. It is an enlargement of the thyroid gland. There may be too little secretion; in hypothyroid goiter the cells increase in order to bring the secretion to a normal amount; in hyperthyroid goiter the gland secretes an excess usually with a great multiplication of cells. Either of these conditions may occur without an enlargement of the gland.

The association of the thyroid and goiter has long been known. Nearly 2,000 years ago, Juvenal, a Roman poet, remarked on the prevalence of goiter in the Alps. In the 16th century the Swiss physician, Paracelsus, wrote of the seriousness of goiter near the famous music center of Salzburg, and agreed with others that the cases were caused by the mineral content of the drinking water. Long before this, about 1180, another physician, Roger of Palermo, had found a remedy for goiter in the ashes of sponges and seaweed. In 1910, David Marine, a physician in a New York hospital, made a study of the goiter occurring in hundreds of brook trout at a hatchery in the mountains of Pennsylvania. He placed small amounts of iodine in the runways, mixed iodine with their food, and, like Roger of Palermo, included seafoods in their rations (Fig. 15.4). A general recovery soon spread through the population. Following this experiment human subjects were similarly treated in a region of Ohio where goiter was prevalent, and again the goiter disappeared. The localities peculiar to this commonest disease of the thyroid, all of them far from the sea, gave the clue to the need of the gland for iodine, and finally led to the prevention of goiter.

CRETINISM AND MYXEDEMA. These diseases are both caused by thyroid deficiency; cretinism arises before the child is born, infantile myxedema afterward. In either one the children become dwarfs, misshapen, and underdeveloped physically and mentally, unless they are treated with thyroid hormone (Fig. 15.6). Thyroid dwarfs are characteristically malformed (Fig. 15.7); pituitary dwarfs are usually of normal shape but small (Fig. 15.17). Typical myxedema occurs after adolescence.

HIGH AND LOW THYROID TYPES. The hypothyroid type of individual has a low rate of metabolism and is relatively calm and slow-moving; among dogs

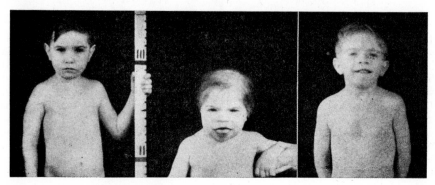

FIG. 15.6. Cretinism, a disease of the thyroid, and the importance of its treatment. *Left,* A normal boy of seven years. *Center,* A cretin of thirteen years, dwarfed physically and mentally subnormal. *Right,* The same boy after receiving thyroid treatment for seventeen months. (Courtesy, Bronstein, *Am. Jour. Med. Sc.* **205:**114, 1943.)

it is the Saint Bernard. The hyperthyroid type, such as the Irish terrier, has a high metabolism, moves rapidly, and is seldom quiet.

Experimental Studies of the Thyroid. Removal of the thyroid glands from rabbits shortly after birth produces dwarfs that are essentially like human cretins. If, while still young, they are fed desiccated thyroid, they will grow to normal size and maturity.

The results of many experiments have shown that the thyroid controls the change of shape that occurs as young animals become mature. This is most spectacular in amphibians which go through a striking metamorphosis from larvae (tadpoles) to adults. Bullfrog tadpoles (*Rana catesbiana*) are literally rushed through metamorphosis, into dwarf frogs by feeding them desiccated thyroid or implanting crystals of iodine in their bodies (Fig. 15.8). The larval tail is absorbed, the legs develop, the mouth widens, and the alimentary canal changes from the long watchspring shape to the more common form of the adult, but the young frog does not increase in size. Merely feeding tadpoles

FIG. 15.7. A "thyroid dwarf"; childhood myxedema. "The Court Dwarf of Don Balthazar Carlos" painted by Velasquez, 1631. The dwarf has the characteristic "saddle nose" and pudgy face and body of thyroid dwarfs. (Courtesy, Boston Museum of Fine Arts.)

with iodine or keeping them in dilute solutions of iodine also hastens metamorphosis.

The skin of human cretins is thickened and dry. If the thyroids are removed from newts (*Triturus viridescens*) their skin likewise becomes thickened and dry (Fig. 15.9). Newts normally shed their skins at intervals but after their thyroids are removed they cease molting and accumulated layers of skin cover the body or hang from it in tatters. The same effect occurs after the pituitary is removed because the pars anterior controls the activity of the thyroid.

PARATHYROID GLANDS

The first important discovery regarding the parathyroid glands was the distinction between them and the thyroid glands on the dorsal side of which they are embedded (Fig. 15.1). In the earlier treatment of goiter the para-

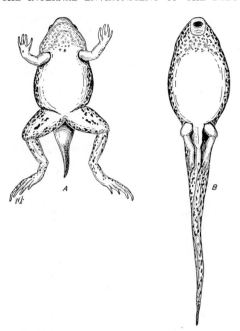

FIG. 15.8. The metamorphosis of tadpoles of bullfrogs (*Rana catesbiana*) is hastened by implanting crystals of iodine in their bodies. *A*, Animal killed two weeks after the crystals were implanted. *B*, The untreated control of the same age. Compare the mouths, tails and paired appendages. In nature bullfrogs are two to three years old before they become adults. (Courtesy, Turner: *General Endocrinology*. Philadelphia, W. B. Saunders Co., 1948.)

thyroids were sometimes removed with the thyroids, with extremely serious results. When the thyroid was removed from cats and dogs, it almost always resulted in tetany, an extreme cramplike contraction of the muscles, and death, but in rabbits the same operation made hardly any disturbance. The reason proved to be that in rabbits one pair of parathyroids was located so far behind the thyroid gland that it was not removed with it. Parathyroids regulate the amount of calcium and phosphorus in the blood and their metabolism in the body (Fig. 15.10). Failure in this regulation produces extreme irritability in the motor nerves and tetany. Tetany may also occur with rickets, a vitamin-D deficiency, the softening of bones being due to lack of calcium.

ADRENAL GLANDS

In man one of the adrenal (suprarenal) glands is in contact with the upper end of each kidney (Figs. 15.1, 15.11) and in animals generally they are near the kidneys. The adrenal gland is actually two glands in one, a central medulla and surrounding cortex.

Medulla. The medulla originates from cells allied to the autonomic nervous

Fig. 15.9. The common spotted newt (*Triturus viridescens*), blackened by the layers of skin that accumulated because a part of its pituitary gland had been removed. Layers of skin began to slip from the head after a duplicate of the missing part of the pituitary had been engrafted into the animal and had activated the thyroid gland to stimulate the molting process. (Photo courtesy A. E. Adams from Adams et al., "The Endocrine Glands and Molting in *Triturus viridescens*," *J. Exp. Zool.*, Aug. 1932.)

system and the cortex from cells near to those that form the sex organs. Epinephrine (or adrenalin) ($C_9H_{13}O_3N$), the hormone of the medulla, is very useful but not essential to life. It has been isolated in pure crystalline form and was the first hormone to be synthesized. Its injection causes a rise in blood pressure and quickened heart rate; more glucose is turned into the blood from the liver and muscles, accompanied by increased muscular power and resistance to fatigue. After making a long series of experiments, an American physiologist, W. B. Cannon, concluded that adrenalin acts as an emergency stimulant in the body, especially for the muscles. It is secreted into the blood in excitement such as fear, pain, or intense effort. Facing the peril of fire a person breaks a window glass with the bare fist; run down by a dog, a cat turns about with hairs up and claws ready. Analysis of the blood of such animals in emotional crises has shown that it contains many times the minute amount of adrenalin (1 part in 1 or 2 billion parts of blood) ordinarily present. At such times the muscles demand more food and more oxygen to combine with it and set energy free. These are provided by glucose, by the increased pumping of the heart, by more rapid breathing, and the higher arterial blood pressure.

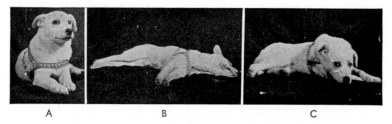

A   B   C

FIG. 15.10. Effects of parathyroid deficiency. *A*, The normal dog before the operation. *B*, The same animal the second day after the removal of the parathyroids in a convulsive condition with twitching muscles. *C*, The same animal 15 minutes after calcium was given to it. The parathyroid glands regulate the amount of calcium and phosphorus in the body. (Courtesy, Turner: *General Endocrinology*. Philadelphia, W. B. Saunders Co., 1948.)

The secretion of the medulla is controlled by the autonomic or involuntary nervous system. The sympathetic fibers of the autonomic nervous system produce a hormone, sympathin, which apparently is distributed to tissues whenever impulses pass over the nerve fibers to them. The reactions to sympathin are similar to those of adrenalin but the two substances are evidently entirely separate. The colors of many fishes are due to pigment cells or chromatophores. Their expansion and contraction are controlled partly by nervous impulses and partly by hormones such as sympathin and adrenalin.

Cortex. The adrenal cortex produces hormones, certain of which are essential to life; if the cortex of both adrenal glands is entirely removed, an animal dies within a few days. Experiments suggest that there are three groups of these hormones, all of which are steroids and some of which have been synthesized. The first group (called the desoxycorticosteroids) controls the

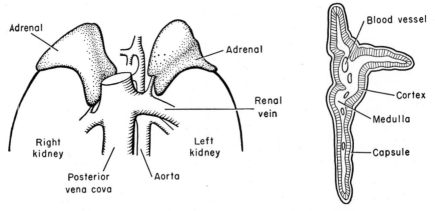

FIG. 15.11. Human adrenal glands. *Left*, A gland caps each kidney but is not a part of it. *Right*, A section of an adrenal. The medulla is within the cortex like the filling in a sandwich. The two parts are different in origin and function; the cortex is essential to life, the medulla is not.

balance of sodium and potassium in the body. The second group (the 11-oxysteroids) includes cortisone, exercises its particular effect on carbohydrate and protein metabolism, and is involved in the series of adaptations called the alarm reaction that occurs after stresses such as shock, extreme cold, and poisons. Cortisone remedies adrenal deficiency either in experimental animals with both cortices removed or in persons suffering from Addison's disease in which the cortices have atrophied. The production of these hormones is under the control of the adrenocorticotrophic hormone (ACTH) of the pars anterior of the pituitary. The third group of hormones is very similar to the sex hormones. Excess production of such hormones, often associated with tumors of the cortex, is responsible for the bearded ladies of the circus.

PANCREAS

Endocrine Glands of the Pancreas and Their Function. Nothing takes the place of the versatile digestive juice of the pancreas as an all-round simplifier of foods that otherwise would be out of reach of the body's metabolism. But the pancreas also contains numerous endocrine glands, literally islands of cells, the isles of Langerhans, that secrete into the blood stream the hormone insulin and possibly lipocaic, a hormone of fat metabolism. Insulin has been called the spark-plug of carbohydrate metabolism because, in some way, it brings about the oxidation of sugar and the subsequent release of potential chemical energy (Fig. 15.12).

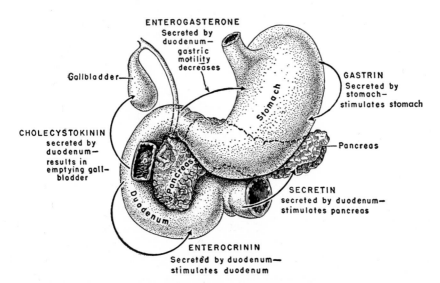

FIG. 15.12. Diagram of the structures from which digestive hormones originate and the parts and processes which they stimulate. (Courtesy, Hunter and Hunter: *College Zoology*. Philadelphia, W. B. Saunders Co., 1949.)

Sugar Diabetes and Insulin Treatment. When the cells in the isles of Langerhans fail to produce insulin, the body cannot use its sugar, no matter how plentiful it is or how well digested. The oxidation of glucose stops, especially in the muscles, and glycogen is no longer stored in the liver and muscles. Sugar accumulates in the blood, is excreted in the urine, and thus is continually thrown away. In the meantime the starving body uses first its fats and then its proteins in the progress of the disease of diabetes mellitus that resulted fatally up to the time when insulin became known. The insulin treatment of diabetes was first used in January 1922. Since then thousands of persons have been able to live successfully by means of it. The saving of all of them has been due to knowledge gained by experiments upon animals.

In 1889 two European physicians, Oscar Minkowski and Joseph von Mering, removed the pancreas from dogs in making studies of digestion. Their caretaker noticed that there were unusual gatherings of flies about the urine of these dogs and when the investigators examined it chemically, they found that it contained quantities of sugar. They immediately tried to remedy the diabetes by feeding the dogs extract of pancreas. But they were without success because they were including the enzyme trypsinogen in the pancreatic juice, which becoming trypsin in the intestine destroyed the insulin, a protein. In 1893, Minkowski published an account of the whole matter. Many experiments followed, mostly unsuccessful because of the destruction of the insulin. Later experiments brought more facts and more clues. Finally, Banting, Best, Macleod, and Collip, investigators at the University of Toronto, discovered a successful treatment and began it in 1922. Banting tied off the pancreatic duct temporarily and, although this brought on bad symptoms, those of diabetes were not among them. Collip destroyed the trypsin with alcohol and acid and thus secured an effective extract of pancreas that included insulin. This is essentially the same remedy which has been used ever since. No cure for diabetes has been discovered and the extract can be taken only by injection.

GASTROINTESTINAL HORMONES

These hormones work in series, each one preparing for the chemical action of another secretion (Fig. 15.12).

Gastrin. The arrival of food in the stomach stimulates the secretion of gastrin by the cells in its lining. Gastrin in turn acts as a stimulant to the production of the gastric juice.

Secretin. When stimulated by the arrival of an acid food-mass from the stomach, cells in the intestinal lining secrete the hormone secretin into the blood. This in turn stimulates the pancreas to produce pancreatic juice and the liver to secrete bile.

Cholecystokinin and Delivery of Bile. Acid food from the stomach stimulates other lining cells of the duodenum to secrete this hormone into the blood. This stimulates the muscles of the gallbladder to contract and pour bile into the intestine.

Enterogastrone, the Antiulcer Hormone. After partly digested food or chyme leaves the stomach, the secretion of gastric juice and the contractions of its muscles are slowed or stopped. Nervous mechanisms are probably involved, but experiments have shown that such rest periods of the stomach are caused by enterogastrone. Its production in the walls of the intestine is stimulated by the arrival of the food, mainly by the neutral fat.

Enterocrinin. Extracts made from intestinal lining will stimulate the release of secretion stored in the lining. The hormone is called enterocrinin.

PITUITARY GLAND

Appearance, Position, and Parts. The human pituitary gland (hypophysis) is the size and shape of a large pea. It is located almost exactly in the center of the head in a cradlelike space on the floor of the cranium above the soft palate (Figs. 15.13, 15.14). It is formed by two outgrowths, an anterior part which grows upward from the roof of the embryonic mouth and becomes the pars anterior, pars tuberalis, and pars intermedia, and a posterior part formed by a downgrowth of the developing brain which becomes the pars nervosa. It remains permanently connected with the brain by the pituitary stalk through which it is well supplied with blood vessels and nerves.

The early anatomists named the gland pituitary (L., *pituitarius,* phlegm) because they thought that its nearness to the nasal cavities meant that it poured a secretion into them. It is commonly known as the master gland since it regulates growth, controls other endocrine glands, and affects tissues and organs. With some variations in structure it is present in the vertebrates from the lower fishes through the mammals.

Functions of the Pars Anterior. Although the manufacture of as many as 10 to 15 hormones has been attributed to the pars anterior, the most recent evidence indicates that it probably produces seven. Three of them influence the development and function of the reproductive organs, the ovaries, testes, and the mammary glands. Three of its other hormones affect metabolism, stimulating growth, regulating the thyroid gland and the cortices of the adrenal glands (Table 15.1). The seventh, not completely established, may be associated with the formation of red blood cells. All of them are proteins; three are glycoproteins, i.e., combinations of a carbohydrate and a protein; and three are simple proteins. Several have been extracted in fairly pure form, but none has been synthesized. It is now believed that the influence of the pars anterior on carbohydrate and fat metabolism which was formerly assigned to hormones called diabetogenic, pancreatrophic, parathyrotrophic,

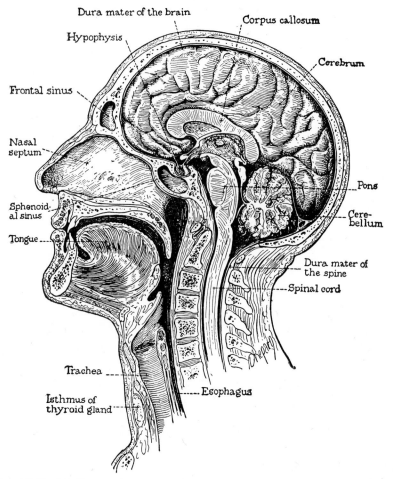

FIG. 15.13. Median section of the head showing the location of the pituitary gland (or hypophysis) in relation to other parts of the head. (Courtesy, Clendening: *The Human Body*. New York, Alfred A. Knopf, 1930.)

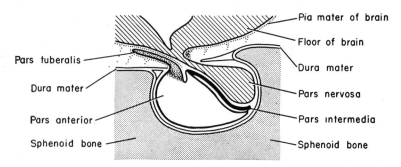

FIG. 15.14. Median section of the pituitary, its parts and their relation to the brain and cranium.

Table 15.1

HORMONES OF THE PARS ANTERIOR OF THE PITUITARY GLAND
GONADOTROPHIC HORMONES

Name	Symbol	Chemical Nature	Main Functions
Follicle-stimulating hormone	FSH	Glycoprotein	Stimulates development of 1) egg-containing follicles in ovaries, which produce estrogen, 2) sperm cells in testes
Luteinizing hormone	LH	Glycoprotein	Stimulates development of corpora lutea (after ovulation), which produce progesterone
or Interstitial-cell-stimulating hormone	*or* ICSH		Stimulates interstitial cells of testes to produce male sex hormone, testosterone
Prolactin Luteotrophic or lactogenic hormone	LTH	Simple protein	Stimulates 1) development of corpora lutea which produce progesterone, 2) secretion of mammary glands; retards development of follicles in ovaries

METABOLIC HORMONES

Name	Symbol	Chemical Nature	Main Functions
Growth hormone	GH	Simple protein	Promotes growth with increase of water and protein content in the whole animal with a decrease of fat; has marked influence on cartilage and bone of skeleton; causes hypertrophy of thymus
Thyrotrophic hormone	TSH	Glycoprotein	Stimulates development of thyroid gland and its production of thyroxin
Adrenocorticotrophic hormone	ACTH	Simple protein	Stimulates cortices of adrenal glands to secrete cortical hormones, e.g., cortisone *et al.;* has growth-retarding action and so is antagonistic to the growth-promoting action of the growth hormone; causes involution of thymus

to name only a few, is exerted by the growth and adrenocorticotrophic hormones.

The hormones of the endocrine glands (gonads, thyroid, and adrenal cortices), whose production is largely controlled by hormones from the pars anterior of the pituitary, also exercise some control on the production of these controlling hormones by the pars anterior. For example, the thyrotrophic hormone (TSH) of the pars anterior stimulates the thyroid to produce thyroxin and release it into the blood stream; in turn a high level of thyroxin hormone (TH) in the blood causes the pars anterior to reduce its production of thyrotrophin (TSH), while a low level causes it to increase its production. This see-saw relation also occurs between the gonadotrophic hormones secreted by the pars anterior (FSH and LH or ICSH) and the sex hormones secreted by the gonads (estrogen and progesterone of ovaries and testosterone of testes) and between the adrenocorticotrophic hormone (ACTH) of the pars anterior and the cortical hormones of the adrenal cortices.

After removal of the pituitary (hypophysectomy) of young animals, the skeleton stops growing, the sex organs do not develop, and the thyroid and cortices of the adrenal glands gradually shrink. However, if a fragment of pars anterior is then transplanted daily into these animals, they will resume growing, the sex organs will develop, and the thyroid and adrenal cortices become normal. Extracts of pars anterior have been prepared which will correct one or another defect caused by hypophysectomy; some of these extracts also cause specific effects upon normal animals. Young rats and puppies thus treated will grow to almost double the size of others in the same litter (Fig. 15.15). Even immature mice or rats implanted with fresh pars anterior or injected with gonad-stimulating hormones at weaning time will become sexually mature in three to five days.

GIANTS, ACROMEGALICS, AND DWARFS. Giants and acromegalics have over-active pituitaries (pars anterior) (Fig. 15.16). Giantism begins in very early childhood, acromegaly in adult life. In acromegaly the nose and lower jaw become abnormally prominent and the forehead and the skin thickened. Individuals dwarfed by underactivity of the pituitary are of two types; one kind has a body like a normal child's (Fig. 15.17), the type of dwarf usually seen on the stage and in circuses; the other has a short, heavy body overlaid with fat.

Function of the Pars Intermedia. In man the function of the pars intermedia is not known. In frogs, toads, lizards, and some fishes it produces a hormone, intermedin, which disperses the pigment in melanophores, the ameba-shaped cells which contain black pigment (Fig. 15.18). Tadpoles from which the pituitary has been removed are very pale but regularly darken when the pars intermedia of normal tadpoles is implanted into them. By an operation on embryos of the small spring-peepers (*Hyla crucifer*) the pars

FIG. 15.15. The effect of extract of pars anterior of the pituitary upon the growth of dogs. Normal dog and giant of the same litter that has been treated with injections of the extract of the gland. (From *The Living Body,* Copyrighted 1952 by Henry Holt and Company. Reprinted with their permission.)

intermedia can be completely suppressed while the remainder of the pituitary continues to develop. In consequence the tadpoles will metamorphose into frogs with silvery-colored skin.

Regarding the relation of the pituitary to color, it is to be remembered that adrenalin also concentrates the pigment in amphibian melanophores. If one cubic centimeter of a solution of one part adrenalin to 10,000 parts of water is injected into the dorsal lymph space of the leopard frog (*Rana pipiens*), it will begin to turn pale in ten minutes and shortly afterward will become thoroughly pallid, remaining so for a day or two.

Functions of the Pars Tuberalis. The function of the pars tuberalis in man and other vertebrates is unknown.

Functions of the Pars Nervosa. The pars nervosa stores and releases at least two hormones, pitressin and pitocin, often included together as pituitrin both probably produced by neurosecretory cells of the hypothalamus of the brain. Pitressin raises the blood pressure by directly stimulating the contraction of smooth muscle in the arteries and arterioles. Adrenalin achieves the same result but by the way of the autonomic (involuntary) nervous system. Pitressin acts to conserve water in the body. When animals are kept on short water rations there is so much antidiuretic substance secreted that it appears in the urine. This holding of water in the

FIG. 15.16. Giantism is produced by overactivity of the pituitary gland (pars anterior) beginning during the natural growth period. Photograph of Robert Wadlow of Alton, Illinois, taken with a man of average height, in a tailor's shop in St. Louis in 1939. His school record was excellent and his personality of high character but he was never physically vigorous and very susceptible to infections from which he died, July 15, 1940, at age 22. In that year he was 8 feet 11 inches and weighed 491 pounds. The record of his growth is the best authenticated of any giantism. (By special permission of Harold F. Wadlow from Fadner and Wadlow: *Gentleman Giant.* Boston, Bruce Humphries, Inc., 1944.)

body during a time of sparse income is one more way in which the internal environment is kept wet. Extracts of pars nervosa are given to check the flow of urine that occurs in diabetes insipidus (Chap. 14, Excretion). The pitocin principle of the extract of pars nervosa is administered as a stimulant to the contraction of smooth muscle of the uterus during childbirth. Pitocin also stimulates the smooth muscle of the intestine and bladder. It has now been synthesized.

NERVOUS CONTROL OF ENDOCRINES

The functions of the pituitary and adrenal glands are at least partially controlled by the nervous system. The thyroid has a rich nerve supply, but there is no evidence of nervous control of its secretion, although nervous tension accompanies high thyroid activity.

Destruction of the pars nervosa of the pituitary results in increase of urine, the consequence of the removal of the antidiuretic effect of pitressin. The same thing occurs after cutting the nerves leading from the hypothalamus of

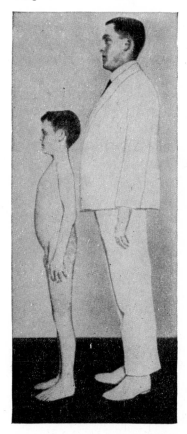

Fig. 15.17. Dwarfism accompanies extreme underactivity of the pituitary (pars anterior) beginning in childhood. The type of pituitary dwarf shown in this figure has the proportions of a normal, not unattractive person. He is 21 years of age. The man on the right is 5 feet, 7 inches tall. (From *The Living Body,* Copyright 1952 by Henry Holt and Company. Reprinted with their permission.)

the brain to the pars nervosa even though the pars nervosa itself is untouched. And since tumors in the hypothalamus result in abnormalities of growth, it is probable that the pars anterior and hypothalamus are associated. The theory concerning the role of the adrenal medulla under stress of excitement suggests that the medulla is being controlled by the nervous system, but this is not known.

Functions of Endocrines in the Sex Organs

In addition to producing eggs and sperm cells the ovaries and testes also secrete hormones that affect allied structures and also secondary sex characteristics such as voice, size, and coloration. Other endocrine glands, especially the thyroid and pituitary, also have a controlling influence on both ovaries and testes.

The antlers of male deer and the brighter colors of male birds are familiar secondary sex characters. If the testes are removed (castration) from a young deer, no antlers grow; a castrated cock has a small comb and a faulty crow or none. In such animals the secondary sex characters are lacking, all repro-

FIG. 15.18. Common grass frogs (*Rana pipiens*): one shows the natural light brown and dark spots; the color of the nearly black one is the result of the powerful stimulation of the pigment cells by the injected intermedin, the hormone of the pars intermedia of the pituitary. When colors are pale or hidden the pigment granules are clumped in the center of the cell and its branches are invisible (Fig. 15.2). Injections of intermedin cause the granules to move into the branches and the animal becomes deep brown or blackish. (Courtesy, *Therapeutic Notes*. Detroit, Mich., Parke Davis & Co., April, 1935.)

ductive structures are reduced, and the body often takes on fat. These changes are caused by the absence of the hormone testosterone ($C_{19}H_{30}O_2$) thought to be produced by cells (interstitial) that are packed in between the tubules of the testes in which the sperm cells develop.

Estrogen, a female sex hormone, is produced by follicular cells surrounding the egg in the ovary, and is responsible for the estrus or heat in female mammals. If the ovaries are removed from young females, they remain sexually immature. On the other hand, if estrogen is injected into these castrated females, the usual maturing is resumed. If it is injected into normal immature females, the secondary sex structures and the estrous periods are hastened into full development but the ovary is not affected and the development of the eggs is not hurried. Another ovarian hormone, progesterone, is produced by the corpus luteum formed from the cells of the Graafian follicle which are left after an egg is shed from the ovary. Estrogen and progesterone, working together, prepare the uterus for receiving the young embryo (Fig. 15.19). These two hormones also stimulate the enlargement of the mammary glands in which the secretion of milk is later induced by the lactogenic hormone of the pars anterior of the pituitary gland (figures and further discussion of the sex organs, Chap. 18).

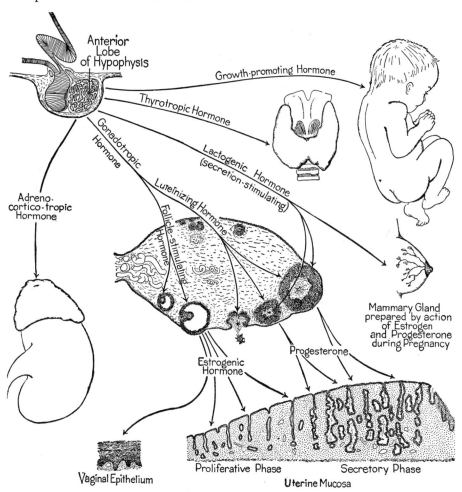

Fig. 15.19. Diagram showing some of the hormones produced in the anterior lobe of the pituitary gland, with especial emphasis upon those taking part in the regulation of the cyclic activities of the female reproductive organs. (Courtesy, Patten: *Human Embryology,* ed. 2. Philadelphia, The Blakiston Co., 1953.)

Uncertainties

The pineal gland located in the middorsal part of the brain is less than half an inch in length and is shaped like a pine cone from which it takes its name (Fig. 15.1). It has excited curiosity for more than three centuries, since the time when it was called the seat of the soul. Its large blood supply and appearance have aroused the suspicion that it may be an endocrine gland and it is often included in figures as an uncertain member of that group. No convincing evidence has confirmed this or established any other function for it.

Thymus Gland. The thymus lies beneath the breastbone in most mammals,

(Fig. 15.1). It is relatively large in infants but becomes much smaller with adolescence. It has been suspected of being one of the endocrine glands, but never proven to be though it is often placed with them. Like the tonsils and other lymphatic structures, it is concerned with the production of lymphocytes.

16

Conduction and Coordination – Nervous System

All living matter is in a unique way excitable and responsive to changes that go on inside and outside of it. Much has been learned about its awareness and response, but a great amount remains to be discovered. Facts concerning it that are clearly shown in laboratory observations and experiments are hard to admit when they are met in the courtroom and the church.

Through our nervous systems and sense organs we stand on the earth and explore the universe. The light of the stars produces chemical changes in the sensory cells of the eye; these start changes in the nerves and brain, and we have ideas about the stars. We know a good deal about those chemical processes, but of the making of the ideas we know almost nothing.

Response and Conduction

Touch an ameba at one point and a wave of motion sweeps over the animal as it gradually draws away. But watch a smart dog pick up the sound of a footstep, the scent of a rabbit! In the ameba the changes spread slowly through generalized protoplasm; in the dog they are received, conducted, and interpreted with great speed through the consummate performance of the nervous system.

Response. It would take an extraordinary light to excite the nerve cells whose fibers compose the optic nerve. On the other hand, an unbelievably faint one will stimulate the rod cells in the retina of a dark-adapted eye because they are specialized receptors of light. The light changes them and the changes are communicated to the nerve cells.

A receptor is a group of cells, one cell, or part of a cell that is particularly sensitive to certain stimuli (Fig. 16.1). External receptors receive stimuli from an animal's surroundings, temperature, light, sound, touch and others.

Proprioceptors (e.g., muscle spindles) receive stimuli arising within the body, such as pain and variations in the tension of a muscle or tendon. Receptors are changed chemically or physically, often in both ways, by stimulation. These stimuli set up impulses, actually changes going through the nerve cells with which the receptors are in contact. Thus the receptors bring to the nerve cells the raw materials with which they work. Many receptors, such as those of the muscle sense of position, are associated with nerves that end in the spinal cord and the cerebellum where their activity is below the

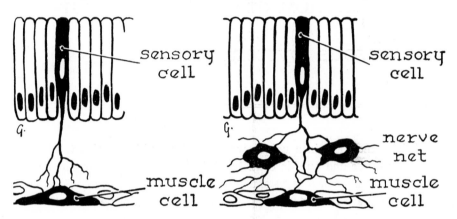

FIG. 16.1. Diagrams of simple associations of receptor and effector cells, those that receive the stimulus and those that act in response to it. *Left,* A receptor cell (sensory) in direct contact with an effector; *right,* a more complex type in which conducting cells (nerve net) act as middle men. Such arrangements occur in simpler animals, e.g., sea anemones. (Courtesy, Parker: *Elementary Nervous System.* Philadelphia, J. B. Lippincott and Co., 1919.)

region of consciousness. We do not decide to turn over in our sleep. Other receptors such as sight and hearing are intimately connected with the higher centers of the brain. Sense organs are parts of the nervous system but are more conveniently discussed in another chapter (Chap. 17).

Conduction. A pinch at one end of a fresh frog muscle immediately starts waves of contraction moving toward the opposite end. When a cell is injured by a microdissection needle a "death wave" begins at the point of injury and quickly overspreads the cell. This is the conduction that is characteristic of all protoplasm. In paramecia and some other protozoans conductile fibrils connect the basal bodies of the cilia with each other and with a center of coordination near the mouth (Fig. 16.2). Conduction reaches its highest development and speed in the nerve impulse.

Nerve Cell

Characteristics. Nerve cells or neurons are the basic units of structure in the nervous system. Each neuron has threadlike extensions called fibers, sometimes of extraordinary length. Currents of energy, the impulses, move along these fibers and by means of them messages are flashed to other neurons. The nervous system contains millions of neurons like electric wires which are protected and insulated from one another except at the tips of their fibers (Fig. 16.3). The body of the neuron is relatively large. Their unique Nissl granules or bodies (named for the neurologist, Nissl) disappear when

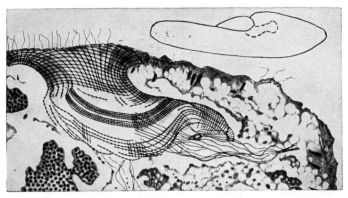

FIG. 16.2. The neuromotor system of a paramecium. The unified action of the cilia on the surface of its body and food passage is controlled through the extraordinarily fine fibrils that connect them. Changes proceed rapidly over these fibrils and they conduct them as our own nerve cells do. A paramecium takes in food because its cilia "agree" to wave it into the mouth. An outline of paramecium with the mouth, gullet and posterior end of the body in the same position as in the greatly magnified view. A cut through the body. The sharp lines of the conducting fibrils are shown in the right half of the mouth and gullet and a particle of food trapped among the fibrils at the lower end. These fibrils are visible only with skilled preparation. To the naked eye the whole animal is only a minute white fleck in the water. (Courtesy, Lund. Univ. of California Pubs. in Zoology, Vol. 39, 1935.)

the neurons are fatigued or injured by toxins as in poliomyelitis (infantile paralysis), but are restored by rest or removal of the harmful agent if the damage is not already too severe. There are two kinds of fibers, dendrites through which nerve impulses come into the cell and the axon through which they leave it (Fig. 16.3). In their evolution as in their embryological development neurons originate from epithelial cells from which processes grow outward.

Dendrites are commonly short with treelike branches. But there are exceptions: certain of the neurons whose cell bodies are located in the ganglia of the spinal nerves may have a dendrite several feet long. These dendrites carry incoming messages of sensation from skin, muscle, and other parts of the body and compose a section of all branches of the spinal nerves. Such dendrites are always figured in diagrams of a reflex arc (Figs. 16.9, 16.11). The

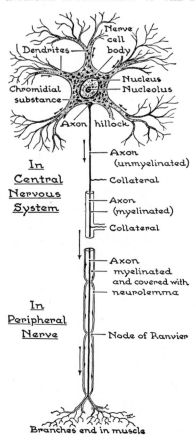

FIG. 16.3. Diagram of a multipolar nerve cell, i.e., one with more than one dendrite (process that conducts an impulse into the cell body). Most of the nerve cells in the human body are multipolar. The processes of nerve cells have contacts or synapses; branches of the axon of one cell in contact with the dendrites of another or with the cell body of another or with both. Such contacts are essential for the coordination of the body and for memory. (Courtesy, Ham: *Histology*, ed. 2. Philadelphia, J. B. Lippincott Co., 1953.)

main distinction between dendrites and axons is a purely functional one: the dendrites conduct impulses toward the body of the nerve cell and the axons away from it.

Axons are usually long, often several feet, since in man many of them extend from the spinal cord to the toes. The axon ends in a brush of short branches which in the case of muscle may actually pierce the cell membranes. The axon of the spinal ganglion cell gives off branches (collaterals) along its course in the spinal cord, e.g., one at the level of the fourth and another at the fifth rib, ending in a synapse with the dendrites of other nerve cells. Many muscle cells are stimulated by impulses from one or a few nerve cells (Fig. 16.4). One pinprick in the back starts impulses speeding over several dendrites via axons and collaterals to the dozens of muscles that one uses in jerking away from the pin.

How are nerve fibers nourished, especially the slender axons that reach far from the cell body? Whether nerve fibers are inside the brain and spinal cord or in the nerves outside, most of them are clothed with a soft, fatty, non-cellular substance, the myelin sheath. Outside the brain and cord, that is, in

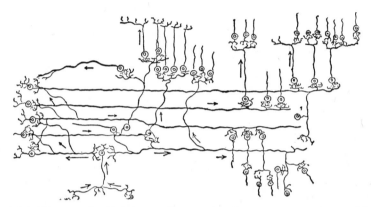

FIG. 16.4. Diagram showing how a few nerve cells may communicate with many others. Responses to one pin prick travel far. Sitting on a pin may cause a high jump. (From *The Living Body,* Copyrighted 1952 by Henry Holt and Company. Reprinted with their permission.)

the nerves, each fiber is further protected by a cellular sheath, the neurilemma (Fig. 16.3). The nerve cells within the brain and cord are supported by the processes of neuroglial cells. These resemble nerve cells but have no conducting power. The fatty myelin causes the whiteness of nerves and the white matter of the brain and cord, which is composed of great numbers of myelinated fibers. Regions where no myelin is present appear gray, as in the gray matter of the brain and cord and in certain nerves of the autonomic nervous system.

Regeneration of Nerve Fibers. A nerve fiber may be completely severed, yet the part between the cell body and the cut may remain alive and regenerate after the injury. On the side of the cut separated from the cell body the fiber disintegrates since no cell body is left to nourish it, but its cellular neurilemma tube persists and takes a remarkable part in the repair. As the regenerating fiber grows longer, it actually enters the empty neurilemma sheath and finally extends through its whole length. Later a new myelin sheath is formed around each fiber, and with this healing of many fibers the function of the nerve is finally restored. Sprouting nerve fibers sometimes cross a distance of several millimeters to reach the neurilemma sheath without which effective regeneration does not occur. In facial paralysis the hypoglossal nerve may be cut and its proximal end sutured to the distal end of the facial nerve. The hypoglossal nerve will then regenerate along the pathway of the facial nerve and will control the facial muscles (Table 16.1).

Ganglia, Nerves, and Neuroglia

A ganglion is a group of nerve cell bodies. In invertebrates, the ventral nerve chain is a series of ganglia connected by nerves (Figs. 16.5, 16.6). In

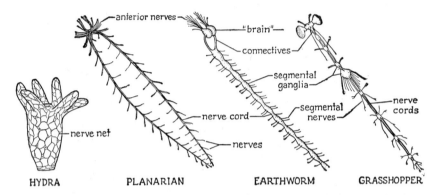

FIG. 16.5. Nervous systems of representative invertebrates; except in hydra, they are on the ventral side of the body, each one a series of ganglia connected by nerves. They show the segmentation that is characteristic of the central nervous systems and very evident in the arrangement of the human spinal nerves. (Courtesy, Storer: *General Zoology,* ed. 2. New York, McGraw-Hill Book Co., Inc., 1949.)

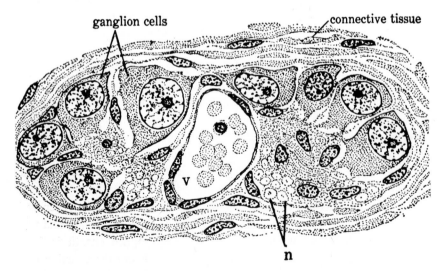

FIG. 16.6. A small ganglion (autonomic). A cross section showing the bodies of eight large nerve cells; *n,* cut ends of fibers of nerve cells; *v,* blood vessel with blood cells. The ganglion is enclosed in a sheath of connective tissue. (Courtesy, Nonidez and Windle: *Textbook of Histology,* ed. 2. New York, McGraw-Hill Book Co., Inc., 1953.)

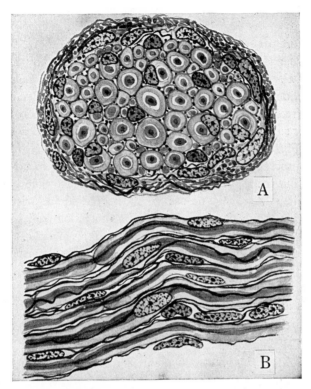

Fig. 16.7. A nerve from a kitten's tongue. *A,* Cross section showing the cut ends of nerve cell fibers. In each one the dark center is the axon; the pale ring around it is the sheath. The nerve is enclosed in a sheath of connective tissue. *B,* Longitudinal section. (Courtesy, Nonidez and Windle: *Textbook of Histology,* ed. 2. New York, McGraw-Hill Book Co., Inc., 1953.)

the vertebrates ganglia are prominent in the dorsal roots of the spinal nerves.

Nerves are bundles of nerve cell fibers that convey sensory and motor impulses between the brain and spinal cord and other parts of the body. Sensory nerves contain fibers that conduct impulses from the sense receptors to the cord or brain, e.g., the optic nerve from the eye. Motor nerves contain fibers that conduct impulses from the brain and cord to muscles or glands. The trunks of the spinal nerves contain both sensory and motor fibers, as do some of the cranial nerves (Table 16.1).

Conduction—the Nerve Impulse

The nerve impulse is not yet understood. The statements that follow may apply to it as a whole or only to a process which accompanies it.

The nerve impulse is an electrochemical process that passes through a neuron. It represents conduction at its highest development and speed. The impulse enters the cell through the dendrites and passes through the cell body and axon. Its rate of movement varies in different animals and within different nerves of the same animal; in warm-blooded animals it may travel 300 feet or more per second, about the speed of a pistol shot.

Experiments and refined measurements have shown that the impulse is not a purely electrical current as was formerly thought. It is an electro-chemical reaction involving the consumption of oxygen, production of carbon dioxide, the freeing of heat, and modification (depolarization) of electrical charges on the surface membrane of the nerve fiber, followed quickly by their restoration (Fig. 16.8). One such change starts another one just ahead and thus the process travels along a fiber. It is something like a fuse burning along a wire but the nerve fiber is in no way harmed by the passing of the impulse. An impulse cannot be started unless the stimulus is of a certain intensity, but beyond that the strength of the stimulation makes no difference in the speed of the impulse. The stimulus is like a spark that may start a small fire or a large one. The processes in the nerve impulse are in some ways similar to those of muscular contraction. The nervous tissue, however, expends an extraordinarily small amount of energy compared to muscle.

Nerve cells are not easily fatigued. Impulses pass over a nerve cell sepa-

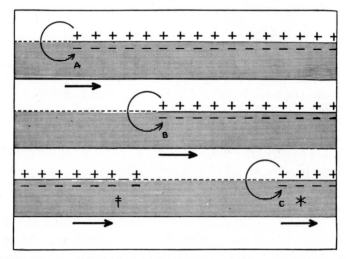

FIG. 16.8. Diagram illustrating the membrane theory according to which the nervous impulse is an electrochemical process that passes through a nerve cell. The resting nerve fiber is polarized, that is, the outside is positively charged, and the inside negatively charged. *A, B, C,* A stimulus passing along a fiber involves a change in the membrane and a loss of polarization. In an interval of from one to five one-thousandths of a second later the fiber becomes repolarized again (±) and the fiber is ready for another impulse to pass over it. In any given nerve, stimulus of a sense organ, perhaps a voice that is heard, results in hundreds of nerve impulses each one on a nerve cell fiber that is insulated by its sheath from others beside it. (By permission from *Biology: Its Human Implications,* 2nd. ed., by Hardin. Copyright, 1952. W. H. Freeman and Company.)

rately and in quick succession like bullets from a machine gun. The time between them is the interval of restoration of the electrical charges, called the refractory period because it is the instant when progress is balked for about one to five thousandths of a second.

Association of Nerve Cells by Synapses

Synapses are points of contact between nerve cells (Figs. 16.9, 16.10). In passing from cell to cell every impulse must go through a synapse, but it can do so in only one direction. (This is in contrast to the movement of an impulse through the axons and other parts of individual nerve cells which experiment has shown may be either toward the cell body or away from it.) A synapse is a junction of resistance through which impulses pass more slowly than along the nerve fibers. The passage of impulses varies in different synapses and in different physiological conditions of the same synapse. It may be rapid and easy or it may be almost or completely stopped. This is true in the brain when words escape one's memory, then suddenly return. By their selective resistance synapses determine that the proper muscles reply to certain stimuli in an orderly fashion while others remain inactive. They are, at least in part, the basis of the relative quickness of accustomed reaction and thinking and also of relative slowness or nervous fatigue.

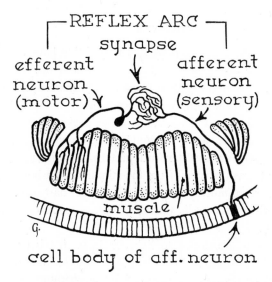

FIG. 16.9. Synapses, the places of communication between nerve cells. Diagram of the synapse of two nerve cells of the earthworm. A change occurring in a sensory cell in the skin is conducted over the axon to its end branches that are intertwined with the dendrites of the motor cell. From there it passes through the cell body and axon of the motor cell to the muscle. At the synapse the fibers appear continuous but observation has shown that they are only in contact. (After Parker. Courtesy, Ham: *Histology*, ed. 2. Philadelphia, J. B. Lippincott and Co., 1953.)

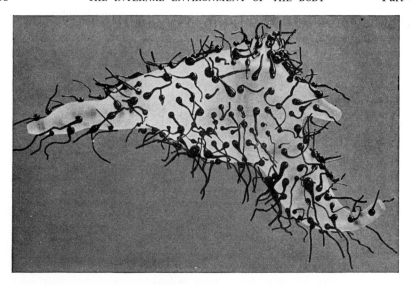

FIG. 16.10. Photograph of a model of the body of a nerve cell from the dorsal (or sensory) horn of the cat's spinal cord. It shows the enormous number of fibers of nerve cells whose end bulbs are in *synaptic* relation with this cell. The model was made by fitting together individual models made from serial sections of the cell. (After Haggar and Barr. Courtesy, Ham: *Histology,* ed. 2. Philadelphia, J. B. Lippincott Co., 1953.)

Tropisms, Responses, and Reflexes

Tropisms and reflexes are responses to stimuli that have a definite standardized pattern. Tropisms make up almost the whole behavior of plants and lower animals. One sunflower plant turns toward the sun; all sunflower plants respond to the sun in the same way. Turn a bright light on a cockroach and it will scuttle to the nearest shadow; any other cockroach would do the same. Almost anybody chokes when a crumb starts down his windpipe; and all chokes have a more or less standard pattern. Tropisms are movements of the whole body toward or away from the stimulus, as a housefly turns toward the light. Reflexes are more often movements of a part of the body, the flick of a cat's ear when its edge is touched, the snapback of one's hand at the touch of a spark.

Tropisms. Insects are drawn to light or dark, that is, they are positively or negatively phototropic to light. But they are so physiologically attuned that their reactions to light are changed by temperature and humidity, and vary with particular phases of their lives. In the mating flight the queen honeybee rises for the first time in her life, high into the sunshine, and for only the second time she flies with the swarm on a brilliant day. Outside of these two occasions, both concerned with the reproduction of her species, a queen bee stays in complete darkness within the hive.

Responses, Unlearned and Learned. Reflexes are the prompt responses of muscle, either voluntary or involuntary (Fig. 16.11). Naturally they are unlearned actions, such as the wink of the eyelids at a flash of light. Learned responses may be established through the conditioning of unlearned ones, and are then called conditioned reflexes or responses. Human behavior is largely made up of reflexes. They begin at birth with the first breathing, a response to an accumulation of carbon dioxide and lack of oxygen in the

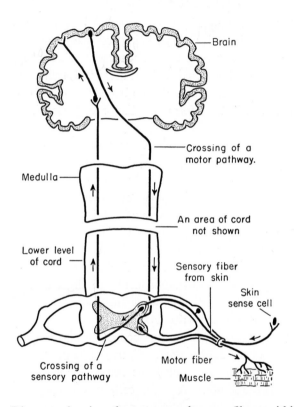

Fig. 16.11. Diagram showing the courses of nerve fibers within sections of spinal nerves, and in nerve cord and brain. A reflex response is represented on the lower right side. It involves: a sensory cell carrying an impulse from the skin to the cord and a motor cell conducting the impulse to the muscle which then contracts. This response may occur without association with the brain. The diagram also shows the course of responses that are associated with the brain. An impulse enters the cord on a sensory fiber. In the cord this passes to the fiber of another cell, and upward over a succession of cells to the cortex of the brain. There, it passes to the fiber (dendrite) of another cell and on through a succession of cells finally reaching the one that bears it along to the muscle. The way upward is the sensory pathway; the way downward is the motor pathway. The diagram shows the crossing of cell fibers from the right to the left side of the nerve cord in the sensory (ascending) pathway and from the left to the right in the motor (descending) pathway. The right foot is pricked and moves but the order to do this comes from the left side of the brain.

blood. This, like other true reflexes, is an experience common to all individuals of one species or to many species within a large group. A young mammal sucks milk whether it is cat, whale, or human. Other pure reflexes are the quick closure of the eyelid when something comes near the eye; the sudden pullback of the hand that is pinched; the sharp recovery of balance lost in a stumble.

Conditioned responses, formerly called conditioned reflexes, were demonstrated by Ivan Pavlov (1849–1936), a Russian physiologist. Over and over he attracted a dog's attention by the sound of a bell, then gave it food, and observed the flow of its saliva. After being fed many times at the ringing of the bell, then the bell was rung but no food was offered. In such cases, the bell alone stimulated a flow of saliva from the dog's mouth. Pavlov christened the response a conditioned reflex but the better name, conditioned response, is taking its place. It is habit formation like eating, sleeping, and waking at definite times.

The Functional Unit—the Reflex Arc or Reflex Response. The action of a great number of reflexes never goes higher than various levels of the spinal cord, never enters the brain at all. Many that seem simple actually involve many nerves and muscles and are very complex. One may touch a hot iron with one's hand and pull it away, skew the body suddenly, and step back. The action is all reflex of which the brain is notified only by means of associated nerve cells. One of the simplest of human reflexes is the knee-jerk. This is well known, not only as an example of a simple reflex, but as the one used in routine tests of nervous adjustments. A slight blow on the kneecap (actually on the patellar ligament) when the legs are crossed will normally cause the foot to jerk forward. The jerk will not occur if the sensory roots of the spinal nerves are damaged, as in locomotor ataxia (tabes dorsalis) or if the gray matter of the cord is damaged, as in infantile paralysis.

The basic unit of function called the reflex arc is typically carried out by five parts: (1) a sensory receptor cell; (2) a conductor, the sensory nerve cell; (3) a connecting or adjustor nerve cell (in the cord); (4) a conductor, the motor nerve cell; and (5) an effector, muscle or gland cell (Figs. 16.9, 16.11).

Actual Conditions of the Reflex Response. The usual diagram of a reflex arc shows a single sensory nerve cell by which an impulse is transmitted directly to a single motor cell or with an adjustor cell between them. Actually, in all vertebrate animals, the simplest stimulus starts impulses through several sensory fibers with a volley of them following one another in quick succession along each fiber. And each sensory cell fiber is not in contact with only one adjustor or one motor cell but with several of them. It is only when impulses arrive at almost the same time via a number of sensory fibers that the motor nerve cells are finally activated. A certain degree of stimulation (summation) must be produced at the synapse before the motor nerve cell receives and transmits an impulse.

The Nervous System of Vertebrates

The nervous system is complex but its parts work together in complete unity. It is divided only on the basis of location, special function, and convenience of description. The central nervous system is the spinal cord and brain; the peripheral system includes the spinal and cranial nerves and their branches, all of the surface nerves; the autonomic nerves control involuntary functions, especially those of the internal organs (Figs. 16.12, 16.13, 16.15).

PERIPHERAL NERVES

The trunks of the peripheral nerves issue from the brain and cord. Their large branches extend through the arms and legs and the walls of the body

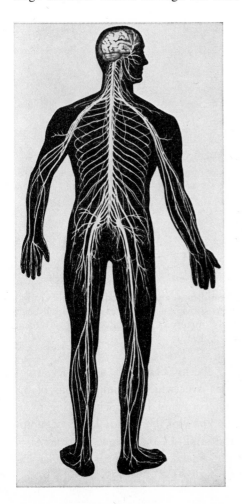

FIG. 16.12. A general rear view of the human nervous system. It presents the brain and certain of the cranial nerves, chiefly the facial ones, the spinal cord and the spinal nerves that divide and subdivide extending to every part of the body. The fusions of nerves at the shoulder and hip levels are called the brachial and lumbarsacral plexuses, respectively. (From Vogel: *Der Mensch.* Leipzig, Barth, 1930.)

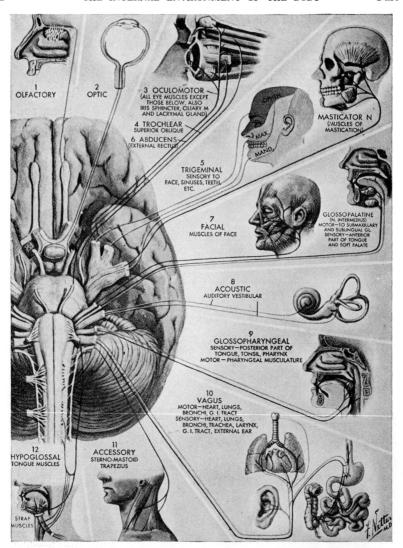

FIG. 16.13. The underside of the human brain and the roots of the cranial nerves. Lines are extended from the roots to show the structures with which each nerve is associated. See also Table 16.1. (Courtesy, Ciba Collection of Medical Illustrations. Drawings by Frank H. Netter, 1953.)

and divide into small branches supplying the muscles, skin, and other structures. They contain the sensory processes over which all impressions of the environment are brought into the spinal cord and brain. They bring to us the raw materials of mind, everything we know of the world. Axons of motor neurons in the brain and cord carry the impulses that direct movements of muscle which largely comprise behavior. Facial expression is muscular exercise; so is a large part of personality.

Spinal Nerves. The spinal nerves occur in pairs, one on either side of the nerve cord. In the higher vertebrates, including man, each trunk branches from the nerve cord by two roots; the dorsal one contains nerve cell fibers that carry sensory messages into the cord, and the ventral one contains those carrying messages to the muscles and glands (Figs. 16.12, 16.14). The cell bodies of fibers in the dorsal root are contained in its ganglion, but those of the ventral root are always in the gray matter of the cord. Soon after the sensory nerve fibers have entered the spinal cord they may come in contact with adjustor neurons and so take part in reflex responses or they may participate in carrying messages to the brain.

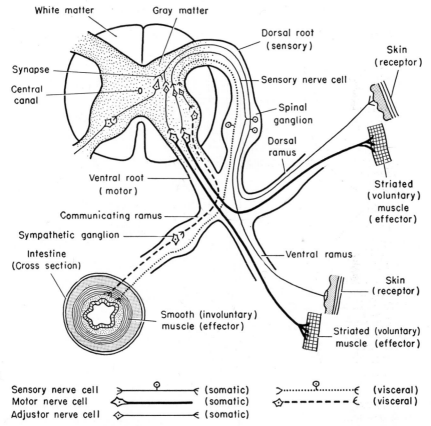

FIG. 16.14. Diagram showing the close association of the nerve cells (autonomic or sympathetic) that control involuntary muscles of the intestine and those that control the voluntary or somatic muscles. Only a few are drawn out of the great numbers of cell bodies and fibers in the cross section of the cord. Cell fibers carrying impulses from sensory stimuli in skin or muscle enter the cord through a sensory root; cells bearing impulses that result in contraction of muscle leave the cord by a motor root. Cell fibers of the autonomic nerve form part of this motor root. All of the thousands of fibers are one way passages. (Modified from Neal and Rand: *Comparative Anatomy.* Philadelphia, The Blakiston Co., 1936.)

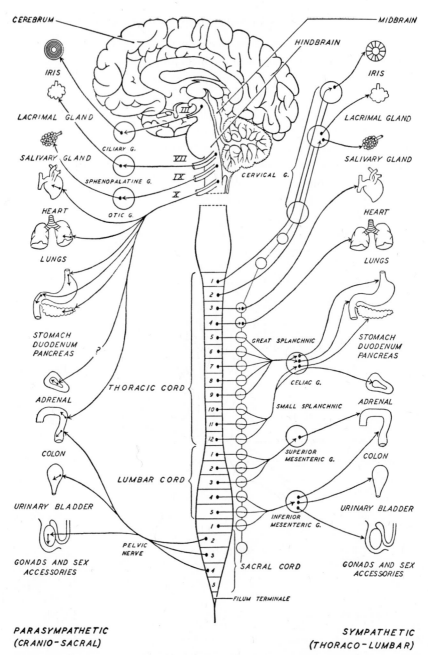

CEREBRUM

MIDBRAIN

HINDBRAIN

IRIS

IRIS

LACRIMAL GLAND

LACRIMAL GLAND

CILIARY G.

SALIVARY GLAND

SALIVARY GLAND

VII

SPHENOPALATINE G.

IX

CERVICAL G.

X

HEART

HEART

OTIC G.

LUNGS

LUNGS

STOMACH
DUODENUM
PANCREAS

?

GREAT SPLANCHNIC

STOMACH
DUODENUM
PANCREAS

THORACIC CORD

CELIAC G.

ADRENAL

SMALL SPLANCHNIC

ADRENAL

COLON

SUPERIOR
MESENTERIC G.

COLON

LUMBAR CORD

URINARY BLADDER

INFERIOR
MESENTERIC G.

URINARY BLADDER

PELVIC
NERVE

GONADS AND SEX
ACCESSORIES

SACRAL CORD

GONADS AND SEX
ACCESSORIES

FILUM TERMINALE

PARASYMPATHETIC
(CRANIO-SACRAL)

SYMPATHETIC
(THORACO-LUMBAR)

FIG. 16.15. Diagram of autonomic nerves that carry impulses to various organs. Figures of the organs are repeated on each side in order to avoid overlapping of the pathways. The diagram emphasizes the fact that each organ receives a double supply of autonomic nerves, the parasympathetic and the sympathetic nerves carrying antagonistic impulses that increase or decrease activity. The Arabic numerals on the cord stand for spinal nerves, the Roman numerals for cranial nerves. (Courtesy, Turner: *General Endocrinology*. Philadelphia, W. B. Saunders Co., 1948.)

BRANCHES. Each spinal nerve trunk contains sensory and motor nerve-cell processes from the respective roots. After a spinal nerve trunk emerges from the vertebral column it divides into several branches, one supplying the muscles and the skin of the back, another the sides of the body, still another branch contains fibers of spinal and autonomic nerve cells (Fig. 16.14). The size of the spinal nerves depends upon the functional demand in the area supplied; in man the largest ones extend into the legs.

PLEXUSES. Different nerves may join and form a plexus in which their fibers are bound together (Fig. 16.12). As a result, one nerve that reaches a muscle may contain fibers of several nerves and all of them may stimulate the muscle.

Cranial Nerves. Most persons are more regularly aware of cranial than of spinal nerves since the former are in control of smiles and toothaches as well as of sight and hearing (Fig. 16.13 and Table 16.1).

AUTONOMIC NERVOUS SYSTEM

The autonomic (involuntary) part of the nervous system is largely in control of internal organs that are more or less continuously active, such as the alimentary canal, blood vessels, lungs, and heart (Fig. 16.15). The activity of most of these is essential to life. Each one, the heart for example, is innervated by nerves carrying impulses that have antagonistic effects; impulses via one nerve hasten its activity, those in the other slow it. In the autonomic nervous system there is an almost total absence of voluntary control. The movements of the heart cannot be slowed by willpower as the tongue can be halted. In this system neither afferent (sensory) nor efferent (motor) fibers are directly connected with the higher centers in the cerebral cortex. Thus stimulation of sensory autonomic fibers does not result in any conscious sensation such as that which results from impulses carried to the brain by the fibers of peripheral nerves. We do not feel the dust in our lungs or food entering the stomach.

In general the autonomic nervous system is one of multiple reflexes and adjustments beyond the direct control of the individual, a great insurance of safety in crises when voluntary action often fails. It is entirely absent in the invertebrates but becomes progressively more elaborate in the vertebrates, especially in mammals. The whole system was formerly called the sympathetic system. It is now divided into two parts, the sympathetic and parasympathetic systems. Of the double sets of autonomic fibers whose impulses have antagonistic effects on various internal organs, one set is in a sympathetic and one in a parasympathetic nerve (Table 16.2, Fig. 16.15). In the autonomic system, two neurons always make up the efferent or motor pathway of an impulse, a contrast to the single neuron in the motor pathway of the ordinary reflex arc.

Table 16.1

NAMES AND MAIN FUNCTIONS OF THE HUMAN CRANIAL NERVES*

Number	Name	Structures Innervated by Motor (Efferent) Fibers	Structures Innervated by Sensory (Afferent) Fibers
I	Olfactory	None	Olfactory mucous membrane of nose (smell)
II	Optic	None	Retina of the eye (sight)
III	Oculomotor	Muscles of movement of eyeballs, with IV and VI Muscles of accommodation of eye Iris (constriction of pupil) Muscles lifting the eyelids	
IV	Trochlear (pulleylike)	Muscles of eye movements, with III and VI	
V	Trigeminal	Muscles of chewing	Structures of sensation in scalp, face, teeth, mouth
VI	Abducens (drawing aside)	Muscles of eye movement with III and IV	
VII	Facial	Muscles of facial expression, salivary glands	Taste buds of anterior two-thirds of tongue
VIII	Auditory Vestibular	None None	Internal ear (hearing) semicircular canals (senses of movement, rotation, balance)
IX	Glossopharyngeal (tongue and pharynx)	Muscles of pharynx (swallowing) Salivary glands	Mucous membrane of pharynx Taste buds of posterior third of tongue
X	Vagus (wandering)	Muscles of larynx (speech) Muscles of pharynx (swallowing) Esophagus, stomach, small intestine (peristalsis) Glands of stomach (secretion), muscles of bronchial tubes Heart	Mucous membrane of larynx Lungs (reflex control of rate of breathing) Stomach (hunger sense)
XI	Spinal accessory	Muscles which turn the head	None
XII	Hypoglossal (under tongue)	Muscles of tongue	None

* Nerves of muscle sense are omitted.

Table 16.2

ANTAGONISTIC ACTION IN THE AUTONOMIC SYSTEM

Organ Innervated	*Action of Sympathetic System*	*Action of Parasympathetic System*
Digestive tract	Slows peristalsis and decreases activity	Quickens peristalsis and increases activity
Urinary bladder	Relaxes bladder	Constricts bladder
Heart	Quickens heartbeat	Slows heartbeat
Arteries	Constricts arteries and raises blood pressure	Dilates arteries and lowers blood pressure
Muscles in bronchial tubes	Dilates passages	Constricts passages
Muscles of iris	Dilates pupil	Constricts pupil
Muscles of hair root	Causes hair to stand erect	Causes hair to lie flat
Sweat glands	Increases sweat	Decreases sweat

SYMPATHETIC SYSTEM

The sympathetic nerves originating in the thoracic and lumbar regions of the cord have a regulating influence on a great number of structures (Table 16.2). The cell bodies of the first of two efferent neurons are located in lateral regions of the gray matter of the cord and their axons extend out through the ventral roots of the spinal nerves along with the axons of ordinary motor cells (Fig. 16.14). After passing through a motor root the axons of the sympathetic neurons separate from it and become the autonomic branch of the spinal nerve leading to a vertebral sympathetic ganglion. These ganglia contain the cell bodies of the second of the efferent neurons whose axons go to the internal organs. They constitute a series of pairs with one member on each side of the spinal cord (Fig. 16.15).

Parasympathetic System. The parasympathetic group consists of nerves with the first of their efferent neurons in the brain stem and the sacral region of the spinal cord. Each vagus nerve which well earns its name arises from the medulla, passes down the chest and abdomen, and mainly innervates the heart, respiratory system, and the digestive system as far as the large intestine.

The peripheral ganglia, containing the second of the efferent neurons of the parasympathetic nerves, are usually near or in the organs innervated. These as well as the vertebral ganglia of the sympathetic nerves are the locations of synaptic connections outside the central nervous system. This is a unique characteristic of the autonomic nervous system.

CENTRAL NERVOUS SYSTEM

The spinal cord is the main connection between the brain and all parts of the body except regions of the head. It varies greatly in length, extends to the end of the body in fishes and snakes, is shortened in mammals, and reaches only to the small of the back in the human body. It contains a central fluid-filled canal, a remnant of the once open gutter of the embryonic nervous system. When the cord is cut across, two substances are readily distinguishable, a central, roughly H-shaped area of gray matter surrounding the canal, and a border of white matter around this (Fig. 16.16). In the gray matter there are many cell bodies, but the white matter consists of great

GRAY AND WHITE MATTER OF SPINAL CORD

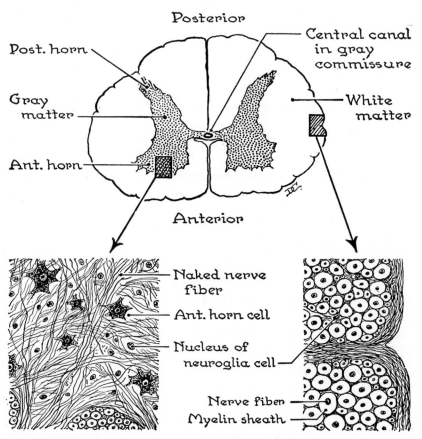

FIG. 16.16. Cross section of the human spinal cord showing the gray matter containing nerve cell bodies and their fibers, and the white matter containing their fibers only. In the brain the gray matter is outside and the white within. The central canal is continuous with cavities (ventricles) of the brain. (Courtesy, Ham: *Histology,* ed. 2. Philadelphia, J. B. Lippincott Co., 1953.)

numbers of myelin-wrapped fibers that extend up and down the cord. The regions of gray and white matter are continued into the brain, but in the cerebellum and cerebrum their positions are reversed and thus the cortex or outer layer of the brain, is gray matter.

The gray matter of the cord contains neurons with various functions. Among them are connecting neurons (adjustors) that transmit impulses from one neuron to another in the same or in different levels; motor neurons, always in the ventral horns of the gray matter, that carry impulses to skeletal muscles and glands; and neurons of the autonomic system that carry impulses to the internal organs and other structures.

In the white matter, the axons are segregated in bundles of fibers of similar function. Great numbers of axons of cell bodies in the spinal ganglia carry sensory impulses to the brain. These are the ascending tracts. There are also axons from cells in the gray matter of the brain, carrying impulses to motor cells in the ventral horns of the gray matter of the cord which then relay them to the muscles. These are the descending tracts (Fig. 16.11). If we are suddenly pricked by a pin, we not only jerk involuntarily, which is the reflex action, we also know about the prick and may remove the pin. The appreciation of the prick and removal of the pin depend on the sensory impulses to the brain, the association of cells in the higher centers, and a complex of impulses to the muscles. In part these relationships have been found out by observing symptoms in persons with injured nerve cords and correlating these with destroyed tracts found when the spinal cord was examined after the patient's death. With some diseases the patient cannot locate his arms and legs without looking at them and must watch his feet in order to walk. This is due to the destruction of the nerve cells responsible for transmitting the sense of position of muscles and joints to the central system.

Vertebrate Brain

The brain is the master coordinator of the bodily activities of an animal and of its awareness and adjustment to the environment. The brain and chief sense organs are appropriately so located that wherever the animal travels, they lead on and arrive there first. Every creeping baby has that experience.

General Description. The vertebrate brain is the bulbous front end of a tube whose walls are composed mainly of nerve cells (Fig. 16.17). In fishes and other lower vertebrates, its outer surface is smooth and the cavity within it is relatively large in comparison to the thickness of the walls. In mammals, and especially in man, its surface dips and bulges and the cavity within it is relatively small compared to the thickness of the walls. The great pile of nervous tissue that makes up the cerebral hemispheres is a comparatively late development in animal history, and the cerebral cortex with its billions of interrelated neurons is largely a mammalian achievement (Fig. 16.18).

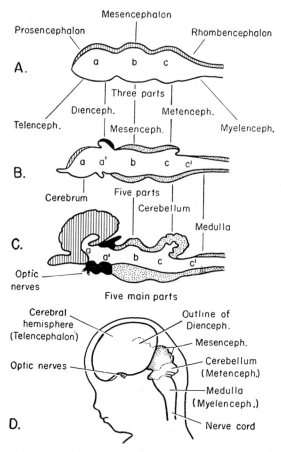

FIG. 16.17. Diagrams to illustrate some of the changes that transform the smooth bulb at the anterior end of the neural tube into a highly complex brain. *A* and *B,* Median vertical sections of brains showing the changes that occur in given regions, e.g., the telencephalon, as they appear in certain primitive chordates and (*C*) certain vertebrates. *D,* Outlines of the brain seen in a human embryo of about 11 weeks' development, 50–60 mm length, about two inches. (*D* redrawn and modified from Patten: *Human Embryology,* ed. 2. New York, The Blakiston Co., 1953.)

During its development the nervous system is at first on the outside of the body. At one period in the life of every vertebrate, fish or human, there is an open groove that extends the whole length of the central nervous system. Later when the system takes its place inside the body, only the central canal in the cord and the communicating ventricles of the brain are left of the former open ditch.

The working parts of the brain are composed of many types of neurons associated in groups for general and specialized functions. Thus the human brain is divided into districts occupied by neurons that control definite parts of the body (Fig. 16.17). Although the cerebral lobes are distinct and the brain is definitely bilateral, there are great numbers of intercrossing fibers that insure synchronous action of the parts. The left side of the brain controls the right side of the body, and vice versa; the fibers from one side of the cord and brain cross to the opposite side. The sensory axons (bearing impulses to the brain) cross over in the brain, in the medulla or above; the motor

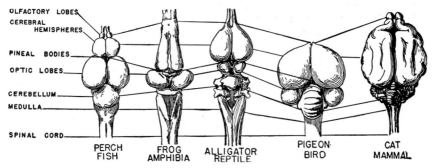

FIG. 16.18. Five types of vertebrate brains. In the cat's brain the pineal body and the optic lobes are present, but are hidden by the cerebral hemispheres. (Courtesy, MacDougall and Hegner: *Biology*. New York, McGraw-Hill Book Co., Inc., 1943.)

axons (bearing impulses to the muscles) cross over in the midbrain, pons, medulla and at various levels below it (Fig. 16.11).

MENINGES. The brain and cord are enclosed in three protective coverings of connective tissue with spaces between them filled with cerebrospinal fluid (Fig. 16.19). The innermost one, pia mater (tender mother) is very delicate and carries many blood vessels. It is intimately associated with the arachnoid layer so called because of its open spaces like a spider's web; these are filled with cerebrospinal fluid. The outermost cover, dura mater (hard mother), is made of tough connective tissue, contains many blood vessels, and adheres tightly to the cranium and vertebrae. Meningitis is an inflammation of the meninges, especially the pia mater and arachnoid.

CEREBROSPINAL FLUID. The central canal and the ventricles are continually moistened by the cerebrospinal fluid. Most of this is formed by vascular glands, the choroid plexuses, located in the ventricles. Much of the fluid makes its way through holes in the choroid plexus of the fourth ventricle and enters the space between the two delicate coverings of the brain and cord so that these organs are actually surrounded by a blanket of fluid (Fig. 16.20). It is produced more or less continuously and the excess is drained off through hollow, button-shaped projections (villi) that dip into open lakes of venous blood in the dura mater. The cerebrospinal fluid diffuses into the blood through the thin caps of the villi whenever its pressure is higher than that of the venous blood.

Brain Size. In evolutionary history, the greatest increase in the size of brains occurred as animals began to live on land. Swimming in the sea was monotony and ease compared with clambering through the ooze and over the hillocks on land. The adaptation to the details and variety of land living left its mark on the brain as it did on the legs and feet. The human brain is heavy in proportion to the weight of the body. Its weight varies with the age and size of the individual. Except in extreme cases such as some defective individuals there appears to be no correlation between size and weight of the brain or number of cerebral convolutions and the degree of intelligence.

PRIMARY DIVISIONS OF THE VERTEBRATE BRAIN

The embryonic brain is the key to the structure of the adult brain. In its earlier development, the brain is a single hollow enlargement whose cavity is continuous with that of the nerve cord. In the third week of human life, two constrictions indicate three regions, the fore-, mid-, and hindbrain (technically called the prosencephalon, mesencephalon, and rhombencephalon). In the fourth week, a constriction forms two subregions of the forebrain, the endbrain and the between brain, respectively the telencephalon and diencephalon. In man, the hindbrain is set off into two regions, the future cerebellum and future medulla (metencephalon, myelencephalon) about the fifth week. The brain is then composed of five primary regions, from anterior to posterior: (1) endbrain, (2) between brain, (3) midbrain, (4) future

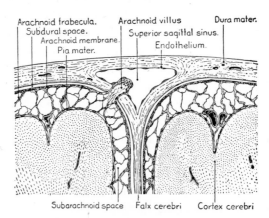

FIG. 16.19. Relation of the meninges, the protective covers of the brain, the pia mater (tender mother) next to the brain, the dura mater (tough mother) next to the skull and the arachnoid (spiderweb) layer between them. The spaces in the latter are filled with the cerebrospinal fluid, a modified tissue fluid. All of the layers also surround the spinal cord including the spinal fluid. Diagram of the layers as they overlie the brain. Excess cerebrospinal fluid drains through the arachnoid villus, one of many that extend into the blood of the sinus. This occurs in many areas of the brain. (After Weed. Courtesy, Ham: *Histology*, ed. 2. Philadelphia, J. B. Lippincott Co., 1953.)

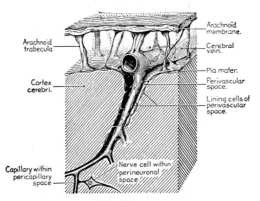

Fig. 16.20. Diagram of the relations of the pia mater, the arachnoid and the blood vessels of the brain. The pia mater dips into the channels of the larger blood vessels. This figure shows the possibilities of broken blood vessels that create hemorrhage of the brain. (After Weed. Courtesy, Ham: *Histology,* ed. 2. Philadelphia, J. B. Lippincott Co., 1953.)

cerebellum, and (5) medulla. Each of them is the location of sense organs and controls for which it is nicknamed: endbrain, "nose brain"; midbrain, "eye brain"; medulla, "ear brain." From the fishes onward through the mammals these sense organs are located according to this plan. In higher animals the main parts that develop from the fundamental regions are as follows:

1. *Endbrain.* In fishes, this region is practically limited to the sense of smell, whereas in mammals this sense is relatively little developed. In mammals, the corpora striata have a stabilizing effect upon the muscles in walking. In man, the cerebrum overtops the rest of the brain and its cortex is a supreme achievement of the human species (Figs. 16.17, and 16.21).

2. *Between brain.* This is the main pathway of the fibers between the spinal cord and the cortex of the cerebral hemispheres, and by means of it all other parts of the brain and the body are connected with the higher centers of control. The main substance of the between brain is in the side walls of the third ventricle which are collectively called the thalamus. So called by certain early anatomists who believed the enclosure to be a room in which vital spirits were imparted to the optic nerves. The thalamus is the anterior end of the primitive brain stem, the oldest part of the brain, a center of the autonomic nervous system, and such functions as temperature regulation and the awareness and expression of emotions (Fig. 16.21).

3. *Midbrain.* The midbrain is a small part that connects larger ones. Its floor is a part of the brain stem, very old in evolution. In fishes, the midbrain is the original eye brain. In mammals, the four-fold bodies (corpora quadrigemina) in its roof are, in a limited way, centers of visual and auditory reflexes.

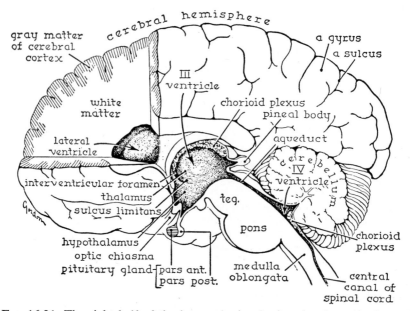

Fig. 16.21. The right half of the human brain. A piece has been cut from the front of the cerebral hemisphere in order to expose the lateral ventricle. This ventricle and its mate in the left hemisphere, and the central third and fourth ventricles have developed from the central canal of the primitive brain and cord. The hypothalamus that forms part of the floor of the third ventricle is believed to have an important part in controlling the secretion of the adrenocorticotrophic hormone (ACTH) under conditions of stress. The cut in the cerebral hemisphere reveals the thickness of the cortex, the shaded gray matter whose area is greatly increased by the folds that are absent in lower animals. It is estimated that there are 10,000 million nerve cells in the cortex of the human brain, each one having synaptic connections with several others. The number of pathways in these highest centers of the brain is beyond imagination. (Courtesy, Ham: *Histology,* ed. 2. Philadelphia, J. B. Lippincott and Co., 1953.)

4. *Hindbrain (cerebellum).* On its dorsal side the hindbrain is composed of the cerebellum and on its ventral side, of the floor of the ancient brain stem. The pons, a bridge of nerve fibers including those that connect the cerebellum and cerebral hemispheres, forms a part of the floor of the fourth ventricle. Some of the main functions of the cerebellum are the maintenance of unconscious muscular coordination, and the preservation of muscular tension or tonus. It contains numerous connections with the eyes, ears, muscles, joints, and other parts of the body.

5. *Hindbrain (medulla).* The white appearance of the hindbrain is due to the fibers of the nerve cells being on the outside as they are in the spinal cord. It is the great passageway for nerve fibers that extend along the sides and form the swollen cords of the pyramids. Its cavity is the fourth ventricle and its thin roof, the choroid plexus, is one of the main sources of cerebrospinal fluid.

The medulla is the entrance and exit way of nerve impulses to and from the spinal cord and brain and to and from the last six pairs of cranial nerves, including the widely effective vagus nerves. It is the center of the autonomic control of important body functions such as respiration and the rate of the heart beat.

Table 16.3

PRINCIPAL STRUCTURES OF THE ADULT HUMAN BRAIN WITH THEIR
LOCATIONS IN THE BASIC DIVISIONS

Forebrain (Prosencephalon)	Endbrain (Telencephalon)	Olfactory lobes, cerebral hemispheres, corpora striata, corpus callosum Contains the lateral ventricles
	Between brain (Diencephalon)	Thalamus, pineal eye stalk, infundibulum (or pituitary stalk), optic nerves with their crossing (chiasma) Contains the third ventricle
Midbrain (Mesencephalon)		Optic lobes Fibers of nerve cells (white matter) form walls and floor Contains the cerebral aqueduct
Hindbrain (Rhombencephalon)	After brain (Metencephalon)	Cerebellum, pons (a bridge of nerve cell fibers in mammals) Contains part of fourth ventricle
	Cord brain (Myelencephalon)	Medulla Great passageway of fibers of nerve cells Contains part of fourth ventricle

FEATURES OF THE HUMAN BRAIN

The history of the cerebral hemispheres of vertebrates is one of the most spectacular in comparative anatomy. It begins with them as smooth paired outgrowths of the forebrain, the centers of olfactory sensation in the nose brain of fishes. Later with the adoption of land life, animals had to clamber and creep, and their cerebral lobes became large and important centers of sensory correlation. Finally, with the mammals, the same lobes became a great superstructure reared on the old primitive nervous system. This newer part of the brain is the center of the nervous functions which in man have been developed far beyond those of any other animal.

The brain is a bilaterally symmetrical organ that acts as a unit in the invertebrates as well as in the vertebrates. The action of the hind legs of a grasshopper is as well timed for a take-off as that in the hind legs of a kangaroo.

Cerebrum. In contrast to its smoothness in other vertebrates the surface of the mammalian cerebrum is usually increased by fissures and by folds called convolutions (Fig. 16.21). The fact that these convolutions give more space for nerve cells is more significant than their arrangement or character which are not unique. They are similar in higher mammals, and the brains of normal human beings greatly resemble one another no matter how different the mental ability of their owners. After years of study, no structure has been found in the human brain which is actually different in kind from those present in the brain of a chimpanzee. In man, the size of the cerebrum compared to the rest of the brain is far greater than it is in the apes. An adult human cerebrum weighs around three times that of an adult gorilla. The layer of gray matter, called the cerebral cortex, is about one-eighth of an inch thick. By counting the cells in small areas and using such counts as a basis of computation, it is figured that the human cerebral cortex alone contains some 9280 millions of nerve cells. Most of these are provided with long nerve fibers, chiefly axons, that extend for relatively great distances and branch in different directions, connecting each cell through the junction-like synapses with the cells in many different centers. The total number of such connections and nervous pathways is inconceivably great.

Fiber Tracts. The wires of a telephone exchange are grouped in cables and distributed on a switchboard according to a system. In like manner, the nerve fibers that have similar functions extend in bundles or tracts through the white matter of the brain and cord (Fig. 16.11), and from there they have synaptic connections with other nerve cells which continue into nerves. In spite of the complexity of their arrangement, the make-up of the main nerve tracts has been analyzed. The courses of various series of nerve cells have been traced from receptors, such as those involved in a pinched toe, to the appropriate center of adjustment in the cortex. Likewise, the motor pathways have been traced, in this case from the cortex to the muscles which move the foot.

In general, nerve cells in the cortex of the right side of the brain communicate with muscles on the left side of the body, and likewise those on the left side of the brain communicate with the right side. Throughout the white matter of the spinal cord and brain there are intercrossing fibers. As a result the spinal cord and the two parts of the brain are bound together structurally and functionally by an unthinkably complex network. Untangling these facts began centuries ago and is not finished. Much has been learned from dissections, microscopic examinations, and experimental studies. Hundreds of observations on how the human nervous system works have been made when injuries to it made this possible.

Functions of Cerebral Cortex. The human cerebral cortex is the location of intelligence, of reasoning powers, of consciousness and of memory. The brain acts as a coordinated whole. However, it is well known that different areas of the cerebral cortex function differently.

At the extreme rear of each cerebral lobe is the visual area (Fig. 16.22).

Destruction of this causes blindness, even though the eyes may be normal; a blow on this part of the head makes one "see stars." The auditory area is near the temple and injury to this causes deafness, loss of the interpretation of sound although the sound receptors may be normal. Along and behind the central fissure (Rolando) which extends from about the middle of the head to the top of the ear is an area associated with various bodily sensations: muscle sense, pressure, temperature, and pain. Patients are able to report their sensations when this region is exposed and is stimulated by electricity. On

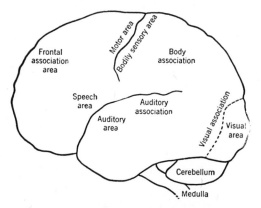

FIG. 16.22. Outline of left half of the human brain with the mental functions of certain areas indicated. For example, the visual association area contains the cells essential to interpret and coordinate the objects seen. (After Morgan. Courtesy, Boring, et al.: *The Foundation of Psychology*, New York, John Wiley and Sons, 1948.)

the opposite side of the central fissure is the motor area. When different parts of this area are stimulated, movements of the fingers, legs, or throat can be produced. A cerebral hemorrhage or "stroke" in this region on the left side causes paralysis of muscles in the right side of the body and vice versa. Both of these areas, the sensory and the motor, are laid out like a map with different places representing different parts of the body. There are also association centers, such as the auditory and visual ones, believed to be concerned with the remembrance of things heard and seen; these regions have been only partially explored. Although the whole cerebral cortex is concerned with thinking, the capacity to direct it and to lay out plans of living appears to be located in the front regions of the cerebrum.

Brain Waves

Several waves per second of electrical activity are produced by the brain even when a person is resting. Recordings of brain waves are obtained by fastening electrodes to different parts of the scalp by adhesive tape and picking up the currents by a recording apparatus. The records (electroencephalograms) show that brain cells are more or less continuously active. This is clearly demonstrated by a frog's brain, which when taken from the body and kept alive, will continue to generate electrical waves for some hours. All brain waves are so feeble that they can be recorded only after being received by a very sensitive apparatus and magnified millions of times. They occur rhythmically, and sleep is the only normal condition in which they are much altered. During sleep, the records show waves that are slower and wider, sometimes broken by irregularities, believed to be caused by dreams (Fig. 16.23). Brain diseases change the brain waves, and epilepsy can be diagnosed by characteristic wave patterns.

Sleep

The average individual spends from a quarter to a third of his lifetime in sleep. All observations on sleep have ended in the conclusion that animals cannot live without it. However, the actual nature of sleep is unknown and this is especially true of the part played in it by the nervous system.

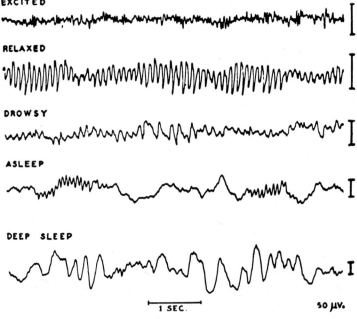

EXCITED

RELAXED

DROWSY

ASLEEP

DEEP SLEEP

1 SEC.   50 μV.

FIG. 16.23. Sleep and excitement in the human brain. Records of electrical waves produced in the normal human brain. Excitement is characterized by very frequent waves and sleep by irregular, less frequent ones. In the (upper) sleep record there was a "sleep spindle" of frequent waves every 14 seconds. (After Jasper. From Penfield and Erickson: *Epilepsy and Cerebral Localization.* Springfield, Ill., Charles C Thomas, 1941.)

17

Responsiveness—The Sense Organs

Sense organs are gateways to the mind. All that we know of our surroundings is brought to us through them. It is difficult to imagine our existence without them. What would it be?

Receptors. Receptors are cells or parts of cells that are especially sensitive to particular conditions in their surroundings. Sense organs include receptors and associated cells. Those that are affected by external things are most familiar for they include sight and hearing, taste and smell, touch and temperature. Other receptors are sensitive to situations within the body, the stretch and pressure of muscles, the movements of internal organs. We feel comfortable in one chair and not in another, we feel thirsty, or we know that we have eaten too much. We make hundreds of adjustments of the body without being aware of any of the sensory signals concerned with them although such signals are constantly being given by these active internal receptors.

A receptor responds to stimuli only when they are of a certain kind and a particular intensity called the threshold of sensation. Within limits, the intensity of a given sensation increases with the stimulus to a certain point, then there is a sensory adaptation and the sensation decreases, and a limit may be reached when there is no sensation at all. The first piece of candy is the sweetest. The stronger the odor, the more quickly it fades. A solution of camphor can be smelled for about five minutes.

External Tactile Senses—Touch, Pain

Protoplasm is in general sensitive to slight differences in pressure whether sensory structures are present or not. Some of the nerve fibers end without any coverings and these probably react to any stimulus from muscular cells or other cells around them (Fig. 17.1). Others end in cellular capsules containing a clear jelly. In such capsules the nerve endings can be affected by slight or by heavy pressure without injury. In man and other mammals, pressure receptors of this type, the Pacinian corpuscles, are located around joints and tendons, in fingers and toes, and in deeper parts of the body, e.g., the mesentery, wherever pressure is apt to be. The Pacinian corpuscle is oval; when it is pressed it elongates and the nerve fiber within it is stretched (Fig. 17.1). Nerve endings are twined around the roots of hairs that are sensitive to the slightest pressure, even of air currents, such as, the hairs in

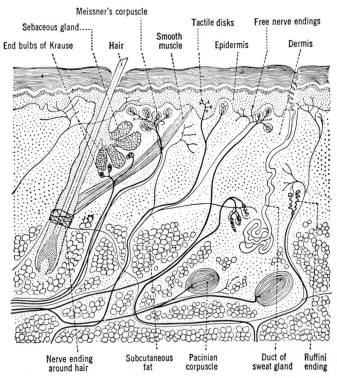

FIG. 17.1. Diagram of the nerves and end organs in a section of human skin. Not all of these endings are to be found in any one area. *Cold receptors;* Meissner's corpuscles, abundant on the palm side of the fingers. *Touch receptors;* nerve endings entwined about the hairs often with end feet applied to them; highly developed association with cat's whiskers. *Pressure and possibly vibration receptors;* Pacinian corpuscles, abundant in skin of palms of hands and feet, internal organs and mesentery. *Heat receptors;* Ruffini endings lie deep in the skin. *Receptors for pain* are not shown; they consist of bare nerve cell fibers extending about and between cells. The number of structures present in a small area of skin may be realized in connection with the sweat glands one of which is shown in this diagram. By counts of limited spaces at least 3000 sweat glands are calculated to be in the skin of the palm of the hand. (Courtesy, Gardner: *Fundamentals of Neurology,* ed. 2. Philadelphia, W. B. Saunders Co., 1952.)

a cat's ear, and the vibrissae or whiskers of cats and rats, and less evidently human hairs.

In the insects and other arthropods, bristles are connected with receptors. Although ants are armored in chitin they are exquisitely in touch with their surroundings by way of their bristles. Human skin contains several types of sense organs. By testing a small area of skin, point by point, receptors for touch, pain, cold, and heat can be found at different locations. Pain may be slight or very intense. The mild pain of pinpricks can be definitely located, but pains deeper in the body are rarely so precisely determined.

Temperature—Thermoreceptors

Little is known about temperature receptors except those in higher animals (Fig. 17.1). Protoplasm is sensitive to temperature although no receptors may be present. Insects are highly responsive to it; ants move their young from one to another part of their underground nests as the temperature changes during the day. In temperatures around 30° C. and under controlled conditions of humidity adult mosquitoes (*Culex fatigans*) react to differences as slight as five-hundredths of one degree.

Internal Senses of Muscles and Viscera

Many impulses from these receptors reach the higher centers of the brain and consciousness, but many others end in the spinal cord and cerebellum below the level of consciousness. Proprioceptors are sensitive to changes in the tension of muscle and tendon. Such changes stimulate impulses to the brain, making us aware of the position and movements of our arms and legs and other parts of the body, the interplay through which the body is kept in a balanced position. Interoceptors are important in regulating the activities of the lungs, alimentary canal, and other viscera in which they are located. They bring about reflex control of internal organs through centers in the medulla and thalamus of the brain. Some of these impulses go through to the higher centers of the brain and are responsible for such sensations as having had "a good dinner."

Chemical Senses

These are the common chemical sense and the twin senses of taste and smell. All chemical receptors are alike in their requirement that particles of a substance must be dissolved and in actual contact with them. We can taste sugar only when it is chemically associated with certain taste buds; we can smell roses, skunks, cheese, or vanilla only when their essences enter the olfactory cells.

Common Chemical Sense. The surface of the bodies of fishes and amphibians is sensitive to chemical substances of a very mildly stimulating character. Taste and smell are closely allied to the common chemical sense from which they sprang. The catfish, Amiurus, has taste buds along the sides of its body and will turn and snap at bait that is suspended near its flank. Its skin can be stimulated by very weak chemical solutions even after its taste buds have been isolated by cutting the nerves leading to them.

Taste. The sensation of taste never acts separately as vision and hearing do. Smell plays the largest part in what is called taste, and pressure and temperature have their shares in it. By one or another kind of receptor we not only perceive the sourness of lemonade, but its temperature, its weight on the tongue, and the consistency which helps or hinders its spread over the tongue. Substances can be tasted only when they are in solution and their molecules are moving about freely.

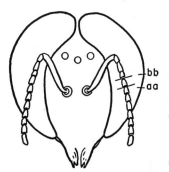

FIG. 17.2. Sense of smell in honeybees. Outline of head showing segments of antennae. Cutting an antenna at the line *aa* leaves one segment that bears sense organs of smell. Cutting at *bb* leaves no sense of smell. See also figure 30.27.

Taste and smell are highly developed in insects and because of this, insects are important to humanity both for good and bad. Bees smell and taste nectar and pollen, and in gathering them accomplish the cross-pollination on which the production of many fruits depends (Fig. 17.2). Their sense of smell guides certain moths and butterflies to lay their eggs on particular host plants on which the young caterpillars will feed. But the same moths and butterflies will readily lay eggs on the wrong kinds of plants if they have been sprayed with extracts of the host plants. Houseflies are quickly attracted by odors of food, fruitflies (Drosophila) by ripening fruit, and female mosquitoes by body odors. Ants, bees, and wasps smell through their antennae, as is readily shown by tests made after these have been removed. Honeybees can taste by receptors in their mouth parts and they as well as the wasps, Vespa and Polistes, can distinguish plain from sweetened water. They also can recognize sweet, bitter, and salt as separate qualities. Out of 34 sugars and related substances, 30 are sweet to human taste, but only nine are sweet to honeybees and all of these are in their natural foods. The sweeter the mixture of cane sugar, the more of it the worker honeybees will drink. The sweeter the mixture that foraging honeybees discover, the more will they excite workers in the home hive by dancing when they return from successful foraging trips.

In order to taste something, mammals must have the substance on their tongues. Nearly all of them are adept at stretching these tongues outside their mouths, cattle licking salt blocks and human beings licking anything.

TASTE RECEPTORS IN MAN. Special sense organs known as taste buds are imbedded in the mucous membrane of the soft palate and upper surface of the tongue. Their name comes from their bud-like shape, but they are quite as much like bottles with small mouths, the pores that open into furrows that surround them (Fig. 17.3).

Anything which is tasted must get into the bottle and bring about the chemical reaction with the receptor cells with which the dendrites of the facial or glossopharyngeal nerve are in contact. These reactions start impulses to the brain, ending in the sour taste of pickles, or the sweet taste of sugar. Salty substances are tasted quickly, bitter ones more slowly, due partly to the distribution of the taste receptors. All four kinds of taste receptors are on

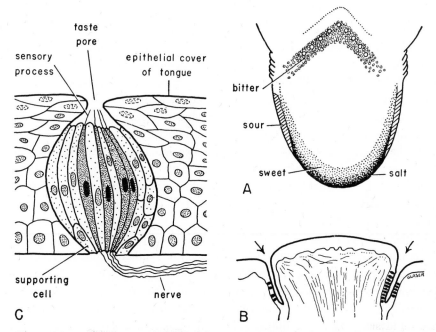

FIG. 17.3. *A,* diagrams of the human tongue and the distribution of the four tastes, *sweet, sour, bitter, salt;* the central part of the tongue is insensitive to taste. The closeness of the dots represents the number of the sense organs. The rings at the back mark the papillae, each holding a battery of taste buds. *B,* section of a papilla of the tongue (much enlarged) with taste buds in the groove that surrounds the papilla. *C,* human taste bud greatly magnified. Saliva mixed with food juice, for example onion, enters the bud through the pore at the top and chemical reactions take place between it and the sensory cells. Impulses pass over the sensory fibers to the brain, where the little understood process of interpretation occurs and maybe the flavor of candy or of onion is revealed. (After Parker: *Smell, Taste and the Allied Senses in the Vertebrates.* Philadelphia, J. B. Lippincott Co., 1922.)

the upper surface of the tongue, salt and sweet in bands near the tip, sour near the sides, and bitter in the center near the root. The receptors of bitter taste are in a few conspicuous papillae ranged in a V-shaped line far back on the tongue. They have been called vallate papillae because each one is shaped like a turreted castle surrounded by a flooded moat, in this case, a tasty flood (Fig. 17.3).

Smell. At least among mammals, smell is the most democratic of the senses. Whatever minute particles there may be in the air, and of whatsoever kind, they are hospitably drawn into the nostrils. The nose of mammals is not only a heater, humidifier, and cleaner of air but through the sense of smell it is a testing place of the chemical nature of the surroundings. In spite of all they smell and think they smell, man and other primates are only feeble smellers as compared with cats and dogs and other mammals. A man looks as he walks; a dog smells as he runs.

In the human nose, the mucous membrane on each side is raised upon three ridges of the turbinate bones that spring from the outer nasal wall. Each cavity of the nose is thus incompletely divided into compartments. The lower ones are passages that are open behind, and air slips through them into the pharynx; the uppermost one is a narrow cleft directly under the floor of the skull. The olfactory organs are pale yellow patches of cells on the walls of this cleft (Fig. 17.4). Their location, as it were, in the attic, sets them off the main roadway of incoming and outgoing air. Each breath of cool air pushes the warmed air up into the olfactory attic where it is poised over the smell receptors till more air comes in. The exposed ends of the receptors bear slender processes that are always wet with mucus. Fibers arising from the other ends of the receptors are grouped together in the olfactory nerves that pass through the skull to the olfactory centers in the brain (Fig. 16.13).

Although man's sense of smell is relatively weak, even so, it will respond to remarkably small amounts of substance. A synthetic substitute for the odor of violets (ionone) can be detected when it is present as one in over 30 billion parts of air. The sense of smell of a particular substance is fatigued in a few minutes, but will then react to a new odor; all recoveries are rapid since odors are diffused through the air. The smaller, lighter particles spread most readily, and as they are scattered farther apart the chance of inhaling them lessens. The aroma of coffee thins quickly; the scent fades on yesterday's rabbit tracks; the odor of last night's cigarette lingers and changes.

Equilibrium—Statoreceptors

The great majority of animals, grasshoppers, fishes, or cows, have an upside and a downside, and it is very important that the owner be informed of

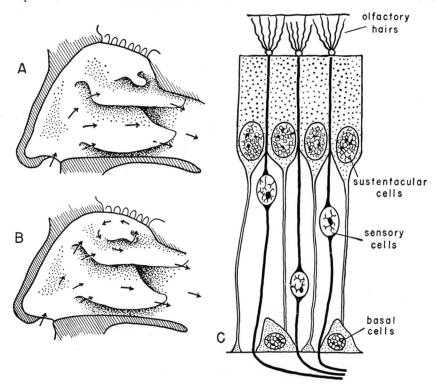

Fig. 17.4. Human olfactory organ. *A,* side wall of nasal chamber with the projecting turbinate bones and the clefts between them. Arrows indicate the course of air in ordinary breathing. *B,* sniffing the air brings it forcibly against the olfactory organ located under the lobe marked by the circle of arrows. *C,* diagram of sensory receptor cells of smell with their supporting cells (*sustentacular*). The sensory cell has a single dendrite which extends to the exposed surface where it is expanded into a bulb which bears delicate processes, the olfactory hairs. These processes extend into a film of mucus that covers the surface of the organ. Extremely minute particles of substance inhaled, whether skunk, garlic, or lily fall into the fluid and upon the ends of the olfactory cells. A chemical change immediately occurs, passes through the sensory cell, and by way of an olfactory nerve to the cells in the brain and the interpretation of the odor. (*A* and *B* after *Biology: Its Human Implications,* 2nd ed. by Garrett Hardin. Copyright, 1952. W. H. Freeman and Company. *C* after Smith, *Canadian Med. Assn. J.,* 1939.)

the positions of these and keep them where they belong. This is brought to them through the statoreceptors.

The majority of active multicellular animals have these paired organs of equilibrium, of essentially the same structure wherever they occur. A statoreceptor is a more or less spherical sac containing fluid and freely movable granules, the statoliths. Minute bristles that project into the fluid are attached to sensitive cells in the wall of the sac, and these in turn touch the nerve fibers. The statolith is attracted by gravity; it rolls about, always resting on the downside, and its pressure upon the bristles is the stimulus of the receptors.

When they molt, lobsters and crabs shed the linings of their organs of balance together with the bristles and statoliths, and new linings and bristles are regained and new grains of sand worked into the sacs. Recently molted crayfishes that have been supplied with particles of iron will work them into their sacs, and thereafter will respond to a magnet. When the magnet is held directly above the crayfish, it pulls the particles of iron against the bristles on the upperside of the sac. In response to the unusual position of the particles, normally on the downside of the sac, the crayfish soon turns over and swims on its back.

Human equilibrium is a complex affair that depends upon vision, muscle sense (proprioceptors), sensitiveness to pressure in the soles of the feet, and paired organs of equilibrium. Each of the latter consists of two small sacs, the saccule and utricle, and three semicircular canals, all a part of the inner ear but not taking any part in hearing (Fig. 17.5). Hairlike processes of sensory cells project into the cavities of the saccule and utricle each of which contains a minute earstone or otolith of calcium carbonate. Gravity pulls the otolith against particular hair cells; this stimulates them and initiates impulses to the brain through the nerve fibers with which they are associated. As the head is tipped this way and that, the otoliths are rolled about, always on the downward side. There are three semicircular canals, each of them connected at both ends to the utricle and arranged so that each is at right angles to the other two. Near one of the openings of each canal

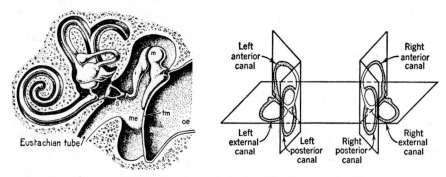

Fig. 17.5. Organs of balance, the human semicircular canals. There is a set of three on each side of the head near the eardrum. *Left,* the three semicircular canals shown in natural location with the bone cut away to show their nearness to the middle ear. The coiled cochlea of the inner ear is deeply embedded in bone like the semicircular canals but has no functional connection with them. Parts of middle ear shown here: *m,* malleus; *i,* incus; *s,* stapes; *me,* cavity of middle ear; *tm,* eardrum; *oe,* cavity of outer ear. *Right,* diagram of the semicircular canals showing their position with reference to the surface upon which the person stands upright, represented by a glass plane. The back of the head is toward the reader. (*Left,* courtesy, Romer: *The Vertebrate Body,* ed. 2. Philadelphia, W. B. Saunders Co., 1955. *Right,* courtesy, Guilford: *General Psychology.* New York, D. Van Nostrand & Co., 1939.)

into the utricle there is a bulbous enlargement containing sensitive "hair cells" like those in the utricle and saccule but without otoliths. These cells are stimulated by movements of the fluid (endolymph) contained in the canals and their tips are turned in whatever direction it flows. Since the canals lie in three different planes, a movement of the head in any direction will affect one or more of them. If the outer ear is irrigated with cold water, convection currents are set up in the fluid of the canals and the person will turn dizzy although his head and body may be kept upright and quiet. The receptors in the canals may be strongly affected by vertical movements like that of an elevator, and by the rolling motions of ships and planes.

Hearing—Phonoreceptors

Ears and eyes work together so closely that we scarcely realize which one brings the news. The eye sees in straight lines in light but the ears hear in light and dark, and around the corner. The eye sees what something is; the ear hears what it does.

Probably relatively few invertebrates can hear. Insects that from very ancient times have been land residents are the great exceptions; their perception of vibrations of air is widespread. Fine hairs commonly borne on the antennae of mosquitoes respond to vibrations. Crickets, cicadas, grasshoppers have tympanal organs or "eardrums" that vibrate in response to the various clicks and squeaks which insects make with their legs and wings.

In the vertebrates, the ears developed and took on their special function as these animals gradually assumed their life on land. The new organ of hearing developed from the saccule which retains its connection with the semicircular canals of equilibrium, but the functions of the old and new organs remained distinct.

The Ear of Mammals—Man. The ears of mammals respond to vibrations that are transmitted through air; this contains comparatively few particles so that the vibrations or sound waves are relatively slow and widely diffused. There is a great advantage in having the outer ear spread out to catch the vibrations and a corridor to conduct them to the middle ear, from which they are transmitted to the real sound receptors in the inner ear (Figs. 17.6, 17.7).

The outer ear includes the outgrowth of flesh called the auricle and the passageway to the eardrum, the auditory canal. Auricles are more or less trowel-shaped and well supplied with cartilage and muscle. Sounds are located by the intensity of the sound waves that stimulate the receptors of the inner ear. We turn our heads and cup our ears to catch more sound waves, as dogs turn their heads and lift both ears or one toward the sound. The ear catches the sound wave; the brain decides where it comes from and what it is. Human auricles are almost immovable; we cannot prick them forward and backward with the attention that is so becoming to dogs and

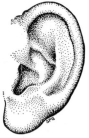

Fig. 17.6. The external ears of tree-shrew and man are strikingly similar in having the rolled edge that is associated with their reduction in size. In some mammals, i.e. bats, there are muscles by which the flap (tragus) can be pulled down over the passage to the eardrum; in the human ear unfortunately this passage can only be stopped with the fingers. The tree-shrew (*Tupaia tana*) of southeast Asia is a small generalized mammal that originated about 100 million years ago and is believed to be an ancestor of the gorillas, man, and other primates.

horses, or drop one ear and lift the other toward the danger as rabbits do. The sizes and patterns of auricles are correlated with the habits of their owners, and picturesquely so, small in the burrowing chipmunks and woodchucks, large in horses and giraffes that gather sound waves on the open plains, largest of all in African elephants, and most elaborate in bats that are aware of ultrasonic sounds (Figs. 17.7, 17.8). A number of mammals, especially seals and others living in the water, can close the entrance to the

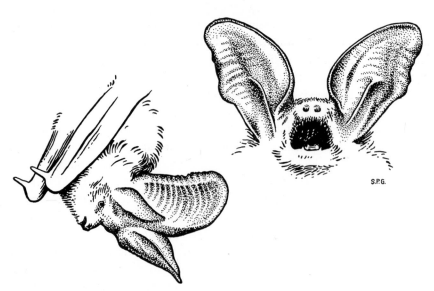

S.P.G.

Fig. 17.7. The enormous external ears of insectivorous bats. *Left*, European long-eared bat; *right*, pallid cave bat of U.S.A. Bats hear ultrasonic sounds, wholly inaudible to human ears. (After Allen: *Bats*. Cambridge, Mass., Harvard University Press, 1939.)

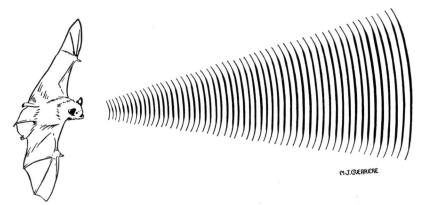

FIG. 17.8. A flying bat makes an ultrasonic cry completely inaudible to human ears. The curved lines represent the sound waves of a single pulse or vibration. Bats emit as many as 50 of these sounds per second and locate obstacles to their flight by hearing the echoes. The sound waves are here represented in true proportion to the size of the bat. When a bat's ears are stopped it strikes whatever is in its path. (Courtesy, Boring et al.: *Foundations of Psychology.* New York, John Wiley & Sons, 1948.)

auditory canal by a fleshy cover (tragus) that works like an eyelid. Man and other primates have only hairs and wax to ward off insects, dust, and water. The human ear has a cover at the entrance but has no means of pulling it down. Neither human noses nor ears can close their doors.

Each middle ear is an air-filled chamber opening into the pharynx by the Eustachian tube. The middle ear contains a chain of three little bones: the malleus or hammer at one end of the chain is attached to the eardrum by ligaments; the incus or anvil is the middle link; and the stapes or stirrup at the other end of the chain is attached to the membrane of the minute oval window in the bony capsule containing the inner ear (Fig. 17.9). Sound vibrations are transmitted from the eardrum over the bony bridge to the internal ear. Under the impact of faint sounds the eardrum is tightened, and under that of loud sounds it is loosened by involuntary muscles that attach it to the bony bridge. Thus the bridge becomes a lever transmitting light or heavy vibrations to the inner ear. Vibrations are also transmitted by the surrounding bone.

The inner ear contains the real mechanism of hearing, the organ of Corti, triply protected by the membranous cochlea or cochlear duct, by surrounding fluids, and by a casing of the hardest bone in the body (Fig. 17.9). The structures of the cochlea are well known, but the details of the way in which they work are still explained only theoretically. Only a bare outline of it can be given here; books containing further details are given in the suggested reading for this chapter.

The cochlea is divided into three fluid-filled cavities, the cochlear duct,

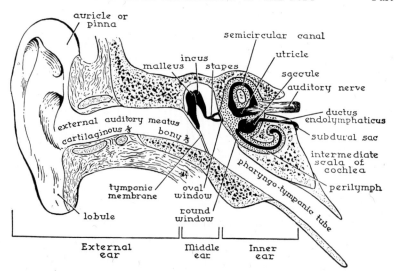

Fig. 17.9. The human mechanism of hearing and adjacent organ of balance, the semicircular canals. A diagram of the general structure shown by a cut through the temporal bone. The inner ear is structurally but not functionally associated with the semicircular canals. The pharyngo-tympanic duct (Eustachian tube) opens into the pharynx. Pressure of air against the outer side of the eardrum is evident in travel through a deep tunnel. It is balanced when the mouth is opened and air goes through the Eustachian tube and presses against the inner side of the eardrum. (Courtesy, Ham: *Histology*, ed. 2. Philadelphia, J. B. Lippincott & Co., 1953.)

and the vestibular cavity above and the tympanic below it. The latter two are continuous, one into the other at the tip of the cochlea. At the base of the cochlea the vestibular cavity comes to an end against the membrane filling the oval window and the stapes. At the base of the cochlea, the tympanic cavity is also ended by a membrane that closes the round window. When the membrane of the oval window is pushed in toward the vestibular cavity by vibrations in the middle ear, the fluid in the cavities is moved, finally pushing against the resilient membrane in the round window (Fig. 17.9). As the minute vibrations surge along through the fluid from the oval to the round window, they vibrate the basilar membrane on the floor of the cochlear duct which contains the actual organ of hearing, the organ of Corti. Fibers of the auditory nerve extend to the receptor cells in this organ. These cells are similar to those of taste and smell in that their hairlike processes protrude into the fluid which floods over them. A delicate membrane (tectorial) projects like a miniature porch roof over and so close to the processes that the slightest jar of the basilar membrane brings them in touch with it. Thus the receptor cells are stimulated, and they in turn excite impulses that are transmitted to the brain by fibers of the auditory nerves.

SUMMARY OF ACTION. Sound vibrations move along the chain of bones in the middle ear and against the membrane of the oval window, thereby pushing it inward. This starts corresponding vibrations that run through the fluid for the length of the vestibular cavity and on into the tympanic cavity toward the round window. As the vibrations travel along the cavities, each one vibrates the basilar membrane and the sound receptors, more or less strongly and in different regions, depending on its own character. Finally, the vibration expends its force against the membrane of the round window which it bends outward a little toward the middle ear. Our ability to distinguish different tones is due to the fact that the vibrations of a particular tone pass more frequently through a certain part of the basilar membrane. The nerve fibers ending in that part carry the impression of the tone to the brain.

Vision—Photoreceptors

Light filters through the air in one direction; if it enters water it passes on in a different direction. This change in direction is refraction and it occurs in greater or lesser degree whenever light passes from one medium into another. The amount of change in the direction depends upon the character of the new medium and the angle at which the light enters it (Fig. 17.10).

Lenses. A lens is a transparent object with a curved surface. A drop of water is a lens. The lens in the eye of a frog or a man contains thousands of cells. Artificial lenses are commonly made of glass, of quartz, or of fluorite. When the surface of a biconvex lens is properly curved all the rays that enter it are brought to a focal point at a certain distance from it, called the focal distance. This distance varies with the curvature of the lenses in cameras and microscopes, as well as with the curvature of the cornea and lens in the human eye.

There are various shapes of artificial lenses; the common foundation lens

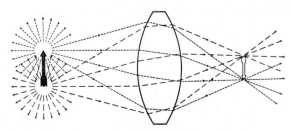

FIG. 17.10. Formation of an image by a lens. Rays of light are reflected from each point of a black arrow pointed end up. Rays from the right of the arrow are intercepted by a glass lens and their courses are bent. Those from the lower end of the arrow are turned upward; those from the upper end are turned downward. Rays from every point of the black arrow are brought to a focus in a point beyond the lens. These points compose a reversed image, shown by a white arrow pointed end down. We see everything upside down. On the retina the legs of a horse point up. The interpretation of the brain points them down. (Courtesy, Walls: *The Vertebrate Eye.* Bloomfield Hills, Mich., The Cranbrook Press, 1942.)

is convex. Biconvex lenses are thick at the center and thin on the periphery. Lenses in the eyes of fishes are spherical; in the eyes of mammals they are usually oval and elastic. The sharper the curvature of a biconvex lens, the shorter its focal distance, as in the nearsighted eye (Fig. 17.18). Light passing through a biconvex lens produces a reverse image (Fig. 17.10). Rays reflected from the lower part of an object meet in the upper part of its image and vice versa, creating a small picture that is upside-down. Likewise, the rays reflected from the right side of the object pass to the left side of the image and vice versa, thus the picture is not only upside-down, but its sides are reversed. We learn the proper position of an object by experience and after that we cannot imagine it otherwise. A cat's eyes show a mouse with feet up, but her brain doubtless shows her a mouse with its feet down.

Image-Forming Eyes. Rays of light reflected from an object fall upon the sensitive receptors and initiate chemical reactions within them which create impulses in the associated nerve fibers. The impulses pass along the fibers to the brain where they are interpreted (Figs. 16.11, 16.22). The number and direction of the light rays and the nature of the receptors on which they fall determine the character of the image they form. Lenses guide light rays to form an image in the eyes of the great majority of animals. There are three main types of image-forming eyes: (1) the exceptional pinhole eyes of Nautilus, in which the rays are brought into diffused focus through a minute hole in the front of each eye (Fig. 17.11); (2) the compound eyes

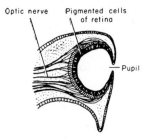

PINHOLE – CAMERA EYE
WITHOUT A LENS

FIG. 17.11. The pinhole eye of Nautilus, the paper sailor, a mollusk related to the octopus, is similar to the pinhole camera which is in focus for all distances, but only a little light is admitted and the image is dim and foggy.

of insects, spiders, and other arthropods, with a lens set into each one of the multiple tubes so that no rays can reach the lens except from directly in front (Fig. 17.12); and (3) the eyes of vertebrates with a single lens set in the front of the eye where it receives light reflected at various angles from the object (Figs. 17.13 and 17.14). The capacities of image-forming eyes are matched by the habits and abilities of their owners to act appropriately for what they see. A fish hawk flying a 100 feet above a lake not only sees a fish beneath the surface but plunges unerringly after it even disappearing into the water to clutch it. The vision of the fish hawk is significant because

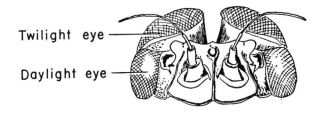

Twilight eye

Daylight eye

A. FRONT FACE

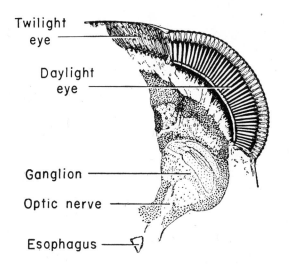

Twilight eye

Daylight eye

Ganglion

Optic nerve

Esophagus

B. SECTION OF COMPOUND EYE

FIG. 17.12. *Top*, face of adult male mayfly, Callibaetis. In the compound eyes of mayflies there are hundreds of lenses each one set so deep in a tube that no rays can reach it except those coming from directly in front of it. The segment at the top, "the daylight eye," provides detailed vision; the other segment, "the twilight eye" provides images or general vision. The daylight eye of this mayfly is twice the size of a period on this page. The majority of mayflies are twilight fliers. *Bottom*, section of the eye of an adult male Callibaetis, highly magnified. (*Bottom*, after Shafer: "Divided Eyes of Certain Insects," *Proc. Wash. Acad. of Sciences*, March, 1907.)

it fits into the bird's whole pattern of behavior (Fig. 17.13). Even if a jellyfish had the eyes of a hawk, it would still lack the plunge of a hawk.

Chemical Reactions of the Light Receptors. Although eyes have developed in different epochs of evolution and in widely different kinds of animals, they almost universally contain lenses and carotenoid pigments (Figs. 17.14 and 17.16). The lens guides the light to the receptors; the carotenoid pigments in the receptors take part in the chemical reactions that create the nerve impulses passing to the centers of vision in the brain.

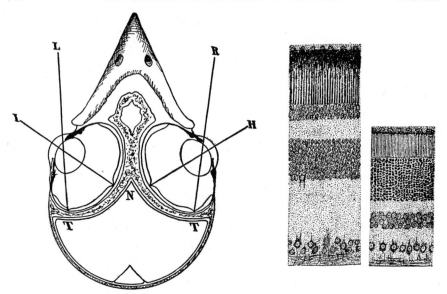

Fig. 17.13. *Left*, a section through the head of the White-bellied Swallow. Three features are characteristic of birds, the most supremely eye-minded of all vertebrates: the eyeball is relatively the largest among animals (the eye of an ostrich is 2 inches in diameter); a vascular nutrient organ, the pecten, is attached to the retina which does not contain blood vessels; the retina, which is the essential, sensory layer of the eye, is the most elaborate among animals, and the foveas or areas of clearest vision, two in each eye are the most perfect. In the diagram the lines *RT* and *LT* represent rays of light. They are reflected on the foveas from an object in front of the bird and fall on the foveas in each eye creating two-eyed or binocular vision. The lines *HN* and *IN* represent rays from objects visible on only one side of the bird and fall only on one fovea creating monocular vision. *Right*, sections of the retina of a crow and a dog, shown with the same magnification. They emphasize the relatively great thickness of the bird's retina. The visual cells are near the tops of the figures. Light enters from the bottom. (Courtesy, Wood: *The Fundus Oculi of Birds*. Chicago, The Lakeside Press, 1917.)

Carotenoids are red and yellow pigments that are most abundant in plants, especially carrots. They can be transformed to vitamin A (Table 11.1) and are stored as such in the liver. Like other substances that have important and common uses, they are plentiful and widely distributed. They are present in light receptors of such great variety as the orange-red light spots of the protozoan Euglena, the eyes of starfishes, squid, and crabs, and the rod and cone cells of vertebrates (Fig. 17.17). Carotenoids are the visual pigments, the purples, violets, and yellows often referred to in connection with the rods and cones, especially of the human eye. They are being found in more and more animals; three of them have recently been extracted by George Wald from the cone cells of chickens (Table 11.1, vitamin A). Similar studies by Wald and others indicate that the perception of light, including color, is basically dependent upon these common pigments. Wald has stated:

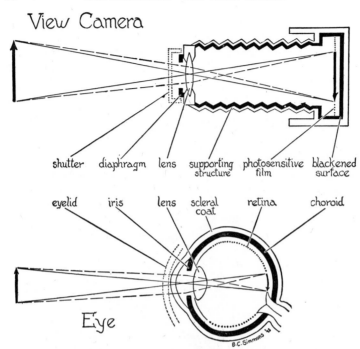

Fig. 17.14. Diagrams illustrating the similarities of the human eye and the camera. In both eye and camera there are two main processes: a physical one by which rays of light are directed to a focus through one or more lenses and a chemical reaction between light and light sensitive substances. In the eye, the latter occurs in the rod and cone cells of the retina; in the camera it occurs within the coating of the photosensitive film. In the camera, the glass lens can be moved nearer or farther from the film in focusing. In the human eye, the shape of the lens as well as its position are changed. In the camera, the amount of light is changed by the diaphragm; in the eye, by the iris. (Courtesy, Ham: *Histology*, ed. 2. Philadelphia, J. B. Lippincott & Co., 1953.)

"It seems likely now that photoreception, visual [image forming] or phototropic [light turned] throughout all living organisms may be founded chemically upon this single group of substances."

THE HUMAN EYE

The Eye and the Camera. The eye is a complex organ that takes pictures again and again on the same light receptors (rod and cone cells) that regenerate their own sensitivity and after one exposure are instantly ready for another. The camera is a complex contrivance that takes pictures when properly operated and its light receptor, the coating of the film, can only be exposed once because it never regenerates (Fig. 17.14). The evolution of eyes has been going on many millions of years. The history of the camera has been relatively short, even including the early suggestions of it in the eleventh century. It has not been copied from the eye but has been built to obtain similar results and automatically resembles the eye.

Path of Light through the Eye. In order to reach the retina light must penetrate through: (1) the conjunctiva, the outermost covering of the front of the eyeball; (2) the cornea, the transparent front part of the outer, tough or sclerotic coat of the eyeball, actually a most important part of the eye that brings rays of light to a focus (Figs. 17.14 and 17.16); (3) a transparent fluid (aqueous humor) that fills the front chamber of the eye; (4) the crystalline lens, important in accommodation (Fig. 17.14); and (5) the transparent jelly (vitreous humor) that fills the back chamber and keeps the eyeball expanded, and finally (6) the retina with its receptors, the rod and

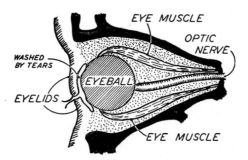

FIG. 17.15. The eyeball in its socket. It is set deep in a bony socket, packed about by fat, curtained by eyelids, and washed by tears. Each eye is equipped with six muscles by which the front of the ball is moved up or down, from side to side and slightly rotated. (Reprinted from *The Machinery of the Human Body* by Carlson and Johnson, by permission of The University of Chicago Press. Copyright 1948.)

cone cells. These curiously enough are seemingly turned away from the light, a condition that can be explained by their development (Figs. 17.14 and 17.16). The back wall of the retina and the choroid coat behind it are heavily pigmented and so absorb excess light. Rays of light pass freely through the pupil which is surrounded by the iris, a circular curtain which is part of the vascular or choroid coat of the eyeball.

A structure usually located in the choroid coat, called the tapetum lucidum (L., bright carpet), acts as a light-concentrating mirror and causes the night eyeshine of many animals. Some tapeta, as in many hoofed animals, consist of shimmering connective tissue fibers. In others, the cells are packed with glimmering rodlets, as in the cat's eye, the brilliance of which encouraged the Egyptians to reverence cats which could reflect the light of the sun even at night.

Accommodation for Near and Far Objects. The image made by means of the cornea and the crystalline lens is a very small picture upside-down on the retina (Fig. 17.14). In sharpening this picture the eye accommodates,

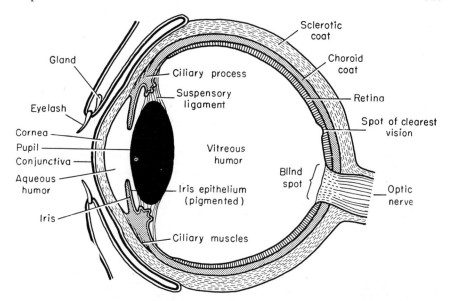

Fig. 17.16. General structure of the human eyeball cut in a vertical section, from the top of the eye downward. The blind spot is the place where the fibers from the cells in the retina leave the eyeball and form the optic nerve. When the eye is directed upon an object it is placed so that the image falls upon the fovea, the area of clearest vision.

that is, changes the focus of the rays from near or far objects by changes in the curvature of the crystalline lens. This is made possible by stretching or relaxing the tension upon the ring of the suspensory ligament attached at one border to the lens and at the other inserted into the circle of ciliary muscles. When these muscles contract they pull the choroid coat forward and relax the tension on the ligament. The lens then becomes more convex, taking its natural more spherical shape. Rays of light from nearby objects are then brought to a focus on the retina in near vision (Fig. 17.14). When at rest, the eye is adjusted for far vision. The eyeball is always distended by the fluids within it and when the ciliary muscles are relaxed there is a chronic pull on the suspensory ligament. This flattens the lens, and rays reflected from distant objects are brought to a focus on the retina.

Imperfections in Convex Lenses. There are imperfections or aberrations in biconvex lenses because the rays that penetrate their thin margins meet in different places from those that pass through them near the center. The spherical aberration of the lens of the eye is partially corrected by the curvature of the cornea. Cameras usually have lenses with compensating curvatures fastened to the convex lens (Fig. 17.14).

Chromatic aberration or color error is also characteristic of single lenses. Short wave lengths are bent more strongly than longer ones. Thus rays of blue light are brought to a focus sooner than those of red light, resulting in a blur of white within a halo of color. All cameras are corrected for this defect by combinations of lenses. In the human eye part of the color error is corrected by the yellow tinge of the crystalline lens, actually a color filter that passes rays of certain wave lengths, i.e., visible light, but stops the ultra violet. Persons who have had the crystalline lenses of both eyes removed because of cataracts can see in ultraviolet light which is not possible to normal eyes.

The Iris—Regulation of Light. Too much light spoils the picture on a film or retina. In the eye, excess light is stopped by the iris and reflections are reduced by the black lining of the eyeball provided by the pigmented layer of the retina and the choroid coat. The iris is a curtain containing a set of circular muscle fibers that contract in bright light and decrease the pupil and a set of radial muscle fibers that contract in dim light and enlarge the pupil. Such responses to changes in light intensity require 10 to 30 seconds. Flashlight photographs sometimes show the wide open pupils that did not have time to close.

The muscles of the iris are controlled by autonomic nerves (Table 16.2). Excitement of the sympathetic system, as in extreme pleasure, dilates the pupil. Certain drugs affect the iris; atropine that dilates it is commonly used during examinations of the eye.

The value of the iris as a curtain is increased by its content of dark pigment. In the white races the front layers of cells of the iris are relatively free from pigment and light passing through them appears blue, paler or deeper depending upon the amount of black in the background. Varying amounts of pigment distributed in the front layers of the iris are the basis for all the varieties of hazel, brown, and black eyes. Absence of pigment lets the blood vessels show, giving the pink eye of the albino.

The Light Receptors. The retina of man and most vertebrates contains two kinds of light receptor cells, the rods and cones, and many associated neurons (Fig. 17.17). The retina is connected with the brain by the bundle of thousands of axons that compose the optic nerve. Its exit from the back of the eyeball is the blind spot on the retina in which there are no receptors (Fig. 17.16).

Each receptor is composed of one part that is much like an ordinary nerve cell and either a rod- or a cone-shaped part that is sensitive to light and contains carotenoid pigments. The cone cells are responsible for vision in bright light, for detail, and for color vision. They are distributed over the central region of the retina and in the human eye are most abundant in a minute spot of clearest vision, the fovea (Fig. 17.16). The rod cells are especially equipped for vision in dim light, are insensitive to color and are numerous in the sides and periphery of the retina. Each cone cell is usually connected

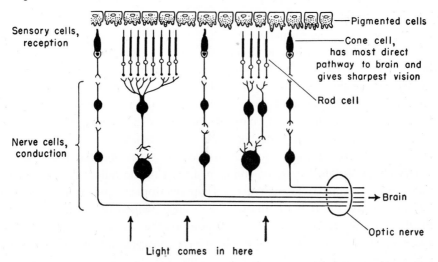

Sensory cells, reception

Nerve cells, conduction

Pigmented cells

Cone cell, has most direct pathway to brain and gives sharpest vision

Rod cell

Brain

Optic nerve

Light comes in here

FIG. 17.17. Section of the central part of the retina (highly magnified). The retina is composed of four layers of cells: an innermost one of nerve cells, the ganglion cells whose long processes (axons) constitute the optic nerve; the bipolar nerve cells that are the intermediates between the ganglion cells and the sensory cells; the sensory rod cells and cone cells; and heavily pigmented epithelial cells. The rod and cone cells are the receptionists of light and are chemically changed by it. The nerve cells are the conductors of effects of those changes. The pigmented layer is a backstop of light; pigment moves within its cells and into their processes. Why light does not first strike the rod and cone cells is explained in the story of the development of the eye.

with the brain by a single chain of neurons, whereas whole clusters of rod cells are connected with the brain by a single chain (Fig. 17.17). The acute vision of the cones seems to be related to their direct connection with the brain, and the less vivid vision of the rods to their indirect connection with it. Cones produce a sharp, detailed image; rods produce a soft, indefinite one. In the starlight, we see with the rods, and the cones, which are relatively insensitive to light, do not function at all. Cones begin to function when the light is of about 1000 times greater intensity than the smallest amount to which the eye can respond. In the gray dawn, the rods dominate vision and there is no color; as the light increases vision is taken over by the cones and the grass is green again. Every rod contains visual purple (carotenoid), a light-sensitive compound related to vitamin A. When light falls on the rods, its energy breaks the visual purple into visual yellow. If dim light is to be perceived, several rod cells must be affected by it at once. The impulse that is created in the associated neurons then passes over them. In the dark, visual yellow is resynthesized into visual purple and the rod cells are charged for another exposure to light. If one comes out of brilliant light into a darkened room, one is completely blinded for a few minutes because the visual purple in the rod cells has been bleached out by the bright light.

The blindness in the darkened room occurs when the visual yellow is being resynthesized to visual purple.

Theory of Color Vision. Rod cells are better understood than cone cells, but the latter are known to contain visual violet. Indications seem to justify the theory that there are at least three different kinds of cones, and that these are sensitive to the different wave lengths of light which produce the sensations of red, blue, and green color. According to this theory, the sensation of white results when all kinds of cones are stimulated equally, and intermediate colors result when two kinds of cone cells are stimulated unequally.

Defects of Vision. The most common defects of the human eye are nearsightedness (myopia), farsightedness (hypermetropia), and astigmatism. In the normal eye, the retina is the proper distance behind the cornea and lens for the light rays to come to a focus or point on the fovea. In the nearsighted eye, the eyeball is too long and the light rays converge in front of the retina and are diverging when they reach it; thus they produce a blurred image (Fig. 17.18). In the farsighted eye, the eyeball is too short and the retina too close to the lens; the rays come in contact with the retina before they converge. With age the lens loses its elasticity, does not become more convex in accommodation, and the eye is chronically farsighted.

Astigmatism, meaning "off the points," results from irregularities in the curvature of the cornea or the lens. In one plane the rays are brought in focus at different points from that of the rays in another plane. On the oculist's chart the upright lines may look clear and black, while horizontal ones look blurred and gray. Astigmatism is so common that this appearance on the chart is familiar to almost anyone whose eyesight has been tested.

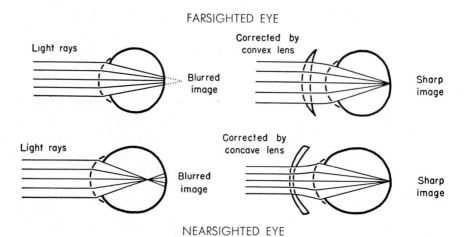

FARSIGHTED EYE

Light rays

Corrected by convex lens

Blurred image

Sharp image

Light rays

Corrected by concave lens

Blurred image

Sharp image

NEARSIGHTED EYE

Fig. 17.18. Diagrams of some common defects of the eye. Nearsighted eye, with elongated eyeball and rays brought to a focus in front of the retina. Farsighted eye, with shortened eyeball and light rays in focus behind the retina.

18

Reproduction

Living organisms have the remarkable power of producing new ones that look and act like themselves, though never exactly so. Many do this by the division of their substance into parts of equal size with nothing remaining to be a parent; all amebas begin life as orphans. Many others divide into parts of very unequal size, a large one, the parent's body and small ones, the cells, two of which, one male and one female must unite to make a new individual. Whatever the case, parental protoplasm is the first substance of the new individual no matter what its kind, ameba, bird, or man.

Asexual and Sexual Reproduction

Either asexual or sexual reproduction increases the population. The main difference is in its variety. By asexual reproduction one cell becomes two cells, and by sexual reproduction two cells become one and this one divides asexually into many (Fig. 18.1). Thus, generations of amebas are produced, and the bodies of multicellular animals increase in size whether small or great, fleas or elephants. Asexual division, the pioneer method of reproduction, has persisted throughout the course of evolution.

Various invertebrates divide into two or more parts, each of them a new individual. In the marine worm, Autolytus, a second head appears part way down the body. There are soon two fully organized worms attached one behind the other. For a time they swim about tandemwise, then separate and each one swims away alone. Sometimes a chain of individuals will form and swim about together. Fresh-water hydras put forth buds that pinch off as independent animals, and thus stop just short of colonial life. The internal buds (gemmules) that form within fresh-water sponges are eventually set free to start new colonies. No higher animals produce buds; cats do not bud off kittens.

Sexual reproduction differs from asexual in that two individuals furnish different kinds of cells, eggs and sperms. When such cells are fully developed

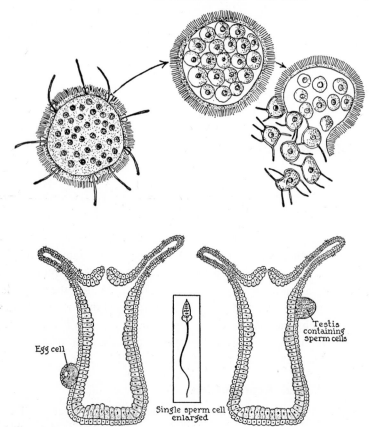

FIG. 18.1. Two methods of reproduction. *Top*, asexual, by which one cell becomes two or more. A one-celled animal (Trichospherium) dividing into many individuals; the substance of the parent is entirely divided up among the offspring. *Bottom*, sexual, by which two cells, egg and sperm, unite in one cell, the first of the multicellular body. A male and a female many-celled animal (Hydra) with the respective sex cells. (Courtesy, Corner: *The Hormones in Human Reproduction.* Princeton, N.J., Princeton University Press, 1942.)

their pattern is set; neither their form nor function can be changed, and by itself the life span of either kind is short. When they are joined, the resulting cell contains the potentiality for longer life, an extraordinary variety of patterns of structure and actions, and unique adjustments. It may bring forth not only the traits of its parents and grandparents but signs of its ancient animal ancestry. Every child is a surprise.

Beginnings of Sex

Conjugation. Paramecia and many other protozoans join in a union or conjugation that resembles the mating of multicellular animals. Ordinarily paramecia swim through the water, passing and repassing their neighbors without response. From time to time, more often in some species than in others, this behavior changes with dramatic suddenness. Mating spreads through the population like an epidemic and for hours a lone paramecium is scarcely to be found. Couples swim about for hours, always in the same position with parts of their oral surfaces held together by a bridge of protoplasm (Fig. 18.2). After preliminary divisions of the micronucleus in each one, two micronuclei of unequal size remain in each individual. The smaller male micronucleus, essentially similar to a sex cell, migrates over the protoplasmic bridge and fuses its substance with the nonmigrating female micronucleus. The female micronucleus becomes a permanent part of each recipient paramecium. After the exchange is completed, the bridge is gradually withdrawn and the mates (conjugants) separate, each animal carrying with it a new strain of inheritance to be distributed to its descendants.

The frequency of conjugation varies in different species, environments, and physiological conditions. After conjugation paramecia divide more rapidly as if mating were the rescue from a physiological depression. However, no such rescue is essential. In a famous experiment carried on at Yale University, L. L. Woodruff kept a culture of paramecia (*P. aurelia*) for over 20 years (12,000 generations) without conjugation simply by changing the water daily and keeping the food and environment satisfactory.

Special mating types of paramecia were discovered by H. S. Jennings who reared thousands of them from natural pond populations. Among them he found certain ones that would and others that would not mate outside their own type, such as type A and B that mated together and a type C that would not mate with either of them. It seems that type C is not a fixed sex but is only generally sexual; animals of this type have not become limited and settled into the bisexual pattern. Their situation suggests that the development of sexes might not have been restricted to two kinds. If a general sexual type had persisted among higher animals including man, would not social behavior have been complex beyond imagination?

Endomixis. In some species of paramecia and under certain conditions there is a nuclear reorganization, called endomixis, and this is followed by an invigoration similar to that after conjugation. This process takes place entirely within one individual.

Sexual Reproduction

The Plan of the System. The bisexual reproductive systems of multicellular animals consist of the gonads, i.e., testes in the male, ovaries in the female, and a series of more or less elaborate tubes and glands located within the system or in another part of the body. The gonads are the essential organs that produce the sex or germ cells. The tubes and sacs provide for the transportation of the sex cells and the developing young that may originate from their

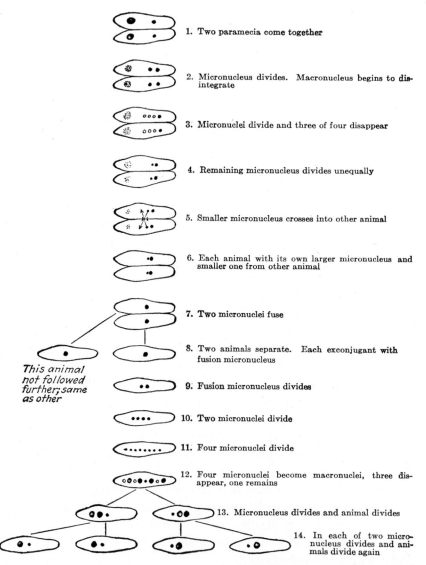

FIG. 18.2. Mating of paramecia, a complicated process by which part of the substance of heredity in the male micronuclei is exchanged between the mates and later distributed to their descendants. The large nuclei or macronuclei, are represented by black spots. They are concerned with the bodily processes, and appear to take no part in conjugation and gradually disappear during it. The micronuclei that are exchanged between the mates are shown by small black dots; those that disappear are shown by circles. (After Jennings. Courtesy, Wolcott: *Animal Biology,* ed. 3. New York, McGraw-Hill Book Co., 1946.)

fusion. The glands produce secretions that control activities of the system.

Similarities of Male and Female. The union of a male and female germ cell is the first event in the life of the great majority of multicellular animals. Since each of them has a male and a female parent it is not surprising that females inherit male as well as female characteristics, and that males inherit female ones as well as male. No animal is entirely male or female in its chemical content, its structure, or its behavior. The pars anterior of the pituitary gland of the male liberates the same gonad (sex organ) stimulating hormones as that of the female. The nipples, developed in all female mammals, are also present in the males.

The characteristics of the opposite sex appear in the sex reversal that occurs in some animals in nature as well as in experiments. The right ovary of most birds is ordinarily only partly developed and the left one produces the eggs. If the left one is removed by careful operation the small and incomplete right one usually develops into a testis and produces sperm cells. This is because the cortex or outer layer of the bird's fully developed ovary secretes a male-suppressing substance that ordinarily prevents the development of sperm cells. Without it they would form in the medulla or central part of the ovary. In the experiment the active cortex was removed with the functional left ovary; it was undeveloped in the incomplete right one. Thus the male part of the right ovary was no longer repressed.

Male and Female Cells—Gametes. In many lower plants and animals, all of them aquatic, the male and female cells are often about the same size and shape and both may swim with tail-like flagella. Within the bodies of multicellular animals, constituting essentially aquatic surroundings, the eggs are moved by cilia or by muscular pressure while the sperm cells are agile, persistent swimmers (Fig. 18.3). Eggs are the energy-conserving cells; sperms are the energy-expending cells. Many eggs are enlarged with food stored for the embryo (Table 19.1). We fry eggs for food, but not sperm cells.

More eggs and sperms are produced than ever fulfill their promise. A bullfrog lays from 10,000 to 20,000 eggs at one time. Counting on one egg matured per month, covering the period between 12 and 45 years, a woman produces about 430 eggs. Yet, within a pair of human ovaries thousands of eggs wait in vain to develop further. George W. Corner quotes an investigator who counted the incompletely developed eggs in both ovaries of a 22-year-old woman and found about 420,000. The numbers of sperm cells are astronomical in the majority of animals. It has been estimated that during his reproductive lifetime, a man produces about four hundred billion sperms or about one billion to each egg released from the human ovaries.

Fertilization. The union of a sperm and egg which constitutes the beginning of a new individual is fertilization. It may be external and occur in the open water, as it does in starfishes and sea-urchins, most fishes, frogs and toads,

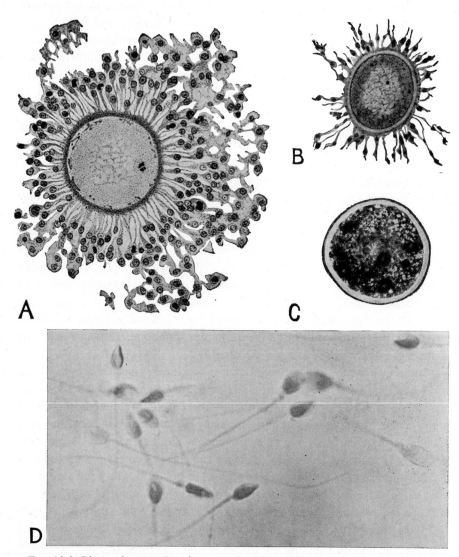

Fig. 18.3. Photomicrographs of eggs and sperm. *A*, human ovum about to burst the enclosing sac and leave the ovary. *B*, a similar stage of the ovum of a macaque monkey. *C*, living human ovum washed out of an oviduct and photographed immediately. The small whitish spots are fatty particles; the nucleus is not visible. The human ovum is about 1/175 of an inch in diameter, barely visible to the naked eye. *D*, living human sperm photographed through a phase contrast microscope. The nucleus of the sperm cell contains the substance of 24 chromosomes, half the heritable material of a new individual. The human sperms are the smallest cells in the body; estimated to take about 2500 of them to cover a period mark such as on this page. (*A*, *B*, *C*, courtesy, Patten: *Human Embryology*, ed. 2. New York, The Blakiston Co., 1953. *D*, courtesy, O. W. Richards, American Optical Company.)

or internal within the body of the female as in some fishes, in salamanders, reptiles, birds, and mammals (Fig. 18.4). Fertilization can occur only in a wet place since sperm cells are swimming cells and all cells are essentially aquatic.

The eggs of sea-urchins and sand-dollars are beautifully translucent and beneath the microscope much of the process of fertilization can be seen. During the spring breeding season the common eastern sea-urchin (*Arbacia*

FIG. 18.4. Courtship of brook sticklebacks (mature fish, two-and-a-half inches long); external fertilization of the eggs. In spring the male leaves the school, stakes out his territory and builds a nest, and at the same time appears in breeding colors. The females are now ready to lay from 50 to 100 eggs. The courtship begins. The male (*left*) zigzags toward the female, swims toward his nest, and repeatedly thrusts his head into it. The female enters the nest and lays the eggs. She leaves the nest. The male enters and sheds the milt (sperm cells) over them. The sperms and eggs meet in the open water. The male fans the water over the eggs and thus increases their supply of oxygen; lines indicate currents in the water. (Courtesy, Tinbergen: *Social Behavior in Animals*. London, Methuen, 1953.)

punctulata) naturally deposits its eggs and sperm directly into the sea. If the mature male and female animals are placed in separate dishes of sea water, the sex cells are discharged. A few eggs, the size of coarse sand grains, can then be slipped onto a glass slide with a little sea water. Under the microscope the nucleus of the living egg appears as a rounded body about one-sixth the diameter of the whole egg and the membrane surrounding the cell and the grainy cytoplasm are clearly visible. If now a droplet of the sea water containing sperm cells is added to the eggs, thousands of sperms can be seen swimming toward one or another of the eggs. At once, the surface of almost every egg becomes fringed by sperm cells headed toward the eggs with tail-pieces vibrating. In less than an instant this activity passes, the sperms cease moving all at once as if a quick shadow passed over each egg and stopped them. Actually, one sperm has pierced the egg membrane and is on its way to the nucleus and as this occurs a special barrier, the fertilization membrane, instantly forms around the egg and shuts out the competing sperms. With the union of the sperm and egg nuclei that soon follows, the inheritance of the coming individual is decided and its sex determined. Without ado or hesitancy the single cell goes through the process of division into two cells, repeating this again and again. Thus a new sea-urchin begins.

Fertilization is a kind of junction between the existence of a sperm and an egg, each of them prepared by meiotic divisions, and a new individual in which mitotic divisions (Chap. 3) and differentiation are preeminent. These processes are discussed under their respective names.

SPECIAL TYPES OF SEXUAL REPRODUCTION

The bisexual method of reproduction is the usual one in higher animals, in all of the vertebrates, and in many invertebrates, jellyfishes, nearly all insects, starfishes, sea-urchins, and their kin. Several varieties and irregularities of sexual reproduction occur.

Hermaphroditism. In some species, each individual normally produces both eggs and sperm cells at the same time, and is called an hermaphrodite. Such animals belong to a few groups of invertebrates, among them planarians and other flatworms, earthworms, leeches, and snails. Among vertebrates, hermaphroditism occurs only rarely. Even in hermaphroditic species, pairs of animals mate and cross-fertilization occurs. In earthworms, the reproductive organs are so located that the eggs of one worm can be only fertilized by the sperm of another worm (Chap. 28).

Although rare, hermaphroditic frogs, birds and even mammals are known; some of these animals have one testis and one ovary, or some other combination of the primary organs. More often, the animal is a partial hermaphrodite having the primary organs of one sex and the ducts and external genitalia of the other. Hermaphrodites with both testicular and ovarian tissue are exceedingly rare in man.

Freemartins. A freemartin is a sterile cow which was born a twin of a bull calf. Her ovaries are usually testislike but contain no developing sperms; the vasa deferentia and other masculine ducts are represented but the external genitalia are mainly female. The twins are known to come from separate eggs. The sterile condition of the freemartin is believed to occur because the membranes (chorions) of the twins are fused in such a way that the blood vessels are joined and there is a common circulation between them. Thus, the hormone of the testes of the bull calf passes into the body of the heifer and acts upon the ovaries. The twin heifer is never sterile unless the membranes of the male and female embryos are fused. Freemartins are known to occur only in cattle, pigs, and goats.

Intersexes. Any normal, sexually produced animal has some structures of the opposite sex. Intersexes are individuals in which the development of such structures is carried to a more or less marked degree, actually degrees of hermaphroditism. Many examples of intersexes show that the plans of the male and female bodies are fundamentally similar and delicately balanced. A tilt in one direction lifts the maleness, in the other the femaleness.

Parthenogenesis. Eggs may develop without fertilization, i.e., parthenogenetically. Natural parthenogenesis is known only in the invertebrates, notably in many small crustaceans and certain orders of insects. In social ants, bees, and wasps the queen can lay either fertilized or unfertilized eggs. Male honeybees develop parthenogenetically. In most aphids (plant lice), there is one generation after another of wingless females, great populations in which every individual produces young from unfertilized eggs. In autumn, these are succeeded by a generation of parthenogenetically produced winged males and females from which fertilized, winter-hardy eggs are produced. In the spring a generation of females hatches from these and the program of the previous summer is repeated. Again every plant louse is busy on the production line; each one means dozens more.

ARTIFICIAL PARTHENOGENESIS. Certain kinds of eggs that normally require fertilization can be stimulated artificially by chemical and physical means to develop into embryos; some even grow into adult animals. This can be done by jolting them in revolving egg-shakers, pricking them with a fine needle, raising the temperature, or changing the content of the fluid about them. Eggs of cold-blooded animals that lay their eggs in open water were the first to be tested, those of starfishes, sea-urchins, and frogs being easiest to manipulate. The possibilities of artificial parthenogenesis were first clearly demonstrated in 1900 by Jacques Loeb who obtained over 200 tadpoles by stimulating frogs' eggs. About half of these lived to become well-grown young frogs of both sexes, the famous "fatherless frogs." When their tissues were examined, the cells of most of these proved to have the usual double number of chromosomes characteristic of frogs of their species and not half that number as might have been expected. More recently, eggs taken from the oviducts of rabbits have been stimulated by changes of fluid and temperature. These cleaving eggs were transplanted into the uteri of unmated foster mothers where some developed normally. After birth, they grew into adults as fatherless as the distinguished frogs of 1900. Such experiments show that an egg is capable of developing without the biparental inheritance, and that development may be started by physical or chemical means, possibly stimulating enzymes within the egg that are ordinarily activated by the entrance of the sperm cell. The puncture of an egg membrane by a fine needle appears to arouse the egg as well as a puncture by a sperm head. It seems that an egg may be as responsive to a physical starter as a motor.

PEDOGENESIS is parthenogenetic reproduction by a young, incompletely developed animal. Its normal occurrence in a species is extremely rare.

Neoteny. Under certain conditions tiger salamanders (*Ambystoma tigrinum*) that have not metamorphosed become sexually mature, mate, and produce fertile eggs. This is neoteny, also a rare condition.

Human Reproductive System

MALE

In man, as in other mammals, the male reproductive system consists of a pair of testes in which the sperm cells are produced and a series of ducts and associated glands by which they are protected, nourished, and transported (Fig. 18.5).

Structure and Function. The testes lie in extensions of the body cavity covered with skin, the scrotal sacs, that hang outside the body. Each testis is the size of a walnut, about an inch long, smooth and oval. It consists of hundreds of seminiferous or sperm-bearing tubules, each a foot or two long, and the thickness of a coarse thread. All of them are tightly coiled in an entanglement which requires exceedingly skillful dissection to unravel (Fig. 18.6). Under the influence of a gonad-stimulating hormone of the

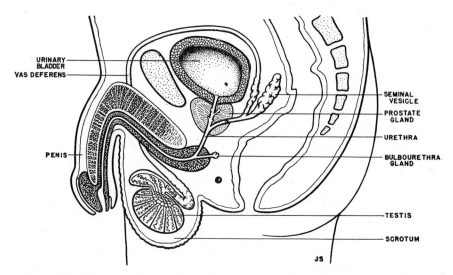

FIG. 18.5. Diagram of a section of human male reproductive organs showing their relation to the urinary bladder and urethra. (Courtesy, Harbaugh and Goodrich, eds.: *Fundamentals of Biology*. New York, The Blakiston Co., 1953.)

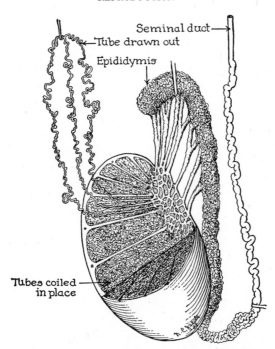

Fig. 18.6. The human testis with a piece removed and some of the seminiferous tubules drawn out of place. The sperm cells develop within the hundreds of these threadlike seminiferous tubules. They mature as they pass through other ducts, especially the epididymis, the much coiled single duct that lies along the side of each testis. (Courtesy, Corner: *The Hormones in Human Reproduction.* Princeton, N.J., Princeton University Press, 1942.)

pars anterior of the pituitary gland, the sperms develop from cells in the walls of the seminiferous tubules. They divide repeatedly, reduce their chromosomes to the half number, finally become very minute, and each develops a single flagellum, a swimming tailpiece (Figs. 18.3 and 18.7). At first the sperms cling to the supporting cells in the lining of the tubules, then they move into the open channels, and are gradually carried toward the outer ducts. In animals that breed the year round, such as rats, rabbits, and man, they are produced more or less continuously. In those with limited annual breeding seasons, such as birds, the production stops between seasons.

The testes develop in the body cavity near the lower ends of the kidneys, locations which the ovaries occupy throughout life. Before birth, however, they gradually slip downward into the scrotal sacs. In man, this location is permanent. In rats, rabbits, and several other mammals, the testes slip in and out of the abdominal cavity. They are outside in the scrotal sacs during the breeding season, and in the abdominal cavity between those seasons. If the testes of certain animals abnormally remain in the body cavity, its higher temperature destroys the sperm cells; such testes are said to be hidden or crypt-

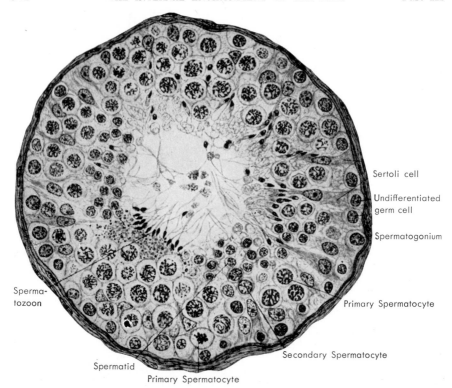

Sertoli cell

Undifferentiated
germ cell

Spermatogonium

Sperma-
tozoon

Primary Spermatocyte

Secondary Spermatocyte

Spermatid

Primary Spermatocyte

FIG. 18.7. Photograph of the seminiferous tubule ($\times$ 550) in which spermatozoa develop. The outermost dark band is the wall of the tubule, mainly connective tissue. All of the other cells are developing sperms and cells (Sertoli) which nourish the sperms. The nearly mature spermatozoa are nearest the fluid filled center of the tubule. Their dark, oval heads are crowded together and their excessively slender tails (flagella) extend into the fluid. Between them and the wall of the tubule are sperms in successive stages of development beginning near the wall. They multiply; their nuclei divide by mitosis and each sperm has 48 chromosomes. Nearer the center others that are further developed divide by meiosis and each mature sperm has 24 chromosomes. (Courtesy, Ham: *Histology*, ed. 2. Philadelphia. J. B. Lippincott Co., 1953.)

orchid. Rarely, as in armadillos, elephants, and whales, the testes remain permanently in the body cavity and yet are not injured by the body temperature. Under some strain of the abdominal muscles a loop of the small intestine may be forced into the passage through which the testis slips; this is called inguinal hernia.

The seminiferous tubules of each testis unite to form a dozen larger ducts which in turn open into the epididymis, a single tortuously coiled duct about 21 feet long. This duct is lined by secretory cells which contribute to the seminal fluid in which the sperm cells slowly mature and develop part of their motility (Fig. 18.6). From the epididymis they move into the sperm duct (vas deferens). These sperm ducts, one from each testis, pass upward into the body cavity and, joining together, enter the urethra which extends through the intromittent organ or penis to the external opening (Fig. 18.5).

Other glands, chiefly the seminal vesicles and the prostate gland, also contribute to the seminal fluid. This fluid contains salts that act as protective buffers against the acids in the urethra of the male and in the reproductive passages of the female, and glucose, a nutrient. The prostate gland almost completely surrounds the urethra near its exit from the urinary bladder. In elderly men, this gland often enlarges. Since its outer surface is covered by an unyielding capsule it can do nothing else but squeeze the urethra and more or less cut off the passage of urine. The gland was named prostate (Gr., standing before) from its position in front of the urinary bladder and is in nowise "prostrate" as it is sometimes called.

The urethra extends through the penis to its external opening (Fig. 18.5). It contains sperm cells only when the penis is erected, that is, when the "spongy" tissues surrounding it are stiffened by the blood that floods into them, and the sperm ducts contract spasmodically, forcing the sperms into it before

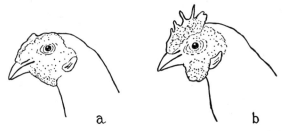

FIG. 18.8. The effect of a hormone of the testis on the comb of the cock. *a,* castrated cockerel, otherwise untreated; *b,* a castrated cockerel after 11 days treatment with extract of testis. Drawn from photographs by Freud and co-workers. (Courtesy, Corner: *The Hormones in Human Reproduction.* Princeton, N.J., Princeton University Press, 1942.)

or during copulation. At the same time urine is shut out of it. The spurts or ejaculations of seminal fluid, a half-teaspoonful or less in bulk, are estimated to contain about 300 million sperm cells. In the ordinary, somewhat shrunken condition of the penis, the skin is very loose and a fold of it, the foreskin, covers the tip. This is very often removed in babies by a simple operation called circumcision. This is a hygienic measure and a very old religious rite.

Testicular Hormone. The testes produce the sperm cells; they also produce fluids. Under stimulation by a hormone (gonadotrophic) of the anterior lobe of the pituitary gland, they secrete a male hormone (androgen) that causes and maintains the development of the secondary sex characters such as voice, form, behavior, and sexual activity (Fig. 18.8). The male hormone is believed to be secreted by interstitial cells lying between the seminiferous tubules. In spite of its name and effects, androgen belongs to the same family of chemical substances as the female hormones, estrogen and progesterone. This is another aspect of the similarity of maleness and femaleness already mentioned and one of the many cases of the likeness of substances that are active in carrying on different functions. Since every human being inherits traits from a male and a female parent, it is not surprising that the male hormone, androgen, figures in the metabolism of women as well as men and that the female hormone, estrogen, is in men as well as women. Both hormones appear in the urine of both sexes. Male hormones administered to animals will counteract the effects of the removal of the testes; a castrated male treated with androgen becomes normal except that it has no sperm cells and is of course infertile.

Castration and Sterilization. Castration of boys and men has been performed for various reasons from ancient times into the present. In the past it was done to produce the eunuchs (Fig. 18.9) who served in courts and harems and, as late as 1870, to preserve the soprano quality of voice in boy choristers. By true castration the testes are removed, thus sterilizing the animal; sterilization may also be produced by cutting or tying the duct (vas deferens) from each testis, thus blocking the passage of the sperm cells which are eventually absorbed. This type of sterilization is sometimes used to prevent the breeding of mental defectives and, with the consent of the person involved, for other reasons.

FEMALE

Structure and Function. The female reproductive system of mammals is more complicated than that of the male since it not only produces and provides for the eggs, but gives protection and nourishment to the developing young. The structures that take part in this double program are the ovaries, the oviducts (Fallopian tubes), the uterus, vagina and external genitalia, and the mammary glands (Fig. 18.10). Like the testes, the ovaries also produce internal secretions.

The ovaries develop and remain in the body cavity a little below the kidneys. Unlike the testes they do not suffer from the high temperature within the body. In mature women, they are the size of a shelled almond, about one and a half inches long and an inch wide. Each one consists of a central core of connective tissue, blood vessels and nerves, enclosed by a covering, the cortex consisting of cords and nests of epithelial cells. This contains the developing eggs and is covered by a single layer of cells, the germinal epithelium, from which the eggs originate. As they develop, they become surrounded by nutrient (follicular) cells. Each egg with its follicular sac forms an ovarian (or Graafian) follicle (Fig. 18.11). Under the influence of an anterior pituitary hormone (gonadotrophic), the follicle grows and a split develops between its outer and inner layers of cells. Into this space these cells or others near them secrete the liquor folliculi, containing the hormone estrogen that is responsible

CASTRATES

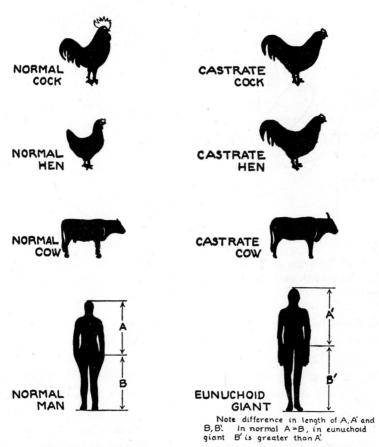

NORMAL COCK

CASTRATE COCK

NORMAL HEN

CASTRATE HEN

NORMAL COW

CASTRATE COW

NORMAL MAN

EUNUCHOID GIANT

Note difference in length of A, A' and B, B'. In normal A=B, in eunuchoid giant B' is greater than A'.

FIG. 18.9. Effects of castration on the shape of the body. These do not occur when sterilization is done by cutting or ligating sperm ducts without removing the testes. (Courtesy, Gregory: *A, B, C of the Endocrines*. Baltimore, Williams & Wilkins Co., 1935.)

for certain changes in the reproductive tract. As the egg matures, it hangs out into the cavity of the follicle which is swollen with fluid so that it protrudes like a minute volcano on the surface of the ovary (Figs. 18.11 and 18.12). At length, the wall of the follicle breaks and egg and fluid are set free; this is ovulation. Human ovulation may occur irregularly in the right or left ovary; ordinarily but one egg is freed per monthly cycle, but there may be two and rarely even more. As an egg matures, the number of its chromosomes is reduced to half that of the parent's body. In the human egg, the number is cut from 48 to 24. This involves two divisions (Chap. 3). The first one occurs before ovulation.

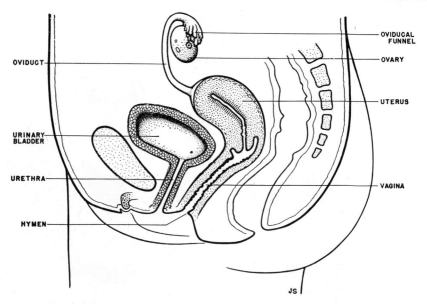

FIG. 18.10. Diagram of a section of the human female reproductive organs. (Courtesy, Harbaugh and Goodrich, eds.: *Fundamentals of Biology.* New York, The Blakiston Co., 1953.)

From the surface of the ovary, the egg ordinarily enters the enlarged funnel-shaped end of the oviduct which clasps the ovary in its soft ciliated folds (Fig. 18.10). The ends of the oviducts contain smooth muscle and have considerable range of position in cupping themselves about the ovaries. Even if the egg is not discharged directly into the funnel, it is apt to be pulled into it by the beat of the cilia always directed toward the uterus. If copulation has recently occurred and sperm cells are present, they usually meet the egg in the oviduct and fertilization results. Once in the oviduct whether fertilized or not the egg is carried on to the uterus by peristaltic contractions of the walls and the urging beat of the cilia. The second meiotic division occurs after the sperm enters the egg. The nucleus of the egg is then ready to unite with the nucleus of the sperm. At fertilization the addition of 24 chromosomes of the nucleus of the egg and 24 of the nucleus of the sperm restores the regular number of 48 in the human body cells. The sex of the individual is also determined at fertilization.

In the ovary, the broken follicle soon enlarges. Influenced by the gonad-stimulating hormones of the anterior pituitary its cells increase in size and number and form an endocrine gland, the corpus luteum or "yellow body" (Figs. 18.11, 18.12). This secretes progesterone which stimulates the further growth of the uterus. If the egg has been fertilized, the embryo developing from it may be gradually making its way into the uterine wall. If so, substances will be produced by its outer membranes and taken by the blood through the

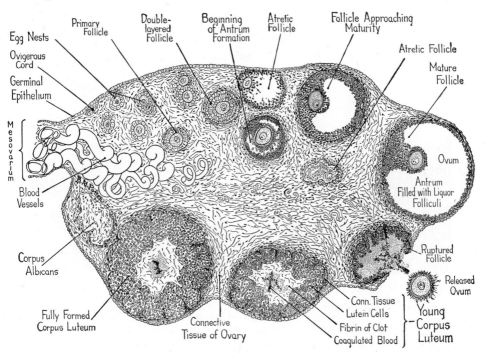

Egg Nests
Ovigerous Cord
Germinal Epithelium
Primary Follicle
Double-layered Follicle
Beginning of Antrum Formation
Atretic Follicle
Follicle Approaching Maturity
Atretic Follicle
Mature Follicle
Mesovarium
Blood Vessels
Corpus Albicans
Fully Formed Corpus Luteum
Connective Tissue of Ovary
Ovum
Antrum Filled with Liquor Folliculi
Ruptured Follicle
Released Ovum
Conn. Tissue
Lutein Cells
Fibrin of Clot
Coagulated Blood
Young Corpus Luteum

FIG. 18.11. Diagram of a cut through a mammalian ovary showing a sequence of stages in the growth and maturity of the ovarian follicle, the egg and its surrounding sac; the rupture of the sac and release of the egg; and the transformation of the sac into a gland, the corpus luteum. At the left, the strands of the mesovarium attach the ovary to the body wall. Follow the sequence clockwise around the ovary, starting at the mesovarium. Note the atretic follicle, one which abruptly ceases to grow before maturity and then degenerates. In the human ovary only one ovum ordinarily matures each four weeks during the active life of the ovary. (Courtesy, Patten: *Human Embryology,* ed. 2. New York, The Blakiston Co., 1953.)

mother's body, inevitably reaching the ovary. During the first half of pregnancy, the corpus luteum is affected by these substances and becomes about the size of a grape. Under stimulation from them and the pituitary gland, the corpus luteum conditions the uterus to hold the embryo until the time when hormones secreted by its placenta take part in this function.

The uterus is the organ within which the mammalian embryo is sheltered and nourished. This period (gestation) may be short or long, three weeks in a mouse, nine months in man, two years in elephants. An embryo enters the uterus as a minute ball of cells and leaves it via the vagina or birth canal as a well-formed individual. The lining of the uterus superficially resembles that of the mouth but has more glands and blood vessels and is physiologically responsive to the embryo and to certain endocrine secretions. It takes part in the formation of the maternal part of the placenta, the organ through which the bodies of mother and child cooperate in the growth and develop-

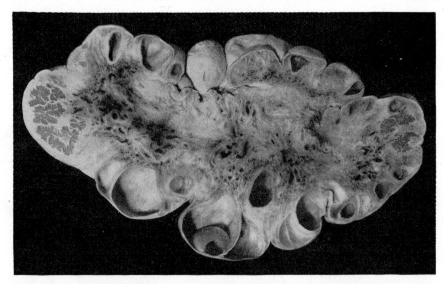

FIG. 18.12. Photograph of a section of the ovary of a whale showing the typical mammalian structure. In the largest follicles, the wall has split giving the appearance of double sacs. In life, the minute ovum (not visible) is in the smaller sac surrounded by fluid. There is a corpus luteum, the solid growth, at each end of the ovary. When taken from the whale this ovary was about 14 inches long. (Courtesy, The South Kensington Natural History Museum, London.)

ment of the latter. Without the embryo the reactions of the uterus are very different; they are outlined in a later paragraph.

Ovarian Hormones. The ovaries produce at least two hormones. Both are secreted under the influence of the gonad-stimulating hormones (the follicle stimulating hormone FSH and the luteinizing hormone LH) of the anterior lobe of the pituitary gland and the luteotrophic hormone (LTH) (Fig. 18.13).

Estrogen, the female counterpart of the testicular hormone, androgen, is secreted by the follicle. Although the ovaries are the principal source of estrogen, it has also been extracted from the placenta, testes, cortices of the adrenal glands, and even from certain plants. A second hormone, progesterone, is secreted by the corpus luteum, also by the placenta and adrenal cortex. Progesterone, acting with estrogen, stimulates the uterine wall to receive and hold the embryo; with estrogen it also stimulates the development and growth of the mammary glands. Both hormones play important parts in the reproductive cycles of the female, in the production of secondary sex characters, and in sexual behavior.

Female Reproductive Cycle

In mammals generally the reproductive or estrous cycle includes the production of one or more mature eggs and the preparations for the protection and nourishment of one or more embryos. Fertilization of the eggs may not occur

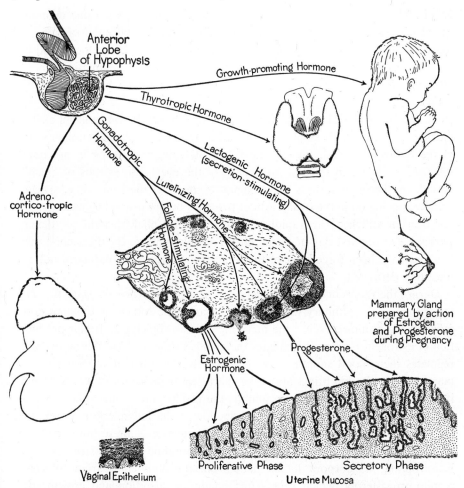

Fig. 18.13. Diagram showing hormones arising in the anterior lobe of the pituitary gland that especially influence the female reproductive cycle. (Courtesy, Patten, *Human Embryology,* ed. 2. New York, The Blakiston Co., 1953.)

and no embryos be produced. Then the cycle of ovulation and preparation will recur again and again. The human reproductive cycle is substantially the same as that of other mammals although in some respects spectacularly different from all except monkeys and other primates. The peculiarities of the human cycle can be much more clearly understood against the background of the reproductive cycle as it occurs in the majority of mammals.

Typical Estrous Cycle. This consists of a cycle of changes in the ovary, accompanied by changes in the entire reproductive tract. As repeatedly stated, the cycle is brought about by hormones of the pars anterior of the pituitary gland acting upon the ovaries, and by those of the ovaries acting upon the pituitary and on the reproductive tubes, especially the uterus, and on certain glands. The ovarian cycle comes to a climax in ovulation, when one or more eggs leave the ovaries. In rats and mice, the interval between ovulations is four and a half or five days; in cattle, horses, and pigs, 25 days. Dogs breed in early spring and fall, irregularly; cats in spring and early fall, sometimes more often. In rabbits, cats, and dogs ovulation occurs only when induced by copulation.

The events of the 21 day estrous cycle in the pig may be taken as an example of a cycle essentially similar to others. For two and a half weeks, the extent of the diestrous period, the pig moves about, eats, and sleeps in apparent satisfaction. Then, in the last three days of the cycle, the estrous or "heat" period, she becomes restless and sexually excited. At the same time, special activity is going on in the ovary. About two days before estrus begins a certain few ovarian follicles grow rapidly and their cavities fill with fluid containing estrogen. On the first day of estrus, they are fully mature. By the second day the eggs have been forced out of the follicles and are in the oviducts, due to meet the sperm cells.

During the reproductive cycle there is a seesaw influence between the anterior lobe of the pituitary gland and the ovary. The follicle-stimulating hormone of the pituitary excites the maturing ovarian follicles and their production of estrogen. Estrogen stimulates the glands in the walls of the uterus and regulates their blood supply, effects changes in the walls of the vagina and mammary glands, and brings about the characteristic behavior of estrus. When it reaches a certain level, it also inhibits the production of the follicle-stimulating hormone and stimulates the production of the luteinizing hormone by the pars anterior of the pituitary. Under the influence of these pituitary hormones, ovulation occurs. Aided by another hormone of the pars anterior, luteotrophin, the corpora lutea, made from the emptied ovarian follicles, secrete progesterone which causes further uterine secretion and growth. By about the sixth day after ovulation, the corpora lutea produce their full quota of progesterone. They continue for a time to make this secretion which further stimulates the uteri (two uteri in the pig), provided embryos are developing in them. Evidently the developing embryos contribute substances to the mother's blood that support the corpora lutea. The placenta (Chap. 19) associated with each embryo produces hormones that help to maintain the embryos in the uteri and prevent more new eggs from maturing in the ovary.

If the eggs are not fertilized, they degenerate, and phagocytic cells consume them as in all mammals. On the fifteenth day after the last ovulations the corpora lutea also degenerate and in consequence the activity and preparations which they stimulated in the uterus likewise subside. Their control of young ovarian follicles is lifted and on the nineteenth day after the ovulations, another group of these enlarges, and another reproductive cycle is about to begin.

Two features of the typical reproductive cycle of the lower mammals are especially significant. (1) Ovulation occurs at a time of sexual excitement, and mating will take place only during that period. (2) The degeneration of the corpora lutea and the withdrawal of preparations for an embryo in the uterus cause very little physiological stir.

Reproductive Cycle. As already noted, the reproductive cycle of menstruating mammals (the human species and the closely related apes and higher monkeys) is similar to that of other mammals except for activities associated with ovulation and the breakdown of the uterine lining.

The changes in the ovary including ovulation proceed as in other mammals. Usually, only one egg follicle enlarges and finally breaks, releasing its egg and the estrogen it contains. Ordinarily, the ovary is already clasped by the ciliated funnel of the oviduct and the egg is at once drawn into it (Figs. 18.11, 18.14). As already stated, even before it leaves the follicle, the number of its chromosomes has been reduced from the 48 of the general human body cells to the 24 of the human sex cells. The egg is carried slowly along the oviduct by the currents created by cilia and by the contraction of its muscle. In other primates, fertilization occurs in the oviducts, and this is known to be true of the human egg. Stimulated by the pituitary (Fig. 18.13), the enlarging follicle steadily secretes estrogen into the blood up to the time when the follicle releases the egg. Stimulated by this estrogen, the lining of the uterus becomes more glandular. After ovulation, the corpus luteum provides the progesterone which further induces the enlargement of the uterine glands, their secretory activity, and the increased blood supply (Figs. 18.11, 18.12, 18.14). All of these changes reach their height in the second week after ovulation. If an embryo arrives in the uterus at this time, it is surrounded by ideal conditions for its reception and nourishment. The embryo is extremely minute. As in the pig it produces important reactions in the uterine wall, and substances are absorbed into the blood that prolong the existence of the corpus luteum. As in the pig, too, the placenta provides hormones which help to stimulate the uterus to hold the embryo.

A very different program follows if no embryo enters the uterus although the latter is highly prepared for one. The corpus luteum degenerates for want of stimulation via the blood from the uterus. Cut off from progesterone, the uterus goes through the violent reactions of menstruation. Its swollen blood vessels are disturbed and ruptured; its lining cells, glands, and inner connective tissue break down. Blood from the broken vessels is mixed with the sloughed off tissues, and the whole cast off debris is gradually drained away through the vagina, a process lasting from one to seven days, but most often for five. Even in the latter part of the period another ovarian follicle is already forming and under the influence of its secreted estrogen the lining of the uterus and its

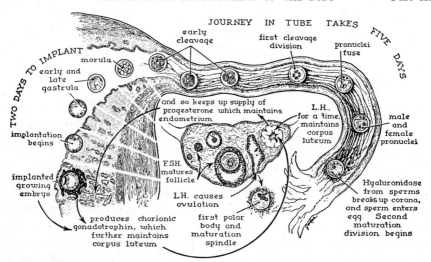

FIG. 18.14. Diagram showing essential steps in the beginning of a human individual, changes in which endocrines are prominent actors in a complex scene. *In the ovary.* An ovum and its follicular sac grow to maturity stimulated by F.S.H., the follicle stimulating hormone of the anterior pituitary. The first of the two divisions of maturation (meiosis) occurs here after which the chromosome number of the ovum is reduced one-half. The luteinizing hormone, L.H., of the anterior pituitary stimulates the follicular sac and causes it to break and release the ovum (ovulation). With luteotrophin (L.T.H.) of the anterior pituitary follicular sac to transform into the corpus luteum, an important gland. *In the oviduct.* Entrance into and movement through the oviduct are largely due to currents produced by cilia. The ovum is surrounded by sperm cells. An enzyme, hyaluronidase, produced by them breaks up its covering (corona) of cells. One sperm enters the ovum. This is a signal for the second maturation division which is completed before male and female nuclei fuse in the fertilization process. The new individual is moved through the tube, at first as one cell, but soon it becomes a ball of cells. *In the uterus.* Under the influence of the luteinizing and luteotrophic hormones, L.H. and L.T.H. of the pituitary, the corpus luteum is now producing progesterone. This substance is carried by way of the circulating blood to the uterine wall and prepares it for the reception of the embryo. The white bands on the uterine wall are drawn to suggest lapses of time during the processes represented. The growing embryo is surrounded by coverings (chorion) that produces the hormone, chorionic gonadotrophin. This is carried about by the blood, stimulates the corpus luteum which in turn produces the progesterone that maintains the capacity of the uterus to hold the embryo. Miscarriages occur without this. The time in the tube varies and probably is often shorter than five days. (After Dickinson. Courtesy, Ham: *Histology,* ed. 2. Philadelphia, J. B. Lippincott Co., 1953.)

blood vessels are being repaired (Fig. 18.15). The physiological anticipation of an embryo begins all over again.

The human reproductive cycle is counted from the first day of menstruation. All of its timing is variable, especially that of ovulation which may occur at different intervals in different individuals, and even at varying intervals within the same individual (Table 18.1).

Table 18.1

SEQUENCE OF EVENTS IN THE HUMAN CYCLES OF MENSTRUATION
AND PREGNANCY

(See also Figs. 18.14 and 18.15)

Days after First Day of Menstruation	Ovaries		Lining of Uterus
	Follicle and Egg	Corpus Luteum	
1–4	New follicle (and egg) begins to develop	Corpus luteum of previous cycle degenerating	Blood vessels in lining rupture in menstruation; lining sloughs off
5–11 variable interval	Gradual development and increase in estrogen	Further degeneration in corpus luteum of previous cycle	Resting condition followed by thickening of lining and increased volume of blood and glands
12–16 variable, average 14	Ovulation, passage of egg into oviduct (where fertilization may occur)	Forms from ruptured follicle; produces hormone, progesterone	Uterine glands more active
17–23	Egg in oviduct or uterus	Enlarges	Fully vascular and glandular condition

IF FERTILIZATION HAS NOT OCCURRED

24–28	Egg probably begins to disintegrate	Gradually begins to disappear	Marked congestion of blood vessels and shrinkage of uterine wall

IF FERTILIZATION HAS OCCURRED

19–280 variable	No ovulation during pregnancy	Remains during first half of pregnancy	Embryo grows within the uterine wall

COMPARISON OF FEMALE REPRODUCTIVE CYCLES

In all mammals, the most important feature of the cycle is ovulation. In most mammals, this is accompanied by marked sexual excitement. Mating is connected with the ovulation period and limited to it. In the human species and higher primates, there are usually few or no outward symptoms of ovulation. Mating occurs at any time and without reference to ovulation.

In most mammals, if no egg is fertilized, the preparation of the uterus for the embryo subsides gradually without rupture of blood vessels or glands. In the human species and certain primates, under the same conditions, the preparations in the uterus are drastically destroyed with the rupture of blood vessels and the sloughing off of much of the uterine lining. The physiological advantages of menstruation are not evident. Nonmenstruating animals experience essentially the same reproductive cycles, and the uterine life of the embryo is quite as complete as in menstruating ones.

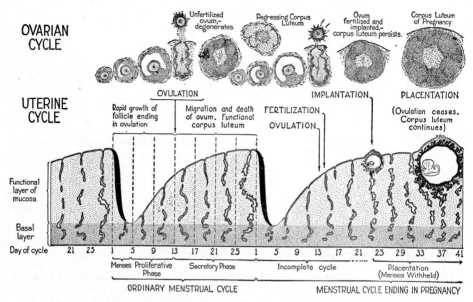

FIG. 18.15. Graphic summary of changes in the inner layers (endometrium) of the uterus in an ordinary menstrual cycle and in another cycle in which pregnancy occurs. The changes in the ovary are placed in their proper relation to the time scale and activities in the uterus. (Courtesy, Patten: *Human Embrvology*, ed. 2. New York, The Blakiston Co., 1953.)

Production of Children

Production is important to the human crop as it is to others How can production of children be encouraged when there is plenty of space and food and, what is more difficult, discouraged when there is not? These two questions penetrate into every society the world around.

Behind both questions is the fact that living matter insists upon reproducing itself. The many cells of our bodies are due to their persistent multiplication. Hard or easy living, much or little food, heat or cold may affect reproduction, but in general and in the long run they do not stop it. Children were conceived and born in the worst prison camps of World War II.

The problem of inducing production of children is a complex one that for thousands of years has been met according to the understanding of various peoples. Social and economic influences are exceedingly important and they as well as the physiological ones are very complex. In our own time, the general trend of experimental evidence has shown that the sperm and egg are capable of fertilization for a shorter time than was previously supposed.

The problem of reducing the production of children is also an old one, dealt with in ancient times and in primitive societies. Fundamentally, it is solved by preventing the egg and sperm cells from meeting. Almost all animals do this for a good part of their lives because they only mate at certain sharply limited and relatively very short periods. In contrast to this, as already pointed out, in chimpanzees, the higher apes, and man mating may occur at any time.

The principal means of preventing fertilization are the mechanical and chemical ones that keep the sperm and egg from meeting, and the "rhythm method," a restriction of the time of sexual intercourse to the periods when no egg is apt to be present, i.e., avoiding those near ovulation. Authorities generally agree that ovulation occurs about 14 days after the first day of menstruation in a 28-day cycle, when these two functions are completely regular and standardized in time. Even so, two days before and two days after the supposed ovulation date are usually included in the possible ovulation time. Two facts, however, must be taken into consideration. Many exceptions and irregularities occur in the menstrual schedule even in the same individual. Ovulation is an unobtrusive physiological process of which few persons are certainly aware. Completely regular and standardized cycles are rare indeed.

Part IV
The New Individual

19

Development

An embryo is a living organism in the early unfolding of its form and function. It has potentiality, and its possibilities for the future contrast with what it is at the moment. This is the root of its compelling interest. The two cells which we see through the microscope would not be so unforgettable if we did not know that they were the first ones in the making of a rabbit. They hold the pattern of lifted ears, of still fright and startled leaping, and of rabbits and more rabbits for years to come.

The development of an embryo is a series of orderly changes in which cells grow and divide and become different. Growth and differentiation are its key processes. Embryonic development may end at hatching or at birth. Birds and other animals that develop and hatch from eggs outside the body are called oviparous. Those that develop from eggs retained in the body are called viviparous. These include man and other mammals with such rare exceptions as the duckbilled platypus of Australia.

As cells grow they become larger and heavier. They take in food and from it make chemical substances like their own. By the time a cell is full grown and ready to divide each of its chromosomes has assimilated food and duplicated itself in quality and quantity. Multicellular animals grow by controlled increase in cell number as well as cell size. Every human being begins as a single cell, smaller than a pin head, scarcely visible to the naked eye. At birth, nine months later, a baby is an organization of over 200 billion cells and usually weighs about seven pounds. Increases in weight and cell number are controlled and limited; men, mice, and elephants have their respective limits.

The animal pole of the egg is the most active in physiological exchange with its environment even while the egg is in the ovary. It usually marks the future anterior end of the embryo. Various regions of the fertilized egg are set off by differences in appearance and function (Fig. 19.1). The gray crescent on the surface of the fertilized frog's egg is the scene of great activity, since its posi-

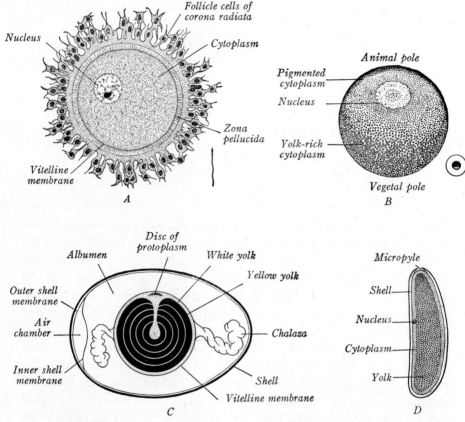

FIG. 19.1. Eggs whose size depends upon the amount of food (yolk) that they contain. *A,* human egg (×200) typical of mammals has practically no yolk and is just visible to the naked eye. At its lower right a human sperm is drawn, very highly magnified, even so its difference in size is striking. *B,* frog (after T. H. Morgan); lower right, a frog's egg surrounded by jelly, natural size. *C,* hen's egg (after Lillie), abundant yolk; shows disk of protoplasm from which the chick develops. *D,* fly; yolk is in the center of the egg and the embryo forms around it. (Courtesy, Arey: *Developmental Anatomy,* ed. 5. Philadelphia, W. B. Saunders Co., 1946.)

tion at the future rear end of the body marks the first ingrowth of the digestive tract. As the cells of the embryo multiply, those of succeeding generations become different from their predecessors. The tall cells in the neural folds of the future nerve cord are descendants of low, rounded ones. Groups of cells acquire special shapes and abilities; potential muscle cells gradually come to look and act like muscle. As differentiation goes on cells actually move about, changing their positions, and by so doing affect their neighbor cells and are affected by them.

Differentiation transforms the potentiality of the fertilized egg into the complex realities of the young animal. In 21 days of incubation the latent power of a fertilized hen's egg is changed to the liveliness of a chick that can aim a peck at another chick's bright eye and strike it.

The Yolk Content of Eggs—Its Food Value and Effect on Development. Because of their content of yolk, eggs are the largest cells in the body. Even in the eggs of mammals a minute amount of yolk is present, a fragment of history from their egg-laying ancestors. The egg cell of a mouse (0.06 mm. in diameter) is one of the smallest eggs of vertebrates; those of some of the huge sharks are the largest eggs known. The egg of an ostrich (85 mm. in diameter) is the largest of any familiar animal. It weighs three pounds and contains the equivalent of one and a half dozen hen's eggs. The ancient birds produced the really large eggs with enough food for a banquet in one yolk. The fossil egg shell of the extinct bird Aepyornis holds a gallon.

Except in mammals, yolk is the complete food for embryos. Its value as human food has greatly added to the economic importance of hens, ducks, and ostriches. The eggs of fishes have not only food value but, in caviar, they add social prestige. It is the yolk that counts; "fried eggs" mean yolky hens' eggs, never cows' eggs. The high value of yolk is due to the completeness of its food content of proteins, fats, carbohydrates, inorganic salts, vitamins, pigments (carotin in birds), and enzymes; water composes about half of its bulk.

Yolk changes the pattern of development because it takes no part in cell division except as it is a hindrance. Obviously, there must be less protoplasm in parts of the cell that are packed with yolk; there cell division is slow because the rate of metabolism is low. Cell division must combat the inertia of yolk or avoid it by taking a roundabout way, as it does in the early embryos of frogs, birds and many other animals (Figs. 19.1, 19.7). Yolk accumulates in one hemisphere of the egg of frogs, and forces the nucleus into the other. Since yolk is heavier than protoplasm, the vegetal pole where it is most abundant is always down and the lighter animal pole is up.

In large-yolked eggs such as those of the frog and chick, the accumulation of yolk in one region is so great that they are known as telolecithal, "end-yolked" eggs (Table 19.1). In small-yolked eggs, like those of amphioxus and man, the yolk is generally distributed and they are called isolecithal, "equal-yolked." Even in these, there is a visible difference between the poles.

Fertilization—The Prelude to Development. The main steps in fertilization are the entrance of the sperm into the egg, and the union of the male and female nuclei (Fig. 19.2). The sperm makes its way into the egg membrane stimulating the rise of a cone of protoplasm that surrounds it and draws it into the egg. At the same time, a thin layer of protoplasm, the fertilization membrane, is suddenly lifted from the surface of the egg and shuts out other sperm cells. The male and female nuclei, each with half the number of chromosomes to be contained in the body cells of the embryo, now approach one another and come in contact. The first cell division of the new individual follows at

Table 19.1

ARRANGEMENTS OF YOLK AND THE ACCOMPANYING TYPES OF CLEAVAGE
IN THE EMBRYO

Amount and Arrangement of Yolk in the Egg Cell	Technical Name of Egg Type	Type of Cleavage (Division)	Technical Name of Cleavage Type	Familiar Examples
Little and evenly distributed	Isolecithal (equal-yolked)	Complete, nearly equal	Holoblastic (cleavage through whole of the embryo)	Starfish Amphioxus Man and other mammals, except marsupials and egg-laying species
Medium amount, less near the animal pole	Telolecithal (end-yolked)	Complete, unequal	Holoblastic	Frogs Toads Salamanders Some fishes
Abundant, except at the animal pole	Telolecithal (end-yolked)	Incomplete, unequal cells in disk on large yolk mass	Meroblastic (cleavage through part of the embryo)	Chick Majority of fishes Reptiles Birds Egg-laying mammals, e.g., duckbill, spiny anteaters
Medium amount in core near center of egg	Centrolecithal (center-yolked)	Incomplete through the peripheral region of egg	Superficial	Insects and other arthropods, except scorpions

an interval varying with the kind of animal and environment but often very soon.

The Substance of the Embryo Arranged in the Egg. In certain kinds of eggs there are special regions in which pigment is present or absent, or yolk is sparse or abundant. Either by following these visibly pigmented zones or coloring them with vital dyes they have been traced to particular destinations in the embryo. In the fertilized egg, these future organ regions are more definite than before fertilization. The substance of the egg takes part in an active organization for the future development of the embryo. In the unfertilized egg of the tunicate, Styela (Cynthia), one of the lower chordates, orange pigment is uniformly distributed through the cell. But by streaming movements of the cytoplasm during fertilization it is later concentrated into a yellow crescent that marks the future posterior end of the embryo (Fig. 19.3). On the opposite side of the egg is the gray crescent that becomes its anterior end. During early development, the protoplasm of the yellow crescent is distributed to form the middle layers of cells or mesoderm; the gray crescent becomes noto-

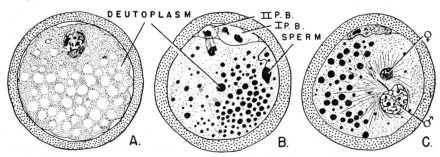

FIG. 19.2. Fertilization in the guinea pig. Microscopic sections of eggs taken before and soon after mating. The eggs are minute, smaller than fig-seeds. Deutoplasm is protoplasm that is permeated with particles of yolk. The yolk may be light (*A*) or dark colored (*B*) depending partly upon the stain used in its preparation. *A*, before fertilization. The first maturation division with the nucleus now in metaphase. This results in two cells, the egg with half its former number of chromosomes and the first polar body (*I P.B.*), a minute cell that contains the other half. The egg is enclosed in a special (vitelline) membrane. *B*, preparation for fertilization. The sperm has just entered the egg. The first polar body (*I P.B.*) is outside the egg cell. The entrance of the sperm stimulates the completion of a second division (*II P.B.*). Changes in the position of particles show that the sperm affects the whole egg. *C*, fertilization. The nuclei of egg (♀) and sperm (♂) are almost in contact. Each one has half the number of chromosomes that is characteristic of the body cells of a guinea pig. The polar bodies are disintegrating outside the egg. (Courtesy, Nelsen: *Comparative Embryology of the Vertebrates*. New York, The Blakiston Co., 1953.)

chord and neural plate; the gray yolk will be the inner layers of cells or endoderm, and the remainder of the egg will become the outermost cells or skin ectoderm. The identity of parts of amphibian embryos has been followed by coloring them and tracing their future careers in the animal, and also by transplanting them to other regions to test the effect of changed locations. Both methods are widely used in experimental embryology.

Development of the Lancelet

A lancelet is a transparent fishlike animal about three inches long. Its lance-shaped tail gave it the name lancelet and its sharp-edged body the name amphioxus (double edged) (Fig. 19.4). There are about two dozen species of Amphioxus distributed in the warmer seas over the world, including those along the southeastern and -western coasts of the United States. Lancelets from the Bay of Naples have long been known to biologists and those from the waters near Amoy, China, to fishermen who may harvest as much as a ton of them per day. In the breeding season, the males and females leave the sand and swarm in shallow water. Eggs and sperm are shed in the open water and fertilization occurs there. At this time the cytoplasm of the egg is apportioned out for particular destinations in the embryo.

The eggs are just visible to the naked eye (0.1 mm. diameter) and contain so little yolk that their processes can be clearly observed through the microscope. The pattern of development is, on one hand, similar to that of hydra and the starfish, animals far older in evolutionary history, and, on the other, similar to that of the vertebrates that are much younger in evolution.

Early Development. The early development of amphioxus proceeds on a

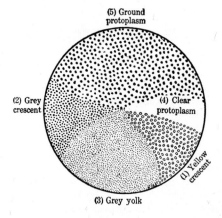

Fig. 19.3. Fertilized egg of the tunicate Styela. A crescent of yellowish protoplasm (*yellow crescent*) becomes the posterior end and a crescent of grayish protoplasm (*gray crescent*) becomes the anterior end of the embryo. Even at fertilization the cytoplasm of the egg becomes arranged for particular destinations in the developing animal. (After Conklin. Courtesy, Shumway: *Vertebrate Zoology*, ed. 4. New York, J. Wiley & Sons, 1942.)

plan followed in essentials by all vertebrates. Development is ordinarily a continuous process. It includes stages such as cleavage, blastulation, and gastrulation that blend into one another.

CLEAVAGE AND BLASTULATION. The first cleavage begins as a slight depression at the animal pole. This deepens and lengthens into a constriction which divides the egg into the first two cells representing the right and left halves of the new animal (Fig. 19.5). The second cleavage also begins at the animal pole, at right angles to the first. The third one is at right angles to the first two

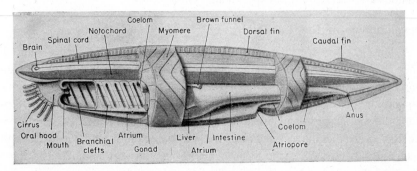

Fig. 19.4. An adult amphioxus with part of the body wall removed from the left side. The essentials to be noted are the relative positions of the spinal cord, notochord and alimentary canal. Amphioxus is generally regarded as an ancient ancestor of the vertebrates. The fundamental plan of its development is followed in all of them. Adults are two inches long. (Courtesy, Rand: *The Chordates*. Philadelphia, The Blakiston Co., 1950.)

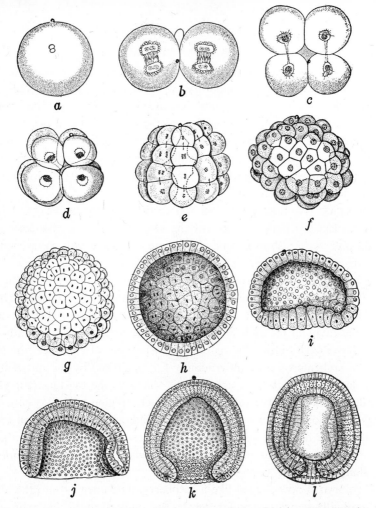

Fig. 19.5. Early stages in the development of Amphioxus. The egg is almost microscopic but has practically no yolk. The processes of development are direct and easier to follow than those of the frog whose eggs contain so much yolk. *a,* fertilized egg. Egg and sperm nuclei in contact. The minute second polar body is at the top; the first one has disintegrated. *b,* two-celled stage with nuclei dividing again. *c,* four-celled stage, two hours after fertilization. Note a temporary cavity (segmentation c.) formed as the cells divide. *d,* eight-celled stage, a side view, showing the smaller cells at the upper or animal pole, the future front end of the animal. *e,* all the cells are dividing at nearly the same rate which would not occur if any of them contained much yolk. The nuclei are in metaphase and anaphase stages of division. The segmentation cavity, open at one end, is traced by a broken line. *f, g, h;* blastula stages. Cells multiply and the embryo grows. Its cavity, the blastocoel, is shown in the half section. *i,* gastrula. The embryo flattens on the side that is finally its posterior end. This is called the gastrulation or stomach forming stage. *j, k, l;* views into the right half of the embryo. *j,* the embryo is now shaped like a broad raspberry; the two layers of its wall are of ectoderm that will form the skin and nervous system, and endoderm that becomes the lining of the alimentary canal, now an open cavity, called the archenteron. The blastocoel is squeezed out of existence. *k* and *l,* the embryo is growing longer; at the rear, its walls draw together except for the small anal opening. Layers of cells, the mesoderm, have spread out between the ectoderm and endoderm. Mesoderm will become skeleton, muscle, blood and other tissues. (After Conklin. Courtesy, Hegner and Stiles: *College Zoology,* ed. 6. New York, The Macmillan Co., 1951.)

and results in cells of unequal size. During these divisions the cells are gradually shifted outward and a temporary cavity is created in the center of the cluster. Cells continue to divide until 200 or more are formed. The embryo is then a hollow sphere called a blastula and the cavity within it is a blastocoel. The cells of the embryo can easily interchange materials with the environment of sea water. They have a relatively high income of oxygen and outgo of excretory products resulting from the rapid metabolism of cell division especially at the animal pole.

GASTRULATION—FORMATION OF PRIMITIVE DIGESTIVE TRACT. Changes now transform the hollow sphere of the blastula to the saclike form of the gastrula (Gr., *gaster,* stomach) in which there is a new cavity, the archenteron, or first digestive tract (Fig. 19.5).

In the early part of gastrulation, the embryo is a double layered cup such as a soft rubber ball would be if you pressed your thumb into its side. The side forced in would be comparable to endoderm and chordamesoderm, and the dent to the cavity of the archenteron; the other side of the ball would be ectoderm and the cavity inside the ball being pushed out of existence, the blastocoel. The archenteron appears gradually foreshadowed by the differentiation of cytoplasm in the fertilized egg and the shape of the blastula (Fig. 19.5). Toward the end of the blastula stage the vegetal region begins to flatten ever so slightly like one side of a waning moon. Hindered by their content of yolk, the cells on the flattened side divide fewer times and thus are larger than the others. Presently the flat region is turned inward or invaginated more and more sharply.

The embryo is now shaped like a raspberry. The opening into the archenteron gradually becomes smaller due to the multiplication and inturning of cells about its rim and finally becomes the minute blastopore. Its rim is the transition zone between endodermal cells and chordamesoderm, and the ectoderm. The endoderm will line the digestive canal. The chordamesoderm will make the notochord and the mesoderm that forms the bulk of the body, of organs such as the liver, the lining of the body cavity, and all muscles and bone. The ectodermal cells are the ancestors of the cells of the nervous system and outer layers of skin. The rim of the blastopore is the germ ring, a growth zone in which cells form rapidly especially in the important side, called the dorsal lip of the blastopore. This is the starting place of the notochord, present throughout life in the ancestors of vertebrates and the forerunner of the backbone in the early embryo and the mesoderm of every vertebrate from fish to man. The development thus far occurs within about seven hours after the fertilization of the egg. As in all eggs, it varies with the temperature and other conditions.

NERVOUS SYSTEM—NOTOCHORD AND MESODERM. As the archenteron continues to enlarge, the dorsal surface of the embryo flattens and a broad band of thick ectoderm extends from the lip of the blastopore to the anterior end of the body, the former animal pole. This is the neural plate from which the nervous system is formed.

At first, the roof of the archenteron is flat. Gradually, three folds arise in it and extend the length of the body. The central one of chordamesoderm becomes the notochord. Those on either side separate from the wall of the archenteron and grow in between the ectoderm and endoderm (Fig. 19.5). A cavity in each one will be part of the future coelom or body cavity. The outer side of each fold adheres to the ectoderm and together they become the somatopleure, the forerunner of the body wall; the inner side of each fold unites with the endoderm to become splanchnopleure, the future wall of the digestive canal. Mesodermal cells differentiate in these layers and form various structures such as muscles.

Development of the Frog

Eggs. Small as they are, frogs' eggs are huge compared with those of amphioxus and their bulk is largely yolk (Fig. 19.1, 19.6). As they float in

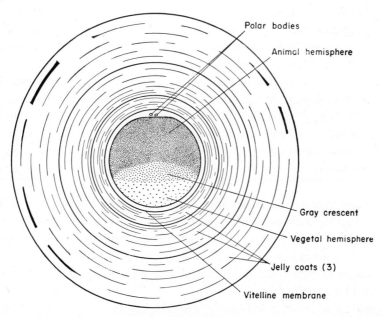

Fig. 19.6. Frog's egg 35 minutes after fertilization. The protective jelly secreted by the oviduct swells as soon as the eggs touch the water. The egg loses water during the rearrangement of protoplasm that occurs at fertilization and the shrinkage allows it to rotate within the fertilization membrane. The unfinished division resulting in the second polar body has been stimulated to completion by the entrance of the sperm. In one region the pigment has moved toward the entering sperm thus creating the gray crescent. (Courtesy, Rugh: *The Frog*. Philadelphia, The Blakiston Co., 1951.)

the ponds, their white vegetal poles are turned toward the dark bottom and their black poles toward the light. This is due to relative weight but it results in excellent concealing coloration. Yolk supplies the tadpoles with food until they are well beyond hatching. Embryos have the same general needs as frogs, plenty of water and food, income of oxygen, and outgo of carbon dioxide, water and urea. They are easily killed from the by-products of their own metabolism and are so sensitive to temperature that they will reach any given stage of development almost three times faster at 20° C. than at 10° C.

Reproduction Ends—Development Begins. Reproduction ends with two processes that are extremely important to the new individual. They are: (1) the maturation of the sex cells whereby their chromosomes are reduced to half the number in the body cells; and (2) fertilization with its immediate effects upon the organization of the egg, followed by the union of the sperm and egg nuclei and the reestablishment of the whole number of chromosomes (Fig. 19.6).

The entrance of the sperm always occurs in the hemisphere of the animal pole and stimulates a reorganization of the egg which makes it repellent to other sperm cells. Even if the egg membranes have been removed, a sperm will not enter a fertilized egg. As before mentioned, experiments have proved that the reorganization and development of an egg can be stimulated by various shocks, pricks, solutions, and shakings. Frogs have grown to young adulthood with only pricks and chemical solutions for fathers.

Among the results of the reorganization is the gray crescent, an area opposite the entrance point of the sperm, from which some of the black pigment retreats. Staining parts of the egg has shown that a plane that passes through the axis of the egg and bisects the gray crescent usually divides the future animal into right and left halves. Since the first cleavage plane bisects the gray crescent it follows that the bilateral symmetry of the embryo is prearranged in the egg.

Cleavage. Successive cell divisions follow one another at intervals of about an hour varying with the temperature. The speed with which new cell membranes grow is slowed down as the membrane formation plows through the yolk. In the animal hemisphere, the wall of the blastocoel is thin because the cells contain so little yolk; in the vegetal pole it is thick because they contain so much (Fig. 19.7).

Within 12 hours after fertilization (at 18° C.) the embryo, usually in the late blastula stage, contains hundreds of cells. The speed with which they multiply makes it hard to realize that with every division a nucleus with its thousands of genes is accurately allotted to each daughter cell. Equal distribution of parental genes begins with the first cell division and is repeated through billions of divisions in the growth of animals from jellyfishes to man.

Gastrulation. Gastrulation proper in amphioxus, for example, includes only

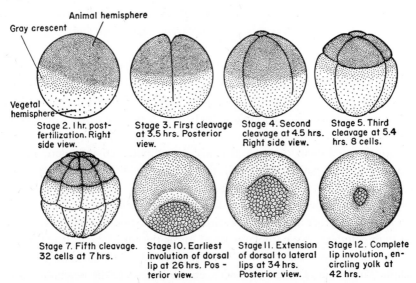

Animal hemisphere
Gray crescent
Vegetal hemisphere

Stage 2. I hr. post-fertilization. Right side view.

Stage 3. First cleavage at 3.5 hrs. Posterior view.

Stage 4. Second cleavage at 4.5 hrs. Right side view.

Stage 5. Third cleavage at 5.4 hrs. 8 cells.

Stage 7. Fifth cleavage. 32 cells at 7 hrs.

Stage 10. Earliest involution of dorsal lip at 26 hrs. Posterior view.

Stage 11. Extension of dorsal to lateral lips at 34 hrs. Posterior view.

Stage 12. Complete lip involution, encircling yolk at 42 hrs.

FIG. 19.7. General survey of the early development of the leopard frog seen in external views. The stages are selected from many intermediate ones. *Stage 2*, the fertilized egg. Polar bodies not shown. *Stages 3, 4, and 5;* cleavage. Continued division creates smaller cells. Where yolk is most abundant, in the vegetal hemisphere, division is slower and the cells are larger. *Stage 7*, early blastula. *Stages 10, 11, and 12;* gastrula. The crescentic groove (*10*) becomes a ring (*12*) as the minute rapidly dividing cells of the ectoderm grow over and around the more slowly dividing yolk-filled cells of the endoderm. These and the cells which will form notochord and mesoderm are thus turned inside (involution). In *12*, only the yolk plug, a pinhead of endoderm, is visible. The opening decreases but remains for a time as the blastopore. (Courtesy, Rugh: *The Frog.* Philadelphia, The Blakiston Co., 1951.)

the processes by which the single layered blastula is converted into the animal with a definite ectoderm and endoderm and chordamesoderm about a future digestive cavity. In the embryos of hydra, starfish, amphioxus and others there is little yolk in the vegetal region of the embryo to hinder the ingrowth of cells that creates the pioneer food cavity. However, in the frog the cells in the vegetal area are burdened by yolk and do not grow inward so readily. Actually, the embryo frog has to swallow a lump of yolky food at its rear end. This process begins with the ingrowth of cells that results in the appearance of the crescentic groove at the junction of the animal and vegetal hemispheres (Fig. 19.7). The crescentic groove deepens because the cells multiply so fast that they not only turn inward, but grow farther and farther over the yolk-filled cells which are also turning in. While this is going on, the horns of the crescent grow toward one another and finally complete a circle. At the same time, the rim continues to close in, and makes the circle smaller and smaller. By now less than a pinhead of white cells, the yolk plug, is visible, and presently not even this because the dark rim has closed the blastopore. The food-filled cells are now appropriately located in the floor of the enteron, the future digestive tract (Figs. 19.7, 19.9). As this cavity enlarges, the blastocoel is practically blotted out.

Mesoderm and Notochord. The ingrown mid-dorsal cells are the future notochord and mesodermal somites (Figs. 19.8, 19.9, 19.10). They form a temporary roof of the enteron whose sides and floor are made of endoderm. The enteron soon acquires an endodermal roof by the upgrowth and meeting beneath the notochord of the endodermal cells that form its sides. The chorda-mesoderm is continuous on each side with other potential mesodermal cells. These have turned in along the lateral lips of the rim of the blastopore and lie between the outer ectoderm and the inner endoderm.

Crevices now appear in the mesoderm along the sides of the body; these widen and extend forward and backward, splitting it into two layers, one that unites with ectoderm (somatopleure) and forms the future body wall, and the other that unites with endoderm (splanchnopleure) to be the future wall of the alimentary canal. The crevices between the layers are the beginning of the future coelom which will contain the digestive canal, kidneys and other organs of the body (Fig. 19.10).

Thus the three principal layers, ectoderm, mesoderm, and endoderm and the notochord are established. Cell division, movement, and differentiation have gone on together. All over the embryo parts are growing and changing partly because of what their inherited genes make them and partly because of their environment, the effects of their neighbor cells.

Nervous System and Epidermis. While the mesoderm and notochord are being established the nervous system is also taking shape largely under their influence. A broad band of thickened ectoderm that extends forward from the blastopore lies directly over the notochord and its adjoining mesoderm. This is the neural plate, the material of future brain and spinal cord (Fig. 19.8, 19.9, 19.10). Along its borders, cells accumulate in ridges, the neural folds which gradually come together and unite to make the neural tube. The neural tube then differentiates; the front part of it becomes brain; the remainder becomes nerve cord. During the closing of the neural tube some of the cells are left along each side. These are the neural crests from which the dorsal ganglia of the spinal nerves arise.

Cilia are now abundant on the skin ectoderm and their steady backward beat keeps the embryo slowly turning over and over while it is still within the egg membranes. After they hatch, tadpoles are moved smoothly forward by their cilia.

FORM AND ORGANS OF THE TADPOLE

The embryo grows rapidly, especially its head and tail. As it lengthens, it loses its stumpy form and looks more and more like a corpulent fish.

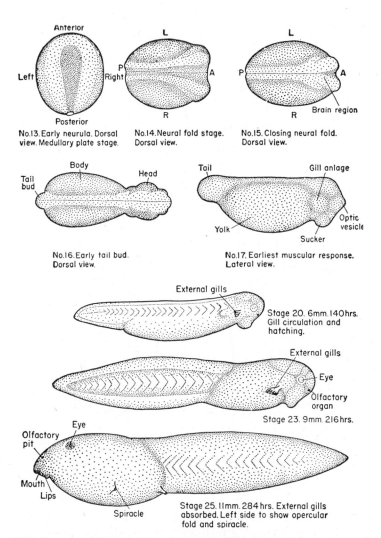

No.13. Early neurula. Dorsal view. Medullary plate stage.

No.14. Neural fold stage. Dorsal view.

No.15. Closing neural fold. Dorsal view.

No.16. Early tail bud. Dorsal view.

No.17. Earliest muscular response. Lateral view.

Stage 20. 6mm. 140 hrs. Gill circulation and hatching.

Stage 23. 9mm. 216 hrs.

Stage 25. 11mm. 284 hrs. External gills absorbed. Left side to show opercular fold and spiracle.

FIG. 19.8. Survey of the later development of the leopard frog, external views. *Stages 13, 14, and 15;* nervous system and epidermis. In the neurula stage, the neural or medullary plate extends forward from the blastopore and lies directly above the notochord and adjoining mesoderm. In *stage 14* the neural folds are present but are separated by an open trough, the future nerve cord and brain. In *15* the folds gradually close together. The central canal of the mature nerve cord and the ventricles of the brain are remainders of the once open trough. In *stages 16 and 17,* the body is lengthening and the developing muscles twitch spasmodically. The optic vesicles are outgrowths of the brain that form the retinas and optic nerves. The cells of the endodermal lining of the gut are still packed with yolk. *Stages 20, 23, and 25* show a rapid increase in size due to absorption of water. At hatching, the tadpole is about 56 per cent water; fifteen days after hatching, it reaches its maximum of 96 per cent water. By *stage 23* the tadpoles hang by their suckers from submerged stems. By *stage 25* they are eating soft plants; their bodies are fish-shaped. The external gills of *stage 23* are replaced by internal ones covered by the opercula. The spiracle, a pore on the left side, is the only exit for water. In leopard frogs the respiratory system changes little until the tadpole is transformed into a frog over two months later. (Courtesy, Rugh: *The Frog.* Philadelphia, The Blakiston Co., 1951.)

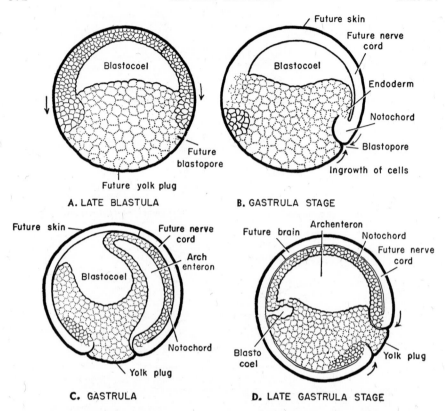

FIG. 19.9. Internal views of frog embryos. (From *Development of the Frog,* as illustrated by the Mueller-Ward Models. Courtesy, Justus F. Mueller and Ward's Natural Science Establishment.)

Skin and Nervous System. After the neural groove is closed there is a short passageway between the neural tube and enteron, the neurenteric canal, that exists but a short time (Fig. 19.10). The forebrain, midbrain, and hindbrain gradually take shape. Beneath and near the front of the forebrain a process of superficial ectoderm extends inward. This later joins a downpushing of the brain and together they become the pituitary body. From the ventral side of the neural tube motor nerve cells send out processes to muscles and glands. Processes from the cells of the dorsal ganglia extend into the cord, to the skin and to other parts of the body. The cord and brain are gradually surrounded by an envelope of loose mesodermal (mesenchymal) cells. In all vertebrates such cells form the coverings or meninges of the spinal cord.

The lining of the neural tube is a center of active cell division and gradually increasing differentiation. Two types of cells are formed, the future supporting cells or neuroglia of the nervous system and the nerve cells or neurons. The latter move out of the lining into the thick wall of the neural tube where they develop into typical neurons with extended axons and dendrites (Fig. 16.3).

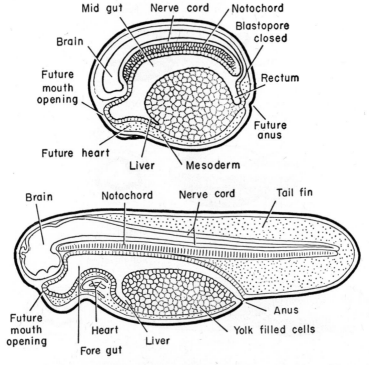

Fig. 19.10. Sections of frog embryos, before and after hatching. (From *Development of the Frog,* as illustrated by the Mueller-Ward Models. Courtesy, Justus F. Mueller and Ward's Natural Science Establishment.)

Similar changes take place in the cells of the neural crest as it is transformed into ganglia.

Sense Organs. An optic vesicle pushes out from each side of the forebrain and makes a well-marked bulge where it is in contact with the skin ectoderm. Each vesicle is shaped like one half of a hollow dumbbell (Fig. 19.11). Its walls are continuous with the wall of the brain, and nerve and sensory cells develop in them. After the vesicle has extended outward, it takes the shape of a double-walled cup. The front or inner wall of the cup will be the sensory layer of the retina containing the light sensitive cells and the cell bodies of the optic nerve fibers; the outer wall will be the pigmented layer. The light-sensitive cells develop from cells that were on the former outer surface of the neural folds. Diagrams of cross sections of the same region of the brain and vesicles at successive ages show how the cells originating on the outer surface of the folds are finally located inside the optic vesicle (Fig. 19.11). This explains why light that comes to the retina strikes the nerve cells, and then the sensory cells seemingly wrong end first (Fig. 17.17). As the optic vesicle grows outward, it touches a plate of skin ectoderm which thickens and dips in to make a sac, the lens vesicle, that fits into the cup. The lens vesicle separates

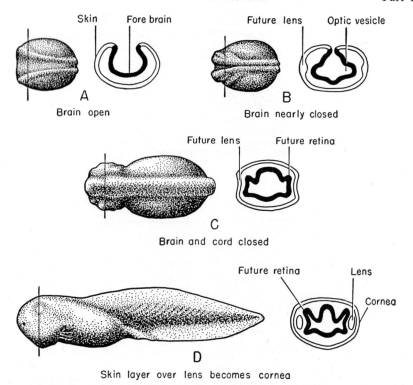

FIG. 19.11. The development of the eye. Diagrams of cross sections of frog embryos showing successive stages of the part taken by the ectoderm in the development of the eye. Except for its part in the sense organs, the superficial ectoderm becomes skin. *A,* embryo with brain open as in Figure 19.8, *stages 14 and 15. B,* on each side of the head an outgrowth of the brain (optic vesicle) approaches the lens, a thickened plate (placode) in the superficial ectoderm. *C,* the optic vesicle at first shaped like a hollow dumbbell is now a shallow cup. The lens bends toward the cup. The neural folds have closed and the future skin is separated from the future brain. *D,* the lens has separated from the future skin ectoderm. The bottom of the optic cup (vesicle) is the future retina. The lens nearly fills the top of the cup. The superficial ectoderm outside the lens will be the cornea.

from the skin ectoderm which later becomes the cornea (Fig. 19.11). The accessory parts of the eye, the coats, blood vessels and muscles, are developed from mesoderm.

The sensory parts of other prominent sense organs, inner ears, nose and taste all develop from ectoderm in fundamentally similar ways. The lateral line system consists of a series of sense buds arranged in rows over the head and body. Each line begins as a thickening of sensory ectoderm which later breaks up into the sense buds that respond to vibrations in the water. Lateral lines are conspicuous in bony fishes and in tadpoles, but they do not persist in frogs and toads.

Digestive System. As the body grows longer, the enteron also lengthens and a ventral outpocketing of it near its front end is the first appearance of the liver. At the posterior end the endoderm grows outward and the ectoderm inward till they meet and break; the latter forms the lining of the future cloaca and its external opening. At the anterior end, a similar ingrowth of ectoderm which will line the greater part of the cavity of the mouth meets the endoderm in an oral plate which also breaks through. Thus, the saclike enteron becomes a tube.

Only the linings of the alimentary canal and its branches are endoderm. In various regions of these, cells are gradually differentiated for their respective functions, such as secretion and absorption. Except for the nerves, mesoderm composes the whole outer wall of the digestive canal and its derivatives such as pancreas and liver and their ducts. The endodermal cells lining the finer branches of the liver ducts become the cells which secrete the bile. Like the liver, the pancreas also arises as an outpocketing of the inner layers of cells in the wall of the digestive canal.

The fundamental processes of ingrowth, outgrowth, and differentiation of cells are repeated over and over again in all embryos.

Respiratory System. The respiratory organs of vertebrates are also derived from the digestive canal. Whether their function demands exposure to water or air, their surfaces are continually moist and are always close to the blood.

The first signs of a respiratory system in the tadpole are the outpushings from the endoderm of the foregut, the region of the future pharynx (Fig. 19.10). There are in all six of these gill pouches on each side. The first and last never open but about the time of hatching, the others meet the superficial ectoderm, break, and become the gill clefts that give free passage to the water outside. The solid bars of tissue anterior and posterior to the gill clefts are the gill arches that support the gills. In the frog, the tissue in front of the first pair of pouches that remain closed will form the lower jaw. In all vertebrates, these pouches become the middle ears and the eardrum develops where the endoderm of the pouch meets the skin ectoderm which will line the tube of the external ear. The Eustachian tube is derived from the part of the pouch nearest the foregut and thus the pharynx and middle ear communicate (Fig. 17.9).

In a newly hatched tadpole, respiration is carried on by external gills that develop as outgrowths of the skin ectoderm of the three arches (Fig. 19.10). These external gills are later absorbed and replaced by internal gills which also arise from the gill arches. At about this time, a fold of ectoderm, the future operculum, arises in front of the gill clefts and grows backward, forming a mantle around the internal gills and gill arches of both sides (Fig. 19.10). It has one external opening on the left side, the only exit for the water that enters the mouth and flows over the gills as the tadpole breathes. Even before hatching, the lungs appear as two small outpocketings from the floor of the future esophagus and are inconspicuously present through the period in which the gills are functioning. Then, with the approach of metamorphosis, the lung sacs enlarge but the endoderm at their tops is constricted in preparation for the future larynx. Although the tadpole is still a true water breather, it is also a presumptive air breather. Before the gills are spent, the lungs are ready to begin work. For the gills and the lungs it is a case of: "The king is dead! Long live the king."

Mesoderm—The Bulk of the Body. The mesoderm produces the connective tissue, the skeleton, the blood and blood vessels, the muscles and other parts including the lining of the body cavity, the kidneys and the reproductive system.

METAMORPHOSIS FROM TADPOLE TO FROG

During the change to adult form in the larvae of frogs and toads, the tail and gills are absorbed; the gill clefts are closed; legs develop; lungs become functional; and the food cavity is changed. The horny lips with which the tadpole scrapes algae are replaced by bony jaws and teeth; the relatively long "watch spring" intestine is changed into a shorter one that functions with a mixed diet of plants and animals (Fig. 34.7).

Provisions for Health and Safety of Embryos

Developing embryos are provided with water and food. They use water continually and it forms a large part of their substance. They have prospered in watery surroundings throughout their histories. The delicate embryos of aquatic animals float and swim in lakes and seas. The equally delicate embryos of most land animals develop within sacs of fluid, individual ponds that take the place of the wider waters of their aquatic relatives.

Earthworms pass their early days within seed-like capsules. Each of these holds a few embryos in a bath of nourishing albumen which they swallow and also absorb through their skins. Like those of other invertebrates, these embryos have no special food-sacs attached to their bodies.

Food and the Yolk Sac. The majority of vertebrates, fishes, reptiles, birds, and mammals, have a yolk sac containing more or less food in the form of yolk. It is a pouch-like extension of the digestive tract, an organ producing enzymes that break the yolk into substances that pass into the blood, are carried into the body of the embryo, and finally converted into its protoplasm. In birds, the body wall closes over the yolk sac before hatching and the latter shrinks and finally merges into the intestine. The rounded front of a one-day chick is due to its yolk sac.

The Watery Environment and the Amniotic Sac. The amnion is a transparent roomy sac that loosely surrounds the embryo (Figs. 19.13, 19.14). It contains the amniotic fluid secreted by the membranous sac and by the embryo itself. The fluid allows the embryo considerable free motion especially during its earlier development and acts as a protection and shock absorber. It is also a catch basin for waste products of metabolism.

Amniotic sacs first appeared in reptiles, the first truly land animals. In them, they are the guarantee of watery surroundings for the embryos even in the desert where many reptiles live. The amnion is also well developed in birds and mammals. All of these are essentially land animals and it functions in them as it does in reptiles.

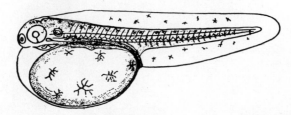

FIG. 19.12. Embryo fish and its food supply. The yolk sac is prominent for some time after hatching in trout and many other fishes. It is a blind sac which opens out of the alimentary canal. The body wall grows completely around it and it is as much inside the body as the intestine. It is highly useful to the embryo in all vertebrates except mammals; in them the yolk sac is history. (Courtesy, Bridge in *Cambridge Natural History*, Vol. VII. London, The Macmillan Co., 1910.)

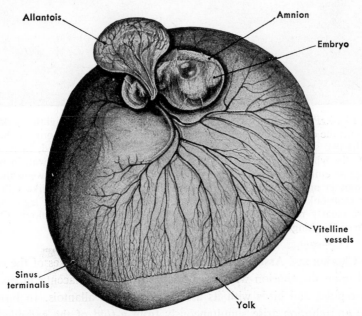

FIG. 19.13. Chick of about five-and-a-half days incubation taken out of the shell with the yolk intact. The albumen and the serosa, a membrane lying next to the shell, have been removed. By means of the allantois the blood receives oxygen and is relieved of carbon dioxide. The yolk sac holds the food supply of yolk easily within reach of the digestive tract of the embryo. (Courtesy, Patten: *Early Embryology of the Chick*, ed. 4. New York, The Blakiston Co., 1951.)

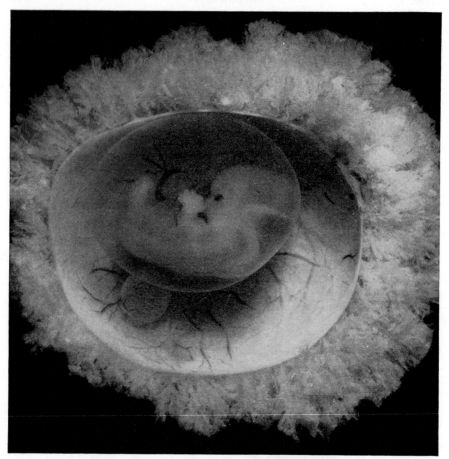

Fig. 19.14. Photograph of human embryo and sacs, in the eighth week of development; the chorion has been cut away to show the embryo, about one half inch long. The two sacs, amnion and chorion, are roomy and fluid-filled. In its natural position, the whole chorion is covered by the tissue of the uterine wall in which it first became embedded. The exchange of gases, food and waste between the blood of the mother and embryo occurs through the walls of the finger-like villi of the chorion that look so feathery in this figure. The left eye, hand, and leg of the embryo are clearly recognizable. (Courtesy, Department of Embryology, Carnegie Institute of Washington.)

The Chorion and Associated Membranes. The life processes of the embryo depend upon the chorion with its specialized part the placenta in mammals and in reptiles and birds with its associated sac the allantois. In birds, the amnion and chorion arise simultaneously from a fold of the extended body wall that first appears in front of the head and then encircles the embryo with its edges closing together as if pulled by a drawstring. The inner part of the fold becomes the amnion, the outer part forms the chorion. They are united for a short time at the meeting place of the folds but the delicate joining usually soon gives way and the layers seem never to have been connected.

The chorion of reptiles and birds is united with the allantois which contains many blood vessels. Together they rest closely against the porous egg shells, and function as a respiratory organ.

The Allantois. Like the yolk sac, the allantois is an outgrowth of the digestive tract but has a different function (Fig. 19.13). In birds, it fills most of the space between amnion and chorion and fusing with the chorion (chorioallantoic membrane) becomes an important respiratory organ. It is also a temporary urinary bladder.

In mammals, except the guinea pig and some other rodents, and the primates including man its walls may fuse with the chorion and become part of the embryonic section of the placenta. It then functions in the transfer of food, respiratory gases, and waste products between mother and embryo.

The placenta is discussed in later paragraphs that deal with the human embryo.

Umbilical Cord. As the embryo grows, the folds of the amnion surrounding the stalks of the yolk sac and allantois come together in a ventral tube (Fig. 19.15). In the higher mammals this tube is the umbilical cord that

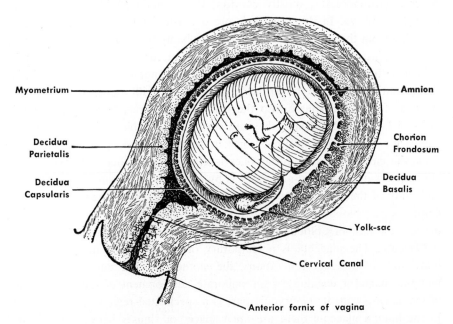

FIG. 19.15. Outline diagram of human uterus showing the placenta, sacs and embryo. The placenta consists of the chorion where the villi have greatly developed —over most of it, they have disappeared—and of the decidua basalis, a part of the wall of the uterus. Compare with Figure 19.14. Decidua capsularis is the part which covered the embryo when it was first implanted. Placenta and sacs are parts of the afterbirth. (Courtesy, Patten: *Human Embryology,* ed. 2. New York, The Blakiston Co., 1953.)

in addition to the yolk sac and allantois also holds the large blood vessels that connect the embryo with the placenta (Fig. 19.18).

Human Embryo

First Days of Life. Different as they may be later, animals greatly resemble one another in the earliest part of their lives (Fig. 38.7). In their youngest stages, rabbits, monkeys, and men look very much alike, though their chromosomes soon tell a different story. In recent years, the microscopic living embryos of mice, rabbits, and monkeys have been removed from the maternal oviducts and uteri, placed in salt solution at body temperature, and photographed in still and motion pictures (Fig. 19.16). The youngest human embryos yet seen, including a 2-celled one, have been removed from the oviducts and uteri of persons undergoing operations (Fig. 19.17). The fertilization of the human egg on a microscope slide has also been photographed.

Implantation in the Uterine Wall. With the help of cilia and contractions of muscles in the wall of the oviduct the human embryo is rolled into the uterus. By the time it arrives there, or soon after that, it reaches the blastocyst stage (Fig. 18.14). This is an almost microscopic sphere, its wall a thin layer of cells (trophoblast), mostly chorion, that contains fluid and a knot of cells, the embryo. In this stage it is presumed to be about 4 to 5 days old, counting from the time that the egg was probably fertilized. Within a day or two, the blastocyst sticks to the lining of the uterus, and then sinks into it, evidently through the effect of its own secretions upon the cells about it. In the meantime, delicate fingerlike processes, the villi, grow out from the surface of the little sphere into the wall of the uterus, like roots into soil (Figs. 18.14, 19.15). There they are surrounded by blood from the uterine capillaries whose walls have been broken during this process of implantation. Thus the embryo's source of supplies is at once established. At first, all exchange of water and food and gases is by absorption through the membranes and body of the embryo. Later, the blood vascular system develops and the embryo's own blood transports materials always to and from the villi extending into the mother's blood. The two kinds of blood never mix.

Placenta. The placenta is a temporary organ formed from parts of two individuals of different generations, the mother and her unborn young. Its maternal part (or decidua) is an elaborate development of the inner layers of the uterine wall. Its embryonic part is a specialized region of the chorion. In the human placenta there are open spaces or sinuses between these two parts into which maternal blood flows from uterine arteries that were first broken during the implantation of the embryo. This blood is constantly changed as it flows from the uterine arteries and slowly returns to the uterine veins. Minute richly branched villi from the embryonic placenta dip into this reservoir of blood (Fig. 19.15). Within each fingerlike villus are

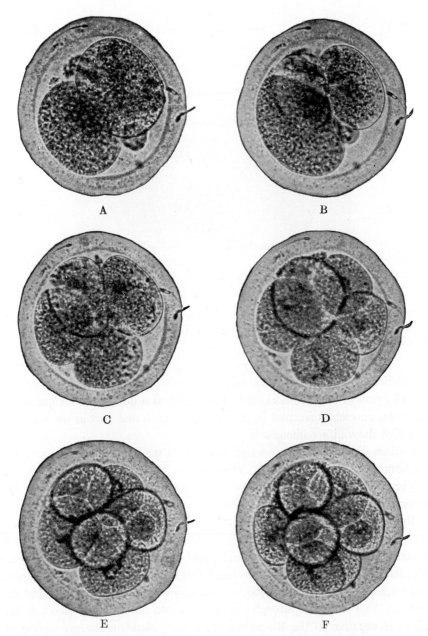

Fig. 19.16. Photomicrographs of living embryos of monkeys showing early stages of division. The fertilized ovum was washed out of the tube, cultivated in plasma and its growth recorded in micro-moving pictures.

The numbers of hours include the time between ovulation and fertilization, and the period of cell division which follows.

A, two-cell stage, about 29 hours after ovulation, the actual escape of the egg from the ovary. *B,* three-cell stage, about 36½ hours. *C,* four-cell stage, about 37½ hours. *D,* five-cell stage, about 48½ hours. *E,* six-cell stage, about 49 hours. *F,* eight-cell stage, about 50 hours. (After Lewis and Hartman. Courtesy, Patten: *Human Embryology,* ed. 2. New York, The Blakiston Co., 1953.)

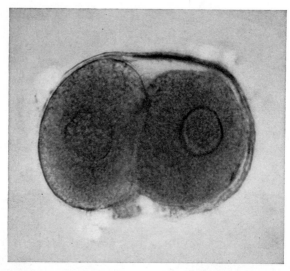

FIG. 19.17. A section of the two-celled stage of a human embryo taken from an oviduct during an operation. (Courtesy, A. T. Hertig and Carnegie Institute of Washington.)

capillaries that join vessels that reach the embryonic placenta from the embryo by way of the umbilical cord. Thus, there is a double circulation in the placenta, an embryonic part in the villi and a maternal part in the reservoir in which the villi are immersed.

Carbon dioxide and other waste products of the embryo pass through the membranes of the villi from the blood of the embryo into the blood of the mother. Food and oxygen from the blood of the mother pass into that of the embryo.

By means of radioactive chemicals, it has been shown that the smaller molecules of matter pass through the membranes of the villi, substances such as salts, sugars, calcium, amino acids, and certain vitamins and hormones. The Rh factor, an antigen or substance that causes agglutination (clumping and sticking together of red blood cells), may be present in the blood of the embryo. This may pass through the placenta into the mother's blood. If her blood is negative to the Rh substance, it can stimulate the production of antibodies which return to the embryo and destroy its red blood cells.

There is no means of communication between the embryo and mother except by substances such as those that have been named. Not a single nerve passes from one individual to the other. In its psychology the embryo is as independent of its environment as any other animal may be.

Hormones. The placenta is not only a filter of foods going inward to the embryo and waste products going out, but it also produces a series of hormones.

As soon as the villi are well developed, they secrete a hormone (chorionic gonadotrophin) promptly circulated by the blood and easily extracted from the urine. Experiments have shown that human urine of pregnancy has a stimulating effect upon the ovaries when injected into the bodies of immature rats and mice, the basis of the Aschheim-Zondek pregnancy test. In the Friedman test for early pregnancy, the urine is injected into the ear vein of a rabbit. If the woman is pregnant, eggs will be shed from the ovaries into the oviducts of the rabbit in about 24 to 48 hours. Obviously this requires an operation on the rabbit. Physicians most commonly use the much simpler test on frogs. Some of the urine to be tested is injected into a dorsal lymph sac of an adult male frog (Fig. 32.20), usually the common *Rana pipiens*. The frog is placed in a dry jar for two hours. Some of its urine is then collected and examined with a microscope. If it contains sperm cells the pregnancy is regarded as certain.

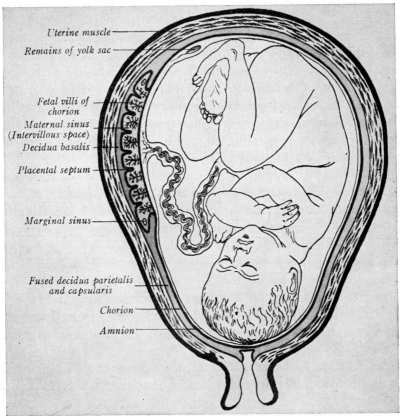

FIG. 19.18. Diagrammatic section through the uterus; infant just before birth in the usual position. As in the majority of mammals the yolk sac is present only as an inheritance from vertebrate ancestors. The placenta and other sacs are forced from the uterus as the afterbirth. (Courtesy, Arey: *Developmental Anatomy,* ed. 5. Philadelphia, W. B. Saunders Co., 1946.)

Other hormones produced by the placenta include estrogen and progesterone which stimulate the enlargement of the uterus, the growth of the mammary glands, and are involved in the uterine contractions that occur at birth.

Birth. The birth process begins with rhythmic contractions of the smooth muscles in the uterine wall, joined later by the striated muscles of the abdominal wall. These are timed with the stretching of the birth canal so that the infant is forced out, normally head first, pulling the umbilical cord after it. Similar contractions expel the afterbirth, which includes the placenta and all the other membranes which were, for a time, of life and death importance to the infant. Birth is in no way such a simple process as this statement suggests. A complex of hormones, changed rate of blood flow, sensitivity of nerves and muscles—a whole system of balanced forces—is concerned.

At birth, a baby meets a great crisis of its life. For nine months it has lived in a soft-walled chamber, flooded with fluid warmed to a steady 98.6° F., protected from jar and vibration and in total darkness (Fig. 19.18). Food ready to use and oxygen have been filtered into its blood. Its lungs are collapsed, without air and with only a fraction of the blood soon to come to them. Instead of going to the lungs, the main supply of blood has taken a short cut and bypassed them; it also has crossed the heart through an opening between the auricles. These arrangements provide for the circulation to the placenta; after birth, they would be useless and worse. If the short routes stay open, a blue baby results because venous blood leaps through the opening from the right to the left auricle, and through the duct from the pulmonary artery into the aorta (Fig. 19.19).

When a baby first emerges into the air its lungs are immediately inflated due to the negative pressure in its lungs and the positive pressure of the air. It must breathe, at once and without practice, a complicated business in which failure is fatal. Before birth, the baby may only swallow amniotic fluid and whatever it contains. After its birth, it deals with food at first hand; its digestive tract is new to this also, the reason for hiccoughs and other digestive rebellions. A baby arrives in a changeful environment, of moving air that may be dry or moist, of shifting temperatures, changing light, food in variety, human neighbors, plants and animals. With unwarned suddenness its ecology is changed and it begins adjustments that must continue throughout its life.

Twins. Multiple births are due to the development of more than one egg or to the division of the fertilized egg into parts each of which develops into an infant.

Fraternal twins are the product of two different eggs which matured at the same time and were fertilized by two different sperm cells. Fraternal twins have different genes and are not any more alike than any children of the same parents. They may or may not be of the same sex. There is a separate

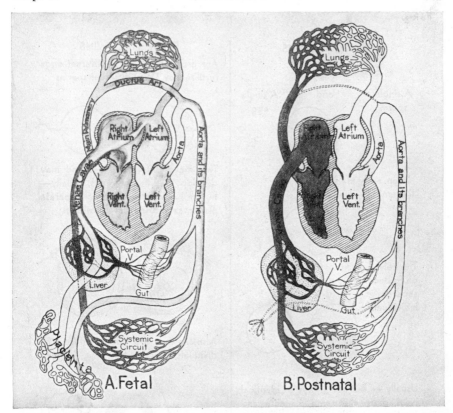

FIG. 19.19. General scheme of human circulation before (*fetal*) and after birth (*postnatal*). *Before birth.* The outstandingly important organ is the placenta through which the embryo receives oxygen, food and other substances from the maternal blood, all of it passing through membranes. Before birth blood passes freely from the right to the left auricles (or atria).

Supplies from the mother's blood are carried to the embryo via the placenta, the umbilical vein and the vena cava (on left side) to the right auricle (atrium) of the heart. Carbon dioxide and substances to be eliminated from the embryo are brought to the placenta via the aorta (right side) and the umbilical artery. *After birth.* At birth the vessels in the umbilical cord shrink and close and the placental blood stream is abruptly cut off. The circulation to the lungs is immediately and completely underway. The passage (ductus arteriosus) between the two auricles is soon closed. (Courtesy, Patten: *Human Embryology,* ed. 2. New York, The Blakiston Co., 1953.)

placenta and amniotic sac for each one and there are two afterbirths (Fig. 19.20).

Identical twins come from a single fertilized egg that divides after fertilization, begins to grow, splits in half and develops into two individuals. Each one has the same inheritance as the other and since sex is inherited they are always of the same sex. They share the same placenta and there is only one afterbirth (Fig. 19.20). Siamese twins are identical twins only partly sep-

IDENTICAL TWINS
Are products of

A single   and   A single
sperm   egg

In an early stage
the embryo divides

The halves go
on to become
separate
individuals

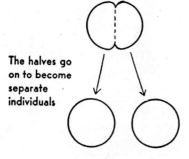

Usually — but not always — identical
twins share the same placenta and
fetal sac

But regardless of how they develop,
they carry the same genes and are
therefore

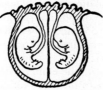

Always of the same sex — two boys
or two girls

FRATERNAL TWINS
Are products of TWO different eggs
fertilized by TWO different sperms

They have different genes and may
develop in different ways, usually—
but not always — having separate
placentas and separate fetal sacs

Also, as they are totally different individuals, they may be

Both
of the
same sex   Two boys

—or two girls

—Or a
mixed
pair

One   One
boy   girl

FIG. 19.20. How twins are produced. (From *The New You and Heredity* by
Amram Scheinfeld. Copyright, 1939, 1950 by Amram Scheinfeld, published by
J. B. Lippincott Co.)

arated. Quadruplets and quintuplets may include fraternals and identicals; the odd one in quintuplets is usually regarded as a twin whose mate did not live long.

In man, apes and many other mammals, only one infant is usually produced at a time. According to estimates from statistics once in every 80 human births, two are born at the same time, and triplets once in 512,000. Only about 30 quintuplets have been recorded, and there are three substantiated cases of the birth of sextuplets. At this date the famous Dionne quintuplets of Canada and a similar series born in Argentina are the only groups of five known to have survived.

20

The Physical Basis of Heredity

*Two influences enter into the making of every plant, animal and man—
their inheritance and their surroundings. Nature and nurture are never separated but nature once set is steadfast and harder to change than nurture.* A
hen sits on ducks' eggs and hatches ducks but no hen broods ducks' eggs into
chickens. Monkeys learn to climb trees; cows never do.

The question "Which is more important, heredity or environment?" has
started endless arguments, but it was never a sensible question for no plant
or animal can exist without both. Although inseparable, they are different.
By the time an animal has come into existence as a fertilized egg, its inheritance has been set, heredity is behind it. Nobody chooses his parents
and the inheritance they give him. But most of his environment is still in
front with chances of change and choice.

What is Heredity? The heredity of a plant or animal consists of the
characteristics brought to it by its ancestors. People of every kind, climate
and time, have had their own ideas and uses of inheritances. In their early
history, the Egyptians selected and artificially pollinated their date palms
and got a better crop of dates. In the middle ages, the big horses capable of
carrying the enormous weight of the armored knights were selectively bred
and became the ancestors of the English Great Horse or Shire Horse. In
later times, many new types, such as mules and Poland-China hogs, have
been produced by crossing different varieties and species. Hardy range-sheep
come from crosses of Merino and "mutton sheep." From time immemorial
human beings have looked at one another and recognized that like begets
like; so have the robins and rabbits and other animals according to their
kind.

What is Genetics? Genetics is the science of the genes, the physical units
of heredity contained in the chromosomes and believed to be protein molecules. Studies of genetics are precise and analytical, usually focused on single
or small groups of inherited characters and often based on experiments.

Beginning of Genetics

The science of genetics has had a lifetime of about fifty years, marked by an extraordinary advance in knowledge and usefulness. From its beginning workers in this field have used precise methods, analysis, experiments upon large numbers of individuals, and meticulous records. The present knowledge of heredity rests upon the discovery that the characters of an organism are inherited independently of each other and not blended together. The discoverer, Father Gregor Mendel, was a gardener, beekeeper, and priest who was interested in flowers, their pollination and the part taken in it by the bees, not only bees in general but the particular varieties that he secured by selecting and cross breeding them (Fig. 20.1). All of his work was illumined by enthusiasm and enjoyment. The flowers were lively and special to him; the fuchsia was his favorite. He finally selected garden peas for his main experiments because they were easy to raise and cross pollinate, and he was especially interested in their inheritance of size and form. So it came about that for his far-reaching work, his material was mainly garden peas grown in a small plot near his monastery. Mendel's enthusiasm was

FIG. 20.1. The garden in the Koniginkloster in Brunn where Gregor Mendel (1822–1884) carried on his experiments (1856–1864). Those experiments were the foundations of genetics, the science of the gene, the unit of inheritance. (Photograph by Hugo Iltis. Courtesy, Sinnott, Dunn, and Dobzhansky: *Principles of Genetics,* ed. 4. New York, McGraw-Hill Book Co., 1950.)

combined with a rare equipment of curiosity, precise observing and record-ing, respect for facts and logical reasoning. His work is an inspiring example of what observation and reason can achieve. He planned his experiments with great care, and set them like traps to catch the facts. The basic principles which he drew from them have been upheld by thousands of experimenters who have followed him.

Gregor Mendel, Founder of the Science of Genetics

Gregor Mendel, 1822–1884, spent his boyhood on an Austrian (now Czechoslovakian) farm where he grew up with orchards and gardens all about him. At 21, he entered the monastery at nearby Brunn (now Brno), was ordained a priest three years later, went to Vienna for a scientific train-ing, returned to his home monastery, and for 14 years was a teacher of natural history in Brunn Modern School. During those 14 years, he conducted the experiments on peas that led him to believe that heritable characters are produced by separate units, and that this separateness is a basic principle of inheritance. Mendel was searching for laws that operate in creating species at the same time that Charles Darwin was writing the *Origin of Species*. His experiments and conclusions were published in a brief paper in *The Pro-ceedings of the Natural History Society of Brunn* (1865). By this time many people were fiercely attentive to the *Origin of Species* (published in 1859) and Mendel's paper went unnoticed. In addition to this, in 1868 he met another handicap in being elected Prelate of Altbrunn, a high adminis-trative office which consumed most of his time. With this new occupation his work in genetics and the adventures of his mind were ended.

RESURRECTION OF A DISCOVERY

Mendel's conclusions remained hidden until 1900, 16 years after his death, when three botanists experimenting in different countries made discoveries similar to those of Mendel. In that same year, and independently of one another, they found his paper. By that time, the first shock from the *Origin of Species* had died down and the theory had begun to stimulate curiosity. People were asking how plants and animals came to be different and how their differences were inherited. Chromosomes had been discovered and biologists were highly excited about their significance. It soon appeared that these things were related to Mendel's inherited characters. Although they were discovered before Mendel's death, he never mentioned them and perhaps never heard of them.

MENDEL'S APPROACH TO THE PROBLEM OF INHERITANCE

Peas are naturally self-fertilizing in one flower. However, it is easy to cross fertilize the eggs of one plant by the male cells (pollen) of another.

Before the flower is quite developed the bud is opened and the stamens containing the pollen are removed (Fig. 20.2). Then pollen from another plant is placed on the pistil through which the male cells make their way to the eggs.

Mendel chose plants of two pure-line varieties, that is, one in which for several generations the plants had been tall and another in which they had been dwarfs, terming these the parental generation (P). He cross-pollinated flowers from these two parent stocks. All of the resulting hybrids were tall plants, the First Filial or F_1 generation (Fig. 20.3). The dwarf character had disappeared. However, when the plants of this (F_1) generation were self-pollinated and another generation (F_2) was produced, the dwarfness termed the recessive character turned up again. Not only that, but it appeared in a regular and predictable ratio of three tall, termed the dominant characters, to one dwarf, the recessive.

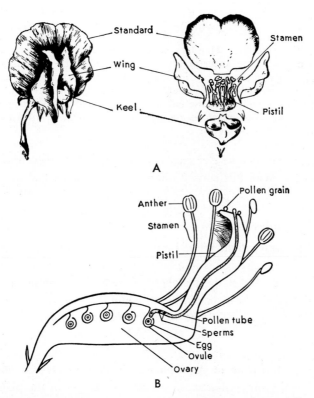

Fig. 20.2. Flower of garden peas, the subjects of many of Mendel's experiments. *A,* diagram of the flower with the petals, consisting of standard, wings and keel, separated to expose the pistil and stamens. The boat-shaped keel and the wings naturally close tightly around the pistil and stamens insuring self-pollination. *B,* diagram of the pistil and stamens of the pea showing the pollen tube that grows downward carrying the sperm that fertilizes the egg. Other sperms unite with nuclei in the ovules (not shown) to produce the nutritive part of the seed. (Courtesy, Colin: *Elements of Genetics,* ed. 2. Philadelphia, The Blakiston Co., 1946.)

Mendel went on rearing the plants to see if their inherited content, the genotype, was what it appeared to be, that is, the phenotype. By analyzing the offspring of self-pollinated plants of the F_2 generation he found that one-fourth of them were pure talls, one-fourth pure dwarfs, and one-half apparently tall but actually hybrids. When crossed with one another these hybrids produced a 3:1 ratio of tall dominants and dwarf recessives as before.

MENDEL'S EXPLANATION

He explained his observations by assuming that all living things transmit hereditary traits by means of physical particles in the sex cells of the parents.

Parents	Tall (tall)	✕	Dwarf (dwarf)	
		↓		
F_1	Tall (dwarf)	✕	Tall (dwarf)	
		↓		
F_2 Tall (tall)	Tall (dwarf)		Tall (dwarf)	Dwarf (dwarf)

FIG. 20.3. The results of Mendel's cross of garden peas of pure ancestry for tallness with peas of pure ancestry for dwarfness. The first generation, first filial F_1, was tall; the second generation, F_2, was tall in a proportion of three talls to one dwarf. Mendel named these characteristics dominant and recessive, terms used ever since. In F_1 the tallness of the tall plant was visible or dominant. The dwarfness of the tall plant was present in its make-up and might be inherited by its offspring but was invisible or recessive.

He called them "formative elements" and assumed that they were units that acted separately. With this correct interpretation Mendel laid the foundation of modern genetics.

Mendel's Principles

The Law of Segregation. While both members of a given pair occur in an individual only one of these is in a single egg or sperm. Thus, characters are segregated. The nature of the members of each pair of opposite characters, e.g., tall and dwarf in peas, or black and white in fowls, is not affected by the other. The black that is inherited from hybrid gray parents proves to be as black as if from pure black ones (Fig. 20.4). Characters are units which do not blend or mix.

The Law of Independent Assortment. Every character is inherited separately from every other character, in peas, the height of the plant from the color of the flower.

Dominance. When organisms, each with a pure-line for opposite characters, are crossed, one character is either completely or incompletely dominant over the other in the offspring (Figs. 20.3, 20.4); the other is completely or incompletely recessive. Some characters are incompletely dominant, such as the red of the red and white plants of four o'clocks that produce the pink

The 3 to 1 Ratio Demonstrated

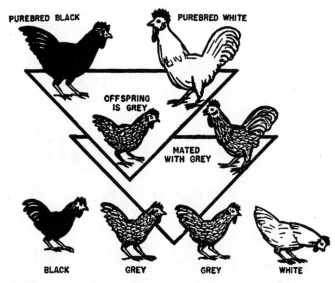

PUREBRED BLACK   PUREBRED WHITE

OFFSPRING
IS GREY

MATED
WITH GREY

BLACK   GREY   GREY   WHITE

FIG. 20.4. The result of crossing fowls of pure lines, one with an unmixed ancestry for black and the other for white feathering; F_1, incomplete dominance of black resulting in dapple gray. Crossing of dapple grays produces a generation (F_2) in ratio of 1 black, 2 dapple gray, 1 white. The blacks are pure black, and the whites are pure white like their grandparents. (Courtesy, *Public Affairs Pamphlet No. 165*. New York, Public Affairs Committee, Inc., 1950.)

ones of the next generation (F_1). Mendel had experience with incomplete dominance for he crossed pure early flowering peas with pure late flowering ones and produced an F_1 generation of plants with a flowering time half way between those of their parents.

Mendel's principles have held true. Since his time, thousands of experiments have been made in plant and animal breeding and the results of the great majority have upheld his principles.

Cellular Basis of Genetics

Chromosomes. In 1902 an American biologist, W. S. Sutton, pointed out that chromosomes are mechanisms that carry out the Mendelian principles. It may be well to review the characteristics of chromosomes in connection with their role in genetics (Figs. 20.5, 20.6). The behavior of chromosomes shows a striking parallel to the dominant and recessive body characters. The chromosomes of the body cells are paired; so are dominant and recessive characters. A character is an inherited quality, e.g., the color black. A factor is the gene or genes that are responsible for it. A gene is a minute part of a chromosome. Factor and gene are used as synonyms. Experimental cross

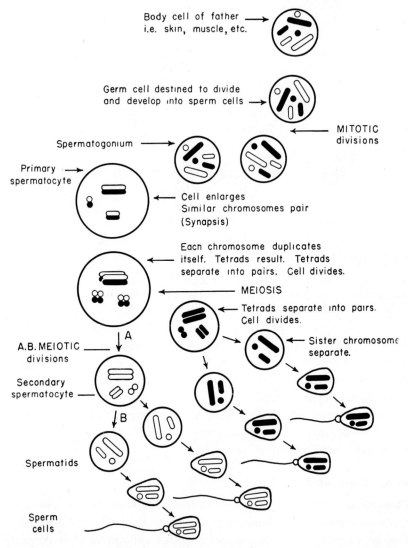

Fig. 20.5. The reduction (meiosis) of the number of chromosomes from the double (diploid) to the single (haploid) number during the formation of sperm. For each sex cell, the process includes: increase in number of cells by MITOSIS; reduction of chromosomes by MEIOSIS. For simplicity, six chromosomes are used in the body cells. Cells of the human body contain 48 chromosomes. Corresponding process in female (Fig. 3.10).

breeding has proven that the genes responsible for characters are segregated in separate sex cells.

The number of chromosomes is normally constant for each species, but varies in different ones. Although each species has its characteristic number, other species may have the same number; man and tobacco plants both have 24 pairs of chromosomes. There are 100 pairs of chromosomes in crayfishes and 24 pairs in man. This tells plainly that there is no relation between an animal's place in evolution and the abundance of its chromosomes.

Chromosomes occur in pairs, except in mature sex cells. One member of each pair is contributed by the egg and the other by the sperm cell of the parents (Fig. 20.5). In the body cells the only chromosomes which may not be paired are those which determine sex and in many species these are also paired but of different shape and size as in man. In other species, usually in the male parent, e.g., grasshoppers, half the sperm cells contain a sex chromosome and produce females, and half are without one and produce males (Fig. 20.6).

During development of human sex cells, the double number of chromosomes is reduced to the single or haploid number, 24 in the human sperm and 24 in the egg (Figs. 20.5, 20.6). Each time a developing egg divides, one member of each pair of chromosomes is segregated in the egg or in the polar body, and likewise for the sperms, a result that is very significant in the ancestry of all of us, whether mouse or man.

Genes. Genes are the units of heredity, probably molecules of nucleoprotein about five millionths of an inch long. By interaction with other genes, with the cell content surrounding them, and the whole environment of the animal, a gene or combination of genes controls the inheritance of such diverse qualities as brown eyes, a soprano voice, and a way of walking. They are contained and transmitted in chromosomes, hundreds of them being located along the cross bands that are visible when certain chromosomes, as in the fruit fly, are highly magnified (Figs. 20.7, 20.8). Although genes have not been clearly seen, their places on a given chromosome have been located exactly.

Genes of fruit flies can be "knocked out" of chromosomes by treating the animals with radium. When the sex organs of such flies are examined microscopically, empty or damaged places may be found on the chromosomes of the sex cells. In such flies, some part of the body may be changed, a new wrinkle in the wings, or some action may be different. Treatments and examinations are repeated over and over again until the changed structure or action of the fly is correlated with the particular spot on the chromosome. Thus, the gene is located. Maps of chromosomes of fruit flies on which genes are located are the results of the combination of experimental breeding and microscopic examination of chromosomes (Fig. 20.8).

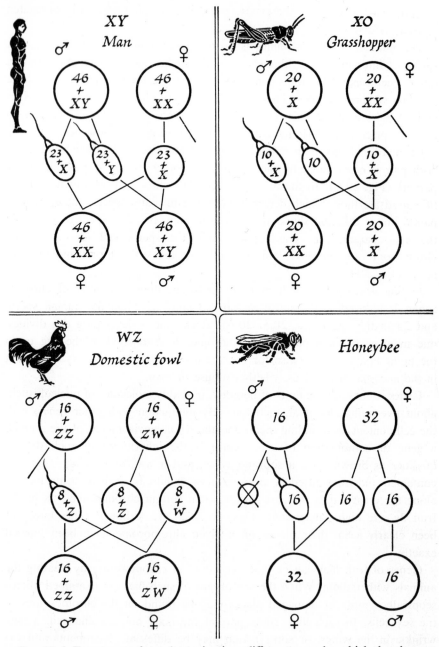

FIG. 20.6. Four types of sex determination, different ways by which the chromosomes determine the sex of an individual. *Man,* cells of the body (except sex cells); male and female each has 48 chromosomes. In males the members of one pair called *xy* are of different sizes, *y* being the smaller. In females, members of the counterpart of this pair are the same size and called *xx.*

All of the eggs contain an *x* chromosome. Half of the sperm cells contain an *x* and half of them the *y* chromosome. Thus the sex of an individual depends upon

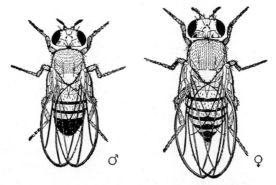

Fɪɢ. 20.7. The fruit fly, *Drosophila melanogaster*. This and other species of these common gnat-like flies have contributed more material to the study of genetics than any other animal. They have 8 chromosomes in the body cells but the genes contained in them are responsible for thousands of structures and actions. Fruit flies were used by Thomas Hunt Morgan in his studies which constitute some of the most important contributions to the science of genetics. (Courtesy, Morgan: *The Physical Basis of Heredity*. Philadelphia, J. B. Lippincott Co., 1919.)

Genes act like enzymes in that they are able to speed up or slow down chemical actions without themselves being used up in the process. They resemble viruses in being extraordinarily minute. Like them they multiply only within living cells; they have specific effects upon cells; they may change (mutate) in nature; and may be caused to change by exposure to x-rays. Genes and viruses differ, genes being orderly and mainly beneficial, while viruses, at least the well-known ones, are usually lawless and destructive.

Genes are inherited but some of the characters which they control may be modified by environment. In man, the ability to smile is inherited, but not the exact smile for those of fat faces differ from those of thin faces and food may create the change.

---

the content of the sperm cell that happens to join the egg from which he or she develops, *xx* a female, *xy* a male. *Grasshopper,* cells of the body (except sex cells); male has 21 and female 22 chromosomes. Every egg has an *x* chromosome. Half of the sperm cells have an *x* chromosome, and half of them have no *x* chromosome. If the latter fertilizes an egg it produces a male $(20+x)$ grasshopper. *Domestic fowl,* cells of the body (except sex cells): male and female each have 18 chromosomes. In males the pair of sex chromosomes are called *zz;* in females the members of this pair are different and called *zw.*

Every sperm contains the *z* chromosome; half of the eggs contain *z* and the other half contain the *w* chromosome. A *z* sperm fertilizes an egg with the *z* chromosome and produces a male *zz.* *Honeybees,* fertilized eggs (sperm 16 chromosomes and egg 16), having the diploid number of 32 chromosomes develop into females (queen and workers); unfertilized eggs (no sperm, and egg 16 chromosomes), having the haploid number of 16 chromosomes develop into males (drones). Their body cells have only half the number of chromosomes (16) that are contained in the body cells of the females (32). (Courtesy, Winchester: *Genetics.* Boston, Houghton Mifflin Co., 1951.)

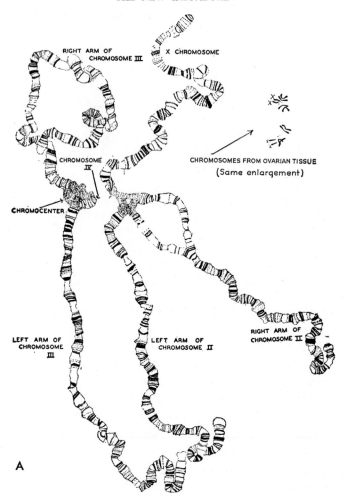

FIG. 20.8. *A,* chromosomes in the salivary glands of a fruit fly. Although they belong to minute flies these chromosomes are among the largest that have been observed. (From Altenburg: *Genetics.* Copyrighted by Henry Holt and Co. Reprinted with their permission.)

Experiments Illustrating Mendelian Principles

Monohybrid Cross. A monohybrid cross may be illustrated by cross breeding one parent having a long line of black ancestors (pure-line), and another parent having a long line of white ones. The offspring produced by animals differing in one character, such as color, are monohybrids.

A pure-line black guinea pig is bred to a pure-line white. The male may be black and female white or vice versa (Fig. 20.9). In a pair of genes, e.g., the gene for white, the recessive, is expressed by w in small type; the gene for black, the dominant, by W in capitals. The formulas for the parents (P)

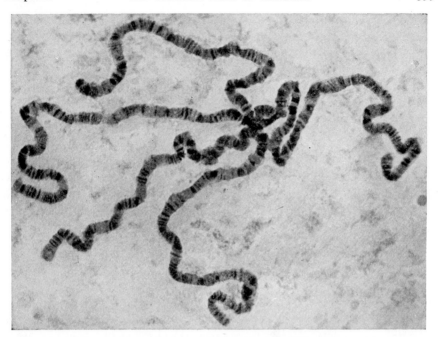

FIG. 20.8 (*continued*). *B,* A microphotograph of normal chromosomes from the nucleus of a cell in a salivary gland of a female fruit fly, *Drosophila melanogaster.* Such chromosomes, among the largest chromosomes that have been discovered in animal cells, have greatly aided the study of the effect of x-rays on the chromosome. If fruit flies are irradiated, e.g., males, the chromosomes in the nuclei of cells in the salivary glands of the first generation of offspring show various changes. Such changes may be losses of parts, shifts in position of parts, combinations of parts involving two or more chromosomes. Changes in the form or habit of the animal accompany these changes, sometimes its death. (Courtesy, B. P. Kaufmann, Carnegie Institute of Washington.)

are *ww* and *WW* since each one has the diploid number of chromosomes, the product of two sex cells each containing gene *w* in one case, and gene *W* in the other. Thus, in each the genes for coat color are similar or homozygous. The sex cells of the black parent (P) each contain a gene for black (*W*); those of the white parent (P) contain a gene for white (*w*). In F_1 only black guinea pigs are produced because each receives one gene for black and one for white, with black dominant. Although each animal is black, it is actually a hybrid for color since half of its sex cells contain a gene for black and half of them a gene for white. Because a trait is dominant in one species it does not follow that this will occur in some other species. Black is dominant over white in rabbits and guinea pigs but white is dominant over black in Leghorn poultry. A different type of gene is involved in the two cases.

Backcross. A backcross (or test cross) of breeding is a method of testing animals that appear alike in one or more characters (phenotypically) but may differ genotypically. It is used commonly in analyzing F_1 dominants by crossing them with their pure recessive parents, hence the name backcross. In the preceding cross of guinea pigs, this would be a cross between a black guinea pig of F_1 and its pure white parent (Fig. 20.10). If the black is a hybrid, the offspring are black and white guinea pigs in equal numbers. In the hybrid black guinea pig of F_1, half of the sex cells carry a gene for black (W) and half of them a gene for white (w). In the white parent P every sex cell carries a gene for white (w). The cross results in the half white and half black of black and white animals (Fig. 20.10). This figure also shows a similar result for another pair of contrasting characters, short-long hair, where short is dominant to long.

Dihybrid Cross. A dihybrid cross is one between organisms that differ

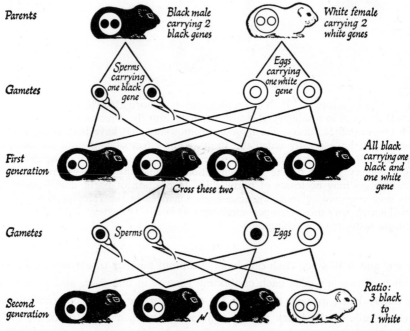

FIG. 20.9. Monohybrids, offspring of guinea pigs which differ in one color. The original parents, P_1, are pure-line blacks and pure-line whites, black W being dominant over white w. The resulting progeny show the behavior of a dominant gene. They also show the effects of the all-important separateness of genes, that the character white which was lost from sight in the first or F_1 generation reappeared unaffected in the F_2 generation. Each animal of F_1 is in appearance (phenotypically) black but in gene content (genotypically) black and white. When the hybrids of F_1 are crossed, their offspring F_2 show the typical Mendelian ratio of three dominants to one recessive. When animals of the F_2 generation are intercrossed, one-fourth are pure black, one-fourth pure white, and two-fourths black (black and white). When crossed these animals that contain genes for black and white produce blacks and whites in the 3:1 ratio. (Courtesy, Winchester: *Genetics.* Boston, Houghton Mifflin Co., 1951.)

from one another in two pairs of contrasting characters. A male guinea pig that has a pure-line ancestry for short, black hair is crossed with a female pure-line for long, white hair, or vice versa for sex (Fig. 20.11). The genes in the body cells are dominant black (*WW*) and dominant short (*LL*) that is *WWLL* in the male, and recessive white (*ww*) and recessive long (*ll*) in the female, *wwll*. During meiosis the genes on homologous pairs of chromosomes, i.e., *WW,* or *LL,* or *ww* or *ll,* go to different sperm or eggs as the case may be (Fig. 20.11).

These gametes form the offspring of the F₁ generation, all of them black short haired guinea pigs (*WLwl*) having the dominant genes for black and short (*W* and *L*) in their body cells as well as the recessive ones for white and long (*w* and *l*). The gametes of the F₁ generation will contain the genes *WL, Wl, wL, wl* (Fig. 20.11). If animals of the F₁ generation are intercrossed the ratio of their offspring will be: 9 black short, 3 black long, 3 white short, 1 white long. The combinations of genes in the eggs and sperm that produce these are shown in Figure 20.11, with the combinations of genes in the body cells. Since in each sex there are four kinds of gametes, there will be 16 possible combinations of gametes with their contained genes in the animals of the F₂ generation.

The foregoing experiment shows that whenever strains of animals differ from one another in two or more pairs of genes the inheritance of one pair is independent of the other (Mendel's Law of Independent Assortment).

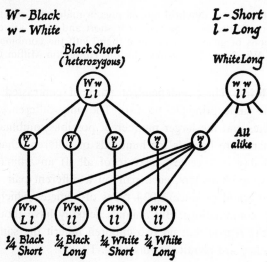

Fɪɢ. 20.10. Back- (or test) cross, a common method of testing the gene content of animals that look alike but may differ genetically. A backcross of a black, short-haired guinea pig to a white, long-haired one shows that the black, short-haired guinea pig carried genes for white color and long hair, i.e., the animal did not breed true to type. (Courtesy, Winchester: *Genetics.* Boston, Houghton Mifflin Co., 1951.)

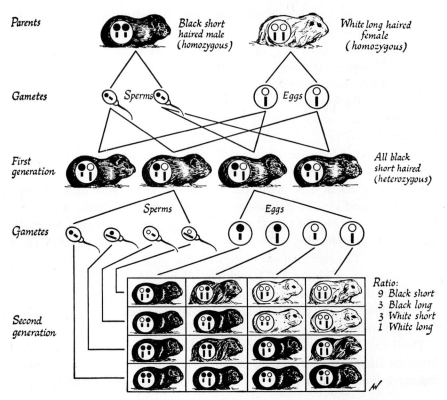

FIG. 20.11. Offspring of dihybrid guinea pigs, a male with short black hair and a female with long white hair. The genes for short and black are dominant. Chart of the combinations of genes that produce them with the combinations in the sex cells. (Courtesy, Winchester: *Genetics*. Boston, Houghton Mifflin Co., 1951.)

Multiple Hybrids. Three independent pairs of contrasted characters are governed by the same principles as two. The only difference is the greater variety of gametes and the larger number of possible combinations of genes. Animals in general are hybrids for hundreds of different characters; human beings are probably the greatest mixture of all. If an animal had only ten pairs of contrasting characters, each pair on a different pair of homologous chromosomes, it could produce 1,024 types of gametes which could in turn form 1,048,576 combinations. But animals actually have thousands of characters. This is the reason that no two children inherit the same combination of traits unless they are identical twins (Fig. 19.20).

Linkage of Genes

Linked genes are those that are located in the same chromosome and inherited together. This is an exception to Mendel's Independent Assortment of Genes which still holds for genes that are located on different chromosomes.

In his experiments, Mendel luckily dealt with no such genes. Linkage works as a check on the independence of genes, a hold-back on too much scattering.

Arrangement of Genes on Chromosomes

Linear Arrangement. Genes are located throughout the length of each chromosome in precise and standardized arrangement (Fig. 20.8). Maps have been made of certain chromosomes of Drosophila showing the locations that have been worked out for a comparatively large number of genes. However, such maps give little idea of the number of genes on a chromosome. In one species of these little fruit flies it is well established that there are certain chromosomes that contain some 2500 genes.

Crossing Over. This change in location of chromosomes occurs during meiosis in the prophase stage when similar (homologous) chromosomes unite in pairs with equivalent genes opposite to one another. A part of one of the pair may change places with a corresponding part of the other (Fig. 20.12). It is as if the residents of a section of one side of a street changed places with those of a corresponding section of the other side.

Crossing over may occur in more than one section of the partner chromosomes in some species and not in others, and in some species only under certain conditions. It may take place in one sex and not the other, as is the case in the female but not ordinarily in the male of Drosophila, although it may be induced by exposing the latter animals to high temperature or x-rays. In most plants and animals, however, crossing over occurs in both sexes. Thus the position of genes on different pairs of chromosomes results in their

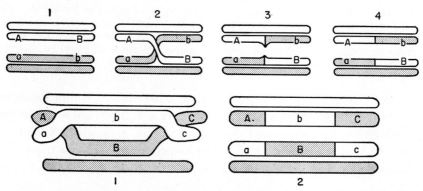

FIG. 20.12. Crossing over of corresponding sections of the homologous partner chromosomes during the "4-strand" phase, in the prophase stage of division of sperm or egg cells. *Upper—1,2,3,4;* example of single crossing. *Lower—1,2;* example of double crossing. Letters represent sections of chromosome strands. In this early phase of synapsis, each member of a future pair of chromosomes has doubled, thus forming 4 chromosomes. In these cases, crossing over occurs in only two of them. Each of the four chromosomes will be distributed into a separate cell in the two later meiotic divisions.

independent assortment when sex cells are formed, but the linkage of genes on the individual chromosomes of a pair reduces their independence of others on the same chromosomes.

Sex Determination

Whether an animal is male or female is determined by the number and quality of certain genes in the egg and sperm from which it originated. Some lower animals are changed from males to females and vice versa by hormones and variations in temperature. This does not happen in higher animals.

Sex Chromosomes. In the body cells of various animals there are either one or two distinctive chromosomes usually smaller than the others. These are the sex chromosomes; the others are called autosomes. Both sex chromosomes and autosomes carry genes influencing sex and it is the balance between these genes that results in maleness or femaleness. In the cells of the human body, there are 48 chromosomes and two of them are sex chromosomes (Fig. 20.13). In a woman, these are the same size, X and X; in a man the two are

A   B

FIG. 20.13. Chromosomes of human cells. Those of the body cells show the characteristic diploid number resulting from the union of male and female sex cells. *A,* the normal pattern of arrangement in a body cell. *B,* the chromosomes arranged in pairs; the presence of *x* and the very small *y* denotes a male; two *x* chromosomes denote a female. (Courtesy, Baitsell: *Human Biology,* ed. 2. New York, McGraw-Hill Book Co., 1950.)

different, X and the smaller Y. All human eggs have one X; half of the sperm cells have an X chromosome; half of them have a Y. Thus, sex is determined at fertilization; the X-egg and X-sperm result in a female XX and the X-egg and Y-sperm in a male (XY). The X-sperms and Y-sperms result from divisions during meiosis (Fig. 20.5). A plan similar to this occurs in many animals.

There are other animals in which half the sperms have an X chromosome, while the other half lacks any sex chromosome (Fig. 20.6). The resulting body cells contain XX in the female and XO in the male. The latter animals appear as typically male as those of the XY plan. Although fruit flies usually have half X and half Y sperm cells, there are rare individuals in which some of the sperms lack any sex chromosome. Male flies develop from the eggs fertilized by such O-sperms and appear typically male. However, breeding experiments have proven that these males are sterile. In other species in which half the sperms regularly lack a sex chromosome (e.g., grasshoppers), the males are fertile. Y-chromosomes contain only a few genes. In fruit flies these appear to be associated with fertility. In the XO male fruit flies that is the main character missing.

Different as males and females are, they are also fundamentally similar. Some invertebrates require but a slight shift in conditions, perhaps of the genes, to tilt the organism toward maleness or femaleness. Sometimes abnormal chromosome numbers resulting in a different balance of the genes may produce supermales, superfemales, or intersexes as in Drosophila (Fig. 20.14). Higher animals are seldom if ever entirely male or entirely female, as the nipples of human males bear witness. The possible explanation may be that every individual carries all the genes essential for both sexes and that certain genes or conditions of the genes tip the balance toward maleness or femaleness.

DISCOVERY OF SEX CHROMOSOMES. Sex chromosomes were first correctly interpreted fifty years ago (1901) by C. E. McClung during his study of the

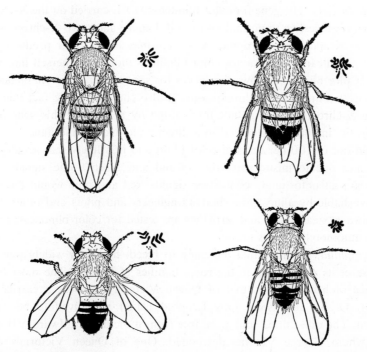

FIG. 20.14. Sex types in fruit flies, Drosophila. *Upper left,* normal female; *upper right,* intersex; *lower left,* supermale; *lower right,* superfemale, and chromosomes of each type. (After Bridges. Courtesy, Snyder: *Principles of Heredity,* ed. 4. Boston, D. C. Heath and Co., 1951.)

spermatogenesis of the long-horned grasshopper. In 1905, Nettie Stevens published an account of the sex chromosomes in a beetle (Tenebrio) and showed that the male had 19 large chromosomes (18 autosomes plus an X) and one small one (Y). In the same year, Edmund B. Wilson announced similar discoveries in insects; one of them, the common squash bug (*Anasa tristis*), has 22 chromosomes in the body cells of the female and 21 in those of the male.

Sex-linked and Sex-influenced Inheritance

Sex-linked. The sex chromosomes, chiefly the X-chromosomes, carry other genes besides those associated with sex. These are known as sex-linked genes. Among the best known of human sex-linked characters are color blindness and hemophilia or "bleeding."

Color blindness varies in degrees from a weakened sense of red-green to the absolute loss of color as in late twilight. Red-green color blindness and hemophilia have long been known to be inheritable in the same peculiar criss-cross way (Fig. 20.15). A color blind man may transmit color blindness through his daughters who have normal vision to half of his grandsons; a color blind woman transmits color blindness to her sons and to her daughters who become carriers. The gene for color blindness (c) is carried on the X-chromosome and is recessive to normal vision (C); females have two X-chromosomes, males an X and Y-chromosome. A woman may be a carrier producing eggs half of which carry the gene for color blindness though she herself has normal vision. Color blindness shows that genes for sex and for other characters may be associated in the same chromosome. It also emphasizes the fact that genes on the X-chromosomes are not transmitted by a father to his sons and so reduces the importance ascribed to a direct male line of inheritance.

Eight out of 100 persons are color blind and it is likely that accidents are sometimes due to misinterpretation of red and green traffic signals. These colors are an unfortunate choice for signals, red and blue would have been distinguishable by almost everybody. Engineers and pilots and other officers on railways, steamships, and airplanes are tested for color blindness; in some states, automobile drivers are not.

Hemophilia, the abnormal tendency to bleed, has been widely publicized because of its distribution in the royal families of Europe. The most famous pedigree of hemophilia is that of Queen Victoria who was a carrier (Fig. 20.16). Of her four sons, only Leopold (II.8) who lived to be 31 was affected. The other three sons were free from it including Edward VII (II.2) from whom George VI was descended. One of Queen Victoria's carrier daughters, Alice (II.3) was the mother of Alexandra of Russia (III.6) whose son Alexis (IV.12) suffered severely from hemophilia. Victoria's other carrier daughter, Beatrice (II.9), was the mother of Victoria Eugenie (III.16)

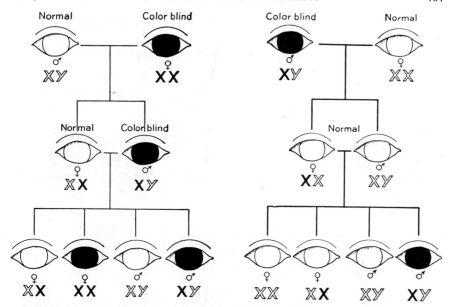

FIG. 20.15. The criss-cross inheritance of color-blindness from a color-blind man, via his daughter, a carrier, to his grandson.

Color-blindness is a recessive c to normal vision C. The gene for color-blindness is carried only on X-chromosomes. A man is color blind because he inherits one X-chromosome carrying color-blindness and no gene for normal vision in the Y-chromosome. A woman is a carrier because she inherits two X-chromosomes, C and c with the C of normal vision the dominant one. If the mother is a carrier and father is color blind, their daughter may be color blind, a rare occurrence. (After Dunn. Courtesy, Sinnott, Dunn, and Dobzhansky: *Principles of Genetics*, ed. 4. New York, McGraw-Hill Book Co., 1950.)

of Spain, two of whose sons had hemophilia, including the Crown Prince Alfonso (IV.16). There appears to be no record of hemophilia among the ancestors of Queen Victoria, and the gene for the disease is believed to have arisen as a mutation. If her consort, Prince Albert, had carried a gene he would have had the disease.

Sex-influenced Inheritance—Baldness. There are many types of baldness; some of them are inherited. Its most striking character is its much greater frequency in men than in women (Fig. 20.17). It seems probable that hereditary baldness is due to a gene that behaves like a dominant in men and like a limited recessive in women. The different expression of the genes in men and women is evidently due to a difference in hormones that makes them more or less sensitive to their inherited genes. Eunuchs (castrated men) seldom become bald. In women, the sparsity of male hormones is said to keep the hair, even though the genes for baldness may be present; in men the excess of male hormone makes the hair follicles sensitive to the genes of baldness.

THE "ROYAL" HEMOPHILIA PEDIGREE*

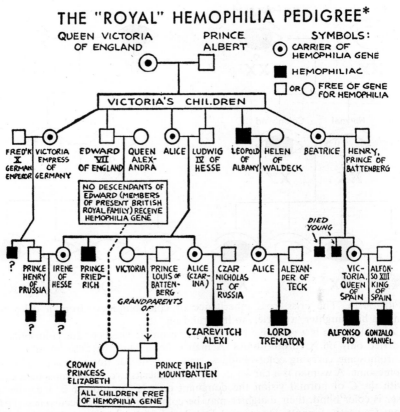

FIG. 20.16. Descendants of Queen Victoria, showing the distribution of hemophilia, evidently a mutation. (Data by Iltis. From *The New You and Heredity* by Amram Scheinfeld. Copyright, 1939, 1950, by Amram Scheinfeld, published by J. B. Lippincott Company.)

Mutations

A mutation is an inheritable change in a gene. This definition applies to changes in the genes of sperm cells and eggs. They are the all important mutations, the ones ordinarily meant by the term, mutation. They are the ones discussed here. Changes in the genes of body cells do occur but are exceptional and never inherited.

Mutation and Evolution. The evolution of living things is possible only because a gene can change and can reproduce itself in the changed form (Figs. 20.18, 20.19). How one gene changes into another kind is one of the greatest problems of biology. The change in one gene on one chromosome of an egg can establish a new kind of plant or animal which in good time may spread over the earth.

Mutations were discovered by Hugo de Vries, one of the rediscoverers of Mendel's pioneer paper on genetics. Since then mutations have been found

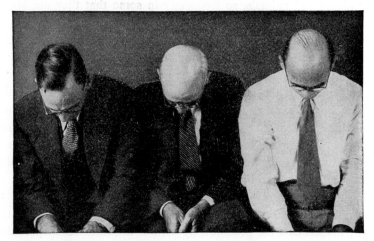

Fig. 20.17. Patterns of hereditary baldness. The gene for baldness is inherited by men and women but has different results. The most convincing theory is that difference in hormones acting on the same kind of gene may be responsible for the baldness in men and the usual lack of baldness in women. (Courtesy, Snyder: *Principles of Heredity*, ed. 4. Boston, D. C. Heath and Co., 1951.)

Fig. 20.18. A mutation for short legs in sheep; short-legged ewe in the center, ordinary sized sheep of the same variety at left and right.

In 1791, a Massachusetts farmer found in his flock a short-legged lamb from which he bred a strain of sheep, valuable to him because they did not jump the pasture walls. This variety, called Ancon sheep, still exists. (Photograph from *Life* Magazine © Time, Inc. Courtesy, Storrs Agricultural Experiment Station.)

in many plants and animals, so frequently in some that they are known as mutating species. In recent years, a thousand or more have been found in fruit flies. Many times that number were examined without discovering a structure suspected of being a mutation. And when some new feature was found, the fly had to be bred and several generations produced in order to show whether or not the new feature was inherited. Fortunately, fruit flies mature and breed quickly. Their lifetime in days is about the same as the human lifetime in years. In 1927, H. J. Muller discovered that if fruit flies were exposed to x-rays, the mutations would occur about 150 times more often than naturally; later treatment with radium increased them to 200 times (Fig. 20.20). The effect of the radiation suggested that mutations might be induced by cosmic rays. Fruit flies were taken to mountain tops where such radiation is more intense and mutations were speeded up. In later experiments, mutations were produced by certain extremes of temperature, by chemical substances, and by other influences inside and outside the flies. Almost every type of mutation found in nature has been induced in them experimentally, and some once believed to be unique results of experiments have been discovered in wild flies. Changes in the genes have gone on through millions of years of evolution as they are continuing quietly now.

Frequency of Natural Mutations. Mutations in any one gene are rare, estimated about one in 50,000 generations. The rate varies in different genes. It is also estimated that a mutated gene occurs in every ten human sperms and eggs. This seeming contradiction disappears when it is remembered that

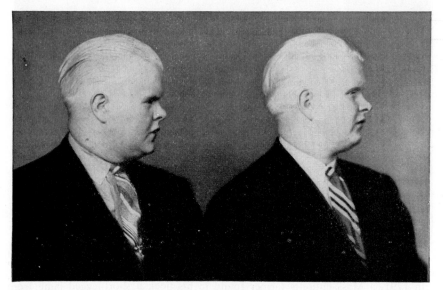

FIG. 20.19. Mutations for lack of pigment. Albino twins, without pigment in hair, eyes and skin, a recessive mutation in a pair of identical twins. (From Rife, Schonfeld, and Humstead in *Journal of Heredity*.)

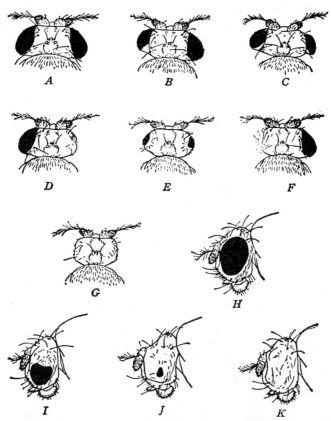

FIG. 20.20. Mutations in eyes of fruit flies (*Drosophila melanogaster*) induced by exposure to radium. *A*, normal eyes, top view; *B–G*, different degrees of eyelessness, top views; *H*, normal eyes, side view; *I–K*, different degrees of eyelessness, side views. (After Hansom and Winkleman. Courtesy, Fasten: *Introduction to General Zoology*. Boston, Ginn and Co., 1941.)

there are thousands of genes in one sperm or one egg and that the majority of mutations effect such slight changes that they are not discovered. In addition, the majority of them are recessives that are carried in the animal but not expressed for a very long time.

On the basis of observations on fruit flies, Muller has estimated that the average time elasping without change in any particular gene may be about 100,000 years. Allowing 10 generations of fruit flies per year, any particular fruit fly would mutate only once in something like a million generations. The mutation rate of the disease of hemophilia in a human line of descent has been estimated by J. B. S. Haldane as one in 100,000 generations.

Some species and some characteristics mutate more than others; fruit flies have many mutations; certain colors of sweet peas and many other garden flowers are mutations.

The genes in the egg and developing embryo may mutate independently of fertilization by the male cell. This has been observed in certain partheno-genetic animals such as waterfleas (Cladocera) by Arthur M. Banta who reared these through 850 generations and observed many mutations.

Effects of Mutations. More mutations are harmful than helpful. Their character shows that any desirable ones that appear are selected by the natural conditions inside and outside the organism. Otherwise they must be preserved by human selection, e.g., the valuable platinum or silver blue mink, the seedless grape.

Some of the most striking effects of environment on the expression of genes are produced by differences in temperature. At 27.5° C. the gene for "short wing" in Drosophila has a more marked effect than at a lower temperature. In Siamese cats the dark pigment is produced only in cooler parts of the body (Fig. 20.21).

FIG. 20.21. Dark pigment of Siamese cats, produced in the extremities of the body which are below a certain level of tempera-ture. (Courtesy, Boyd: *Genetics*. Boston, Little, Brown and Co., 1950.)

Giant Plants—Giant Cells. Polyploidy is a type of mutation in which the whole number of chromosomes, diploid or haploid, is increased two to several times. Such increased numbers are hereditary and are accompanied by marked changes. Polyploid plants are very large. Various garden flowers and vegetables, crop plants and fruit trees are polyploids. Plant polyploids are frequently found in nature, animal polyploids rarely if ever.

Many plant polyploids have been produced experimentally, largely by means of colchicine, a solution derived from the bulbs of the autumn crocus (Colchicum). The buds are bathed in colchicine solution which penetrates into the developing reproductive organs and affects the cells. The chromo-somes double their number but the rest of the cell fails to divide. In most plants, fertilization goes on as usual except that, for example, instead of 4 chromosomes in the sex cells, there are 8 and the fertilized egg has 16. Thus the young plant starts with double the number of chromosomes and larger cells than those of its parents. Giant tomatoes (Fig. 20.22) and giant flowering marigolds are polyploids. The radiant "Tetra Snaps" of certain seed catalogues are "Giant Tetraploid Snapdragons" that have giant flowers and four times the usual haploid number of chromosomes. Animals make a poor showing of polyploidy. It has been induced experimentally in Drosophila, and in several species of salamanders chiefly by subjecting the animals to low temperature (Fig. 20.23).

Inbreeding and Outbreeding

Inbreeding is the mating of near kin; cross breeding and outbreeding are the matings of unrelated individuals. In many communities there is a great deal of the former. Obviously, the more closely individuals are related, the more hereditary traits they have in common; the better or worse are their traits, and the better or worse for their descendants. Charles Darwin and his wife Emma Wedgwood were first cousins, each with a long heritage of desirable genes. In their case, nature and nurture joined in producing the gifted and cultured Darwin family. Cleopatra was the descendant of six generations of brother and sister marriages, yet the story of her life does not imply that she was dull or helpless.

Outbreeding usually produces individuals with unlike genes in which re-

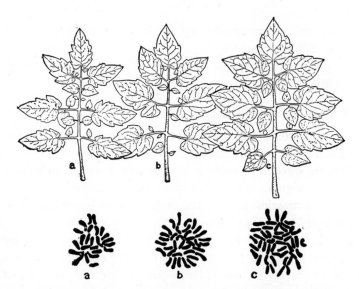

FIG. 20.22. Giant plants. Polyploidy in the tomato resulting from treatment with colchicine. *a,* leaf and usual diploid number (12 pairs) of chromosomes; *b,* leaf and chromosomes of triploid (3 sets of 12); *c,* leaf and chromosomes of tetraploid (4 sets of 12). (After Jörgenson. Courtesy, Snyder: *Principles of Heredity,* ed. 4. Boston, D. C. Heath and Co., 1951.)

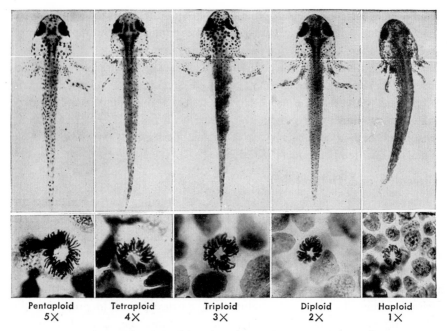

| Pentaploid | Tetraploid | Triploid | Diploid | Haploid |
| 5× | 4× | 3× | 2× | 1× |

FIG. 20.23. Giant cells. Polyploidy in salamanders (*Triturus viridescens*). The salamander larvae are all at about the same stage of development. Since they are about the same size, the changes in cell size due to polyploidy result in a reduced number of body cells. (Courtesy, G. Fankhauser, Princeton University.)

cessives, often defects, are hidden by dominants. Cross breeding of plants or animals of different varieties leads to increased vigor. This is often described as hybrid vigor, for example, the offspring of a male ass and a mare is a mule, a hybrid tougher than either parent.

Mistaken Ideas about Heredity

Acquired Characters. Nothing is inherited unless it changes the genes in the sex cells. Bodily injuries do not do this; neither do acquired habits or training—eating olives or building bridges. An overwhelming number of experiments and arguments has been presented in fruitless attempts to prove that effects upon muscles, nerves, and bones may be inherited. Tails of rats bobbed for many generations have left the last generation of rats growing tails as long as those of the first; the sex cells are untouched by the afflictions of the tails. Only the capacity is inherited, a tail to be cut, a mind to be trained.

Does one or the other parent take a greater part in inheritance? Only if one has the dominant members of pairs of genes and the other the recessives. A recessive must await its chance of expression until it can pair with another recessive.

Telegony. This is a theory that in case two or more males mate with one female the influence of an earlier mating may be carried on to the offspring that result from the later one. This is the favorite reason that dog breeders propose when puppies have been due to "mistakes." Similarly, among cattle dealers there is a notion that if a "blooded" bull is mated to a "scrub" cow, the latter may infect his offspring of later matings. Such beliefs are numerous but have no foundation in fact.

Human Inheritance

Value of Knowledge. Knowledge of human heredity is of great practical value, (1) in medical treatment, especially public health, (2) in forming wise opinions and judgment of the special and economic problems that crowd the present world, and (3) as an aid in reaching legal decisions, such as disputed parentage. With a knowledge of heredity it is also to be remembered that children cannot choose their parents. The parents do the choosing; the children take the results.

The inheritance of many physical and mental defects and diseases is becoming more or less clearly understood. It is important to know whether a defect is a dominant or a recessive since no recessive even if present in one parent will crop out in a child unless a matching recessive is transmitted by the other parent. At present, prospective parents can secure a clearer idea than ever before of what benefits or dangers they may pass on to their children. There are blood tests which detect the presence of hemophilia and hereditary anemia in carriers who otherwise give no hint of the diseases.

Genetics holds a leading role in the investigations of cancer and thousands of experimental studies are being made in this field. Clues to the behavior of breast cancer have been discovered in inbred mice and rats susceptible to the disease. Globular particles (the "milk factor") visible under the great magnification of the electron microscope have been isolated from these inbred mice that regularly transmit cancer to nursing offspring.

Heredity is in the kernel of racial problems. There is at least a better chance for clearer thinking and wiser judgment about social problems when the facts of human inheritance are kept in sight. The facts overtop the notions of pure human breeds and superior races. All human beings are multiple cross breeds. All are superlative mongrels, that are like kaleidoscopes whose patterns may be changed but only insofar as the material allows.

Knowledge of blood types has entered the courts, as in New York, where a man claimed that he was not the father of his wife's child. The tests showed that his blood was type O, "universal donor"; his wife's type was A, and the child was AB. Since the parents could not pass on a combination of genes for the AB type, the court decided with the father.

Examples of Inherited Qualities. Blood is an extremely sensitive and complex chemical compound. Even in closely related species of animals the chemical compositions of blood are different. Only a little blood from an animal of one species is harmful or fatal to an animal of another species if injected into the vessels of the latter. The blood of different persons also differs. It is well known that human blood is affected by the chemical composition of blood in certain persons and not in others. This is the basis of blood groups, the inherited chemical compositions of blood discussed in Chapter 7. It is also the basis of Rh, an hereditary characteristic in the chemical content of the blood. In dealing with this the meaning of the terms antigen and antibody should be clear.

An antigen is any substance, often one injected into the body, that stimulates the formation of the chemical substances called antibodies. The toxin of an infection is an antigen which stimulates the formation of antibodies (antitoxins) that turn about and work against it.

RH PROTEIN. Up to a comparatively few years ago, the cause of deaths of many infants before birth or soon afterward was a mystery. However, in 1940 a new type of human blood group was discovered which proved to be the cause. It was named the Rhesus or Rh type after the Rhesus monkeys whose blood was used in making tests that led to the discovery. About 85% of the human population are Rh-positive, that is their red blood cells contain the characteristic Rh-protein, an antigen, which reacts to the tests. The Rh protein is inherited through dominant genes, Rhrh or RhRh. The remaining 15% of the population inherit recessive genes, rhrh. Their red cells lack the Rh substances and they are termed Rh-negative.

The connection between the Rh blood and the harm to children arises only when the mother is Rh-negative and the unborn child is Rh-positive (Rhrh), through inheritance from its father. The Rh-proteins (antigens) pass from the blood of the child to its mother's blood where they stimulate the production of "anti-Rh" substances, that is, antibodies against themselves. Eventually some of this anti-Rh passes into the child's blood (Fig. 20.24). There it may cause such agglutination (sticking together) of the red cells that the child cannot survive. This does not usually happen with a first baby because not enough anti-Rh is then produced, but more accumulates with the second or third child usually with grave results.

The "anti-Rh" substance occurs in the blood and tissue fluid and can penetrate the membranes that separate the blood of mother and child. But the Rh-protein is in the child's red blood cells which would not be expected to get through the membrane. How this happens remains to be discovered.

Testing for Rh blood is a common procedure. When a Red Cross blood donor is typed, the identification card includes an Rh+ or Rh—. Babies that are born alive but with damaged blood may be saved by transfusions of Rh— blood. The damaged blood with its dangerous anti-Rh is literally washed out of the blood vessels by the donor's blood.

SKIN COLOR. The natural color of skin is complex and several genes take part in its inheritance. Three pigments are involved in any human complexion, melanin (black or brownish), carotene (carrot color), and hemoglobin (varying reds of the blood). The blue of skin, e.g., on the wattles of male turkeys, is due to the scattering of light upon the layers of cells, not to pigment. The predominance of one or more of these pigments determines what the skin color will be. The key genes are those which govern the melanin. The genes remain separate and only in their effects is there any blending, as in mulattoes. Changes of skin color may also be due to jaundice, glandular and other disturbances that may or may not be related to heredity.

EYE COLOR. The colors of skin, hairs, and eyes are produced by virtually the same kinds of pigments. In eyes as in skin, the genes for the dark pigment

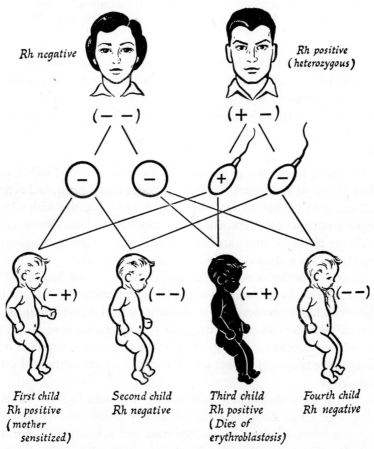

FIG. 20.24. Diagram of the possible action of the Rhesus (*Rh*) protein in the bloods of mother and child. The types of children that may result from a cross of an Rh negative woman and a man who is Rh positive; in this case only half of the sperms carry the Rh+ genes. (Courtesy, Winchester: *Genetics*. Boston, Houghton, Mifflin Co., 1951.)

melanin play key parts. Melanin is present in all human eye colors from black to pale blue (Chap. 17). Black and brown eyes occur in a majority of the human race, and the genes for dark pigments were probably the pre-eminent ones in early human history.

Table 20.1

CERTAIN TRAITS INHERITED IN MAN

Dominant	*Recessive*
Dark hair	Blond hair
Curly hair (incomplete dominance, wavy)	Straight hair
Black skin (incomplete dominance)	White skin
Brown eyes	Blue or gray
Hazel or green	Blue or gray
Nearsightedness	Normal vision
Blood group A, B, and AB	Blood group O

MENTAL DISORDERS. A number of mental disorders are known to be inherited. The inheritance of a few of these is known; for others it is suspected and still being studied. Superior mental ability and special aptitudes run in families but are also strongly influenced by upbringing and other surroundings.

Eugenics

The increasing knowledge of human inheritance has brought with it numerous plans for racial betterment. Eugenics includes study, plans, and action for the betterment of the human race. Eugenics may be negative with education and regulations against the reproduction by which feeble-mindedness, insanity, and appalling physical defects are continued. Positive eugenics encourages the continuation of the qualities of health and good citizenship.

The greatest problem of negative eugenics is feeble-mindedness since 5 per cent of the American population has an intelligence rating of 70 or much less. This group includes: paupers due to laziness and inability; criminals, large numbers of them hopelessly defective; many persons who have grown up in institutions for defectives and must remain there; and great numbers of morons who hang to the fringes of life but contribute nothing but inertia and children like themselves.

The reproduction of definitely unfit persons has been to some extent prevented by segregating them in institutions and by sterilization. However, confinement is a heavy financial load on the state and is unhappiness for the individual. Sterilization, on the other hand, is a simple operation; severance of both sperm ducts of the male (Fig. 18.5) or both oviducts of the female (Fig. 18.10). It prevents the outlet of the sex cells, but in no way affects the sensations or health of the person. The operation is performed upon the advice of committees of physicians and, where feasible, the consent of the person involved. The laws of twenty-seven states provide for sterilization of the feeble-minded and permanently insane under such well-guarded provisions. California has carried out the law extensively and with satisfactory results. The American performance of sterilization was settled by the Supreme Court in a decision given on May 2, 1927, in which Judge Oliver Wendell Holmes made his famous remark, "Three generations of imbeciles are enough."

Positive eugenics is largely education in the ideals of what good citizens should be and the power which they have upon society. Awards for large healthy families have been more frequent in the eagerly militaristic countries than in America. For the most part the positive aspect of eugenics takes care of itself.

Part V

Evolution of Animals

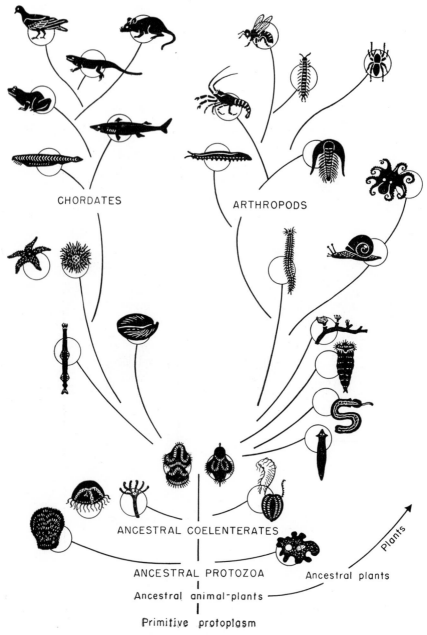

CHORDATES

ARTHROPODS

ANCESTRAL COELENTERATES

ANCESTRAL PROTOZOA

Ancestral animal-plants

Primitive protoplasm

Plants

Ancestral plants

PLATE I. A suggestion of relations within the animal kingdom. See Plate II. (After Allee et al.)

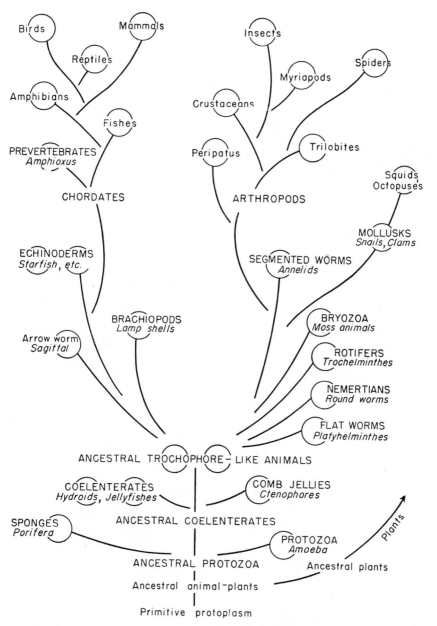

PLATE II. A suggestion of relations within the animal kingdom. See Plate I.

21

The Protozoans—Representatives

of Unicellular Animals

Living organisms are the centers of relationships that reach out and connect with numberless other things, living and nonliving. These relationships have multiplied through the long past as they are still doing. This is evolution. Learning about relationships is a universal and exciting occupation, whether it occurs in telephone conversations, in political campaigns, in searching out the what and wherefore of plants and animals and other things. Because of this, protozoans have place and importance; no matter that they are little, largely unknown, and hardly ever seen. Discoveries of their far-reaching relationships are the lively rewards of exploration into their daily lives.

Protozoans—The Pioneer Animals

The great advances in the evolution of animals occur in flights of steps on the long stairway of living. The protozoans were the pioneers and dominating animals on the first steps. Multicellular animals with innumerable complexities dominated the second great flight of steps. Continuing their own evolution, many protozoans moved into the bodies of the multicellular animals and became successful parasites in these new surroundings. Others persisted in free living, becoming adjusted for various conditions in the always-changing environment of the earth.

Gradually many kinds of animals were gathered into communities, held by bonds of food and shelter. Organized societies appear on the highest steps, and are still continuing to change. Social insects became prominent, and after long ages primitive human societies developed. The human groups became divided; some scattered widely; others intermixed. They often came together to eat, to fight, and to acclaim their works. All of this greatly benefited the distribution of the protozoans; gave them new places to live and easy ways to reach them. They became, and still are, successful parasites of the human digestive tract and, with the help of man's insect associates, have been widely introduced into human blood.

Compared with multicellular animals, protozoans are only relatively simple; many are extraordinarily complex. No near kin of the ameba has come to fly like a bird, but neither can birds make a living on bacteria, as many protozoans do. The multicellular animals created opportunities for the protozoans; they have never displaced them.

Characteristics. Protozoans are minute unicellular animals that carry on all the fundamental processes of the life of higher animals. They live in all sorts of places and in different ways with one limitation, that for at least part of their life span their surroundings must be wet, actually a limitation of every animal.

Most protozoans have animal-like structures, flagella, cilia, and special openings for the entrance of food; some have light receptors containing the visual pigment carotene probably present in all types of eyes; others have neuromotor fibrils suggestive of nervous systems; many bear paralyzing trichocysts that are shot out in defense or attack (Fig. 21.1). Likewise, most protozoans are animal-like in their activities, such as the digestion of food and elimination of water, the conjugation or mating of paramecium, and the fiercely carnivorous behavior of Didinium. Contrasting with these are the plant-like flagellates that are green with chlorophyll and contain cellulose, such as the green spheres of Volvox, and the myriad euglenas that give a pasture pond the look of a spring greensward. Euglenas carry on photosynthesis as truly as maple trees yet they continually travel about, their eye-spots in front according to the general custom of animals. It is easy to tell John Doe from a rose bush, but it is hard to tell whether green flagellates are plants or animals. They fit partly into each kingdom, not wholly into either.

Sizes and Numbers. All protozoans are minute. Only the larger ones are visible to the naked eye; a colony of Volvox only large enough to be a dot of green; *Stentor coeruleus* to show its trumpet shape; the giant ameba (*Chaos carolinensis*) of the laboratories to look like a minute splash of water, and the white *Spirostomum ambiguum* to cover a hyphen on this page (Fig. 21.2). In general, the largest protozoans are marine radiolarians and foraminiferans, shell-forming relatives of the ameba. There are great numbers of microscopic protozoans; the parasitic ones are especially minute. In a human red blood cell there may be space not only for one parasite, but for many young ones resulting from its division. Protozoans outnumber all other animals in individuals and perhaps even in species. Euglenas are scarcely visible to the naked eye, although it is common for countless millions of them to create a green layer on an acre of pond water.

Distribution and Habitats. Protozoans live in moist and watery places. Many

RESULTS OF A LONG EVOLUTION

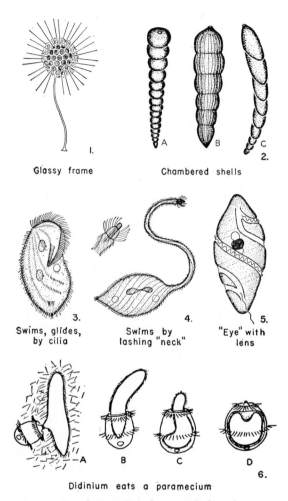

FIG. 21.1. Protozoans are the results of an evolution that was under way long before multicellular animals appeared. Here are a few examples of their special structures. *Protecting shells. 1, Clathrulina elegans* extends its delicate pseudopodia through the openings in its glassy basket. *2,* three types of the multichambered shells of foraminiferans that are secreted and occupied, one chamber after another until in the last one the owner reaches full size. *Locomotion. 3, Kerona polyporum* glides by means of cilia over various species of hydra. *4, Lacrymaria olor* swims by lashing movements of its swanlike neck. *Sensory organs. 5,* Pouchetia has a relatively enormous light receptor, a lens and cup containing the visual pigment carotene similar to that in eyes of multicellular animals. *Weapons of attack and defense. 6,* Didinium attacks and devours a paramecium which has thrown out its poisonous trichocysts without effect. (Courtesy, Jahn and Jahn: *The Protozoa.* Dubuque, Iowa, Wm. C. Brown and Co., 1949.)

can resist drying while in cysts or spores, but only for a time. This limitation has not hindered their success.

In spite of their remarkably long history of life in watery environments, they are the most widely distributed of all animals, both geographically and ecologically; they have found the greatest number and variety of homes. They live in the upper soil along with hordes of bacteria, worms, and rotifers. They swarm through the surface waters of the seas, both polar and tropical. The luminescence of Noctiluca lights the surfaces of temperate as well as tropical seas. Protozoans live in hot springs and in the snow and ice of the Rocky Mountains, at times covering the glaciers with pinkish films.

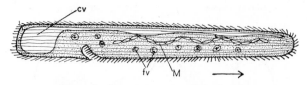

One of the largest protozoans

FIG. 21.2. One of the largest protozoans, *Spirostomum ambiguum*, easily visible to the naked eye. They look like white flecks against the dark bottoms of fresh-water pools where they are occasionally abundant. Contractile vacuole (*cv*) connected with a canal; (*fv*) food vacuoles; the macronucleus (*M*) is shaped like a string of beads. (Courtesy, Jahn and Jahn: *The Protozoa*. Dubuque, Iowa, Wm. C. Brown and Co., 1949.)

Many live in the wet surroundings within the bodies of land or water animals, usually as parasites, sometimes only as passengers. Within flies, bees, horses, cattle, and man protozoans can travel far and wide in the safety of a fluid environment.

Ways of Living. Protozoans live more or less independently. They are free living or in loose association with plants and animals.

Free-living ones, paramecia and others, ingest solid food—bacteria, diatoms and other protozoans; some of them absorb food in solution through the body covering. Those that contain chlorophyll—Euglena, Volvox, and others—make their own food from inorganic material elaborated by photosynthesis (Fig. 21.3).

ASSOCIATIONS. Colonies of Vorticella and Epistylis are attached to submerged objects in ponds; to the naked eye they may seem to be patches of mold, but through a lens they are like miniature gardens of nodding flowers. Kerona creeps louse-like over hydra (Fig. 21.1). Green paramecia (*Paramecium bursaria*) and green stentors (*Stentor polymorphum*) are colored by unicellular algae (*Chlorella vulgaris*) that live within them. There are mutual benefits in such associations; the protozoans receive food and oxygen from the algae, and the algae secure protection from the protozoans. Wood-eating

WAYS OF LIVING

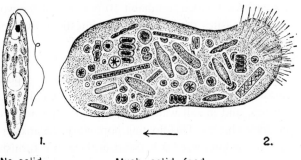

1.   2.

No solid   Much solid food
food

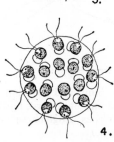

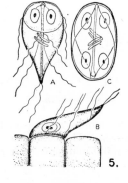

Colonies   Parasites

FIG. 21.3. Ways of living. *Free living and solitary. 1,* Euglena is brilliant green
with chlorophyll and makes its own food by photosynthesis. *2, Pelomyxa palustris*
is relatively very large and ameba-like. It consumes so many small organisms that it
may have a hundred food vacuoles at one time. *In colonies.* In spheres of transparent cellulose, *3,* Pandorina and *4,* Eudorina. *5, Giardia intestinalis* and related
species live in the intestines of various vertebrates including man. *A,* active form
with two nuclei and eight flagella. *B,* side view of the active animal attached to the
lining of the intestine. *C,* two young animals that are about to separate. (Courtesy,
Jahn and Jahn: *The Protozoa.* Dubuque, Iowa, Wm. C. Brown and Co., 1949.)

cockroaches (*Cryptocercus punctulatus*) and termites have a similar relation
with certain flagellates.

Their minute size and preference for fluid environments open the way for
protozoans to be successful parasites. Among the parasites are species of
Plasmodium that in one stage of their lives invade human red blood cells and
cause malaria, and in another live in anopheline mosquitoes without doing the
latter any apparent harm. *Entameba histolytica,* the most important intestinal

protozoan of man, is the cause of amebic dysentery in temperate as well as tropical climates and is estimated to inhabit 10 per cent of the world's population. All protozoan parasites of the blood and intestines live completely immersed in fluid food (Fig. 21.3).

Place of Protozoans in the Food Supply. Protozoans feed upon bacteria and unicellular algae, mainly diatoms and desmids. They are important food, in some places almost the sole food, of multitudes of minute animals, crustaceans, rotifers, larval fishes, and in salt waters the ciliated swimming young of jelly fishes and other invertebrates. This floating population (plankton) is the food of larger animals, of medium-sized fishes that in their turn furnish food to still larger ones. The bluefish and the cod would die in infancy if it were not for the protozoans, and the bacteria and algae which support the protozoans.

Locomotion. Protozoans move about by means of flagella, by the flowing of protoplasm in pseudopodia, or by cilia. All of them have one or the other of these structures through some period of their lives, except the sporozoans

Fig. 21.4. Swimming motions of Euglena. The blunt end containing the reddish eye spot is forward. The flagellum lashes sidewise and backward, pushing the body forward in a spiral path and turning it over as it goes. Euglena swims toward the light except when too strong. (Data from Jennings.)

which have no locomotor organs. The classes of Protozoa are arranged on the basis of their ways of locomotion.

FLAGELLA. The flagellum is a whip-like extension from the cell, with a contractile core. Its simplest motion is like that of a swimming eel or a snake that glides through the grass, bending its body from side to side in one plane. In most flagellates the flagellum moves in a spiral that turns the body obliquely, at the same time rotating it as in Euglena (Fig. 21.4).

PSEUDOPODIA. The flowing of protoplasm is the most primitive means of animal locomotion. It is caused by the changing states of protoplasm from mobile watery plasmasol to the firmer plasmagel and vice versa (Fig. 2.11). Such changes occur in response to those in the animal's surroundings and to conditions within its body. A pseudopodium looks like a spreading spatter of egg white. Its significance appears when the ameba moves in a definite direction, only after several small pseudopodia have been overcome by larger ones (Fig. 21.12).

CILIA. The ciliates are the fastest, most versatile swimmers of all protozoans.

Their cilia are similar to flagella but finer and more numerous. Each one makes a backward power stroke and a return drag, the whole movement being rapidly repeated in unison with others (Fig. 21.5). In salt-water shallows the surface water often teems with minute ciliated swimmers; many are protozoans; many others are newly hatched marine invertebrates.

Structures similar to the locomotor organs of protozoans appear over and over again in multicellular animals. In man, and in the majority of higher animals, ameboid blood cells creep along the capillaries by outflowing protoplasm; sperm cells swim by means of flagella; and the cilia of the lining of the trachea keep the way clear for breathing.

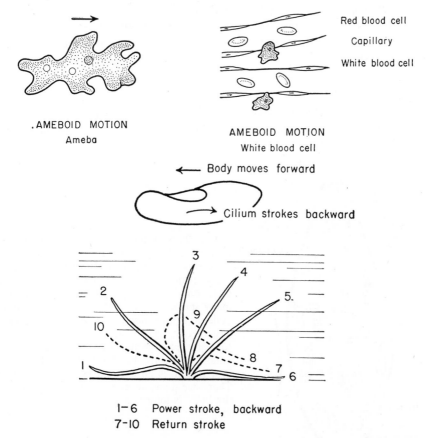

. AMEBOID MOTION
Ameba

Red blood cell

Capillary

White blood cell

AMEBOID MOTION
White blood cell

Body moves forward

Cilium strokes backward

3

4

2

5.

9

10

8

7

1

6

1−6 Power stroke, backward
7−10 Return stroke

FIG. 21.5. The motion of pseudopodia and cilia is important in both unicellular and multicellular animals. *Upper,* motion by pseudopodia in the ameba and in white blood cells of higher animals. Ameboid locomotion is prevalent throughout the animal kingdom. White blood cells are continually crawling about and in and out the blood capillaries of the human body. *Lower,* diagram of the power stroke of a cilium that pushes the animal forward, e.g., a paramecium, and the return stroke that is actually a hindrance. The same thing would happen in rowing if the oars were kept in the water on the return stroke. In the lining of the human trachea the power stroke of the cilia is toward the mouth.

There are five classes of protozoans:
1. Mastigophora, or flagellates, with one or more flagella.
2. Sarcodina or rhizopods, with pseudopodia.
3. Sporozoa, with no locomotor structures.
4. Ciliata, or ciliates, with cilia throughout life.
5. Suctoria, with cilia in the young and tentacles in the adult stages.

Class Mastigophora or Flagellata

This class includes both the plantlike phytoflagellates that contain chromoplasts with chlorophyll and often other pigment, and the zooflagellates that are clearly animals and without chlorophyll. The phytoflagellates make their food from inorganic matter and are basically constructive organisms in whatever community they live. The zooflagellates take their food from plants and other animals.

Phytoflagellates

Structure. The brilliantly colored euglenas of several species are common in fresh waters (Fig. 21.6). Among their characteristic structures are the green

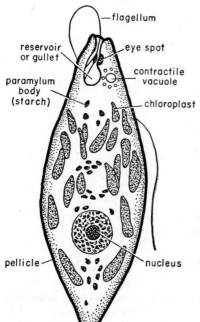

Fig. 21.6. Euglena, a fish-shaped green protozoan that lives in many stagnant pools of fresh water. It is just visible to the naked eye but the millions of them often turn the surface of a pool brilliant green. There are many species, in some the mouth leads to a gullet as in this one, others are without these structures, and probably make all of their food by photosynthesis. The flagellum, a bundle of contractile fibrils bound together in a sheath, is an efficient swimming organ. There are many species of Euglena, in some the body is long and slender.

chloroplasts, (disks, ovals, stars, or bands) scattered through the body and about the central nucleus. The flagellum that arises from a minute body (blepharoplast) in the side of the cytopharynx is associated with the control of movements. Excess fluids and metabolic products collect in its enlarged base from whence they are discharged from the body. The reddish, light sensitive eyespot is a markedly animal characteristic. The whole body is enclosed in a thin elastic cover or pellicle that adjusts itself easily to the organism's squirming movements.

Nutrition. The chloroplasts are vital organs, the centers of photosynthesis by which the carbohydrate food is formed with the help of water, carbon dioxide, and radiant energy from the sun. Free-living flagellates also absorb dissolved nutrient materials from the water in which they live; in fact, in nutrient solutions euglenas will live and multiply even in the dark after losing their chlorophyll. Their stored paramylum is a food similar to the glycogen in the tissues of multicellular animals. Chlorophyll-bearing flagellates are the constructive organisms of their communities. In both fresh and salt water they are the great carbohydrate producers.

Pigments. Phytoflagellates may be yellow green, blue green, orange, and at times some are red. The colors are due mainly to carotene and allied pigments that cloak the chloroplasts that are then called chromoplasts. Like the related green of chlorophyll, the pigments of carotene are generally sensitive to light. Protozoans that contain chromoplasts usually have a reddish stigma or eyespot similar to that of the euglenas. "Red snow" and pasture pools "colored by red rain," common in midwestern United States, are usually due to dense populations of red euglenas (*Euglena rubra*) (Fig. 21.6).

Colonies. Some phytoflagellate colonies contain but a few individuals, 4, 8, 16 and thereabout, held together in jelly; others such as Volvox contain thousands of them (Fig. 21.7). Many colonies show distinct polarity or difference between the ends; in Pleodorina and Volvox the individuals at the anterior pole are sterile while those farther back produce new colonies asexually by repeated cell divisions. Volvox and others reproduce sexually and asexually; some cells enlarge and become eggs, others divide and produce flagellate sperm cells. The fertilized egg secretes a shell in which it can remain for a long period, through drought or winter. When favoring conditions return, the egg divides and a young colony emerges.

Dinoflagellates. Composing a large part of the microscopic surface fauna of the sea, dinoflagellates include the luminescent noctilucas that float in coastal waters, and the armorbearers that are typical plankton forms of both ocean and inland waters (Fig. 21.8). Dinoflagellates usually bear two flagella, each one originating in a groove of the body surface. Their bodies are clothed in membranes, or in two shells or several plates. Thus they are armored and earn their name, *dino* or terrible flagellates. Their nutrition is generally plant-like but some have lost the chromoplasts, have become ameboid, and feed on small organisms in typical ameboid fashion. Still others get their living as parasites in the intestines of copepods and other small floaters of the sea. Larger inverte-

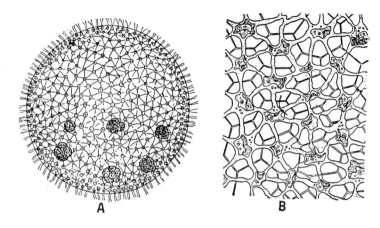

A   B

Green volvox of the ponds

FIG. 21.7. *A*, Volvox, a colony of thousands of cells, most of them with two flagella, a red eyespot, contractile vacuole, and chlorophyll. Strands of protoplasm
unite the asexual cells and make them physiologically continuous. Certain of the
cells reproduce by division. Certain cells in some colonies enlarge and become
female sex cells; in others certain cells divide and become male sex cells. These
fuse with the large cells in the female colonies and form daughter colonies which
remain for a time within the parent colony. *B*, a detailed view of the surface of
Volvox highly magnified showing the protoplasmic connections between the cells.
(*B*, courtesy, Hyman: *The Invertebrates*, vol. 1. New York, McGraw-Hill Book
Co., 1940.)

brates feed upon them especially along the coasts. Epidemics of human food
poisoning have been traced to eating mussels (*Mytilus californicus*) which had
fed upon a species of Gonyaulax that produces an alkaloid poison (Fig. 21.8).
The "red tide" that came in along the Florida coast in 1947 brought poisonous
dinoflagellates in untold numbers and tons of dead fishes were strewn for many
miles upon the shore.

ZOOFLAGELLATES

Definitely animal-like, zooflagellates do not contain chlorophyll, and usually
have one or two flagella. They may be solitary or colonial, and many are parasitic. The collar-flagellates (choano-flagellates) that live mainly in fresh water,
have transparent protoplasmic collars. The single flagellum swings forth from
within the collar and draws food against the cell along with the currents of
water that it creates (Fig. 21.9). In the sponge-like colonial Proterospongia,
the individuals are embedded in a blob of clear jelly; collared cells protrude
from the surface and collarless ameboid ones migrate into the interior of the
jelly. Collared cells are very characteristic of sponges, and Proterospongia
appears like a hesitant step in an evolution toward a structure similar to
sponges.

DINOFLAGELLATES

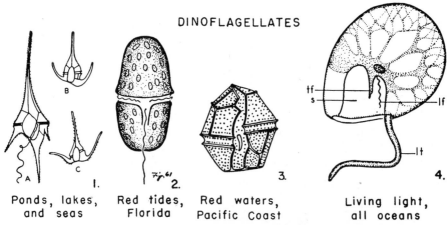

| Ponds, lakes, and seas | Red tides, Florida | Red waters, Pacific Coast | Living light, all oceans |

FIG. 21.8. Dinoflagellates: armored and unarmored types. *1*, Ceratium, with the typical armorlike shell and flagellum. *2*, a dinoflagellate (Gymnodinium) that often sheds its armor and becomes a naked swimmer. They occur in vast numbers in the "red tides" of Florida. Tons of dead fishes are thrown on the beaches whenever these protozoans abound. *3, Gonyaulax polyhedra*, a main cause of some of the red water of the oceans. Several kinds of shellfishes feed on them after which they are poisonous as human food. *4*, Noctiluca, a relatively large translucent sphere. They float on the sea in vast numbers, each one flashing light. Together they create miles of bioluminescence. *lt*, tentacle; *lf*, flagellum; *tf*, flagellum; *s*, groove. (Courtesy, Jahn and Jahn: *The Protozoa*. Dubuque, Iowa, Wm. C. Brown and Co., 1949.)

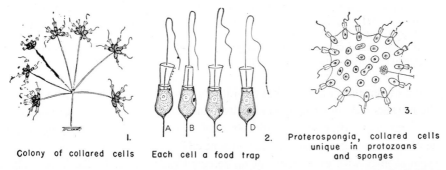

| Colony of collared cells | Each cell a food trap | Proterospongia, collared cells unique in protozoans and sponges |

FIG. 21.9. Protozoans that suggest sponges. *1, Codosiga botrytris*, each individual of the colony has a kind of food trap called a collar cell or choanocyte. *2*, four cells of the colony in different stages of catching and ingesting food; *A*, a particle caught by the flagellum is whipped against the collar which contracts; *B*, slides the particle against the body of the cell; *C* and *D*, finally it enters the cell body. *3*, Proterospongia, so called because of the resemblance of its cells to the collared cells (choanocytes) of sponges. (Courtesy, Jahn and Jahn: *The Protozoa*. Dubuque, Iowa, Wm. C. Brown and Co., 1949.)

Trypanosomes

The trypanosomes are blood parasites in all classes of vertebrates, but so far as known are pathogenic only in man and domestic animals where, in an evolutionary time sense, they have but recently developed. They are transmitted from one vertebrate to another by blood-sucking invertebrates—those of fishes, salamanders, frogs and reptiles by leeches—those of land vertebrates by ticks and insects. Within these carriers they go through a cycle of several days' development without which they cannot be transmitted into their second host (Fig. 21.10).

The trypanosome of the rat (*Trypanosoma lewisi*) is nonpathogenic and common in our native wild rats, often so abundant that the blood literally

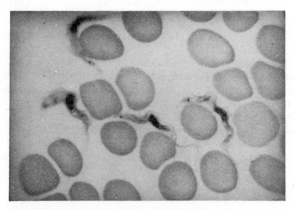

FIG. 21.10. *Trypanosoma gambiense* among the red cells of human blood. These microscopic blood parasites are the cause of trypanosomiasis, the sleeping sickness of tropical West Africa. They pass one period of their life history in the tsetse flies that are essential for their distribution. Aside from that they are parasites in the blood of man and certain of the wild game animals of Africa. (Courtesy, General Biological Supply House, Chicago, Ill.)

twinkles from their motions. Yet the rats thus infected show no signs of harm. The rat becomes infected by licking its skin and thus gathers the feces of infected rat fleas. After an incubation time of two weeks the parasites appear in the blood as typical trypanosomes and multiply enormously. Fleas suck up the trypanosomes with every meal of an infected rat's blood. In the lining cells of the flea's stomach, they multiply by repeated divisions and transform into the mature trypanosomes then ejected upon the rat's skin in the feces of the fleas.

This life history shows important characteristics of such parasites; their great capacity to multiply, and their ability to change form and adjust themselves to environments in which they thrive and are carried about and distributed. This life history also displays the ability of a host animal to become more or less immune to injury from its parasites. Natural immunities occur on every hand commonly because of chemical content or structure, or both. Immunities to protozoans include that of wood-eating insects which are not only immune but are benefited by the flagellates that live in their digestive tracts.

Trypanosomes and Sleeping Sickness. The most widely injurious of pathogenic trypanosomes are those that cause the African sleeping-sickness of man and domestic cattle, not to be confused with the sleeping-sickness or encephalitis, a paralysis, that has no relation to trypanosomes. The African disease occurs throughout central Africa and is due either to *Trypanosoma gambiense* or its near relative *Trypanosoma rhodesiense*. They are transmitted from man to man or from wild mammals to man by blood-sucking tsetse flies (Glossina) that inject the parasites into the blood when they bite just as mosquitoes inject malarial parasites into the blood. The trypanosomes go through an essential part of their life history in the body of the tsetse fly. This takes 14 days at the end of which they have bored their way into the salivary glands of the fly and are ready to enter the mammalian blood and cerebrospinal fluid (Fig. 21.10). The big game animals of Africa are the reservoirs for these parasites and the only known transmitters are the tsetse flies. Like wild rats and fleas, the big game animals and tsetse flies have become practically immune to trypanosomes. Only man and domestic mammals are mortally harmed, an indication that for them the trypanosomes are still relatively new parasites.

Class Sarcodina or Rhizopoda

The Sarcodina—amebas, radiolarians, foraminiferans, and others—move by means of flowing protoplasm, many of them by pseudopodia. They feed on bacteria, microscopic plants and animals and next to the bacteria, algae, and phytoflagellates are basic food supplies. Fresh-water species have one or more contractile vacuoles; salt-water and parasitic species usually lack these altogether. Reproduction is mainly asexual, by binary fission or by budding; sexual reproduction is known in comparatively few species, such as foraminiferans.

THE AMEBA

Habitat. Fresh-water amebas live in ponds and streamsides, on decaying leaves and slimy stems. All of them likely to be found there are microscopic. The only way to see them is to collect pond water and plant debris, let it stand several days, and then examine it bit by bit under a microscope. The relatively large amebas of most laboratories have been grown in cultures, purchased from specialists in rearing them. *Ameba proteus* and *Ameba carolinensis* (also called *Chaos chaos*), the giant ameba, are commonly used for study.

Appearance. At first glance, through the microscope, an ameba seems to be a strangely active spatter of peppered egg white. It gives no sign that it is carrying on the same basic essentials of living as are one's own cells. Amebas are generally colorless, or gray to black (*Pelomyxa palustris*) from the bacteria that live in the cytoplasm. Two regions are distinguishable in the body, a clear outer layer of ectoplasm and the central endoplasm which contains the vital organelles and the nucleus, separated from the endoplasm by the nuclear membrane (Fig. 21.11). There may be clusters of green particles in the endoplasm, bacteria and diatoms in the food vacuoles which are temporary stomachs in which digestion prepares the food for absorption and assimilation. The contractile vacuole widens and vanishes only to appear again in nearly the same place. Such vacuoles eliminate metabolic waste products and are important guardians of the water content of the body. They are active when the animal contains too much water, and disappear when it contains too little. Neither marine nor parasitic amebas have contractile vacuoles. Since their bodies and the sea water or the protoplasm of their hosts contain about the same proportions of salt, the sea water does not flood into their bodies as it does into the amebas of fresh water.

Locomotion. Amebas commonly move about by means of pseudopodia although these are usually greatly reduced in parasitic species.

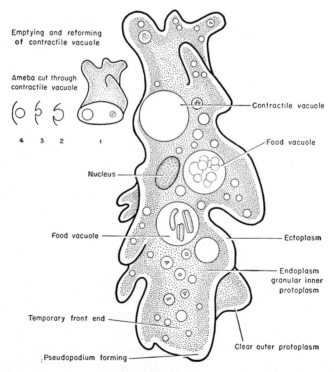

FIG. 21.11. An ameba, showing its principal structures. *Inset,* section of ameba with the contractile vacuole in successive stages of emptying and refilling.

Digestion, Absorption, and Assimilation. Amebas have no permanent reception place for food. When an ameba first touches an inviting particle its protoplasm rapidly flows around it and the food is engulfed as the ameba passes over it (Fig. 21.12). Amebas never ingest dry food. Each bit is filmed with water as our own food is cloaked with air or liquid. As soon as the food is engulfed in the endoplasm, the digestive ferments flow into this temporary stomach from the surrounding protoplasm. These digest the food, mainly the proteins. The digested foods, the water and ferments are gradually absorbed into the protoplasm. The indigestible remainders, such as diatom shells, stimulate the wall of the vacuole which squeezes them out of the body and all signs of the food vacuole disappear. Finally the absorbed substances are assimilated, arranged within their kindred materials in the living ameba.

Respiration and Excretion. Oxygen held in the water diffuses through the body of the ameba and unites with carbon and other substances within it. This oxidation liberates energy and heat and leaves a by-product, carbon dioxide, that either diffuses out through the body covering or collects in the contractile vacuoles with other metabolic products, and is discharged with them.

The natural growth of the whole animal is a constructive process of change

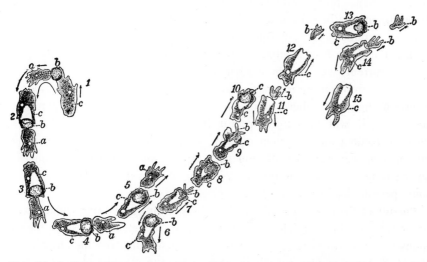

Fig. 21.12. "Pursuit, capture, and swallowing" of one ameba by another; escape of the captured ameba and its recapture; final escape. The whole action took about fifteen minutes. *1*, an ameba (*a*) from which the part *b* has been almost severed by a glass rod; *c* is an ameba which has come in contact with part *b* and tries to ingest it; *2–4*, are stages in the ingestion, which are accomplished in *5* and *6* when ameba *a* moves off and out of the story; *7–10* show that *b* is restless in the food vacuole of *c*; at *11* and *12*, *b* escapes and moves away entirely out of contact with *c*; *13*, *c* pursues and captures *b*; for the second time *b* escapes, this time permanently leaving *c* at *15* with temporarily vacant food vacuole. (Courtesy, Jennings: *Behavior of Lower Organisms.* New York, Columbia Univ. Press, 1906.)

and addition that goes on through its early life. Assimilation of food is its essential preliminary. The extent of growth is determined by heredity and by surrounding conditions, regulators that are as effective for an ameba as for a horse.

Reproduction. Amebas reproduce by division into two approximately equal parts and by mitotic division of the nucleus. At a temperature of 24° C. the process takes about half an hour. There is no real metamorphosis; an ameba that has just come into existence by division looks like any other one of its kind only smaller.

Reactions to Stimuli. In their natural surroundings amebas are touching something, are resting, or moving upon water soaked and decaying leaves. One ameba described by H. S. Jennings touched the end of an algal filament, after which a pseudopodium was extended along each side of the filament. Then the protoplasm on one side stopped flowing and the filament was avoided as part of the current was reversed and turned into another direction. If an ameba is touched with a glass rod it behaves the same way. Reactions to contact are not all negative, however. If an ameba comes in touch with a surface, while it is still suspended in the water, it immediately spreads itself as a cat landing from a jump will spread its toes to contact the ground (Fig. 10.1). In general, amebas react positively to gravity; they creep on the bottom of a dish, or on the mucky bottom of a pool, a contrast to the usual open water swimming of paramecia. If salt solution from a very fine capillary tube diffuses against the side of an ameba, the part affected will contract and the protoplasmic currents will start in another direction.

Amebas are no more responsive in one part of the body than in any other to touch, light, or other stimuli. In general, if light interferes with their activities, they will move away from it. If it is suddenly thrown on them when they are feeding on a filament of alga, they will stop and even squeeze out bits of alga that were already ingested. Over-stimulation by light makes an ameba refuse food as interference with equilibrium and other senses makes some persons lose their appetite.

Pursuit of Prey. In general, amebas draw away from things which would be harmful to them and toward those that are beneficial. Most of their responses are due to direct physical or chemical stimuli from the environment. Yet H. S. Jennings was not wholly able to analyze pursuits of one ameba by another, although he observed them several times and devoted years of study to the behavior of protozoans. One such pursuit and capture is described in the figure and legend (Fig. 21.12). The captor (ameba c) pursued its prey (ameba b) with great persistence. The climax came at numbers 11 and 12 when the captive (b) escaped completely out of contact with its captor (c) yet the latter continued the pursuit and repeated the performance. Does this not suggest that the ameba depends upon a primitive kind of memory?

OTHER SARCODINA—SHELLED AMEBAS

A few common species of Sarcodina are presented according to their habits of life, free living in fresh water; free living in salt water; and parasitic (Figs. 21.13, 21.14).

Fresh Water. Arcellas glide over submerged pond weeds with pseudopodia

NEAR RELATIVES OF THE AMEBA

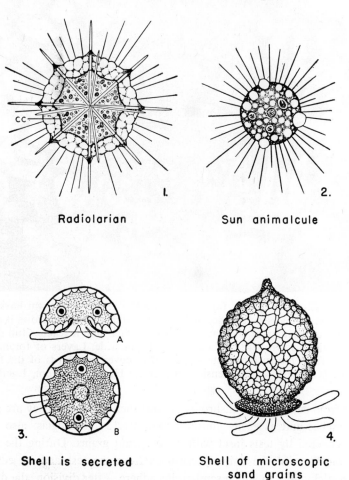

FIG. 21.13. Ornate relatives of the amebas. *1*, Acanthometron, whose radiating needles are attached by musclelike bands, the myofrisks by which needles and body are moved. *2*, the sun animalcule, *Actinophrys sol,* a splendid relative of the better known amebas. This one is common on the submerged vegetation of ponds. *3*, *Arcella vulgaris,* an amebalike animal with a tam-o'-shanter-shaped cover. *A,* section showing the two nuclei and the pseudopodia extending from under the shell. *B,* view through the top of a translucent shell. *4,* Difflugia makes its covering of microscopic sand grains firmly held together by a secretion. (Courtesy, Jahn and Jahn: *The Protozoa.* Dubuque, Iowa, Wm. C. Brown and Co., 1949.)

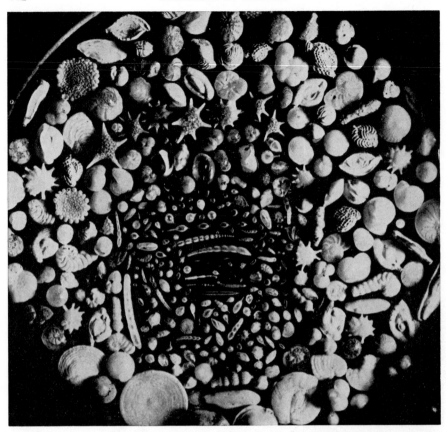

FIG. 21.14. Shells of marine foraminiferans. The majority of them have several chambers. The animal secretes the shell of one chamber but as it grows it slips out of this and secretes a larger chamber and then another until it reaches full size. The whole collection shown here is about seven inches wide. Layers of foraminiferan shells fallen from the surface waters are said to cover two-thirds of the floors of the oceans. (Courtesy, South Kensington Natural History Museum, London.)

extended from beneath the mushroom-shaped shell-like tests. They are actually shelled amebas and as easily cultured (Fig. 21.13). Difflugias, also ameba-like, are covered by tests inset with minute sand grains. During the asexual division one part of the animal protrudes from the test and its ectoplasm secretes a sticky fluid to which sand grains adhere. After division, the difflugias separate, one covered by the old test, one by the new. Heliozoans or sun animalcules whose bodies are decked with crystal clear filaments are the splendid relatives of amebas.

Sea Water. Foraminiferans (hole-bearing) are ameboid protozoans that secrete many-chambered shells, most of which are chalky; others are of chitin or silica (Fig. 21.13). The young foraminiferan makes a shell with an opening from which it extends its body as a snail does. As it grows, its protoplasm flows out of the chamber, spreads over the shell it has made and secretes another shell, a second chamber. Delicate pseudopodia extend through pores in the shell as well as through the main opening. Adult foraminiferans are dimorphic, that is, some individuals divide asexually into many new ones; others divide into flagellate gametes (sex cells). The gametes fuse in pairs and produce individuals that divide asexually when full grown. This alternation of sexual and asexual phases suggests the "alternation of generations" of the coelenterates (Chap. 24).

The "white cliffs of Dover," England, and the chalk-beds 1000 feet or more deep of Mississippi and Georgia are made of foraminiferan shells that once dropped downward through deep seas that flooded these lands. Foraminiferans live in surface waters and Globigerina is one of the commonest of them. These animals are constantly dying and their shells form the "globigerina ooze" that covers some 40 million square miles of ocean floor.

Radiolarians are among the most beautiful objects in nature. They are a vast array of animals with clear glassy skeletons, radiating needles and latticed spheres of silica fashioned like delicate crystal toys. The protoplasm that is foamy with vacuoles, holds fat drops, oil spheres, and red, yellow, and brown pigment granules. Many of them contain "yellow cells," very minute protozoans that live within them.

Radiolarians are exclusively marine, living chiefly in surface waters; some species have been found in samples taken at depths of over three miles. Their skeletons fall upon the sea bottom in more perfect shape than those of foraminiferans of the same size because the silica is so resistant to the corrosive effects of the sea water. Probably for the same reason, radiolarians are among the oldest and most perfect fossils known. Many of the old patterns are almost identical with those of present-day species although their microscopic sculpturing must have been in the making long ages before multicellular animals appeared.

PARASITIC SARCODINA

Parasitic amebas occur in many vertebrates, in man, and in such distantly related invertebrates as hydras, leeches, and cockroaches. Practically all of them inhabit the alimentary canal and all enter an encysted stage at one time or another in their life history. It is then that they pass out of the body of the host and are freely distributed. *Endameba histolytica,* the cause of amebic dysentery, lives within the human intestine (colon). In its encysted stage, it is transmitted from one person to another in drinking water and by flies and food. *Endameba gingivalis* is a common parasite in the human mouth where it lives near the base of the teeth. The colons of cockroaches often contain numbers of *Endameba blattae* that ingest bacteria from the intestinal content.

Class Sporozoa

Characteristics. The sporozoans are without exception the parasites with complicated life histories, often including an alternation of sexual and asexual reproduction. Their hosts are animals of many types from protozoans to man. As spores they commonly pass from one host to another. A spore is a young individual or group of them (sporozoites), usually enclosed in a capsule, capable of establishing the parasite in a new host.

In addition to malaria in man and birds, sporozoans cause the serious diseases of coccidiosis in fowls and rabbits, certain fevers in cattle, and the pebrine disease of silkworms.

Gregarines. The Gregarines are chiefly parasites in the body cavities of invertebrates. They are common in grasshoppers, cockroaches, and in the seminal vesicles of earthworms. The latter are easily examined and beautiful when taken from freshly killed worms; the viscera of pickled worms are drab and sterile. Pieces of earthworm vesicle can be teased out in a little water on a glass slide. If they are infected, the ciliated adult parasites will swim through the mealy debris and the spores containing the young parasites will be scattered through it or packed in cysts.

Coccidia. The Coccidia live in the epithelial cells of many vertebrates and a few invertebrates. Their life history is complex and, in essentials, similar to that of the malarial parasite. That of a coccidian (*Eimeria schubergi*), a parasite of centipedes, is typical of others. It is swallowed with the food and passes on into the intestine as a cyst (oocyst) containing several young individuals (sporozoites). The sporozoites enter the cells of the intestinal lining. They divide repeatedly producing two kinds of individuals; asexual ones that enter cells and divide asexually; and sexual ones that enter cells and enlarge into egg cells (macrogametes) or enlarge and undergo multiple division into sperm cells (microgametes). A micro- and a macrogamete fuse forming a zygote as in ordinary sexual reproduction. The zygote surrounds itself with a secretion which hardens into a shell. Within this shell or cyst (oocyst) it divides several times until the cyst is packed with young parasites (sporozoites). While this division is going on, the cyst is either in the lower intestine or has been thrown outside the body. There along with millions of its kind it wins or loses a chance to be ingested by another centipede.

Hemosporidia. These sporozoans are parasites of vertebrates, blood sucking insects and other arthropods. In the vertebrates, they inhabit the blood cells and plasma. In arthropods that transmit them from one vertebrate to another, they occur in the stomach and salivary glands. Those that most affect human welfare are the species that cause human malaria.

MALARIA. Malaria, meaning bad air, is the name of a group of infections caused by microscopic protozoan parasites (Class Sporozoa) that live mainly in the blood and are transmitted solely by female anopheline (Anopheles) mosquitoes. During its complete life history, the malarial parasite passes one part of its existence in man and another part in the mosquito. Although other vertebrates have malaria-like parasites and symptoms, the parasites causing human malaria have been found only in man and anopheline mosquitoes.

The paroxysms of malaria known as chills and fever may occur every day, every other day, or every third day. These differences are due to peculiarities in the life cycle of different species of malarial parasites which occur in human blood. More than one of these may live in the blood at once and thus a person may have more than one type of malaria at the same time and the distinctness in the succession of temperature changes may be irregular.

Immunity. Human beings have some natural resistance to all malarial parasites and certain races show a greater degree of it than others. In the United States, the Negro race has a greater immunity to *Plasmodium vivax* than the white. Some degree of acquired immunity is evidently developed by people living in tropical regions where they have been subjected to malaria since babyhood. Immunity to malaria artificially acquired by a vaccine as it is in smallpox has not been accomplished and the prospects for it are not regarded as promising. There are several reasons for this. One of them is the existence of so many malarial parasites each of which may create its own type of immunity, and the immune person is prone to carry latent infections of them.

Plasmodium Causing Human Malaria. There are four species of Plasmodium that cause malaria: *Plasmodium ovale* is very rare; *P. vivax* is the cause of "tertian" or "benign tertian" malaria, has a 48-hour cycle of development in man, and is widely distributed in tropical and temperate zones; *P. malariae* is the cause of "quartan" malaria and has a 72-hour cycle; and *P. falciparum* is the cause of "malignant tertian" malaria and has a 40- to 48-hour cycle.

Life History of Plasmodium vivax. Benign tertian malaria caused by the parasite, *Plasmodium vivax,* is the commonest type of the disease in the United States. When they bite human beings, female anopheline mosquitoes carrying these parasites introduce them into the blood in an infective stage of development known as sporozoites (Fig. 21.15). The sporozoites travel to the liver cells and divide for 6 to 10 days (exoerythrocytic stages). When they are released from the liver cells they enter the red blood cells and give rise to nonsexual and sexual forms. In a red blood cell, each sporozoite grows and divides into from 15 to 20 new individuals, the merozoites, nonsexual forms, within about 48 hours. During this time, the parasite splits the hemoglobin in the blood cell, and absorbs the hematin part of it known as malarial pigment which accumulates in the parasite. After 48 hours, the red blood cell bursts and the contained merozoites are freed in the blood plasma along with the debris of the broken cell. This is the period of fever and general disturbance of temperature in the person who has the disease. The merozoites soon attack

LIFE CYCLES OF MALARIAL ORGANISM IN MOSQUITO (ANOPHELES) AND MAN

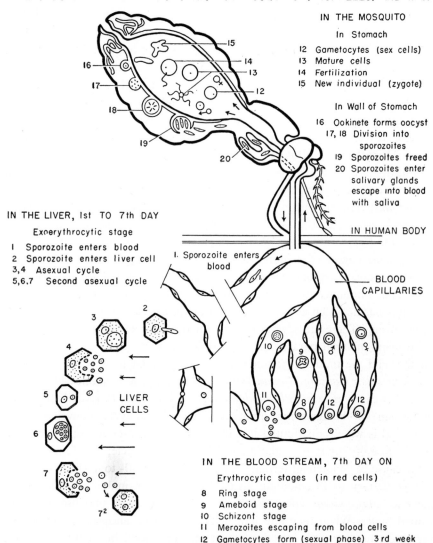

IN THE MOSQUITO

In Stomach

12 Gametocytes (sex cells)
13 Mature cells
14 Fertilization
15 New individual (zygote)

In Wall of Stomach

16 Ookinete forms oocyst
17, 18 Division into
          sporozoites
19 Sporozoites freed
20 Sporozoites enter
      salivary glands
      escape into blood
      with saliva

IN THE LIVER, Ist TO 7th DAY

Exoerythrocytic stage

1 Sporozoite enters blood
2 Sporozoite enters liver cell
3,4 Asexual cycle
5,6,7 Second asexual cycle

1. Sporozoite enters
   blood

IN HUMAN BODY

BLOOD
CAPILLARIES

LIVER
CELLS

IN THE BLOOD STREAM, 7th DAY ON

Erythrocytic stages (in red cells)

8   Ring stage
9   Ameboid stage
10 Schizont stage
11 Merozoites escaping from blood cells
12 Gametocytes form (sexual phase) 3rd week

FIG. 21.15. Life history of the parasite, *Plasmodium vivax*, which causes benign tertian malaria. *In the human body.* An infected female Anopheles mosquito bites and injects saliva containing the parasites into the blood of its victim. Stages *1,2;* the parasites travel in the blood and enter the liver cells. Stages *3–7;* the parasites multiply in the liver cells. Stages *8–12;* the parasites leave the liver, enter the blood; many but not all invade the red blood cells, multiply and the red cells burst; gametocytes (sexual phase) develop in some of the red blood cells. *In the mosquito.* A female mosquito of the genus Anopheles bites and sucks blood from a person whose blood contains developing gametocytes of *Plasmodium vivax*. Stages *12–15;* in the stomach the male and female cells mature, fertilization occurs and young parasites develop. Stages *16–20;* phases of growth and multiplication occur in the wall of the stomach, followed by release, migration and entrance into the salivary glands. The parasites are now ready for distribution into any individual whom the mosquito may bite.

other red blood cells and the cycle of growth and asexual multiplication just described begins over again. Sexual development starts with a stage that differs scarcely at all from the sporozoite from which the asexual generations develop. It also grows in the red blood cell but instead of dividing into merozoites it gives rise to either a male organism (microgametocyte) or female (macrogametocyte). If left in the human body, these male and female organisms usually die.

Description of the parasite's life in the female mosquito. If the gametocytes are taken into the stomach of a female anopheline mosquito they develop into easily recognized male and female individuals (Fig. 21.15). The nucleus of the male gametocyte (microgametocyte) divides and within a few minutes 6 to 8 microgametes, each with a flagellum, are formed. The female gametocyte (macrogametocyte) does not divide and is the macrogamete. Into it one of the microgametes enters. The union of these two cells makes a zygote (corresponding to the fertilized egg in higher animals). It becomes wormlike and is called an ookinete. The ookinete bores into the stomach wall of the mosquito and there, surrounded by a kind of cellular capsule (oocyst), it divides into many sporozoites. There may be more than 10,000. These grow until they burst the capsule and are freed in the body cavity of the mosquito, usually within 10 days to three weeks depending on the temperature. In their migration in the body cavity, many of them reach the salivary glands and bore into them, finally lodging in the tubes which carry saliva into the mouth. As many as 200,000 sporozoites may be packed in one mosquito's salivary glands. When an infected female mosquito bites (only the females suck blood), she always injects her saliva into the blood capillary which she has pierced, at the same time injecting parasites into the blood.

Benign and Malignant Malarias. Benign malaria is characterized by periods of fever, the malarial paroxysms, broken by periods of normal or below normal temperatures. The period of fever consists of a seemingly cold stage of chills during which there is actually a rise in temperature, a hot stage of high temperature and a sweating stage, all of these occurring within about 10 to 12 hours.

The nonsexual cycle of the life of the parasite occurs in the period between the paroxysms. For *Plasmodium vivax* of benign tertian malaria, this period lasts 48 hours and the paroxysm occurs on the third day. *Plasmodium malariae* of benign quartan malaria has a nonsexual period of 72 hours and there is a paroxysm on the fourth day. In malignant malaria the temperature changes are likely to be less regular than in benign types and the paroxysms last longer.

Malignant tertian malaria is caused by *Plasmodium falciparum*. This parasite multiplies in very great numbers. Corpuscles containing their asexual stages tend to clump in the capillaries. When such a clogging of capillaries occurs in the brain ("cerebral malaria"), the patient becomes unconscious. In this and certain other conditions, the symptoms of malignant tertians are quite different from those commonly supposed to belong with malaria. "Blackwater fever" is probably a type of malaria caused by *Plasmodium falciparum*.

Treatment of Malaria by Drugs. A considerable number of drugs have been found to have antimalarial effects. The four which arrest the development of the merozoites of all species of Plasmodium and in sufficient doses are curative in the malaria of *Plasmodium falciparum* are quinine, atabrine, chloroquine, and paludrine. More recently developed than any of these is the powerful antimalaria drug, darasprim, which holds the possibility of eliminating the disease.

Class Ciliata

All ciliates bear cilia at some period of their lives; many throughout life (Fig. 21.16). Ciliates are complex, and specialized mainly for independent living. They live on or in many plants and animals, myriads of them in protecting capsules on grass blades. Sheep, cattle and other cud-chewers swallow them into the first stomach or rumen along with great numbers of bacteria. Ciliates and bacteria become active in the warmth and moisture of the rumen and the bacteria provide a rich food supply for the protozoans (Fig. 11.14). Ciliates always abound in all healthy cud-chewers after they are old enough to eat grass. They disappear as the food is moved on into other sec-

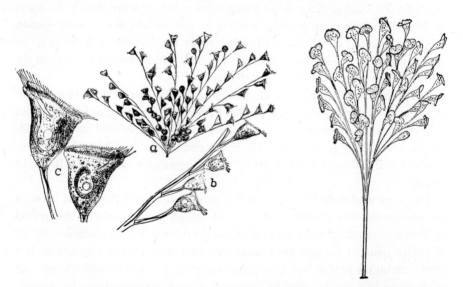

FIG. 21.16. Two colonial protozoans that like paramecia are dependent on cilia for the intake of food and are common residents of fresh water. *Left,* Vorticella, bell animalcule. *Right,* Epistylis, often attached to aquatic insects. (*Left,* courtesy, Conn: "Protozoa of Connecticut," *Conn. State Geol. and Nat. Hist. Survey Bull.* #2, 1905. *Right,* courtesy, Hyman: *The Invertebrates,* vol. 1. New York, McGraw-Hill Book Co., 1940.)

tions of the stomach, apparently killed by the digestive fluids. It has been estimated that two per cent of a sheep's daily protein requirement may be met by digested ciliates. They are present in the alimentary canals of other animals apparently sharing the food supply, but without damage to their hosts. Most slugs and many snails, planarians and sea urchins contain them.

Paramecium and other ciliates have systems of contractile fibrils and neuro-fibrils concerned with responses, coordination, and control of the cilia. The trichocysts are minute poisonous rods arranged at right angles to the body surface. They are discharged with great vigor particularly when a paramecium is attacked by its constant foe, Didinium. Most ciliates are peculiar in having two kinds of nuclei, a large macronucleus important in general metabolism, and one or more smaller nuclei that take part in conjugation. The latter is an approach to the mating relation and the fusion of sex cells in multicellular animals. In certain individuals, there may be a reorganization of nuclei called endomixis that always occurs within single animals. This brings about an upswing of physiological activity similar to that which follows conjugation.

PARAMECIUM

Appearance. Paramecia are common animals in both ponds and labora-tories. This "slipper animalcule" was among the "little things" which were first seen in the seventeenth century, when the newly devised microscopes were being tried out with great enthusiasm. A drawing of it was made by Joblot in 1718. Paramecium came on the human stage then and has never left it. No one will go far into the most recent studies of heredity, of variation and sex, of re-sponses and behavior, and of populations, without finding paramecia a focus of attention.

General Structures. Its form and structure show the definite shape, differ-entiation of front and rear ends, a definite position of mouth and gullet, path-way of food vacuoles, anal opening, and contractile vacuoles (Fig. 21.17). All of these localizations suggest a trend toward permanence in the location of organs familiar to us in multicellular animals. The endoplasm is enclosed by ectoplasm that secretes the flexible non-living pellicle and bears the cilia that extend through the pellicle.

Support and Movement. A paramecium swims by the beating of its cilia. Strong oblique backward strokes drive it forward and, in addition to the forward movement, continually rotate the body on its long axis (Fig. 21.18). The forward movement may stop or be reversed, yet the body will continue to turn. The cilia in the oral groove beat more strongly than elsewhere. This turns the anterior end away from the oral side as a boat turns toward the side that is rowed more strongly. The boat eventually swings in circles and the paramecium would do the same if it were not that it rotates on its long axis.

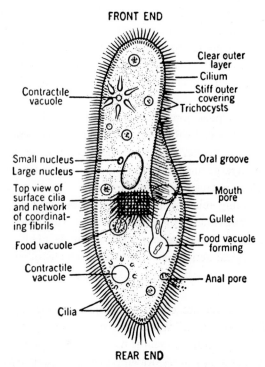

FRONT END

Contractile vacuole

Clear outer layer

Cilium

Stiff outer covering

Trichocysts

Small nucleus

Large nucleus

Top view of surface cilia and network of coordinating fibrils

Food vacuole

Contractile vacuole

Cilia

Oral groove

Mouth pore

Gullet

Food vacuole forming

Anal pore

REAR END

FIG. 21.17. Paramecium, a general view, with its main structures and functions indicated. Gullet, food vacuole, and other organelles are embedded in the protoplasm. (Courtesy, Gerard: *Unresting Cells*. New York, Harper & Bros., 1940.)

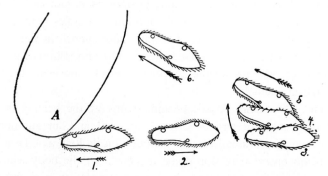

FIG. 21.18. Diagram of an avoiding reaction, the basic pattern of behavior in paramecia (*Paramecium caudatum*). *A* is the source of stimulation; *1–6* are successive positions of the animal. The habitual rotation on the long axis of the body is not shown. (Courtesy, Jennings: *Behavior of Lower Organisms*. New York, Columbia Univ. Press, 1906.)

Nutrition. Paramecia live surrounded by swarms of bacteria. These are swept into the oral groove and down the gullet by cilia that move so rapidly that a microscopic stream of water seems to run through the protoplasm. Fortunately for the paramecium, food is not always pouring into it. Granules containing enzymes form about the food vacuole as soon as the food creates it. In the first stage of digestion, the content of the vacuole is acid and the microorganisms in it are killed. In the second stage, the granules swell and dissolve; the content of the vacuole becomes alkaline; part of the food is dissolved and absorbed in the protoplasm and the indigestible residue is squeezed along in a regular circuit toward the anal pore. The vacuole disappears when its function ceases, but a successor appears in the same location as soon as more food arrives.

Respiration, Water Content, Excretion. Oxygen is secured from the surrounding water and carbon dioxide is given off into it. The fresh water that surrounds the paramecia has a lower osmotic pressure than protoplasm and therefore is continually diffused into them. This creates an income of oxygen, but necessitates the outlet supplied by the contractile vacuoles or else the animal would burst. The vacuoles eliminate metabolic waste though they also have the very important function of maintaining water balance just as the kidneys of the frog do.

Mechanisms of Sensory-motor Functions. Complicated neuromotor systems in paramecia and other ciliates have been demonstrated by special preparation and high magnification. Beneath the pellicle each cilium originates in a rounded base and these are connected with one another (Fig. 16.1). These fibrils are associated with a latticelike network of fibrils surrounding the mouth and gullet. It is probable that the fibrils are conductors and serve to coordinate the cilia while ingesting food. Some of the fibrils are joined in a minute body (motorium) located in the lattice. Destruction of this in the ciliate Euplotes upsets the coordination of the animal.

Behavior. The behavior of a paramecium consists of only a small number of definite movements. By one, or another, or combinations of these few movements, it responds to all the stimuli that act upon it. The basic pattern is that of an avoiding reaction (Fig. 21.18). By means of it, the paramecium rejects one stimulus and accepts another. An avoiding reaction occurs immediately after a stimulus such as contact with an object. The animal slows up, stops or banks off, then moves in a different direction. In doing so it enters a new place, comes upon different chemical, mechanical, and electrical stimuli, light or temperature. The repetition of the avoiding reaction by trial and error results in the rejection of some stimuli and acceptance of others. However significant the process may be, it ends in a generally consistent choice of favorable food and surroundings.

Reproduction—Conjugation and Sex. Paramecia reproduce asexually by transverse division with the macronucleus and one or more micronuclei, depending on the species, leading the division (Fig. 21.19). The old oral groove goes with the anterior half and a new one is formed in the posterior half. A new contractile vacuole forms in each part. Under favorable conditions the process takes about two hours. At temperatures of 15° to 17° C. the animals grow rapidly to mature size and at the end of about 24 hours each one divides again.

Conjugation is similar to fertilization, a mixture of nuclear materials from two individuals thereby creating new hereditary combinations. Conjugation rejuvenates the animals that take part in it, but it is not an essential process and may not occur. Endomixis, the nuclear reorganization, that may take place in single individuals, also rejuvenates the animals and stimulates division. A description of conjugation is given in Chapter 18, Reproduction.

Class Suctoria

Adult suctorians have no cilia or other locomotor organs. Neither do they have a mouth but take their food through tubular tentacles. The tips of these tentacles are attached to other protozoans, thrust into their protoplasm which then streams into the invader apparently by suction (Fig. 21.20).

Suctorians are common in fresh water and salt; many live as commensals, in fresh water attached to such various objects as algae, and the shells of turtles; and in salt water, to sea weeds and hydroids.

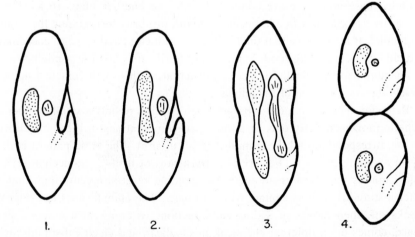

1.   2.   3.   4.

Fig. 21.19. Division of *Paramecium caudatum: 1,* micronucleus beginning division; *2,* macronucleus lengthening, micronucleus in mitosis; *3,* nuclear division continuing; cellular division beginning; *4,* two animals of the next generation. Paramecia multiply only by division. Occasionally there is a temporary union (conjugation) with exchange of nuclear material followed by the division of each of the partners. An individual's life span is the period between divisions; in the natural plan a lifetime is ended by a division not by death.

Like ciliates, suctorians have two types of nuclei, larger and smaller and of different function. The animals conjugate and all the embryos are ciliated.

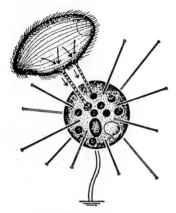

Sucking tentacles in use

FIG. 21.20. Suctorians. *Podophyra fixa,* common protozoans of fresh water. The tubular tentacles are attached to a ciliate and the suctorian sucks in the substance of its prey. (Courtesy, Jahn and Jahn: *The Protozoa.* Dubuque, Iowa, Wm. C. Brown and Co., 1949.)

Such similarities make it seem probable that suctorians were originally ciliates, now greatly changed in structure and habits.

22

Sponges—A Side Line
of Evolution

Cellular Organization. Sponges are living waterways. Water is constantly moving over them and into and out of them, continually flowing through the labyrinth of canals and chambers which they contain. These countless watercourses are keys to their livelihood. Some sponges are radially symmetrical but many more have fantastically irregular forms that are named after fancied resemblances, dead men's fingers, Neptune's cup, and Venus's flower basket (Fig. 22.4). Water is drawn through the microscopic pores that give the name Porifera to the phylum and flows through the many passageways that are unique among animals.

Protozoans are minute and unicellular while sponges are relatively large and multicellular (Fig. 22.1). It is hard to find any other real difference between members of the two groups. The organization of sponges is relatively simple, but the structure of the individual cells is complex and specialized. Except for those that secrete the units of the skeleton, the cells carry on their functions independently. Sponges have neither mouth nor digestive tract, neither organs nor systems. There are no nerve cells or central controls as in other multicellular animals, or as in some protozoans (Fig. 16.1). The skeleton is an outspread network of spicules or fibers. Except for the extensive development of skeleton, a simple sponge resembles Proterospongia. In this colonial protozoan the flagellated collared cells project from a blob of jelly in which ameboid cells move about freely as they do in the jelly layer of sponges.

Although sponge cells are relatively independent, they are also deeply cooperative in maintaining the entity of the sponge and they stay together as the cells of young embryos do without any apparent binding. Sponges, like early human embryos, are held together by the insistent cohesion of their cells. Certain sponges may be pushed through a fine cloth and their cells separated,

FIG. 22.1. A cluster of common calcareous sponges that grew hanging from a harbor wharf pile. The loosely branched one is Leucosolenia, each branch an individual sponge. The others are: (*left*) the crowned sponge, Sycon (Grantia), its long fingers with crowned tips; and (*top*) a shapeless bread-crumb sponge, Halichondria. (Photograph of living sponges by Douglas P. Wilson, Marine Biological Laboratory, Plymouth, England.)

yet in favorable conditions they will come together and become perfectly reorganized into their former shape (Fig. 22.9).

Sponges are undoubtedly multicellular animals. But in very ancient times they drew away from the developments going on in other multicellular animals. In their early history they must have adopted a static existence, thoroughly adjusted and dependent upon the come and go of water, a sideline and blind pocket in the trend of animal evolution (Fig. 33.1).

Structure. Leucosolenia, a simple sponge, illustrates the fundamental characteristics of all the sponges (Fig. 22.2). Colonies of various species of Leucosolenia grow just below the low tide mark. The body of each individual is a sac whose open top is the excurrent opening or osculum. The current of water that flows from this opening, carries particles outward and was the clue by which Ellis in 1765 discovered that sponges are animals. Thousands of incurrent pores perforate the body wall, each one opening through a single pore cell into the large central cavity or spongocoel (Figs. 22.2, 22.3). The outer surface is covered with epithelial cells and flooded with mucous secretion that hinders small animals from settling upon it. The central cavity is lined with choanocytes or collared cells whose lashing flagella produce continual currents through the waterways of the sponge. Water enters through the incurrent pores bringing oxygen and microscopic particles of food with it. It passes

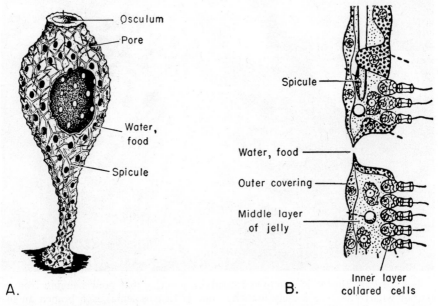

FIG. 22.2. *A,* a stage of a simple sponge with part of its wall cut away to reveal the central cavity. This illustrates the fundamental characteristics of sponges. It is a hollow vase with pores in its wall through which water and food enter a central cavity. Water, waste and doubtless much food pass out through the main opening (osculum). The intake and digestion of food is carried on by collared cells (choanocytes) that project into the cavity. *B,* a long section of the wall shows the lining of the central cavity with its collared cells that catch particles of food, digest it, and pass it on to the ameboid cells within the body wall. The spicules forming the skeleton are each secreted by two cells that move inward from the outside layer. The *stage* shown (known as Olynthus) occurs in the development of certain spicule-bearing sponges. It is not a species. (Courtesy, Borradaile & Potts: *The Invertebrata.* Cambridge, England, The Macmillan Co., 1932.)

out through the excurrent pore taking with it the various by-products of metabolism. Each collared cell is a provider of food. Its flagellum brings in the water that carries food; it captures and ingests the particles that the current throws against it, and it partially digests them before they are passed on to the ameboid cells that complete the process. Particles of solid waste are eliminated from the various cells that perform the digestion. Each cell comes very close to carrying on the whole process of nutrition essentially as it is in the ameba, only a few degrees more specialized.

The outer cellular covering of the body and the lining of the spongocoel are separated by a layer of clear jellied secretion, the mesenchyme (Fig. 22.3). It contains the versatile ameboid cells that move about easily in the yielding jelly. When in contact with the collared cells, certain of the ameboid ones receive food particles from them and complete the digestion of these. Certain others secrete the crystal clear spicules of calcium carbonate; others are often packed with excretory inclusions and pigment granules; still other cells are filled with food and evidently act as storage reserves.

Skeleton. Many people know sponges only as skeletons because the natural sponges in general use are cleaned and bleached skeletons (Figs. 22.4, 22.5). The skeleton is produced in the mesenchyme. It determines the shape of the sponge, holds the water canals open, and is the support of the body. It is doubt-

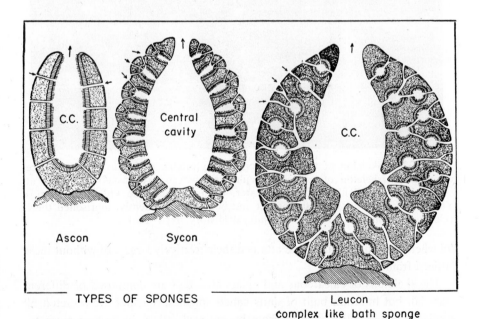

C.C.

Central cavity

C.C.

Ascon

Sycon

TYPES OF SPONGES

Leucon
complex like bath sponge

FIG. 22.3. Body plans of three types of sponges: *A*, simple sponge; *B*, sponge with folded wall; *C*, complex structure, e.g., bath sponge. Arrows denote currents of water; short lines indicate flagella of the collared cells that line the food chambers.

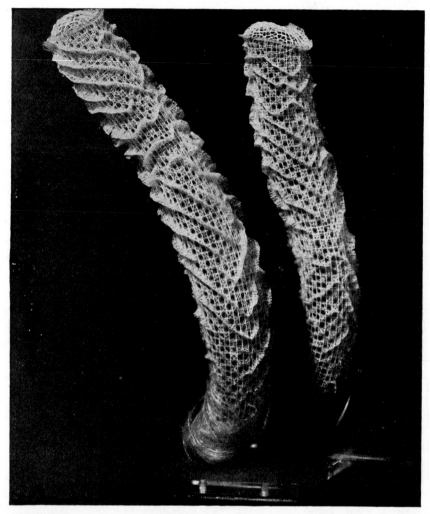

FIG. 22.4. Skeleton of the glass sponge, Euplectella, or Venus's flower basket which has a skeleton of silicious spicules interwoven like basketwork. It is attached by "glassy" fibers, in deep water. Common near the Philippine Islands. Young shrimps often enter the basket and become permanently imprisoned there. (Courtesy, American Museum of Natural History, New York.)

ful whether sponges could have attained their relatively large size without these latticed frames.

The skeletons of calcareous and "glass sponges" are composed of different material, but both are built of units called spicules. Spicules are secreted by special ameboid cells, some of them by one cell, others by two or more together, a cooperation that is rare among sponge cells except in spicule production. The secretion of a single shaft of spicule (monaxon) is begun within a cell as a minute axial thread around which calcium carbonate is deposited.

This cell divides into two as the process continues and when the spicule is complete both cells move away. Spicules vary in shapes and sizes according to the species. In general, they are elaborations of the single needle form. The most beautiful spicules are the silicious ones composed of opal, a form of hydrated silica. They are present, not only in the deep-sea glass sponges, but in the fresh-water sponges, several of them very common (Figs. 22.6, 22.7). Bath sponges contain interjoined fibers of spongin, a protein similar to that in hair and feathers. The skeletons form an important basis for the classification of sponges.

Reproduction. Sponges reproduce sexually as well as asexually. In sexual reproduction, female cells are produced in one individual and male cells in another. Both kinds develop in the mesenchyme from especially large ameboid cells. The sperm cells enter other sponges, whether male or female, by way of water currents, and in the females the eggs are fertilized in the locations where the embryos develop. In Sycon (older name, Grantia) the egg takes in food, enlarges and protrudes into a cavity lined with collared cells pushing some of the food with it. During the breeding season the large numbers of sperm cells freed from male sponges in a vicinity make it inevitable that many of them are carried through the incurrent pores of sponges whether male or female. When they are brought into the female they enter the collared cells that are adjacent to the ripe eggs. In the meantime one or more of the cells loses its collar and flagellum, becomes ameboid and applies itself to the sur-

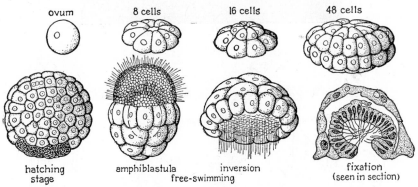

FIG. 22.5. Development of a calcareous sponge, Sycandra: the ovum fertilized by sperm from another sponge; the early embryo, 8, 16, and 48 cells, which is embedded in the jellied middle layer (mesenchyme) of the parent's body wall; an opening formed on the underside of the 48-celled stage functions as a mouth for the embryo; blastula and beginning of hatching when the embryo makes its way into the water passages of the parent; collared cells are already formed with flagella extending into the blastocoel; amphiblastula: the embryo turns inside out by way of an opening that first appeared in the 8-celled stage; the future upper end is up; inversion; the future excurrent opening (osculum) is down; the larva is floating in open water; fixation, compare Fig. 22.2. (After Schulze. Courtesy, Storer: *General Zoology,* ed. 2. New York, McGraw-Hill Book Co., 1951.)

face of the egg. The sperm enters the modified choanocyte, its own shape changed by the loss of its tail and capsule-like cover. It passes through the choanocyte, enters the egg and fusion of the male and female nuclei finally occurs.

After fertilization, the egg divides completely and at the 16-celled stage the embryo is a disk-shaped cushion of cells (Fig. 22.5). The eight cells next to the collared cells are the layout of the future outer cover or epidermis of the sponge. The other eight cells are the future collared cells. The latter divide rapidly and develop flagella. In this stage the embryo of calcareous sponges, now a hollow sphere, makes its way into the water currents in the parent sponge and is borne out of the excurrent opening as a free-swimming animal. Later, the layer of collared cells bends inward and the epidermal layer grows over it forming an outer sac around it. By this stage the young sponge has attached itself to a rock or seaweed and settled down for its further development and to a life of complete dependence upon the currents of the sea.

Sponges reproduce asexually by budding and branching somewhat after the fashion of plants. This habit produces the familiar "fingers" of sponges, as in

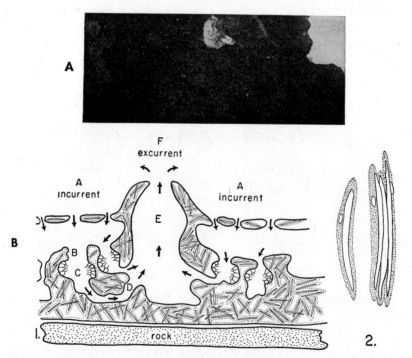

FIG. 22.6. Fresh-water sponge. *A,* living Spongilla, spread over a stone. The outlines of the water canals are faintly visible. Spongilla often covers submerged twigs and if exposed to sunlight is green with algae that grow within its cells. *B1,* diagram of a section of the wall of a fresh-water spicule-bearing sponge. *B2,* microscopic spicules within the cells which formed them. Greatly enlarged. (Courtesy, Morgan: *Fieldbook of Ponds and Streams.* New York, G. P. Putnam's Sons, 1930.)

the eyed Finger Sponge (*Chalina oculata*) of the Atlantic coast and *Leucosolenia eleanor* of the Pacific coast. Buds broken off and carried by currents established themselves in protected crannies and other places, such as wharf pilings and the backs of crabs.

Fresh-water sponges are mainly annual growths that die out in autumn except for the gemmules that can resist both drought and cold. These winter over in safety and germinate into young sponges in the spring (Figs. 22.7, 22.8). A gemmule is a ball of foodfilled ameboid cells and mesenchyme enclosed within a capsule. The outer wall is pierced by a minute outlet through which the growing sponge spreads forth. In autumn, the flourishing summer colonies of Spongilla are reduced to thousands of spicules sticking to the rock with many gemmules appearing like fig seeds packed among them.

All animals, especially invertebrates, have some power to replace lost or injured parts. With their relatively simple organization, sponges have a great capacity for these processes of regeneration even to the extent of a complete rearrangement of their parts after they are separated. When certain sponges are pushed through silk bolting cloth, their cells are nearly all separated from one another. If the redbeard sponge, Microciona, is thus treated and its cells allowed to fall into a large flat dish of sea water, they will spread and the solution soon resembles tomato soup. The amebocytes immediately begin random movements and certain of them become centers about which special food-carrying amebocytes congregate (Fig. 22.9). Collared cells that have been injured regrow their collars and take their proper places as living cells of

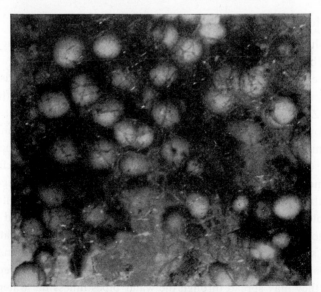

FIG. 22.7. Spongilla and other fresh-water sponges frequently overwinter as gemmules which resist cold and drying. Held among the spicules of the summer colony they look like fig seeds caught in the meshes of torn lace.

the flagellate chambers. A considerable bulk of sponge should be put through the cloth. There must be a sufficient number of cells, especially food-carrying amebocytes, or regeneration will not occur. Collared cells will not collect

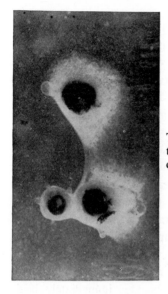

FIG. 22.8. Germinating gemmules of Spongilla. The young colonies have surrounded the capsules of the gemmules from which they grew. Readily reared on glass.

except about amebocytes. If bodies of two different species of sponges are put through the bolting cloth, their cells may at first intermingle, but soon those of each kind congregate by themselves.

Fresh-water Sponges

All fresh-water sponges are classified in the family Spongillidae, of which there are about 20 American species (Fig. 22.6). They grow in clean water, in ponds, lakes, and streams, upon stones, the undersides of lily pads, and submerged stems and sticks. When they are in full light they are often colored green by Zoochlorellae, the unicellular algae, within their cells. Many are annual growths, germinating from gemmules in the spring, reaching full size in mid-summer and dying away toward autumn except for the new crop of gemmules (Fig. 22.7). Fresh-water sponges are inhabited by a few minute residents, not large or as numerous as those that live in marine sponges. Among them are the larvae of Spongilla flies that puncture the sponge cells and suck up the protoplasm. They are about a quarter of an inch long and match the sponge color exactly. The best way to find them is to watch for what appear to be bits of sponge moving about through the sponge colony. Compared with marine sponges fresh-water ones are small, scanty growths. Nevertheless, in reservoirs they may spread through the water pipes unless the water is chemically treated. This has occurred in the water systems of more than one large city.

SCATTERED SPONGE CELLS REORGANIZE

A. Red sponge
Cells reunite when
pressed apart.

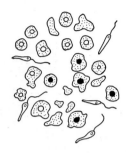

B. Scattered cells
Ameboid cells:
collared cells that
will regain collars.

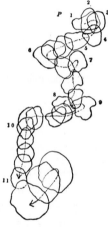

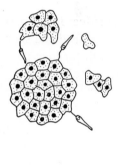

C. Ameboid cells move about,
make contacts with other cells.

D. Groups of cells are reformed.

FIG. 22.9. Regeneration of the redbeard sponge, *Microciona prolifera. A,* its natural growth; *B,* cells of the living sponge after it was broken up by being pressed through a fine cloth strainer; *C,* random movement of an ameboid cell (archeocyte) observed two and a half hours; *D,* the amebocytes have begun the reorganization which continues until the canals and chambers are reformed and new spicules are produced. (*C,* courtesy, Galtsoff, *Jour. Exper. Zool.,* **42:**197.)

Marine Sponges

Marine sponges are notable for their characteristics and biological and economic importance (Fig. 22.10).

Uses. The absorbent quality of sponges has long been known. Roman soldiers carried sponges with them to use for drinking cups. The era of bath sponges was followed by one of sponges for automobiles, and both have been displaced by plastic sponges. Needless to say, the sponge industry has been

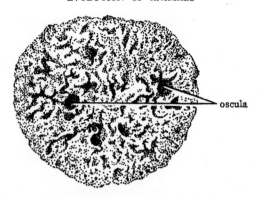

Fig. 22.10. Commercial sponge, Hippospongia, a typical sponge of commerce. When cut open, living sponge looks like raw liver. The chief American region for sponges is the west coast of Florida, centering at Tarpon Springs. The skeletons of commercial sponges are composed entirely of spongin fibers that are horny and elastic. The preparation for market consists of removing all soft matter and bleaching the skeleton. (Courtesy, Brown: *Invertebrate Types.* New York, John Wiley and Sons, 1950.)

greatly reduced. The sponge-fishing grounds of Florida and the Bahamas have been overfished and sponges are subject to diseases which occasionally reduce the growth for long periods.

Comparisons with Other Phyla

Likenesses

Simple sponges resemble the colonial protozoan, Proterospongia.

Collared cells of sponges are similar to those in Proterospongia and some other protozoans. They occur nowhere else among animals.

The wandering amebocytes of the mesenchyme of sponges are similar in habit and form to amebas.

The tube-shaped body, the colonial habit and attached state of sponges are suggestive of the corals (Phylum Coelenterata).

Differences

The characteristic spicules of sponges are different from skeletal structures in any other animals. Sponges differ from protozoans in that their cells are more dependent upon one another than the cells of colonial protozoans. They differ from other multicellular animals in that their cells are less dependent upon one another.

23

Coelenterates—Simple Multicellular Animals

Clusters of orange and yellow sea anemones, colonies of pink hydroids and plumy sea pens well deserve their old-time names of "plant-animals" and "gardens of the sea." No marine animals have such translucent beauty as the coelenterates. Nor have any truly multicellular ones so long a lineage—at least five hundred million years. They are direct descendants of the protozoans and are the ancestors of all multicellular animals (Fig. 33.1). Sponges are also directly descended from protozoans, but they long ago became set apart on an offshoot of evolution.

The two basic forms of coelenterates are the polyp and the medusa. The polyp has a cylindrical body and, in its more typical condition, has one end that bears the tentacles and mouth and another end attached to a surface or joined to a colony. Hydra is a polyp; so are the sea anemones and corals. The medusa or jellyfish has an umbrella- or bell-shaped body, is usually free-swimming, and bears the sex cells (Fig. 23.1).

Ecology. Almost all coelenterates are marine. Of about 10,000 species only a few, mainly the hydras, live in fresh water. Coelenterates are widespread and abundant, chiefly in surface waters and between the tide lines. Jellyfishes thrive in sheltered coves rich in organic matter. They are carried about by currents, great numbers of them often suddenly appearing in harbors and the shallows along bathing beaches. There they feed heavily upon the swarms of minute crustaceans (copepods) that become sparse soon after the jellyfishes move in. Bathers know jellyfishes as sea nettles.

Sea anemones and corals are numerous and colorful in warm seas. A few inconspicuous ones occur along the more northern Atlantic and Pacific coasts of the United States. Sea anemones cling tightly to rocks and wharf pilings. When the tide is out, they draw their tentacles in and their bodies down almost

465

hidden against the rock surfaces and seaweeds. Corals do not flourish in water below 66° F. or in the deep sea. The white coral Astrangia, which lives on the Atlantic coast as far north as Massachusetts, grows only in small colonies, never in the lush growths of the corals of tropical waters (Fig. 23.1). Except for corals, coelenterates of one kind or another are at home from the far north to the equator; the giant or pink jellyfish, *Cyanea capillata,* of the Atlantic is common about Greenland.

Food. All coelenterates are carnivores. Drifting jellyfishes are surrounded by protozoans, entomostracans and numberless young larvae which they constantly consume. To the sessile hydroids, sea anemones and corals, the tides daily bring fresh supplies swept from the bottom and deeper waters off shore.

Appearance and Size. Coelenterates occur in great variety. Branching colonies of little hydroids are attached like plants upon the seaweeds. Jellyfishes are bell- or umbrella-shaped and there are sea anemones more delicate and colorful than their namesakes. The common names of corals are descriptive of their forms—sea pen, sea fan, organ pipe, staghorn, brain, and mushroom. Some jellyfishes are as transparent and colorless as crystal; others are translucent brown, deep red, yellow, lavender, or milky white. Colonies of the hydroid, *Tubularia crocea,* common on the Atlantic coast, are rose-pink; polyps of the organ pipe coral, Tubipora, have bright green tentacles and the limy pipes of their skeletons are red. The Portuguese man-of-war floats on the sea like a great opal, one of the most beautiful of marine animals.

Hydroid polyps are usually very small, often microscopic, but colonies of them extend over bands of seaweed for 50 yards or more. The diameter of jellyfishes ranges from an inch, to 8 feet in the great pink Cyanea. Likewise, sea anemones range from little ones with oral disks half an inch wide to giants with a five-foot span. Although individual coral polyps are minute, the countless numbers of them in the colonies have built thousands of miles of coral reefs and islands.

Characteristics. Coelenterates are radially symmetrical and without head or segmentation. The body is composed of two layers of cells, the external epidermis or ectoderm and inner gastrodermis or endoderm, with a middle layer of jellied mesoglea between them. Unique stinging cells containing the nematocysts occur in one or both layers. The mouth, surrounded by soft tentacles, opens into a saclike digestive cavity, the enteron, that may be branched or divided by partial partitions and has no other opening. The skeleton is limy, horny, or absent. There are no blood, respiratory, or excretory organs. A network of nerve cells conducts messages through the body wall. Reproduction is commonly by alternation of generations, with asexual budding from attached polyps (hydralike) and with sexual reproduction by sex cells in the free-swimming medusa (jellyfish) stage.

Classes of Coelenterates. HYDROZOA. These are the little hydroids that grow

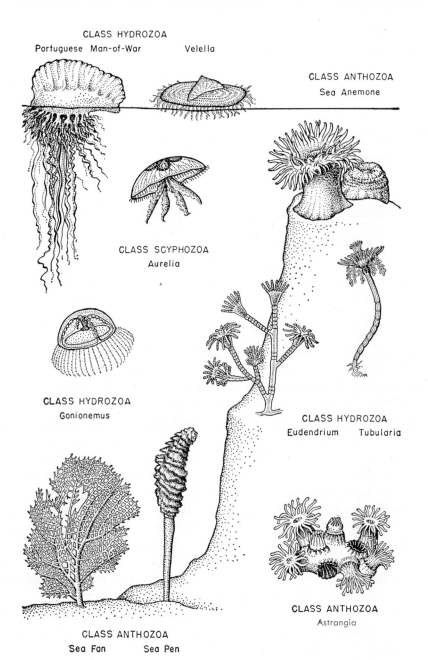

CLASS HYDROZOA
Portuguese Man-of-War   Velella

CLASS ANTHOZOA
Sea Anemone

CLASS SCYPHOZOA
Aurelia

CLASS HYDROZOA
Gonionemus

CLASS HYDROZOA
Eudendrium   Tubularia

CLASS ANTHOZOA
Astrangia

CLASS ANTHOZOA
Sea Fan   Sea Pen

FIG. 23.1. Representatives of the three classes of coelenterates, all are greatly reduced but not to the same scale. These or nearly related species live in both Atlantic and Pacific coastal waters. *Class Hydrozoa,* hydroids: Eudendrium, colony of polyps, 5 inches high; Gonionemus, medusa, ¾ inch in diameter, cosmopolitan; Physalia, Portuguese man-of-war, colony of polyps beneath a gas float, 10 inches long, tentacles up to 50 feet long when fully extended, float 6 to 8 inches in diameter; Velella, the "little sail" of the California coast. *Class Scyphozoa,* jellyfishes: Aurelia. *Class Anthozoa,* sea anemones and corals: Metridium, brown anemone, length to 4 inches; Astrangia, white coral, colonies of 5 to 30 individuals, 10 inches diameter, Florida to Cape Cod; Gorgonia, sea fan, a colony of horny corals, in warm waters on coral reefs; sea pen, a colony of fleshy polyps, warm coastal waters.

in tufts on rocks and seaweeds (Fig. 23.1) and the hydrocorallines, among them the "stinging corals." The class also includes the Siphonophora, the Portuguese man-of-war, and others that live in the open sea and have no sessile stage.

SCYPHOZOA. Larger medusae or jellyfishes with notches in the margin of the umbrella, as in the common jellyfish, Aurelia.

ANTHOZOA. These are either solitary or colonial coelenterates, with a great development of the polyp and no medusoid stage. Figure 23.1 suggests the form of the sea anemones, the brown anemone, Metridium, and the true corals.

Hydra—A Representative of Simple Multicellular Animals

Hydra is a link between older and newer ways of living. It digests its food partly by the old method of the ameba, partly by the newer methods of the grasshopper, frog, and man. Many of its characteristics are like those of higher animals, but simpler.

All hydras live in fresh water. They look like bits of coarse thread frayed out at one end, are semi-transparent and, except the green ones, are almost colorless. Their movements are visible to the naked eye and they are easily examined with the microscope. They are also common, widely distributed, and easily kept in aquaria. Only when they are undisturbed in considerable space do they display the deliberate grace of their searching tentacles and their sudden capture of minute water animals.

Ecology. Hydras live in sunlit pools, hanging from submerged plants and decayed vegetation. With the help of a gas bubble at the base of the body they are often buoyed up against the underside of the surface film (Fig. 23.2). Enormous numbers occasionally appear in lakes as they have done at Douglas Lake, Michigan, when the seines spread for fishes have been weighed down by the millions of hydras clinging to them. Under certain peculiar conditions, they may turn red, especially toward fall, and large patches of pond surface may be colored by them. Other aquatic organisms do this; the redness of blue-green algae gave the Red Sea its name.

Hydras reach their full activity in summer and then they frequently produce buds asexually. They usually reproduce sexually toward the end of the season on a lowering temperature, down to 50° F. They make a definite adjustment to winter temperatures. Brown and green hydras collected in winter from ponds in which the temperatures were 46° to 56° F. and placed in pond water at 35° F. contracted into balls and stayed so for two weeks, as long as the water was kept at the same degree of cold. When it was warmed to 46° F. they stretched out and began feeding. Active and semiactive hydras are certainly not confined to summer conditions. Various species with flourishing growths of buds have been found thriving beneath the ice.

Food. Hydras are carnivores that forage freely on protozoans and crusta-

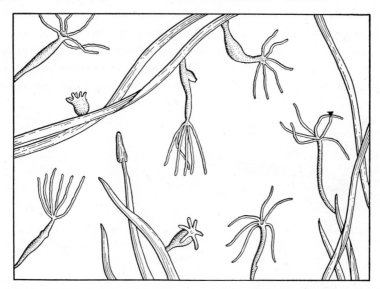

FIG. 23.2. Hydras in natural positions on water plants and buoyed up beneath the surface film. They swing and stretch downward like pieces of elastic thread frayed out at their ends.

ceans. They are avid feeders commonly swallowing fingernail clams and ejecting the shells after the soft bodies have been digested. Attached to the side of an aquarium they hang outward slowly swaying their bodies through the water with their tentacles trailing. Let a water flea graze one tentacle and it instantly shortens, carrying the water flea toward the hydra's mouth while the other tentacles join in paralyzing the victim. The body soon bulges with the water flea whose movements grow feebler as the digestive enzymes begin to work on it (Figs. 23.3, 23.4).

Common Species. Of the eight species of hydra known in North America, three are widely distributed and common. The green hydra, *Chlorohydra viridissima,* owes its brilliant color to the single-celled algae called zoochlorellae which live within the inner cells of its body. They are thus protected and, during photosynthesis, they use the carbon dioxide that they and the hydra give off in respiration (Fig. 23.4). Two other species are the gray hydra, *Hydra americana,* in the eastern United States, with short tentacles and no stalk to its body, and the brown hydra, *Pelmatohydra oligactis* (*Hydra fusca*), with a basal stalk and tentacles which stretch three or four times the length of body and stalk combined. Pale-colored hydras are larger, more translucent and better for study than the green ones.

Fresh-water jellyfishes or medusae (Craspedacusta) have bells about half an inch in diameter. They are rare yet occasionally occur in large numbers as they did in Gardiner's Lake, Connecticut, in the summer of 1952.

The following account of hydra applies to most of the species.

Movements and Locomotion of Hydra. When they are searching for food hydras sway their tentacles and stretch them gently in all directions. They move from place to place, imperceptibly by gliding upon their bases, sometimes by turning somersaults (Fig. 23.5). Such end-over-end steps are repeated again and again. Green hydras move about more than other species;

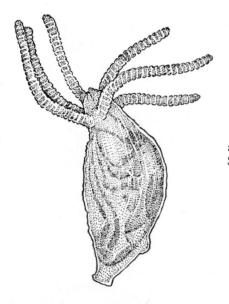

Fig. 23.3. A hydra which has caught and swallowed a "full meal" of water flea. Sketched from life.

the brown and gray ones will attach themselves and sway or hang almost motionless in one place for long periods.

Responses and Coordination of Behavior. Hydras react to mechanical contacts, light, electricity, and chemical solutions. The firmness of their attachment to the side of an aquarium as they swing out in the water regardless of gravity is an example of their reaction to contact. They respond to the slight current created by a passing water flea with the simultaneous contraction of the tentacles and the body, showing how quickly the reaction spreads through the animal. In unevenly lighted jars, hydras will retreat from the dark areas as well as from the strongly lighted ones moving about until by trial and error they finally reach their optimum degree of light. All of these responses may be affected by some special physiological state of the animal.

Form and Structure. GENERAL PLAN. The radial symmetry of hydra is at once conspicuous in the arrangement of the tentacles (Fig. 23.3). It has a distinct oral end with some of the characteristics of a head. The other end functions as the base by which it is attached and on which it glides about. One end of hydra is permanently different from the other, a foreshadowing of the polarity so evident in higher animals. The front end of an ameba is distinguishable mainly by the fact that it is forward during locomotion. Hydra's bodily

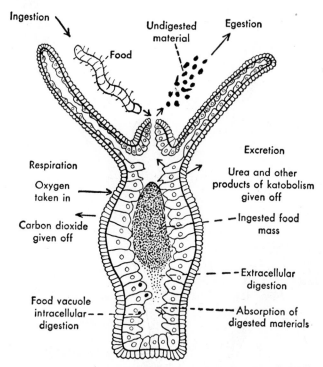

FIG. 23.4. Hydra, its general metabolism. Excretion is carried on by all cells; exchange of respiratory gases likewise. (Courtesy, Mavor: *General Biology,* ed. 3. New York, The Macmillan Co., 1947.)

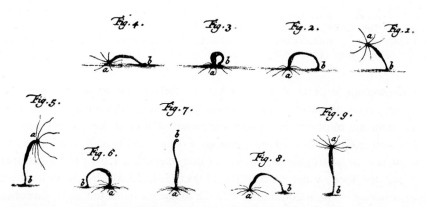

FIG. 23.5. The more rapid ways by which hydras travel. Figures *1–4,* by looping; *5–9* by somersaults. Drawings from work of Abraham Trembley (1700–1784), a pioneer in the study of hydra and of experimental zoology. (From Trembley: *Mémoires pour l'Histoire des Polypes.* Leyden, Jean and Herman, 1744.)

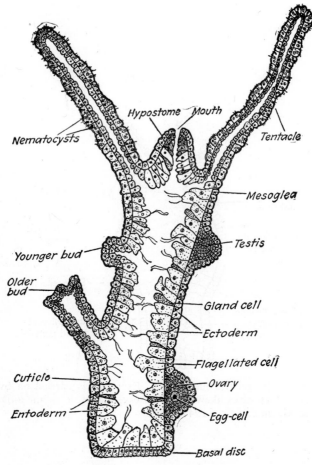

FIG. 23.6. A long section of hydra with the bud of asexual reproduction and the male and female organs. Such a composite is unusual; in the majority of species the sexes are separate. (Courtesy, Wolcott: *Animal Biology*, ed. 3. New York, McGraw-Hill Book Co., 1946.)

functions occur in exact places. Food enters through the mouth and nowhere else. Stinging cells are most abundant on the tentacles which grapple the prey. Nerve cells are most numerous near the mouth, the usual locality for a brain.

Like all coelenterates, hydra contains a single cavity called the enteron, coelenteron, or gastrovascular cavity. Its one opening functions as an entrance and exit for food, water, and waste (Figs. 23.4, 23.6). In all hydras, the gastrovascular cavity is continuous into the tentacles, but is not so in the corals and other hydroids. The body wall enclosing the cavity consists of the three layers already mentioned, the epidermis (ectoderm), the lining of the enteron, (endoderm), and the extremely thin gelatin-like mesoglea (Fig. 23.6). In jellyfishes, mesoglea forms the bulk of the body and contains fibers and cells which move into it from the true cell layers; in sea anemones, it is a tough fibrous tissue.

EPIDERMIS. The epidermis is composed of epithelial tissue containing supporting cells, epithelio-muscular, glandular-muscular and glandular cells, sensory nerve cells, formative and stinging cells (Fig. 23.8). The supporting cells protect and support other cells. The outer ends of the epithelio-muscular cells are likewise protective but their inner ends are drawn out into contractile strands which extend along the mesoglea lengthwise of the body. When these strands contract, the tentacles and body shorten and widen. Glandular cells are crowded about the mouth and in the basal disk along with epithelio-muscular cells. Hydras attach themselves to objects by means of a sticky secretion and the contraction of epithelio-muscular cells. Gas is also secreted in the basal region; a bubble of it caught in the mucus often buoys an animal up beneath the surface film (Fig. 23.2).

The neurosensory cells reach to or near the outer surface and their processes extend to the nerve plexus close to the mesoglea. These are the receptors of touch and other stimuli, called neurosensory cells because they look so much like nerve cells. Cells of the nerve plexus or "net" rest against the processes of the epithelio-muscular cells (Fig. 23.7). The neurosensory, nerve and epi-

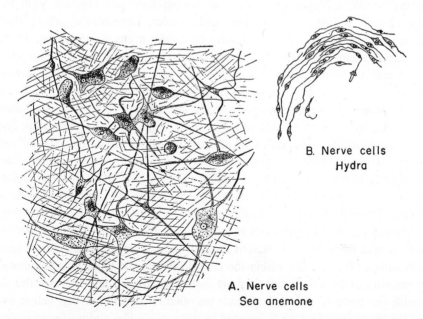

B. Nerve cells
Hydra

A. Nerve cells
Sea anemone

FIG. 23.7. Nerve cells. *A*, sea anemone. A layer of nerve cells from the oral disk, more elaborate but similar to the layer of nerve cells in the body wall of hydra. Note the lack of continuity of the cells. *B*, hydra, part of the ring of nerve cells in the base (pedal disk) of the body. Note that these cells are not regularly continuous. (Courtesy, Hyman: *The Invertebrates,* vol. 1. New York, McGraw-Hill Book Co., 1940.)

thelio-muscular cells equip hydra to respond to its environment. The nerve plexus acts as a unit and the impulses appear to travel in either direction over a given process, as in a telephone conversation the speaking goes first one way and then the other on the same wire. In higher animals the incoming and outgoing impulses travel on different pathways. There is a concentration of the plexus about the mouth which suggests the more prominent nerve ring around the mouth of a starfish. Investigators have shown that in hydra the processes of different nerve cells may touch but are not continuous. Thus, there is a synapse, a break over which the nerve impulse jumps from one cell to another as in higher animals.

Formative (or interstitial cells) are small cells wedged in between those of the epidermis and gastrodermis, the lining of the enteron. They behave like embryonic cells, still capable of developing into something different; some of them become sex cells, many become stinging cells (Fig. 23.8). In the human bone marrow, there are embryonic cells that differentiate throughout life into specialized blood cells.

A stinging cell (cnidoblast) is one that forms within itself the nonliving mechanism called a nematocyst (Fig. 23.8). In the epidermis, mature stinging cells occur close to the outer surface, are numerous on the body, and abundant on the tentacles. Nematocysts are microscopic harpoons expelled from the stinging cells against the hydra's prey and enemies. They are the unique stinging mechanism of coelenterates. Each one carries a charge of poison. Those of hydra are harmless except to minute animals, but the stings of larger jellyfishes and the Portuguese man-of-war are very painful. The fully formed nematocyst is a transparent capsule containing a minute coil usually termed a thread, shown to be a tube in some species and believed to be so in all. Poison is secreted by the stinging cell and is in some way carried by the nematocyst when the latter is discharged. One side of the cell is ordinarily exposed and the triggerlike cnidocil that projects from it is supersensitive to stimulation. Stinging cells respond directly to stimuli. The threads of some nematocysts pierce their prey (Fig. 23.8C). There are four kinds of stinging cells each of slightly different structure, usually not visible except by special preparation.

The expulsion of nematocysts is too sudden to be clearly observed. As the tentacle of a living hydra is viewed through the microscope, they can be seen each with a thread coiled within the capsule. When the tentacle is stimulated by pressure or by weak acid, they are instantly expelled and the capsules lie outside the tentacle with their threads uncoiled. It is believed that before expulsion the threadlike tube is inverted in the capsule like a glove-finger pulled inward. When the nematocyst is expelled the tube is rapidly everted by the pressure on the capsule as it is shot out of the cell.

Stinging cells are wandering cells. Many of them migrate from the epidermis, across the mesoglea, go through the gastrodermis into the enteron and

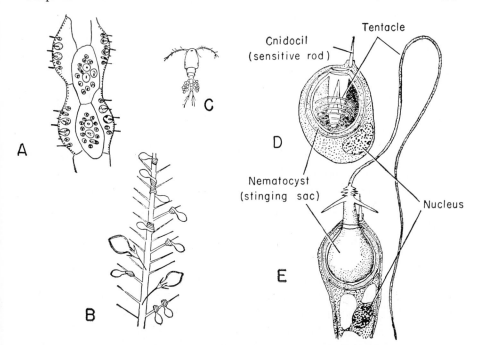

FIG. 23.8. The stinging capsules (nematocysts) of hydra. *A*, a bit of tentacle magnified to reveal the batteries of stinging capsules. *B*, tail bristle of Cyclops with the stinging capsules thrown upon it during its capture by hydra. *C*, Cyclops, a favorite food of hydra, is only a white speck to the naked eye. Note its single eye, the eggs it carries and the tail bristles. *D*, a stinging capsule highly magnified within the cell that formed it. *E*, the stinging cell with the thread unloosed and poison discharged. (*A* and *B*, courtesy, Hyman: *The Invertebrates*, vol. 1. New York, McGraw-Hill Book Co., 1940. *D* and *E*, after Schneider. Courtesy, Dahlgren and Kepner: *Animal Histology*. New York, The Macmillan Co., 1908.)

enter the cell layers at some other point. Wherever they enter they finally lodge in the ectoderm. Not all of them migrate; some remain in the ectoderm where they developed. Their structures and functions are entirely different from those of the wandering cells (macrophages) of mammals that pick up foreign substances in the human body, yet both types move about in similar ways. Each illustrates the flexibility of form and function that is highly characteristic of living matter.

ENDODERM. The gastrodermis of the enteron and its extensions in the tentacles is in general similar to the epidermis. It is composed of epithelial tissue and contains glandular, sensory, and nerve cells—the latter less frequent than in the epidermis. There are fewer formative cells and no stinging cells except those that migrate into it (Figs. 23.6, 23.8).

Nutritive muscular cells are the predominant cells of the gastrodermis. Their bases are extended into muscular processes which run in a circular direction opposite to the processes in the epidermis but like them rest against the mesoglea. Their contraction makes the body and tentacles more slender and stretches the comparable processes in the epidermis. Their bases are specialized for movement and their inner ends contain vacuoles usually filled with particles of food that has been partly digested in the enteron. Glandular cells are abundant about the mouth and in the gastrodermis. In hydra, and more evidently in sea anemones, the cells near the mouth produce mucus. A slippery surface must ease the slide of a struggling water flea into the "stomach" (Fig. 23.3). The glandular cells also secrete digestive enzymes.

MESOGLEA. In hydra, mesoglea is noncellular and so thin that in stained sections of the body it appears only as a dark line. This is far from true in jellyfishes whose bulk and shape are largely due to their mesoglea, but when they are washed up on the beaches and the water evaporates only papery wisps remain.

Digestion, Respiration, and Excretion. Food is brought to the mouth by the tentacles and drawn into it by contractions of the body. It is partly digested in the enteron by enzymes which reduce it to a semifluid. Any partly digested particles of food which remain are then engulfed by the nutritive muscular cells and digestion is completed within them. Thus hydra employs two methods of digestion, an extracellular one like that of higher animals, and an intracellular one like that of an ameba. Finally, the completely digested food is absorbed through the cell membranes and passed on from one cell to another. Indigestible wastes are ejected through the mouth.

There is no special "breathing mechanism" in hydra. The cells take oxygen from the water or from one another and give off carbon dioxide likewise. There is no transporting fluid such as the blood, and no need of it since the body wall is thin and there is no body cavity to separate the digestive tract from the outer cells. Individual cells eliminate nitrogenous waste but have no contractile vacuoles or other special means of doing so.

Reproduction. Hydras reproduce asexually by budding or under unusual conditions, by transverse division of the body, and sexually by the fusion of male and female sex cells (Fig. 23.6).

The buds develop near the junction of the enteron and stalk, when the latter is present. In dioecious (separate sexed) species the individuals produced from buds have the same sex as their parent. In a well-fed hydra, a bud will form and separate from the parent within two or three days. Before it separates there is a free passageway between the enterons of the parent and bud, and food swallowed by the parent may be absorbed by the buds.

The testes and ovaries develop from formative cells in the ectoderm. During the maturation of the sex cells the number of chromosomes in each one is reduced by half (meiosis). When the sex cells are brought together the chromosome number is returned to that of the body cells.

In the ovary, formative cells are absorbed by the future egg until it becomes a large food-filled cell. It is soft and irregularly shaped, with outspreading processes which are withdrawn as the egg matures. Sperm cells swimming free in the water go through the thin cellular sac enclosing the egg and fertilization occurs while the egg is still attached to the parent. The now one-celled embryo divides many times and becomes a hollow sphere of cells (blastula), then a double layered sac (gastrula), in the meantime slipping out of its protective sac. The embryo secretes a capsule in which the embryo may remain dormant for several months. There is no evidence, however, that the eggs have a definite resting period or that they are latent over the winter except as low temperature slows down the development of those produced in the fall.

Regeneration and Grafting. Like other coelenterates, hydras can replace lost parts. If one is cut transversely and the parts are kept in good conditions, a new basal piece will grow on the one bearing tentacles and a new set of tentacles on the basal piece. Or if a central part of the body is removed it will grow new oral and basal ends in their original relationships. If properly fed, hydras will regain the full size of a lost part within a few days. Regeneration follows a variety of cuts (Fig. 23.9).

Studies of Hydra. Aristotle knew that coelenterates could sting, thought they looked like plants, and named them zoophyta along with other soft-bodied animals. This name stayed with them for several hundred years.

Regeneration in animals was first described in hydra. In 1744 Abraham Trembley (1700–1784) made a thorough study of hydras and published a

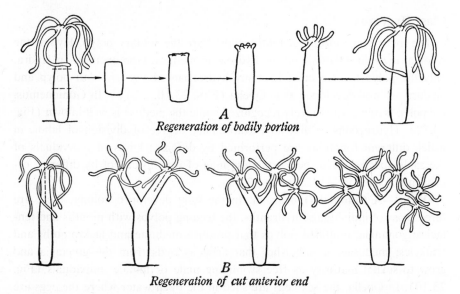

A
Regeneration of bodily portion

B
Regeneration of cut anterior end

FIG. 23.9. Regeneration of hydras. *A,* successive stages in regeneration of a piece cut from the mid-region of body. *B,* regrowth of parts of heads—a five-headed animal from original single head. (Courtesy, Fasten: *Introduction to General Zoology.* Boston, Ginn and Co., 1941.)

monograph, "Polypes d'eau douce." He described them as animals, portrayed their locomotion, and gave accounts of his experiments upon them. He discovered that if one were cut into two, three, or four pieces, each piece would form a new animal; and if the oral end of one were split it would form a two-headed animal (Fig. 23.9). Hydra has continued to be a subject of experimentation and R. L. Roudabush (1933) turned hydras inside out as Trembley did. The striking result of the later experiments was the migration of cells, discovered by studying sections of the animals killed and fixed at periods of 10 minutes, 2 hours, and 24 hours after they had been turned inside out. They showed: the epidermis on the inside and the gastrodermis on the outside as they had been turned in the experiment; and later also the cells of the gastrodermis in migration toward the inside and those of epidermis toward the outside; and finally, cells of the two layers in position as they were before the experiment.

GRAFTING. Trembley's grafting experiments were the first of many others. Pieces of different hydras, even those of different species, have been grafted together. Pieces may be too small to regenerate but will fuse and grow, the ectoderm joining with ectoderm and endoderm with endoderm.

The Invertebrates. Protozoa through Ctenophora, by L. H. Hyman, contains an unequaled store of knowledge about coelenterates, including the results of the author's own extensive work on the hydras and comprehensive lists of references.

Class Hydrozoa

The hydrozoans most frequently studied are the solitary polyp, Hydra, the colonial hydroid, Obelia, and the hydrozoan medusa, Gonionemus. In Hydra, only the polyp form occurs. In many hydrozoans, however, both polyp and medusa are well developed as in Obelia (Figs. 23.10, 23.11). In Gonionemus, the polyp is minute and rarely recognized while the medusa is well known (Fig. 23.12). Hydrozoans exhibit an extraordinary degree of division of labor, in which different functions are performed by different kinds of individuals of the same species, as in the Portuguese man-of-war instead of by different organs in the same individual (Fig. 23.13).

Obelia—A Colonial Hydrozoan. In the fully developed colony, there are three types of individuals: hydranths, the feeding polyps with mouths and tentacles; gonangia, modified polyps that produce medusae and lack mouths and tentacles; medusae or jellyfishes that arise as buds from the gonangia and grow to sexual maturity as free swimming male or female individuals (Fig. 23.10). In Obelia, the sex cells are shed in the open water where the eggs are fertilized. In some hydroids, the sperm cells are shed and the eggs are fertilized while the medusa is still attached. In its complete cycle, the life of Obelia includes an alternation of generations. One generation, the colony, is asexual and

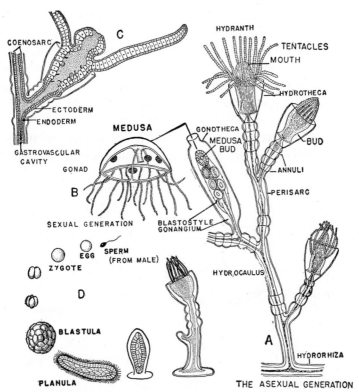

FIG. 23.10. The structure and life cycle of Obelia, a marine colonial hydroid. The mature colony is about one inch high with swollen joints from which the branches, vegetative and reproductive individuals, are given off alternately. *A,* a mature colony, the asexual generation. *B,* the minute jellyfish or medusa (greatly enlarged), a free swimming sexual individual, of which there are males and females developed in different colonies. *C,* section through a vegetative individual (hydranth) showing the gastrovascular cavity that extends throughout the colony. *D,* the early development of a colony, from the fertilized egg, through the free swimming ciliated planula, to the young attached colony. (Courtesy, MacDougall and Hegner: *Biology.* New York, McGraw-Hill Book Co., 1943.)

produces new individuals (feeding and reproductive polyps) by budding. The next generation, medusae, is sexual and by the fusion of sex cells produces the first polyp of a new colony. In this cycle, an individual is the image of its grandparents but looks like a stranger to its parents.

HABITATS. Various species of Obelia live on both coasts of North America. Colonies of them, an inch or two high, grow by millions on the long ribbons of kelp and other seaweeds. Attached and branched as they are, even a good observer might well take them for plants just as Aristotle did. They can be examined satisfactorily only with a strong lens.

THE COLONY—ITS FORM AND WAY OF LIVING. The colony is held fast by the root-shaped hydrorhiza and from this springs the upright branch (hydrocaulus) that forms the main stalk of the colony (Fig. 23.10). The hydrorhiza extends along the seaweed with many colonies springing from it.

The tentacles of the feeding polyps are armed with stinging cells (Fig. 23.8). These and the persisting motion of its tentacles are the hydranth's equipment for catching the minute animals which swarm through the surrounding water. The reproductive polyps (gonangia) bear the medusae which bud off from its stalk much as buds of hydra develop from its body.

The bodies of Obelia and Hydra are essentially similar. As in hydra, the body wall is composed of two cellular layers, epidermis and the thin layer of

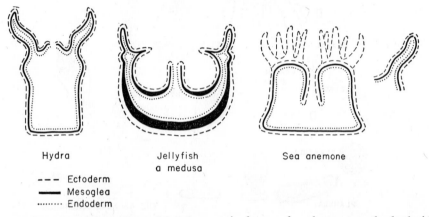

Hydra   Jellyfish   Sea anemone
        a medusa

– – – Ectoderm
——— Mesoglea
········· Endoderm

FIG. 23.11. Ground plans of the three main forms of coelenterates: the hydroid polyp, the medusa or jellyfish, and the polyp of the anemone, are constructed on the same general plan. The mouths of hydra and sea anemone are held upward; a jellyfish swims with mouth down.

mesoglea. In Obelia, the body is encased in a transparent casing (perisarc), complete except at the tips of the polyps. The digestive processes are essentially the same as those of hydra. The gastrovascular cavity is continuous throughout the stalks and branches of the colony and food is shared by the community. Lively protozoans are swept into the mouths of feeding polyps, moved along while still in tremors through the enteron, and gradually digested and absorbed along the way.

THE MEDUSA—ITS FORM AND WAY OF LIVING. Medusae are the sexual links in the hydrozoan life cycle. Medusae are specialized individuals devoted to reproduction in contrast to the ovaries and testes of higher animals which are only organs of reproduction. Hydrozoan medusae are always small, and those of Obelia are minute. They live in tide pools and shallows, swimming about by vigorous contractions of their umbrellas. But they are powerless against currents and are carried into harbors in enormous numbers though they are so small that they go unnoticed. It is the larger scyphozoan jellyfishes that everybody sees (Fig. 23.14).

The medusa's umbrella-shaped body is largely the jellied mesoglea containing at least 95 per cent water and the scattered fibers and cells that have migrated into it. Both the upper convex and under concave surfaces are covered by epidermis liberally supplied with stinging cells and sensory nerve cells. The mouth is at the end of a short tube (manubrium) which hangs from the center of the under surface (Fig. 23.10). The passage from it opens into a central cavity from which four radial canals lead to the circular canal that extends around the margin of the umbrella. All of these canals are parts of the enteron which in its evolution has added the distribution of food to its already established functions of digestion and absorption. As might be expected of an active free-living animal, the nerve cells and their associations in the medusa are much more highly developed than in the attached polyps. A nerve ring lies along the margin of the umbrella. This receives processes of nerve cells acting in a simplified way like the central nervous system of higher animals. A sensory organ of equilibrium (statocyst) is located at the base of every other tentacle. These and similar sensory organs in other medusae are considered as the first real organs to be developed in the invertebrates.

REPRODUCTION. The medusae of any one colony are either all male or all female. They closely resemble one another and the ovaries and testes develop in the same relative position beneath the radial canals. The sex cells are shed into the open water where fertilization occurs. The embryo becomes first a spherical blastula, then a swimming larva. Its wanderings are important to the distribution of the species but they last only a few hours before it settles upon rock or seaweed and the development of the colony of polyps begins (Fig. 23.10).

Gonionemus—A Hydrozoan Jellyfish. In Gonionemus, the medusa is well developed and the polyp is diminutive. The medusa is as transparent as glass and less than an inch in diameter (Fig. 23.12). This was formerly a common jellyfish among the eel grasses along the eastern coast of the United States.

When feeding, Gonionemus swims toward the surface with its mouth down. There it turns over and floats slowly downward, its mouth up and its tentacles extended in a wide open snare for any small animals within reach of their stinging clutch. When at rest it likewise lies mouth up, with its tentacles attached to the bottom by the adhesive pads.

Other Species of Hydrozoa. The skeletons of hydrocorallines are peppered with minute pores but the polyps are seldom seen extending from them since they expand at night. The "stinging coral" (*Millepora alicornia*) well known along the coast of Florida contributes largely to the formation of coral reefs.

The colonies of Hydractinia which live on the shells of hermit crabs have a division of labor similar to that of Obelia but in these colonies there are feeding polyps, reproductive polyps with medusa buds, and protective polyps without mouths, only stubby tentacles and a great supply of stinging cells.

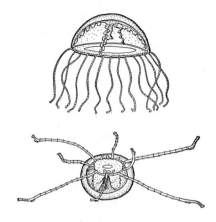

Adhesive disks holding to surface

Fig. 23.12. *Upper,* adult *Gonionemus murbachi,* a beautiful jellyfish with a disk hardly an inch in diameter and 60 to 80 tentacles that bear rings of stinging cells. It goes through a medusa and a polyp stage, the latter so minute it is little known. Very abundant in the quiet inlets of Cape Cod. *Lower,* a young jellyfish resting on the bottom and holding fast with its suction disks. (*Lower,* after Perkins, *Proceeds. Academy of Natural Sciences,* Philadelphia, 1902.)

The Portuguese man-of-war (*Physalia pelagica*) floats on the surface of warm seas in many parts of the world and was named Portuguese only because seamen saw it floating near Portugal (Fig. 23.13). It occurs in the Gulf Stream from Florida northward, occasionally drifting into harbors in New England. Its gas-filled float, about ten inches long, is translucent blue and rose-tinted, colors that are continued in the polyps which trail backward for 10 to 40 feet. Their beauty is strictly for the eye, nothing to be fondled. Colonies and pieces of tentacles that have been picked up half dead upon the beach have caused serious poisoning. The long defense polyps paralyze a good-sized fish and, due to their extraordinary contractions, are able to present the fish which they have snared at the mouths of the short feeding polyps.

The "little sail" (Velella) is a similar hydrozoan colony supported by a float about two inches wide that bears an erect projection, the "little sail." These are common drifters often whole fleets of them, in the warmer waters of the west coast.

Class Scyphozoa

The Scyphozoans include the larger jellyfishes. Their radial symmetry is based upon four or a multiple of four structures, such as the eight notches in the margin of the umbrella (Fig. 23.14). The polyp stage is either lacking or the polyps are minute. A full-grown polyp suggests a stack of diminutive

FIG. 23.13. Portuguese man-of-war, Physalia, eating a fish held by the feeding polyps. The float (about 10 inches long) is tilted over on its side with the crest toward the camera. Physalia is a colony of hydrozoan polyps fitted for different functions—feeding, defense, reproduction. They act together in such close cooperation that they form an individual. Physalia frequents warm ocean currents and is often carried to the shores of Europe and America. (Photograph courtesy, Douglas P. Wilson, Marine Biological Laboratory, Plymouth, England.)

saucers (strobilas). Some jellyfishes are crystalline clear and colorless; others are rose-tinted, yellow, lavender, blue, or deep red; all their swimming motions have characteristic grace and rhythm.

Aurelia—A Scyphozoan Jellyfish. Aurelia is one of the commonest of jellyfishes and most often studied. Drying fragments of them litter the beaches after a storm, great bounty for the sandpipers. The polyps are small and usually hidden in seaweeds (Fig. 23.15).

A long folded lip trails from each corner of the square mouth (Fig. 23.14). The edges of these are well armed with stinging cells and the fold encloses a groove along which cilia drive minute animals toward the mouth and thence to the four-pouched stomach. There they come in contact with gastric filaments

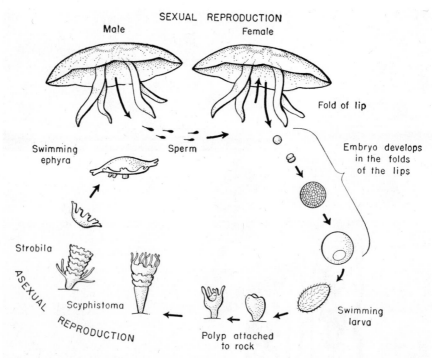

SEXUAL REPRODUCTION

FIG. 23.14. The life cycle of the common jellyfish, Aurelia. During their complete cycle jellyfishes have different forms and habits. The largest of these are the male and female medusas, 6 to 10 inches across the disks in Aurelia. All the other forms are minute. The embryo is produced by the union of sperm and egg, and sheltered in the streamer-like lips of the parent. The larva swims by cilia and transforms into a hydra-like polyp. In the following stages, scyphistoma and strobila, the animal divides into a series of saucer-shaped young ones. Finally these separate and as ephyras, developing males or females, they swim free.

heavily loaded with more stinging cells. Within a few hours, they are reduced to broth by secretions strong enough even to digest chitin. Particles of food are engulfed by nutritive cells and digestion is completed within them as it is in the similar cells of hydra.

Jellyfishes have a very definite sense of balance. If one of them is tilted out of horizontal position it will contract more strongly on the upper than on the lower side and bring itself back to a horizontal position. If the organs of balance in the notches are all removed from one side and that side is upturned as before, the animal will not attempt to right itself. The ovaries and testes, always borne on separate individuals, are the four horse-shoe-shaped bodies in the floor of the central enteron, the most conspicuous structures in the animals.

The embryo goes through its early development within the folded lips of the female, becomes a ciliated free-swimming larva, and then a polyp that settles upon a rock or seaweed. There it may grow for months budding off one young medusa after another; the oldest one at the end the first to separate and swim away (Fig. 23.15).

Class Anthozoa

Sea anemones and true corals. These are the fleshy sea anemones and the limestone secreting corals. All are polyps, solitary or colonial with no medusa stage. They are distinguished from hydrozoan polyps by the vertical partitions or septa which partially divide the gastrovascular cavity into alcoves opening into a central space below the gullet.

Sea-anemone—A Representative Anthozoan. *Metridium marginatum* is the common sea anemone which attaches itself to wharf piles and gathers by

FIG. 23.15. An underwater photograph of living polyps of Aurelia. Polyps (about one-half-inch long) of *Aurelia aurita,* growing on a hollowed rock. Jelly-fishes (medusae) are being formed by the transverse division of the polyps. A young jellyfish (ephyra stage) has just separated from a polyp and is swimming into open water. (Photographed from life by Douglas P. Wilson, Marine Biological Laboratory, Plymouth, England.)

dozens in the tide pools along our north Atlantic coast (Fig. 23.1). Metridium has a cylindrical body topped with a crown of hollow tentacles arranged in circlets around its slit-shaped mouth. When full grown and expanded it is about 4 inches high and its oral disk may be three inches wide. Its skin (epidermis) is soft and slimy but tough even to sharp scissors.

Partial septa extend vertically from the body wall; some are attached to the gullet, others extend only part of the way toward it (Fig. 23.16). Their free edges are thickened by digestive filaments containing the nutritive cells. Some of these secrete digestive fluids into the gastrovascular cavity; others engulf particles of food and digest them within food vacuoles in the cells. The structure of hydra, jellyfish, sea anemone, and coral is fundamentally similar (Fig. 23.11). Stinging cells are active and abundant on the tentacles and on the stinging threads (acontia) borne near the bases of the digestive filaments. These threads may be shot through pores in the body wall or out of the mouth and extended three or four inches into the water, paralyzing animals which the tentacles cannot reach.

Ovaries and testes are in separate individuals and the young develop from fertilized eggs. Anemones also reproduce asexually by longitudinal division and by pedal laceration, the pinching off of fragments of the basal disk. In an aquarium, the base of the anemone may be spread against the glass side and

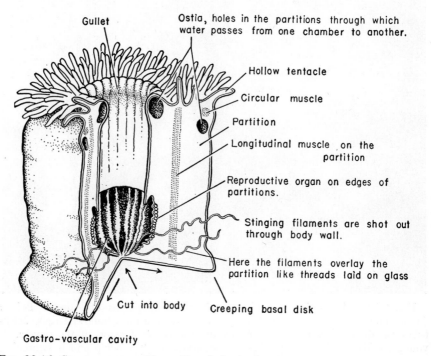

Gullet

Ostia, holes in the partitions through which water passes from one chamber to another.

Hollow tentacle

Circular muscle

Partition

Longitudinal muscle on the partition

Reproductive organ on edges of partitions.

Stinging filaments are shot out through body wall.

Here the filaments overlay the partition like threads laid on glass

Cut into body   Creeping basal disk

Gastro-vascular cavity

FIG. 23.16. Sea anemone with a side of the body cut away to show the partial partitions in the coelenteron.

firmly attached along the edges. The attachment is so strong that the central part can be pulled away leaving a ring of torn tissue behind it. Each piece will develop tentacles and a mouth and finally a complete minute anemone, ultimately a ring of little anemones.

Anemones can glide on the pedal disk, but at the slow pace of about four inches per hour. When conditions are good they stay in one place for long periods. An anemone contracts its body tightly and quickly; the tentacles disappear suddenly, and its mouth appears tied up like a bag. Water is squeezed out through pores in its body wall and the acontia are also forced out through them. It may not expand for a long time and then very slowly while water gradually flows into the enteron through smooth ciliated furrows on one or both sides of the gullet (Figs. 23.1 and 23.16).

The tentacles are very sensitive to stimulation and move excitedly if meat juices are added to the surrounding water. If a water flea happens to come in contact with the tentacles it is immediately snared in the sticky mucus, then paralyzed by the stinging cells and brought to the mouth by the ciliated tentacles (Fig. 23.17). Immediately the whole oral disk is in motion, the mouth opens and, with the further help of tentacles and lips, it takes in the food. In the gullet, the food comes in touch with currents of cilia, always inward when the anemone is feeding though they may be outward at some other times. Anemones are carnivores that will eat any animal flesh, living or dead. They often attach themselves to crab shells and to the shells appropriated by hermit crabs. The crab is hidden and the sea anemone rides to new feeding grounds, foraging as it goes, probably a truly symbiotic relation.

Astrangia—A Coral Polyp. *Astrangia danae* form little colonies of a couple of dozen polyps on the rocks, in sheltered places from North Carolina to Massachusetts (Fig. 23.18). They feed upon small crustaceans and young fishes and can be kept alive quite successfully in cold salt-water aquaria. They are like smaller editions of the sea anemone except for the limy coral cup secreted by the ectoderm. This is laid down at the base of the polyp, in thin ridges and as more coral is produced the bottom of the cup is also thickened. Astrangia is closely related to the most important builders of coral reefs.

Coral Building. In tropical waters, where they abound, coral animals have built the foundations of large areas of land. The Bermuda Islands are at the northern limit of coral building and are comparatively small, yet they include more than 19 square miles of coral. The Great Barrier Reef of Australia, crowded with coral, is 1350 miles long (Fig. 23.20). Such areas have been built by the epidermal cells of millions of minute polyps each one slowly secreting its cup-shaped home. Polyps die and new generations of them secrete new cups upon the old ones. Only the surface of the coral mass is alive.

Other animals live in the crevices and chasms of the coral ledges—protozoans, sponges, boring mollusks, case-making worms, seaweeds, and brilliantly colored fishes. Probably no place on earth is so replete with life as the undersea gardens of coral reefs. All of these plants and animals leave their remains on the coral and gradually build it up toward the surface where it then receives the drift brought by winds and waves.

CORAL REEFS. There are three main types of coral reefs and they are among the most interesting of land masses (Fig. 23.19). A fringing reef is near the coast, separated from it only by narrow strips of shallow water. It is a platform of coral which projects outward from the shore and ends steeply on the seaward side of the reef. Breaks occur here and there in the reef, letting currents into the shallows, but little or no navigation is possible. Barrier reefs resemble the fringing ones but differ in that there are wide, deep channels between the mainland and the reef. The world famous one is the Great Barrier Reef of Australia (Fig. 23.20). The atoll is a ring-like reef with an opening in one or several places into a lagoon which may be less than a mile or as much as 50

FIG. 23.17. Snake-locks anemone (*Anemonia sulcate*). The tentacles and cilia bring food to the central mouth. No garden is more beautiful than are colonies of sea anemones—ivory, yellow, purple, rust-colored, and orange, with their translucent tentacles shifting and stretching in the currents. (Photograph courtesy, Douglas P. Wilson, Marine Biological Laboratory, Plymouth, England.)

miles wide. None of the reefs is continuous—all of their fronts being subject to incessantly breaking waves. The booming of surf is a characteristic voice of the reefs.

THEORIES OF REEF BUILDING. Charles Darwin suggested *The Subsidence Theory:* that in past ages all corals had lived in fringing reefs; that in places

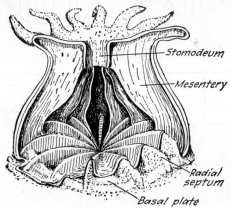

FIG. 23.18. *Upper,* polyps of the coral, Astrangia, cup half an inch high. The white *Astrangia danae* lives on the eastern coast, as far north as Cape Cod and the orange and red *Astrangia insignifica* on the western coast of North America. (Courtesy, American Museum of Natural History, New York.) *Lower,* diagram of a coral polyp with one side of the body cut away to show the general structure. The polyp is resting on the basal plate and partitions (or septa) of the limy cup which it has secreted. Only the basal parts of the cup are included. The mouth, tentacles, and walls (mesentery) of the alcove-like parts of the central cavity are similar to those in sea anemones. (After Pfurtscheller. Courtesy, Wolcott: *Animal Biology,* ed. 3. New York, McGraw-Hill Book Co., 1946.)

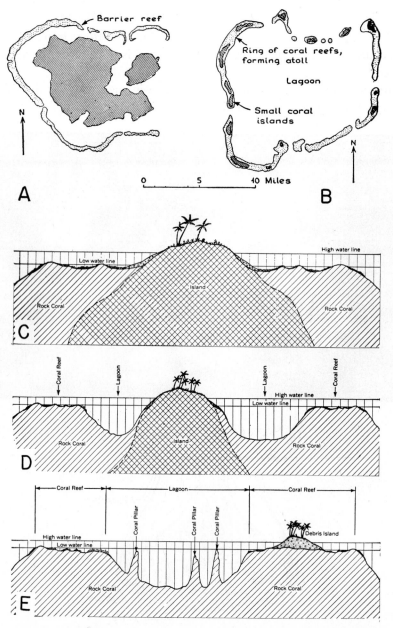

Fig. 23.19. Coral reefs: fringing, barrier, and atoll reefs. *A*, a barrier reef in the Caroline Islands, Polynesia; the land is crosshatched. *B*, an atoll in the Chagos Archipelago, Indian Ocean. *C*, profile of a fringing reef. Living coral cannot survive more than brief exposures to the air and usually does not grow above the low water line. *D*, profile of a barrier reef (see Fig. 23.20, corals of a barrier reef). *E*, profile of an atoll reef. Taken in a different place the section might have gone through another island like the one included. (*A* and *B* from *Principles of Geology* by Gilluly, Waters, and Woodford. Copyright, 1952. W. H. Freeman and Company. *C, D,* and *E*, courtesy, McCurdy: *Manual of Coastal Delineation*. Washington, Hydrographic Office, 1947.)

FIG. 23.20. *Upper,* the edge of the Great Barrier Reef and the overwash of the sea at Heron Island, Australia. The Great Barrier Reef is 1350 miles long and in places 30 miles wide. It is a natural factory where billions of coral animals take lime from the sea water and build the cups that protect them and bury their ancestors. *Lower,* corals on the Great Barrier Reef at South Malle, Australia. (Courtesy, Australian News and Information Bureau.)

the land had sunk creating wide channels and barrier reefs; that in the case of islands the land might have sunk completely out of sight and formed the lagoon. The relatively recent *Glacial-control Theory* states: that during the last glacial period the amount of water frozen in the great ice caps may have lowered the ocean by about 200 feet. Shallows resulted covering many platforms of the ocean with water too cold for corals. However, as the ice melted and the waters were warmed coral growth began and kept pace with the rising ocean level. This theory accounts for the uniform depths of coral lagoons whose bottoms may represent the platforms which existed when the ocean was at its ancient low level.

Attempts to unravel the mystery of reef formation have been made by boring deep into a reef and identifying the coral skeletons found at low levels. This was done on Funafuti Atoll, in the South Pacific north of Fiji. One boring about five inches in diameter was carried down 1114 feet without reaching the base of the reef. Twenty-eight reef-building corals were identified and of these 22 are now living on the reef in water around 100 feet deep. Borings on other reefs have given similar results, all of them supporting the glacial-control theory.

24

Ctenophores—Comb Jellies
or Sea Walnuts

The ctenophores or comb bearers constitute a small phylum whose members live in the surface waters of warm seas and ocean currents. They are commonly taken for jellyfishes and were formerly classified with them. Their differences from coelenterates, the absence of stinging cells and the peculiarities of sense organs and radial bands, are now regarded as important enough to place them in a separate phylum. They are transparent and glimmering, some pink or bluish or orange, but many colorless except for the continually shifting coppery bronze iridescence of their combs. All of them are luminescent and the millions occasionally swarming through the ocean surface create fantastically beautiful illuminations.

General Features. Ctenophores are moderately small, often about the size of a plum. One of the smallest, Pleurobrachia is no larger than a garden pea (Fig. 24.1). The pale violet Venus's girdle (Cestum) is a ribbon 2 to 3 feet long. It is usually oval or globular, sometimes pear-shaped.

Its conspicuous distinguishing feature is the eight rows of combs that radiate from the mouth at one pole of the animal and extend to the opposite one like the ridges of a cantaloupe (Fig. 24.1). These rows are arranged in radial symmetry, but the long tentacles usually present are located one on each side of the body and Venus's girdle is clearly bilaterally symmetrical. Ctenophores are regarded as a higher group than coelenterates because of their tendency toward this balance of two sides of the body. Another mark of progress is the three-layered body wall, ectoderm, endoderm, and a middle layer closely approaching the cellular mesoderm of higher animals. In ctenophores whole cells are muscular, not merely the processes as in the epithelio-muscular cells of hydra. They have no stinging cells. Neither is there asexual reproduction nor alternation of generations as in coelenterates.

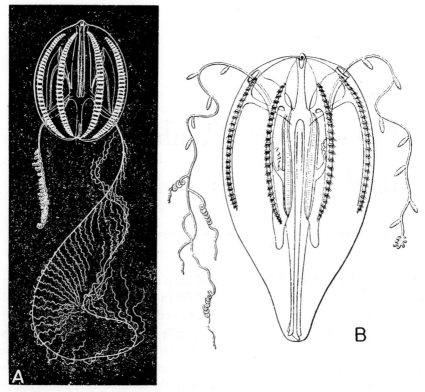

FIG. 24.1. Ctenophores. *A, Pleurobrachia pileus,* the "sea gooseberry," named because its size, streaks and translucence suggest a gooseberry. Common on the northern Pacific and Atlantic coasts. *B, Hormiphora plumosa,* barely an inch long. Tortugas, Florida. (Courtesy, Mayer: *Ctenophores of the Atlantic Coast of North America.* Washington, Carnegie Institution, 1912.)

Ecology. Ctenophores are carried about by currents but they also swim feebly by means of their combs. Venus's girdle swims by undulations of the body similar to those of a leech or an eel.

Ctenophores are carnivores that feed voraciously upon any animals that they can swallow. Swarms of billions of little Pleurobrachia can sweep the surface water clean with their tentacles that trail for several inches behind them. In his study of the food relationships of animals in the Gulf of Maine, H. B. Bigelow writes that "of all the members of the plankton [surface organisms], the most destructive to smaller or weaker animals are the several coelenterates, and especially the ctenophores, genus Pleurobrachia, a pirate to which no living creature small enough for it to capture and swallow comes amiss." All ctenophores have a unique means of catching their prey, the glue cells presently described.

Structure. Each comb is composed of long cilia fused together as if the teeth of a comb were united nearly to their tips (Fig. 24.2). A ctenophore swims

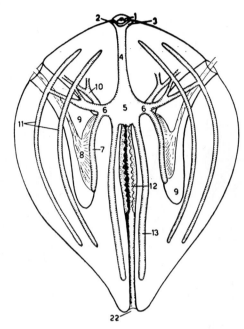

FIG. 24.2. Diagram of the digestive system of a ctenophore. *1*, statocyst (sense organ of balance); *2*, anal pore; *4*, aboral canal; *5*, stomach; *6*, transverse canal; *11*, meridional canal; *12*, pharynx; *22*, mouth. Several labels omitted. (Courtesy, Hyman: *The Invertebrates*, vol. 1. New York, McGraw-Hill Book Co., 1940.)

mouth forward. The motion in each row usually begins with the last comb at the aboral end and goes forward like a wave. Each beat is a strong backward flap of the comb which drives the water out from under it and helps to push the animal forward. If a ctenophore strikes head on against an object, the beat is at once reversed. Experiments have shown that the movement of the combs is controlled by the nerve cells that lie beneath the rows. At the rear, or aboral pole, of the body there is an area of nerve and sensory cells. In the center of this is a pit containing a sense organ, the statocyst, which holds a little cluster of limestone particles supported by tufts of cilia that are connected with sensory cells. This is believed to be a balancing or steering mechanism since any turning of the body causes the limestone to rest more heavily on one or another of the tufts. This would stimulate the sensory cells, and the stimulus carried to the combs would cause them to beat faster on one side than the other. From this polar area a nerve net extends through the body and is concentrated in eight strands, one under each row of combs.

On each side of the body is a sac into which the tentacles can be retracted. The latter are often very long in proportion to the body and are the ctenophore's catch-traps for small animals. Their epidermis consists largely of glue cells (colloblasts) each of which in action is a combination of a lasso and glue-

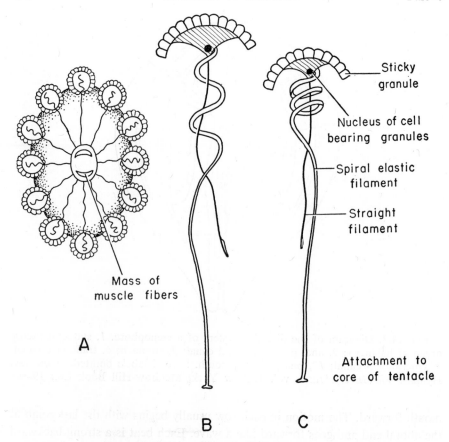

Sticky
granule

Nucleus of cell
bearing granules

Spiral elastic
filament

Straight
filament

Mass of
muscle fibers

A

Attachment to
core of tentacle

B   C

FIG. 24.3. Adhesive cells: these sticky "lasso cells" compose a large part of the epidermis of the tentacles. Still attached to the tentacle by the lasso threads they are thrown against unfortunate little animals that are then stuck fast to them. When the tentacle has collected its prey, it contracts and wipes itself across the expectant mouth of its owner. *A,* a section through one of the branches of a tentacle (Fig. 24.1.). The outer surface is covered with the sticky heads of the "lasso cells." Each cell is attached by a coiled filament which acts as a spring preventing the cell from being wrenched off by the struggling victim. *B* and *C,* sticky cells with filaments uncoiled and coiled. (*B* and *C,* redrawn after Wolcott: *Animal Biology,* ed. 3. New York, McGraw-Hill Book Co., 1946.)

pot (Fig. 24.3). Each cell discharges a sticky secretion. It is fastened to the tentacle by a coiled contractile fiber encircling a straight fiber which acts as a special holdfast while the contractile one is stretched out into the water. The core of the tentacle contains a central strand of nervous tissue concerned with the responses in the tentacle and a cord of muscular cells which provides for its extreme contractility. As in coelenterates, the extensive branched enteron provides for digestion, absorption and transport of food, water, and metabolic waste. The only opening in the enteron is the mouth which leads into a pharynx and stomach. From there a series of ciliated canals extends through the body, often especially prominent in luminescent individuals (Fig. 24.4).

Reproduction and Regeneration. All ctenophores are hermaphrodites and in most species eggs and sperm cells are shed into the open water where the eggs are fertilized.

Ctenophores have high powers of regeneration and can repair severe injuries to their frail bodies. They have been subjects for many experiments on regeneration and grafting. Any parts removed, including the statocyst, are regrown. Whole rows of combs are replaced. Halves of an animal, cut in either direction, will regenerate but parts containing the statocyst grow more rapidly than others. Pieces of one animal may be grafted into another. Bands of combs may be grafted onto another ctenophore in reverse of their natural position. Such grafted combs will continue to beat as before in opposition to those on the recipient animal, causing the latter to turn round and round.

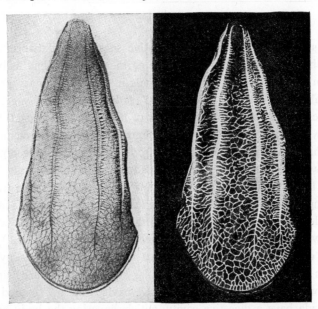

FIG. 24.4. Luminescent ctenophores. Beroë photographed by daylight and in darkness except its own light. Vividly shown here are the meridional canals and network of intercommunicating canals. Beroë is less than two inches long and has no tentacles. At certain seasons swarms of ctenophores illuminate wide expanses of the seas. (After Panceri. Courtesy, Harvey: *Bioluminescence.* New York, Academic Press, 1952.)

25

Flatworms—Vanguard of the Higher Animals

There is a vast difference in the relative speed of a flatworm and a race horse, yet bilateral symmetry, always the partner of speed, had its beginning in the flatworms. They were the first animals in the evolutionary procession to firmly establish the likeness of two sides of the body feebly suggested in the ctenophores (Fig. 24.1). Other features of higher animals begun in the free-living flatworms are a definite head, a centralized nervous system, the meso-derm or middle layer of body cells, and complex reproductive organs.

Along with their advances in build and behavior flatworms are strikingly primitive. In the majority of the free-living species the digestive tract has but one opening, the mouth. Instead of being located in the head, it is in the center of the underside of the body suggesting the wheel-like symmetry of the jelly-fishes, in which the mouth takes the place of the hub (Figs. 25.1).

Classes of Flatworms. There are three main classes in the Phylum Platy-helminthes and each one has its particular successes: 1, Turbellaria are, for the most part, free living, have a digestive cavity and are covered with cilia; 2, Trematoda have a digestive cavity, cuticle covering the body but no cilia, and are parasitic; 3, Cestoda lack an enteron and have a cuticle, but no cilia.

TURBELLARIA—PLANARIANS AND OTHERS. The power to regrow lost parts permits planaria to survive and even to multiply after injury. Three planarians may live and flourish because one was cut into three pieces. All turbellarians are aquatic. A considerable number live in fresh water and a few on moist soil. Most of them are marine. Some are marked with striking patterns in yellows, reds, and black and white and all are graceful swimmers and gliders. They are named for the turbulent movements of their abundant cilia.

TREMATODA—LIVER FLUKES AND OTHERS. All trematodes have great capacity to multiply. They are parasites, with a wide distribution assured them

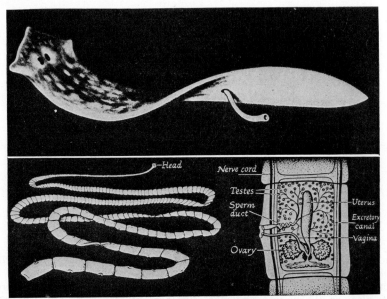

FIG. 25.1. Two flatworms: the planarian, free living, and the tapeworm, a parasite. The planarian (mouth and pharynx extended) shows the thorough bilateral symmetry of the flatworms, a feature that brought great changes into the evolution of animals. The tapeworm has developed extraordinary reproductive capacity by means of the many sections (proglottids) of the body almost all of which are capable of producing hundreds of fertilized eggs. (Courtesy, Pauli: *The World of Life*. Boston, Houghton Mifflin Co., 1949.)

by the animals on or in which they live. All have an outer covering of resistant cuticle and no cilia.

CESTODA—TAPEWORMS. All cestodes have extreme capacity to multiply. All of them are parasites with a world-wide distribution assured them by the far-ranging vertebrates that are their hosts. They travel by land, sea, and air, in goats that scale the mountains, in salmon that swim the Pacific, in bobolinks that fly from Brazil to New England.

Class Turbellaria

Turbellaria are free-living flatworms. The most familiar of them are the fresh-water planarians, one-half to one inch long (Fig. 25.2). They are common in streams and lakes and in many laboratories they are among the classic subjects of experimental zoology. Some are white or translucent; others are sober colored, gray, brown or black, a contrast to the brilliance of the marine species.

A Representative Planarian

The commonest planarian in the United States is *Dugesia tigrina* (= *Planaria maculata*) (Figs. 25.2, 25.3). It glides over alga-covered stems in ponds

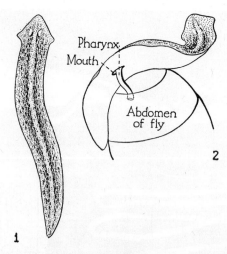

Fig. 25.2. Habit sketches of a common fresh-water planarian. *Dugesia tigrina* (*Planaria maculata*). *1,* full grown, about three quarters of an inch long, *2,* feeding on the water-soaked body of a dead fly, its sucking pharynx extended through a soft place in the insect's abdomen. The eggs of planarians are usually protected in cocoons, about the size of pinheads, and attached to submerged rocks and leaves.

and quiet streams, its dark body so soft that it can be cut with the edge of a leaf.

A Pioneer Head. Planarians are pioneers not only in their bilateral symmetry, but in having two uniquely different ends to their bodies, one of which is a recognizable head. Dugesia cannot be credited with a neck, yet the head is clearly set off from the rest of the body. It bears the eyes and many sensory cells, and holds the brain. As with cats and other more astute animals, the head of the planarian always arrives first. It is lifted slightly and bent from side to side testing and exploring the way, a faint foreshadowing of the wise end of a cat. On its surface are many microscopic pits containing cells that are sensitive to chemical substances. On the pointed flaps, fancifully called auricles, similar chemical perceptors are set in ciliated troughs. Planarians are attracted by such foods as snail blood or crushed earthworms and in a dish of water they will follow a capillary tube that contains them. If certain very weak acids are used as bait, a planarian will grip the tube that holds them and push its pharynx up into it as if the acid were a choice flavor, comparable to grapefruit and pickles to human taste. On the other hand, when certain other substances are offered, it will turn sharply away as if in a hurry. With one auricle removed it travels in circles in a dish of dilute snail blood, curving its body toward the unhurt side by which it still responds to the attractive blood. If its brain is removed it will not react even to the most desirable snail juice.

The whole body surface will respond to a delicate touch though the head is

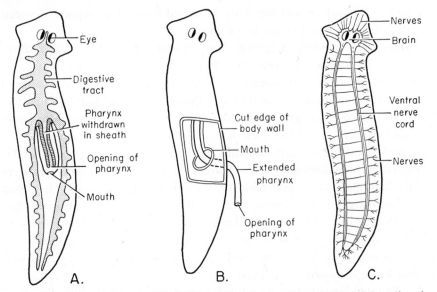

FIG. 25.3. Digestive and nervous systems of a planarian. *A*, the digestive system, so distributed through the body that digestion and absorption take place in every locality. *B*, view showing the pharynx extended to capture food. *C*, the nervous system. Compared to hydra and the sea anemones, the nervous system is distinctly centralized.

by far the most sensitive part. Planarians strive to keep their undersides in contact with a supporting surface and in their attempts to do so, the head takes the lead just as it does when a turtle turned wrong side up flops over to gain a foothold. Turned onto its dorsal side, a planarian twists into a spiral so that the ventral surface of its head comes in contact with the substratum. The head then glides forward and the body unwinding the spiral follows after.

In the eyes of Dugesia and other planarians the pigmented cells form a cup into which one to many neurosensory cells project. These are retinal cells comparable to the rod and cone cells of the human eye. Turbellarians, in general, avoid the light; fresh-water planarians seek the darker sides of stones, the undersides of submerged leaves. When placed on contrasting backgrounds, such as an experimental one of black and white circles, planarians (*Dugesia lugubris*) followed the black circles. After they were blinded, they made no distinction between white and black.

Locomotion. Planarians glide about by means of the assembled help of millions of cilia located on their ventral sides and by muscular contractions, the latter more important than the cilia. The roles of the cilia and muscles have been separated by treating planarians with lithium chloride which paralyzes the cilia, but not the muscles, and with magnesium chloride which paralyzes the muscles but not the cilia. The slime trail secreted by mucous cells is an important asset for gliding. The cilia are whipped into the slime, strike against the underlying surface and the body is moved forward in rapidly repeated microscopic lurches that merge into a glide.

Feeding. The majority of turbellarians are carnivorous. The smaller fresh-water ones feed upon crustaceans and worms that are nearly microscopic, the larger ones on snails, earthworms and insect larvae, often on their softened remains. Even in quiet waters they can detect juicy meat two or three feet away. As the worm recognizes the food it pauses, swings its raised head about and starts directly toward it. First it touches, then rubs its head against the piece and glides onto it, finally stretches and dips its pharynx into it (Fig. 25.2).

Digestion, Assimilation and Food Storage. Flatworms are strikingly different from other bilaterally symmetrical animals in having the mouth half way down the body, curiously enough not in the important head region (Figs. 25.3, 25.4, 25.5). The pharynx leads into the three-forked (in triclads) intestine whose many branches reach throughout the body. Practically any piece that may be torn from the body takes digestive and excretory cells with it; thus it can be nourished and can grow.

Feeding experiments and microscopic examinations of the intestine have shown that the entire processes of digestion, absorption, assimilation and storage of food occur within the partly ameboid cells of the intestinal lining. A planarian grows fat in its linings, usually of the intestine; food stored there is largely fat, rarely glycogen. Nothing is known of the actual processes by which the stored food is transferred and used by the other cells of the body. In one series of experiments, planarians (Dugesia) were starved for two weeks, then fed on beef liver. At frequent intervals, some of them were killed and examined microscopically. The partially ameboid cells began to engulf the bits of liver as soon as they came in contact with them. Swollen with absorbed fluid, they bulged into the intestine and embraced the food with their pseudopodia. Within them the bits of food and fluid were digested in food vacuoles like those of amebas. It took about eight hours for the content of a full intestine to be taken up by the ameboid cells. During digestion planarians take in two or three times more oxygen than usual and utilize the stored fat for the extra energy expended.

Fresh-water planarians can endure starving for six to 14 months but at the end of that time they may be reduced to one three-hundredth of their original size. The greatest degeneration is in the reproductive system, part of which entirely disappears. Their condition suggests that of worker honeybees that are chronically underfed and have undersized reproductive organs. The heads of starved planarians are relatively large because the nervous system is not reduced.

Respiration. Oxygen and carbon dioxide are exchanged by diffusion through the body as in ordinary aerobic respiration, a contrast to the anaerobic respiration of parasitic flatworms (see cestodes p. 515).

Excretion and Water Balance. The excretory system consists of many large flame cells each of which faces into a kidneylike (protonephridial) tubule (Fig. 25.4). A network of these tubules opens out on the surface of the body by minute pores. As in other animals, water is continually coming in and going out of the body. Water that regularly diffuses into the body and collects in the flame cells is waved into the tubules and passes through the microscopic outlets, thus completing the circuit. Nothing is known about the excretion of nitrogenous waste.

Nervous System. Planarians have a bilobed brain from which two main nerves reach backward through the body giving off frequent branches (Figs. 25.3, 25.5). By skillful operating the brain can be removed. Following this the animals remain quiet, unless stimulated, then they move about freely showing that muscular action is independent of the brain and can be coordinated by the branches.

The sensory cells with which the head is richly supplied have already been mentioned. Planarians are responsive to chemical substances, to changes of

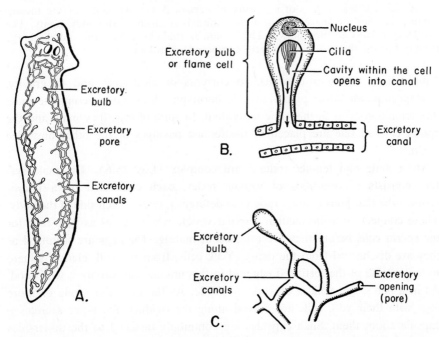

Fig. 25.4. The excretory system of a freshwater planarian. *A*, the entire system, excretory bulbs (flame cells) in which excess water and metabolic waste is collected and waved by cilia into the microscopic canals which finally carry it out of the body through microscopic pores. Detail of canals: arrows mark the flow of fluids from the bulbs. Highly magnified excretory bulb, called a flame cell from the flicker of the cilia, which project into the cup-like cavity in the cell and create a current of fluid into the canal. Like all kidney systems the function of this one is the regulation of water content and the elimination of metabolic waste, especially nitrogen.

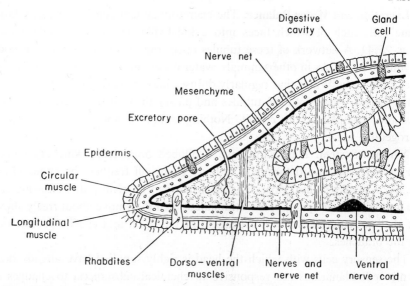

FIG. 25.5. Cross section of a mature planarian. A net-like tissue of the mesen-chyme occupies the space that in higher animals is taken by the body cavity. The excretory organs are not shown. The glandular rhabdite cells form and discharge minute bodies, the rhabdites, largely composed of calcium.

temperature, to water currents, to currents of electricity, and to gravity.

Reproduction. Most planarians are hermaphrodites having complete male and female systems in the same individual. In spite of this, they mate and the sperm cells of one are placed in the female passages of the other and vice versa.

Both male and female systems are complex (Fig. 25.6). The male system consists of hundreds of minute testes, each connected by a microscopic tube that joins a larger tube (vas deferens), one on each side of the body. These connect with the median seminal vesicle which serves as a storage for the sperm cells before they are released at mating. The eggs are fertilized as they are discharged from the ovary. Yolk cells, from the yolk glands, adhere to the outside of the fertilized egg and in this unique way supply it with food. As in a hen's egg, yolk is universally inside. As the planarian's one or more eggs with their yolk cells are moved along the oviduct, the latter secretes a capsule about them. Such capsules are commonly fastened to the undersides of submerged rocks; those of Dugesia resemble fig seeds on short stems. Capsules collected from rocks usually hatch in two or three weeks if kept in clean, cool water and subdued light at ordinary temperatures.

Planarians commonly reproduce asexually by transverse division or fission. Fission is most common during the summer, sexual reproduction in winter and spring. When about to divide, the animal suddenly fastens its rear end down and pulls its front end forward, till the two separate. In a lightly greased dish, a planarian is completely frustrated; it can neither fasten its body to the surface nor divide.

Regeneration. The common Dugesia and certain other free-living planarians have remarkable powers of regeneration. Parasitic flatworms, like parasites in general, are unable to replace damaged parts. Experiments upon the regeneration of sponges, hydras, and especially planarians have shown important principles governing the organization and growth of the body. The possibility of grafting human tissues was discovered by experimenting on lower animals. The experiments on the regeneration of planarians carried on by T. H. Morgan about 1890 are among the classics of experimental zoology.

Pieces of a planarian's body maintain the natural polarity of the whole body. Remove the head and tail leaving only the middle part of the body, and a new head will grow from the front edge and a new tail from the hind edge (Fig. 25.7).

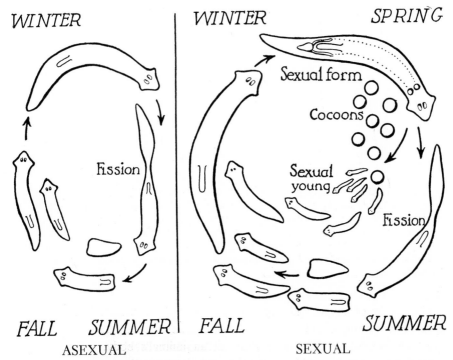

WINTER   WINTER   SPRING

Sexual form

Cocoons

Fission

Sexual young

Fission

FALL   SUMMER   FALL   SUMMER

ASEXUAL   SEXUAL

FIG. 25.6. Diagrams of the life cycles of *Dugesia tigrina* (*Planaria maculata*) as they vary under different ecological conditions. *Left,* purely asexual reproduction. Transverse divisions occur throughout the warmer months. The parts of the animals grow to a certain size; the rear end adheres to the surface and the front part proceeds forward, pulling at the middle of the body which quickly breaks. *Right,* the more common succession of sexual and asexual reproduction; the sexual organs are highly developed in spring; many egg capsules are laid; by midsummer sexual reproduction ceases and asexual reproduction by fission begins. (Courtesy, Morgan: *Animals in Winter.* New York, G. P. Putnam's Sons, 1939.)

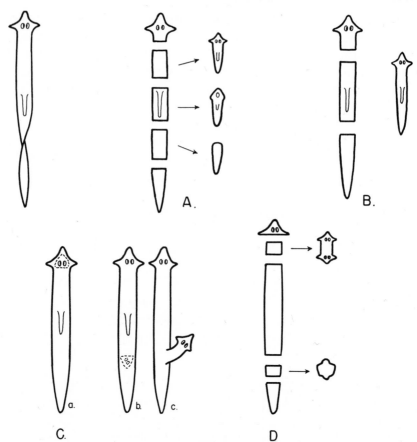

Fig. 25.7. Regenerating planarians. *A*, their capacity to regenerate is greatest at the anterior end; *B*, a regenerating piece shows its natural polarity, that is, the head grows from the front and the tail from the rear as it does in normal animals; *C*, a piece removed from the head and grafted into the body produces a head; *D*, a short piece taken near the head may regenerate a head at each end. (After Child: *Patterns and Problems of Development*. Chicago, University of Chicago Press, 1941.)

The results of experiments upon planarians support C. M. Child's theory of the axial gradient. This theory postulates that there are different rates of metabolic activity in different regions of an animal's body, commonly the highest at the anterior and lowest at the posterior end. Planarians confirm this since pieces taken from the front end of a planarian grow faster and larger than those taken from the rear. In some species, only the pieces from the front will produce heads. Experiments show that the head dominates adjoining regions and leads them to cooperate in their growth. If the central part of the head of one planarian is grafted into an open wound in another planarian, it will not only develop a whole head, but will influence adjacent tissues to produce a pharynx (Fig. 25.7). Tails thus engrafted are simply absorbed. A small cross section of a planarian taken close to the head will produce a head on each cut surface. The dominance of the head over the rest of the body is limited for parts that are at some distance. In the natural asexual reproduction of a planarian, the rear end gets beyond the control of the head and constricts off as a separate animal. Similar constriction and division can be brought on by cutting off the head. All such behavior indicates that there is a gradation of physiological activity from stronger to weaker and of control from front to rear of the body, an anterior to posterior gradation of metabolism.

OTHER TURBELLARIANS

Acoela. The most primitive turbellarians are the Acoela (without a cavity) that have a mouth, but no definite digestive cavity. They swallow their food directly into the loose mesenchyme where ameboid cells gather about it and engulf the particles. Thus, digestion is intracellular like that of the amebas. All the Acoela are marine, usually only one-tenth of an inch long and generally little known.

Rhabdocoela. The Rhabdocoela, named from the rod-shaped gut, are common throughout the world in fresh waters and along sandy and muddy seashores (Fig. 25.8), a few in hot springs. Most of them are less than half an

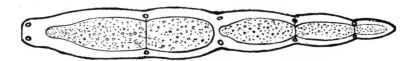

FIG. 25.8. A rhabdocoel, Stenostomum: various species of this genus are among the commonest of invertebrates, cosmopolitan in standing waters but little known because of their minute size. A chain of connected individuals is formed by incomplete divisions of the body. (Courtesy, Morgan: *Life of Ponds & Streams.* New York, G. P. Putnam's Sons, 1930.)

inch long, faintly colored and little noticed. The digestive cavity is straight and unbranched. The rhabdites, rod-shaped bodies of unknown function, are very abundant in them.

Tricladida. The Tricladida include land and marine planarians as well as fresh-water ones. All triclads have a three parted digestive cavity. Many land species live in the humid tropics, some of them marked with brilliant colors and several inches long (Fig. 25.9). They are limited to localities where there is a heavy rainfall, and much of the time lie under logs and leaves surrounded by mucus. They travel on their own slime tracks and in tropical rain forests they swing from the branches on slime threads as caterpillars swing on silken ones.

Polycladida. The Polycladida have a digestive tract that is branched many times. They are commonly two to six inches long and all are of leaf-like thinness (Fig. 25.10). They live almost entirely on the rocky seashore, gliding over the rocks or swimming by the undulating motions of their fluted bodies. Many are inconspicuous; others are strikingly dappled and striped; all swim with a peculiar grace and rhythm that has made them the "butterflies of the sea," competitors with a group of the snails for that name.

Class Trematoda

General Characteristics. Trematodes are called flukes (Anglo-Saxon, flok = flat) because of their flat shape. They are built on the turbellarian plan, but are parasites that have become extremely dependent upon other animals. The

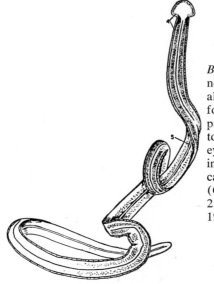

FIG. 25.9. A cosmopolitan land planarian, *Bipalium kewense,* sometimes brought to northern greenhouses on tropical plants; also found in Florida, Louisiana, and California. It is nearly a foot long, has an expanded head and is marked by long purple to black stripes on a yellowish ground; *4,* eye; *5,* creeping sole. It moves on a creeping sole like the fresh-water planarians, occasionally hanging off into the damp air. (Courtesy, Hyman: *The Invertebrates,* vol. 2. New York, McGraw-Hill Book Co., 1951.)

adults cling to their host by one or more suckers, and their bodies are covered with tough cuticle. They have an enormous reproductive capacity and live parts of their life span in alternate hosts. Like other parasites, they lack some of the features that are present in their free-living relatives, external cilia, an epidermis, rhabdites, and eyes.

Flukes attack large numbers of vertebrates, including domestic animals and man. Their life cycles are complicated and their existence a gamble. Certain trematodes have relatively direct development and one host (Order Monogenea). Most of these are ectoparasites on the gills and skin of freshwater and marine fishes; some of them live mainly in the urinary bladders of frogs. The fertilized eggs are shed into the water and there develop into ciliated larvae that gradually become like their parents, first in their clinging habits and then in structure including the gradual loss of cilia and of eyes.

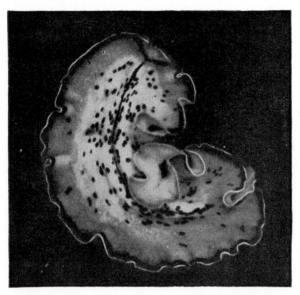

FIG. 25.10. A black and white flatworm of the Pacific coast (*Pseudoceros montereyensis*) called a polyclad because of its many-branched digestive tract. Natural size. This and other polyclads swim and glide about through the water, the fluted borders of their bodies undulating like living ruffles. They are among the most beautiful of marine animals, comparable to the butterflies on land. (Courtesy, MacGinitie and MacGinitie: *Natural History of Marine Animals*. New York, McGraw-Hill Book Co., 1949.)

Many other trematodes have an elaborate life history and develop indirectly (Order Digenea). The fertilized eggs develop into young flukes that look unlike their parents and go through several phases before they are adults. During the life span they live in alternate hosts, the adults in a warm-blooded vertebrate, the young ones in snails, crustaceans or other invertebrates. If there are three hosts in one series, they are usually, first, a mammal occupied by the adult; second, a snail; and third, a fish.

SHEEP LIVER FLUKE

The liver fluke, *Fasciola hepatica,* is often chosen as a type for study because of its large size, economic importance and its well-known life history (Fig. 25.11). The hosts of the adults are sheep, cattle and other herbivores, and man. There are sheep flukes all over the world wherever sheep are raised, especially in mild climates; in the United States, they are most common in the states bordering the Gulf of Mexico. Where the cysts are thickly distributed over pasture grass the infection of the sheep may be enormous, killing 50 to 60 per cent of a flock.

The adult liver fluke looks like a small dead leaf. At the pointed tip of its body is the muscular mouth with which it punctures the tissues of its host and

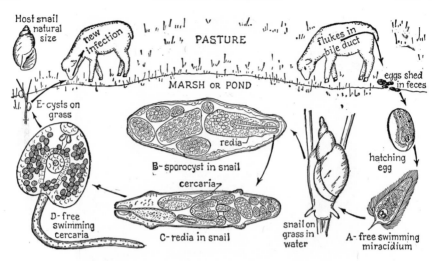

FIG. 25.11. Life history of the liver fluke of sheep, *Fasciola hepatica*. (After Thomas. Courtesy, Storer: *General Zoology*, ed. 2. New York, McGraw-Hill Book Co., 1951.)

sucks up their fluids. With minor differences, the digestive, excretory, nervous, and reproductive systems are similar to those of planarians. They are all hermaphrodites.

Life History. During its life cycle the liver fluke of sheep resides in two hosts, the adults, usually in sheep, the larvae in fresh-water snails of the genus Lymnaea. Without both of these hosts, the fluke cannot complete its life history.

The adult flukes inhabit the ducts of the sheep's liver. The fertilized eggs are carried down the bile duct, into the intestine, and from there are cast out of the body. One sheep may support, on an average, 200 mature flukes. Although each of these may produce its half million eggs, only those that happen to fall into fresh water have any chance of survival. In the water, they hatch into minute ciliated larvae (miracidia) that are active swimmers. In order to survive, the larvae in this particular stage bore their way into the body of the common water snail Lymnaea (Fig. 25.11). In the liver of this snail, they transform into stationary sporocysts within which the egglike cells develop into very minute active larvae (rediae). These work their way about in the snail, become stationary and then produce active larvae (more rediae). Several generations of these active larvae may develop resulting in great increases of numbers. Instead of changing into sporocysts, the later generations transform into active tadpole-shaped larvae (cercariae), which are discharged into the water by the snail. In order to survive, they must reach the grass and leaves along the shore where they enclose themselves in resistant cysts and await their fate of being eaten by a sheep or left to perish. Billions of them are lost.

However, in the infected grass it now takes only the right nibble from one sheep to insure a fluke population. In the sheep's stomach, the digestive juices free the larvae (cercariae) which then migrate to the liver, chemically and physically their home niche. They attach themselves by means of the ventral suckers and in three to six weeks develop into adult flukes, the parents of another generation.

The two greatest gambles in the fluke's life history are on its chances of entering its hosts, the pond snail and sheep. Both ends are achieved by the production of vast numbers of young, the chief tool of a parasite's existence. Probably one fluke among untold numbers secures the necessary lodging in both hosts. Yet, the great reproductive capacity of that one hermaphroditic fluke— half a million eggs from a single adult, 300 larvae from a single egg—maintains the exuberant success of the species.

SALMON-POISONING FLUKE

The salmon-poisoning fluke, *Troglotrema salmincola,* is prevalent in the extreme northwestern United States. The adult flukes live in the intestines of dogs, foxes, bears, bobcats, and other mammals. In dogs, the parasites cause salmon-poisoning—violent illness often resulting in death.

In order to live, the fertilized eggs must reach the water and enter their intermediate host, a snail called a periwinkle (*Goniobasis plicifera*). Larvae similar to those of the sheep liver fluke develop and finally the active ones (cercariae) make their way into the water. When these come in contact with trout or salmon they bore into the muscles and become encysted. If a dog or other possible host eats salmon raw or semi-cooked, the young flukes are freed from their cysts and take up their ultimate residence in the intestine and their business of creating the next generation.

IMPORTANT HUMAN PARASITES

Human flukes are frequent in tropical and Oriental countries; none is native to North America. However, infections are occasionally discovered in persons who have been residents of countries where they abound and these may be a source of further infection. There are four main types of human parasites in this group.

Blood Flukes. The adults live in the blood vessels of man and several domestic animals. Like those of other flukes the larvae inhabit water snails. One species, *Schistosoma haematobium,* is distributed in parts of southern Europe, Asia, and Australia. It causes the disease called bilharzia in about fifty per cent of the population of Egypt. The fertilized eggs are expelled from the human body in the urine. The embryos hatch in fresh water and ultimately enter mainly one kind of snail (Bulimus) and undergo part of their development within it. Then, the active young cercariae swim out into the water and the stage is set for the human infection through the skin or by swallowing infected water. Blood flukes with life histories similar to this are encountered in the West Indies, the Philippine Islands, China and Japan.

Lung Flukes. Known in Oriental countries, including the Philippine Islands, and in Central America and Peru, lung flukes occasionally appear in the United States in former residents of the Orient. The adults of one well-known species, *Paragonimus westermani,* deposit their eggs in the cavities of the human lung, and the fertilized eggs are set free in mucus coughed from the lungs. The larvae first enter fresh-water snails, and next fresh-water crabs and crayfishes in which they become inactive and encysted. They then have two chances to live; meat from the crab must be eaten raw by human beings or water in which larvae have been freed from dead crabs must be used for drinking.

Intestinal Flukes. Probably the most destructive of these is the giant intestinal fluke, *Fasciolopsis buski,* common in man and pigs, particularly in Central and South China, but also encountered in India, Siam, and Malaya (Fig. 25.12). The adult flukes, about two or three inches long, inhabit the small intestine and produce the fertilized eggs. In order to live, these eggs must reach quiet fresh water, the haunts of several species of snails which the larvae (miracidia) may then enter. About 50 days later, the larval flukes leave the snails and swim about freely as cercariae. They then encyst themselves on

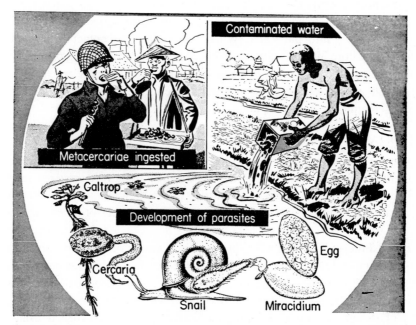

FIG. 25.12. Life history of the giant intestinal fluke, Fasciolopsis, abundant in South China. In one stage the larvae are in cysts on water-chestnuts (water caltrop) that are commonly eaten raw. (Courtesy, Mackie, Hunter and Worth: *Manual of Tropical Medicine.* Philadelphia, W. B. Saunders Co., 1945.)

water plants, abundantly on water-chestnuts such as those that were introduced into the United States and have now crowded other plants and animals to extinction in a considerable number of American waterways.

The success of this parasite's gamble for life has come with the custom of eating water-chestnuts. The outer husk is peeled off and the succulent "nut meat" is eaten raw, an abundant and cheap food in the Chinese summer markets. In China, as many as 1000 larvae of giant flukes have been picked from a single water-chestnut.

Liver Flukes. A half dozen or more species of liver flukes are frequent parasites of man mostly in Oriental countries. The Chinese liver fluke, *Clonorchis sinensis,* is a common parasite of man, cats, and other mammals that eat raw fish. Enclosed in minute capsules, the encysted larvae can live for many months in the muscle of 40 different species of fresh-water fishes thus awaiting a cat or a man to eat them. In an earlier stage, the larvae live in snails. The great numbers of canals and the farm fish ponds in sections of South China and Japan are ideal meeting places for the snails and fishes. The people who eat the fishes give the parasites their final home in the liver.

Class Cestoda

The life histories of such parasites as the flukes are mystery stories compared with the plain histories of their free-living relatives, the planarians. Parasitic living has made a still deeper mark on the tapeworm (Cestoda), especially on their appearance. They are hardly recognizable as flatworms and are well named after tape measures. It is believed that any vertebrate may be host to one or another kind of adult tapeworm.

General Characteristics. The cestodes are internal parasites that are deeply committed to the parasitic habit. Like the trematodes, they have no epidermis; neither have they a mouth or digestive tract, either in immature or mature stages. They have no sensory receptors except free nerve endings that are sensitive to touch. They can move about only feebly, but are amply provided with holdfasts such as hooks and suction cups. In a few species the body is a unit, like those of flukes, but in the great majority it is divided into many units or sections commonly called proglottids from some very highly imagined resemblance to the shape of the tongue. It is a question whether proglottids might not be more appropriately termed segments since they are repeated as true segments are in the earthworm. The general structure of tapeworms is too degenerate to establish this.

Adult tapeworms inhabit the intestines of vertebrates entering as larvae, always by way of the mouth. The total length of adults of different species ranges from about that of an ordinary typed hyphen to 40 feet. Like the flukes they require one or more intermediate hosts, vertebrate or invertebrate, to complete their life history.

Most tapeworms are hermaphrodites. Each proglottid contains at least one set of reproductive organs of each sex, and in some species two sets (Fig. 25.13). The eggs may be fertilized by sperm cells from the same proglottid. However, mating proglottids have been observed in tapeworms immediately after being taken from the intestine. The physiology of tapeworms is difficult to investigate since they live only a short time outside the intestine, even in normal salt solutions. The youngest proglottids, behind the neck, constitute a zone of growth. Those farther back have definite organs; in the middle parts of the worm they contain mature reproductive organs; toward the posterior end these organs lose their form and the proglottids become sacs filled with hordes of eggs and embryos. Although lilies and tapeworms are far kin, the stages of development in the chain of proglottids are comparable to a

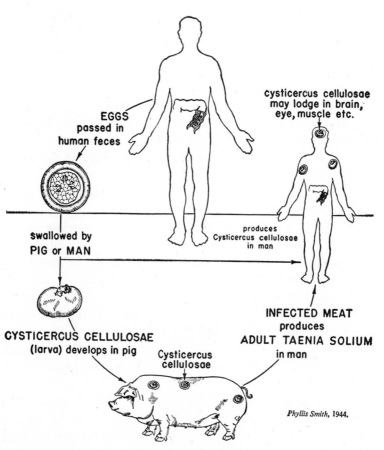

FIG. 25.13. Life cycle of pork tapeworm, *Taenia solium*. (Courtesy, Hunter and Hunter: *College Zoology*. Philadelphia, W. B. Saunders Co., 1949.)

bud, a perfect flower, and finally a seed pod. Fertilized eggs and early embryos are shed freely into the intestine (Figs. 25.13, 25.14). A ripe proglottid at the end of the body occasionally separates off, carries the pregnant uterus with it, and sets free the eggs wherever it may fall with the waste from the intestine. Proglottids may be eaten by animals of many kinds. They will survive only if they are swallowed by their secondary hosts. In them, they hatch out in the intestines and bore their way into voluntary muscle where they become encysted. Within the cysts they develop into minute bladder-shaped worms, the cysticercus stage. Their lives now depend on having their final host feed upon the secondary one, such as a cat or man eating raw fish or pork. The encysted worm is then freed in the intestine and begins its growth as an adult.

Physiology and Ecology of Adult Tapeworms. Tapeworms live in the dark, in very special chemical surroundings; shifting hosts is a gamble for life; they endure a long waiting period (cysticercus); and they perish by thousands. This is the price of parasitism which tapeworms pay and yet survive.

In making its home in the intestines of vertebrates, the adult tapeworm adjusts itself within an elaborate canal that is functioning for another animal. Such canals are in no way modified for the tapeworm. The worm must maintain its location against the constant shifting of the walls and the pressure of moving food. Yet its only anchor is its minute head (scolex) hanging attached by hooks and suction to the intestinal wall.

Tapeworms live regardless of the presence or absence of oxygen in their environment. There is very little of it in the intestines.

The content of the host's intestine, the tapeworm's only source of food, is absorbed through its body wall, but little is known of the process. Glycogen constitutes about 60 per cent of the dry weight of tapeworms, however, and is essentially similar to that stored as a reserve food in the bodies of the majority of animals.

PORK TAPEWORM

The two common tapeworms of man are the pork tapeworm and beef tapeworm, *Taenia solium* and *T. saginata*. The latter is distributed throughout most of the world, especially in parts of Africa and eastern Europe. The rate of infection is high among the Mohammedans who merely sear the outside of large chunks of beef. In the United States, less than one per cent of inspected beef has been found infected. The pork tapeworm is also distributed throughout the world, wherever raw or inadequately cooked pork is eaten. Adult pork tapeworms rarely occur among Jews and Mohammedans since they seldom eat pork.

The beef and pork tapeworms are similar in structure and plan of life history. Man is the only final host of the pork tapeworm and the hog the usual intermediate host. The adult pork tapeworm lives in the human intestine with

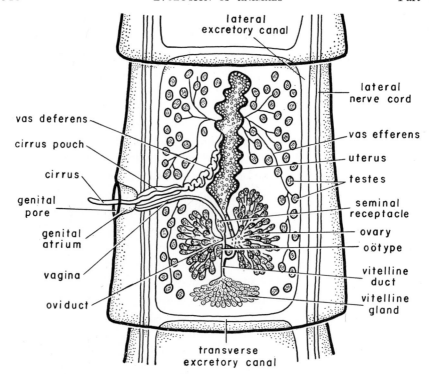

FIG. 25.14. Mature proglottid (or segment) of *Taenia pisiformis,* a tape-worm of dogs, showing the male and female reproductive systems. *Male System.* The male cells are produced by many minute testes; they are carried by micro-scopic tubes (*vasa efferens*) to a larger tube (*vas deferens*) and discharged through the genital pore during the mating between proglottids of the same or of different tapeworms. *Female System.* Great numbers of microscopic eggs are produced in the ovaries. They are moved through the oviduct into the vagina and are there fertilized by sperm cells received from the mating proglottid. The eggs are then moved backward into a small structure (*oötype*) where they re-ceive yolk from the vitelline gland. The fully formed eggs then pass forward into the uterus that becomes so crowded with them that it finally fills the whole proglottid, a bag of eggs ready to develop into young tapeworms. (After Good-child. Courtesy, Brown: *Selected Invertebrate Types.* New York, John Wiley and Sons, 1950.)

its head, about the size of a pinhead, attached to the intestinal wall. Posterior to the short neck is the chain of proglottids which make up the body, from six to 25 feet long in mature worms with about 1000 proglottids. Each mature proglottid contains 150 or more testes and at least one complex ovary. Fer-tilized eggs burst from the proglottids either before or after the latter are cast out of the intestine. They are protected by shells and on moist soil or vegetation the embryos may remain alive for weeks.

When swallowed by hogs or man, the embryos hatch soon after reaching the intestine. The embryos soon pierce the intestinal wall, enter the blood vessels and are distributed through the body. Parasites in general not only have their own hosts but their particular niches in the host to which they are chemically and physically adjusted. So it is with young tapeworms. Their particular niche is the subcutaneous tissue and muscle, usually voluntary muscle such as that in the shoulders and back—ham and spare rib. In these tissues, they become encysted and begin their waiting period.

Within 60 to 70 days the encysted embryos have metamorphosed into bladder worms (about 5 mm. long and 8 mm. broad), the cysticercus stage, often confusingly called *Cysticercus cellulosae* as if they were a separate species as they were first thought to be. Bladder worms are capable of growth into adult worms if they are freed from their enclosure in the muscle and reach the human intestine (Fig. 25.13). This is the point at which eating infected and inadequately cooked pork is a favor to tapeworms. In the intestine, the worm becomes mature in five to ten weeks but it may live there for several years continuing to produce and cast off proglottids as well as millions of fertilized eggs free in the intestinal contents.

Larval tapeworms may make their way out of the human intestine and become encysted in the muscle of the same person. They remain there a long time and are ultimately absorbed. Cannibalism would be their only gate to freedom.

Fish Tapeworm

The broad or fish tapeworm, *Diphyllobothrium latum,* is common in persons living in the Baltic countries, northern Wisconsin, Minnesota, Michigan, and regions of Canada bordering these states (Fig. 25.15). The adults live in the human intestine. In order to progress further, the developing eggs must reach fresh water, where the larvae, then free-swimmers, are eaten by various

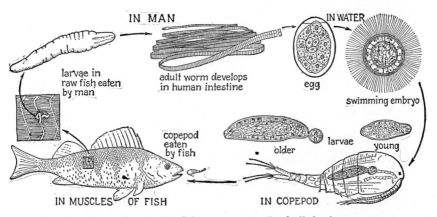

IN MAN

IN WATER

larvae in raw fish eaten by man

adult worm develops in human intestine

egg

swimming embryo

copepod eaten by fish

older

larvae

young

IN MUSCLES OF FISH

IN COPEPOD

FIG. 25.15. Life cycle of the fish tapeworm, *Diphyllobothrium latum.* Adult fish much reduced; larval stages variously enlarged. (Courtesy, Storer: *General Zoology,* ed. 2. New York, McGraw-Hill Book Co., 1951.)

species of minute crustaceans (copepods) in which they develop into the inactive phase. Even so, they travel far since about 22 species of fishes feed upon copepods. In the fishes the larvae migrate into the muscle, the "clean white meat." The human infection occurs and the progress of the parasite goes on when the meat is eaten without thorough cooking.

CONSEQUENCES OF PARASITISM

Parasitism is an unbalanced relationship between organisms that has developed from a balanced one. Parasites and their hosts are close intimates. A parasite must get on or into one host and stay, or it must have first one and then another host. At one time or another, or all the time, it must cling to its host. Its whole success depends upon this.

Parasites ride about on or in their hosts. Those that ride most can move about least by themselves. In general, the more they depend on the possessions of the host, the fewer they have of their own. Tapeworms do indeed travel light, without locomotor organs, without mouth or digestive tract, without skin cover, without eyes, almost without sense organs.

26

Roundworms—The Tubular Plan

Phylum Nemathelminthes—Nematodes

Roundworms are spread over the earth in every region where animals live (Fig. 26.1). Great numbers of them contribute to plant, animal, and human welfare. Hosts of them live in the soil—minute, hidden, and little known. Still others are parasites of plants, of invertebrate animals, and probably of all vertebrates.

Their evolution has included structures of very great importance to higher animals. The tube-within-a-tube plan of the body first came into existence in them, the digestive canal as the inner tube, the body wall as the outer one. Less obvious in a peacock or a man, the plan is as really present in them as it is in a hookworm or a vinegar eel, both of them roundworms.

There are widely varying degrees of similarity and relationship among roundworms. Formerly all of them were included in the Phylum Nemathelminthes. Now the more closely related roundworms are grouped together in a phylum, the Nemathelminthes, by some zoologists and in a class, the Nematoda, by others. Still other more diverse forms are included in the small phyla and the classes that are discussed briefly in the next chapter.

Characteristics and Structure Illustrated by Ascaris. Nematodes are slender worms, pointed at head and tail ends, many of them microscopic, others several inches long. The structure of the widely distributed species of Ascaris that parasitize man and pig is typical of nematodes in general (Fig. 26.2).

A HUMAN PARASITE. *Ascaris lumbricoides* is among the longest-known human parasites and is still common in localities where the soil is polluted with sewage. They probably became established in the human body when wild pigs were first hunted and eaten, when agriculture was in its beginnings and pigs were being domesticated. The human parasite (*A. lumbricoides*) is indistinguishable except in habit from the Ascaris of the pig (*A. lumbricoides,* variety *suum*) from which it doubtless originated. Probably infection with

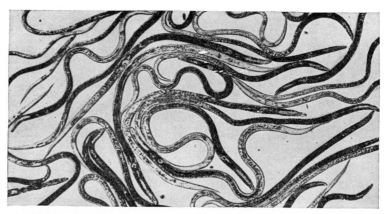

FIG. 26.1. A free-living nematode worm. Vinegar eels (*Turbatrix aceti*) cultured on an agar (gelatin) plate. They are minute, little longer than the width of a pinhead. They flourish on the fungus that abounds in the "mother" of raw cider vinegar; they also live in sour paste. (Courtesy, General Biological Supply House, Chicago.)

Ascaris usually spreads from man to man with no other animal implicated. Ordinarily eggs from the Ascaris of pigs do not develop in man nor those from the Ascaris of man in pigs. However parasites may be otherwise regarded, they deserve respect for their sensitive discrimination of environments.

LIFE HISTORY OF *Ascaris lumbricoides*. The adults live in the small intestine where they feed mainly upon the partly digested food of the host, also upon blood from the intestinal walls. The mature worms mate and each female produces over 20 millions of eggs. These are freed in the intestine and as embryos within the thick, resistant egg shells they pass out of it with the

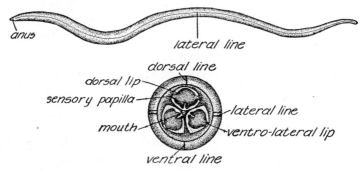

FIG. 26.2. *Ascaris lumbricoides*, a human parasite probably introduced to mankind when pigs were first domesticated. *Upper,* outline of the body of the female. *Lower,* the sucking mouth guarded by three lips by which it can grasp and suck blood from the lining of the intestine although it feeds more regularly on the digesting food. Length of adult females, 8 to 14 inches; males, 3 to 5 inches. (Courtesy, Curtis & Guthrie: *General Zoology,* ed. 4. New York, John Wiley and Sons, 1947.)

excreta. Under favoring conditions of temperature, moisture, and air the active embryos develop in about two weeks. In another week, while they are still in the shell, the minute worms molt and become active larvae. They are now capable of infecting a host. When the eggs are swallowed, often on uncooked vegetables, the larvae hatch in the small intestine. After repeated investigations upon animals which harbor the parasites for a time, it has been discovered that the larvae do not continue to develop in the intestine. Instead, they pierce the intestinal lining and enter the blood stream thus reaching successively the liver, heart, and lungs. They burrow out of the lungs, reach the trachea and esophagus, and finally the intestine. This journey takes about ten days during which the larvae increase from microscopic size to a length easily visible to the naked eye. In the intestine they grow to maturity, six to 12 inches long, the females larger than the males (Fig. 26.2). The average length of their mature life in the intestine is about a year. The number of eggs in the mature female may reach 27,000,000, probably more.

Knowledge of the life cycle of this species of Ascaris and the successful treatment of its human host are among the thousands of benefits to human life that have come from experimentation upon animals. These parasites have not lived out their life cycle in any animals which have been experimentally infected with them. Yet, the larvae will migrate through the body in mice and guinea pigs as well as in their human host. And this was the hardest part of their life story to discover—why and how they take their roundabout route away from the intestine through membranes and passageways and back to the intestine again.

GENERAL STRUCTURE. Nematodes are clothed with a tough, usually transparent cuticle secreted by a layer of protoplasm in which there are nuclei but no cell membranes (syncytium). Beneath the syncytium a layer of longitudinal muscles is divided into four bands that extend the whole length of the body. When the dorsal band contracts the ventral one is stretched and vice versa; likewise, when the right side of the body is contracted the left side is stretched and vice versa. The action of these muscles and probably some rebound from the bent cuticle compose the entire locomotor outfit of nematodes. It is responsible for their thrashing gait, a swinging whip in one direction, and backward whip in the opposite. Even so, they make good progress when they can push against particles of soil, or against food in the intestine, or as they squirm through tissues. Water gives them little help. On a microscopic slide a group of flexing nematodes might be taking a gymnastic exercise, much bending and no locomotion.

Between the muscles and the digestive tube there is considerable space, a body cavity in that it holds the organs. However, it is not lined with epithelium, and thus not a true body cavity or coelom comparable to that of the earthworm and of higher animals.

Nematodes have no special circulatory or respiratory systems. The fluid contained in the body cavity distributes digested food and collects metabolic waste. The microscopic nematodes of the soil evidently exchange respiratory gases through the outer cuticle just as minute insect larvae exchange gas through their extremely thin chitinous covering. Ascaris is mainly anaerobic, obtaining oxygen from the body fluids of its host and energy from the breakdown of its own stored glycogen. Ascaris has a definite excretory system. Two canals, one running along each side of the body, come together at the anterior end and open to the outside through a ventral pore. The nervous system is a delicate ring of nervous tissue about the esophagus. Two large nerves connected with the ring extend the length of the body, one on the dorsal and one on the ventral side with connecting branches. The higher invertebrates have a main ventral nerve chain and the vertebrates a dorsal nerve cord. Ascaris is not committed to either plan.

The male and female reproductive systems are in separate individuals and in either one the organs occupy a large part of the body cavity. The eggs are fertilized in the uterus. Each one is later surrounded by a hardy chitinous shell. The egg shells are so resistant to chemicals that they will develop while immersed in a weak formalin solution.

Free Living Soil Nematodes. Myriads of little animals find pasture on the plants in the shallows of fresh waters. These millions feed on one another, on the algae that cloak the living plants, and on the soft tissues of decaying ones. Among them in untold numbers are the nematode worms recognizable under the microscope by their glassy smoothness and translucence. Among other wigglers of different kin, bristle worms and gnat larvae, the sweeping curves of the nematodes are distinctive.

Numerous as parasitic nematodes may be, those that live independently in fresh and salt water and soil probably far outnumber them. Their home niches are astonishingly various, on lake bottoms, in hot springs, and in polar seas, in soils, even in deserts.

VINEGAR EELS. Who has seen live vinegar eels? Probably nobody who has used only "store vinegar," pasteurized and bottled. Vinegar eels are the nematode worms (*Turbatrix aceti*) of raw cider vinegar. They are about one-sixteenth of an inch long and their characteristic nematode thrashing movements are recognizable when the vinegar containing them is held up against strong light (Fig. 26.1). They are distributed on the fruit mainly by fruit flies, *Drosophila melanogaster,* the famous fly of genetics. It is also the fly of rotting apples.

PLANT PARASITES

Minute nematodes bore into the roots of a great variety of plants. Some of them, such as the sugar beet worm, *Heterodera schactii,* live in only a few species of plants while the closely related common garden roundworm, *Melo-idogyne marioni,* inhabits plants of over 1000 varieties. The worms lay their eggs either in the roots or in nearby soil. In either case, the young larvae bore their way into the rootlets. The plant cells are stimulated by the foreign body and divide rapidly, forming little galls, or root-knots, in which the parasite is walled in by scar-tissue (Fig. 26.3). The roots soon become so deformed that they cannot function and the plant dies. In both plants and animals, the tissues of the hosts often develop growths or secrete substances that wall in the parasite. Nematodes also enter leaves, usually through the breathing pores (stomata), and move about the latticed interior, eating out the contents of the cells as they go (Fig. 26.1). On the outside, the disturbance is marked by twists in the leaves and by whitened trails. Nematode parasites are harbored by water as well as land plants. Even sea weeds (Ascophyllum of the Atlantic coast) may be burdened with nematode galls.

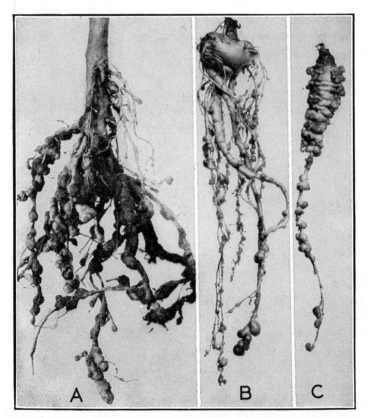

FIG. 26.3. Knot-root caused by a microscopic nematode, *Meloidogyne marioni.* Knot-root galls cause great loss to vegetables especially cabbage and its kin, cotton, and several of the grains: *A,* tomato; *B* and *C,* parsnips. Every knot-root gall is populated by millions of nematodes. (After Jeffers and Cox. Courtesy, Walker: *Diseases of Vegetable Crops.* New York, McGraw-Hill Book Co., 1952.)

ANIMAL AND HUMAN PARASITES

Pinworms. Many parasites are highly favored by tropical climates but one of the commonest, the pinworm (*Enterobius vermicularis*) is equally abundant in temperate climates. These are strictly human parasites, most frequent in children of the Caucasian race. The adults live and reproduce in the intestine, feeding only upon its content. They are most active at night and then emerge through the anal opening and lay their developing eggs upon the skin and clothing; eggs are also freed in the intestine. They are taken into the human mouth via many kinds of infected objects and eventually hatch and mature in the intestine. The effects of the infection are irritating rather than dangerous.

Hookworms. Exclusively human hookworm disease like malaria paves the way for other diseases and often brings whole communities into distress and poverty. Medical treatment of hookworms is relatively easy and successful. Teaching people to avoid them is difficult. There are many parts of the world in which hookworm disease is still an important health problem, in our own southeastern coastal states, in the West Indies—especially Puerto Rico, in Central America, in some parts of South America, in Egypt, and in parts of Africa and Asia (Fig. 26.4). The disease is stopped wherever the ground is frozen all winter.

There are two widely distributed species of hookworms—the Old World hookworm, *Ancylostoma duodenale,* and the American hookworm, *Necator americanus.* Their habits are essentially similar but Old World hookworms are

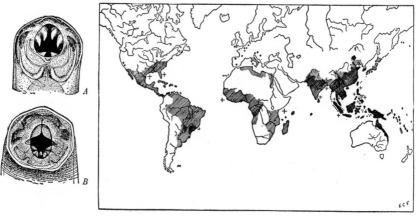

FIG. 26.4. Hookworms of man. *A,* mouth of the European hookworm, *Ancylostoma duodenale,* armed with hooks. *B,* mouth of the American hookworm, *Necator americanus,* armed with cutting plates and hooks.
The world distribution of hookworm. Areas that are criss-crossed and deeper black indicate infection by two species, *Necator americanus* and *Ancylostoma duodenale.* The + marks indicate *Ancylostoma braziliense,* in Central America, Brazil, Africa, and Pacific Islands. (Courtesy, Craig and Faust: *Clinical Parasitology,* ed. 5. Philadelphia, Lea and Febiger, 1951.)

more dangerous to the host and more difficult to eliminate. The fertilized eggs are extruded in the intestine and, as early embryos, pass out of it with the feces. On moist warm soil, the larvae hatch within 24 to 48 hours. They bore downward a little way into the soil but never travel far in any other direction. Their very presence on the ground or in water means that human excrement, known as night soil, has been deposited in the immediate vicinity. This insures an abundance of bacteria on which the larvae feed. At the end of about five days they molt a second time although the loosened cuticle is not cast off but stays on until it is worn away by the worm's movements against the soil.

They are now in the infective stage, with bodies that are slender, sharply pointed, and of microscopic size. They become not only different in shape but their appetites change. They forsake the bacteria on which they have fed, are restless and go without food. Instead of boring downward as they did earlier, they now squirm upward and lie as close to the surface of the soil as possible and still keep moist. They are now prepared to bore into human skin, usually on the feet. The country may be one in which night soil is used as a fertilizer as is common in Asia. In that case, the larvae wander over the vegetables and so have a good chance at the human mouth and a direct route to the intestine. If they enter through the skin, they burrow until they reach a lymph or blood vessel, and in the circulation they are ultimately taken to the lungs. There they are caught in the capillaries and this particular environment stimulates them to burrow out into the air chambers. This is nicety of discrimination at its height. In the lungs, the upward movement of the cilia acts as an escalator that carries them to the throat from which they are swallowed. They are then on the way to their final stop in the intestine. There they bury themselves for a short time between the villi, go through a third molt and develop a mouth by which they grasp the intestinal wall (Fig. 26.4). They grow rapidly until they are about one-quarter of an inch long and then molt for the fourth and last time. With this molt, the mouth is changed to its final form and the worms become mature. They are now able to clamp their mouths to the intestinal lining, to wound the capillaries and to suck blood. Eggs begin to appear in the feces about six weeks after a known infection, a sign that the parasites constitute a growing population and are steadily drawing blood from their host. By ingenious calculations upon the number of the female population it is figured that each female sucks one cc. of blood from the host per day. In doing so they are provisioning a metabolism that according to careful estimates enables a female of *Necator americanus* to produce from 5000 to 10,000 eggs per day. Each one is fertilized internally and the embryo leaves the female body in the four-celled stage of development.

Fortunately, this multiplicity is reduced by circumstances. The embryos will not develop beyond four cells unless they are exposed to air. This hinders the succession of one generation after another within the intestine. Whatever substance surrounds the developing embryos must be moderately warm and moist, must contain bacteria and be well mixed with air. Temperature between 70° F. and 85° F. is the optimum; if it is much lower or higher than that, the embryos are injured or destroyed. Direct sunshine and drying kills them. Wriggling through soil is rugged business and clay or salty ground injures them. Hookworms are not long-lived, at most about five years. Infections tend to die out unless repeated, the chemical environment having changed, and immunity being established. Such obstacles as these are set against the daily litters of 10,000 eggs.

Trichina. Adult trichinae (*Trichinella spiralis*) are parasites of the intestine. But it is young ones, not the adults, which are responsible for the serious disturbance called trichinosis. Unlike most parasitic worms, they live in temperate climates and are almost completely absent from the tropics; they occur mainly in Europe and the United States. According to data of 1947 and more recent estimates, the United States had three times as much trichinosis as all other countries combined.

Trichinae most often parasitize man and pigs but can live in other animals (Fig. 26.5). Rats and cats are easily infected, dogs are less so, and birds are resistant to them. Human infections usually come from eating imperfectly cooked pork, hurriedly cooked roasts with red parts left in the center, and ham improperly cured and cooked. In the United States at this date, the prevalence of infections in man and pigs is highest in the Atlantic States, especially in

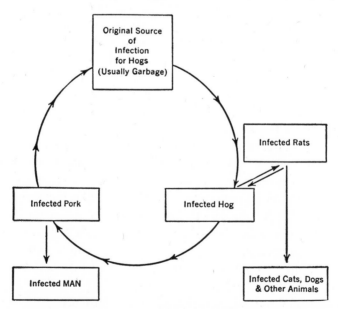

FIG. 26.5. Diagram illustrating the common methods of exposure to trichinosis (caused by *Trichinella spiralis*) in the continental United States. (Courtesy, Craig and Faust: *Clinical Parasitology,* ed. 5. Philadelphia, Lea and Febiger, 1951.)

Massachusetts, and on the west coast. Essentially, it occurs wherever pigs are fed on garbage that contains bits of infected pork. However, marketing of meat products into different regions of the country does not leave any locality free from suspicion. Uninspected pork from farms and small butchering places has proven more dangerous than government inspected pork. Trichinae have not been eliminated anywhere. More effective than inspection is the fact that pork is usually refrigerated for long intervals which kills trichinae.

LIFE HISTORY. Trichina worms are usually swallowed as immature larvae enclosed in cysts embedded in pork muscle (Fig. 26.6). The cysts are digested off and the microscopic larvae bore into the intestinal wall where they grow to maturity, mate and reproduce within five to seven days after they are swallowed. The adults may or may not cause intestinal disturbances depending upon the number of larvae that were swallowed. An ounce of heavily infected pork sausage may contain 100,000 encysted larvae.

The embryo trichinae develop in the uterus of the mother. The microscopic larvae are born alive, burrow into the capillaries and become numerous in the blood between two and three weeks after their parents were swallowed. They are distributed all over the body but finally settle into muscles that have a large blood supply, those of the diaphragm, the thorax, the legs, but not the heart (Figs. 26.5, 26.6).

After they enter the muscles, the larvae grow rapidly but are still practically microscopic. They are then in the infective stage. Their only chance for life is that the muscle which they occupy may be eaten by an animal in which they

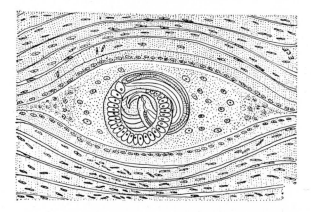

FIG. 26.6. Drawing of microscopic cyst of trichinae about three weeks old. The walls of cysts contained in infected pork are digested off in the human stomach and the larvae develop into adults within five to seven days. Mating occurs and the females produce living young, larvae that invade the body within about three weeks, finally settling into muscles and other tissues in the encysted state shown here. See also figure 26.1. The harm to the body is done by the migrations of larvae, rather than by the cysts. (Courtesy, Craig and Faust: *Clinical Parasitology*, ed. 5. Philadelphia, Lea and Febiger, 1951.)

can survive. Otherwise, they die in the cysts and become calcified. The trichinae in the human body constitute great populations of suicides since human cannibalism is almost extinct. The survival of trichinae is kept up only by the eating of infected scraps of meat, mainly by pigs and rats.

Trichinae differ from other intestinal parasites in that the young do not leave their native host and take their chances for a new one. The majority of young trichinae stay within their home hosts, although this means destruction for so many. How well the species can afford this is shown by the prevalence of trichinosis. The invasion of the muscle is a critical step for the larvae and in heavy infections highly dangerous for the host. The symptoms include intense pain in particular muscles, great difficulty in breathing, and in movements of the eyes and jaws. The surrounding muscle fibers become inflamed and disintegrate. About six weeks after the original infection walls form about the larvae then curled up among the muscle fibers. Gradually one, sometimes two or more larvae are walled into the capsule that at first is delicate but after a year or more becomes hard and chalky. This encystment phase is the second dangerous one for the host. Other symptoms continue and pneumonia is often a complication. The host does not recover until eight weeks to several months after the infection. Even after that there is a period of a year or longer when the jarring and stretching of the muscles is made painful by the cysts.

Filariae. With infections of trichinae the immature young are the chief cause of disturbance; with infections of filariae the adults are the main trouble makers. The adults, living in the human passages, produce young called microfilariae. The embryonic microfilariae must go through a stage of development in a blood-sucking insect before they become infective to man (Fig. 26.7).

Filarial parasites (*Wuchereria bancrofti*) are widely distributed in tropical and subtropical countries, especially in coastal regions and on islands (Fig. 26.8). In the western hemisphere they occur throughout the West Indies, Panama, and northern South America. The adults are the cause of elephantiasis. They live in the lymph passages, tangled together like snarls of coarse white threads, the females about three inches in length, the males half as long.

LIFE CYCLE. Within the lymph passages the females give birth to the microfilariae. These are microscopic (about 0.2 mm.) slender squirmers that at once bore into the blood and lymph capillaries, and are carried over the body by the circulating blood (Fig. 26.7). Their further development depends on their being sucked up with the blood by a biting mosquito (female) that may belong to one of several genera, Anopheles, Culex, and others. Experiments have shown that there must be at least 15 microfilariae per drop of blood in order to infect the mosquito. Evidently they must be numerous enough to condition their surroundings by their metabolic by-products. Blood containing 100 or more microfilariae per drop will kill a mosquito, even one of the transmitting species. Yet, the blood of heavily infected persons commonly contains

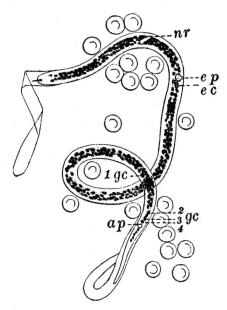

Fig. 26.7. The microscopic filaria worms, *Wuchereria bancrofti,* swarming in human blood at night. They are parasites in human lymph glands and in certain species of mosquitoes which are essential to their complete life cycle and which transmit them to their human hosts. They are the cause of filariasis (elephantiasis). (Courtesy, Craig and Faust: *Clinical Parasitology,* ed. 5. Philadelphia, Lea and Febiger, 1951.)

several hundred of them per drop. Many mosquitoes must be killed by large meals of them. Thus, millions of microfilariae are swallowed into death traps as surely as human muscles are death traps for trichina larvae.

Within the mosquito, the microfilariae immediately bore through the stomach wall and enter the muscles of the thorax. There they develop into larvae; their form changes from slenderness to sausage shape, and back again to slenderness and lengthening. This takes about 10 days at the end of which they are physiologically set for a change. They wriggle out of the thoracic muscles of the mosquito and make their way into its mouth parts (Fig. 26.7). The mosquito is now loaded with infective larvae. Mosquitoes that carry microfilariae live near human dwellings, not far to go for a blood meal.

Everybody must have seen mosquitoes feel the skin for an easy place to bite. The filaria-loaded mosquito does this like any other mosquito, and the larvae in its mouthparts stimulated by the warmth and pressure of the flesh at once bore their way through the mosquito's labium (lower lip) and into the skin. The next chapter of filaria life history is almost a blank. Into what part of the human body the larvae go and how long before they are full grown inhabitants of the lymph passages is mostly unknown. Their arrival there is a certainty.

Phylum Nematomorpha

Horsehair Worms. Adult horsehair worms writhe slowly like living wire or lie in still coils in the edge-waters of ponds. They used to be common in drinking troughs and the wayfarers who saw them added their testimony to the belief that horsehairs "turn to life" after a night in the water. Adult hairworms are from a few millimeters to a yard in length; in shallow water they are easily noticeable; coiled in the body cavity of a freshly killed grasshopper they are spectacular.

The names of the genera, Gordius and Paragordius, come from the Gordian knot that their coils suggest.

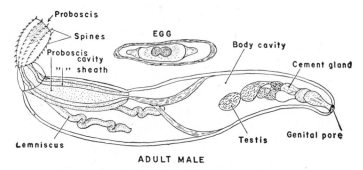

ADULT MALE

Fig. 26.8. Structure of typical spiny-headed worm or Acanthocephala. These worms are parasites of fishes, birds, and mammals in most of the world including the Arctic and Antarctic. They range in size from less than an inch to more than one foot. (Courtesy, Hunter and Hunter: *College Zoology*. Philadelphia, W. B. Saunders Co., 1949.)

GENERAL STRUCTURE—ADVANCE OVER FLATWORMS AND NEMATODES. The body cavity is lined with epithelium and is thus a true coelom. Partitions of loose tissue divide the cavity into compartments. It is not filled with tissue (parenchyma) as the comparable cavity is in nematodes. A single midventral nerve connects with the brain by way of the ring around the esophagus, an arrangement suggesting the one in the earthworm and insects.

The adult worm is uniformly cylindrical and slender. Its covering of cuticle is very thin but the thickness of the body wall makes the cuticle look opaque. There is no special circulatory, respiratory, or excretory system. The digestive canal is open throughout its length in young worms but may close or degenerate in adults. The sexes are separate. The eggs are shed from the ovaries into the coelom and then pass into the oviducts which are structurally separate from the ovaries as they are in the vertebrates.

LIFE CYCLE AND ECOLOGY. Several stages in the life history of horsehair worms were discovered many years ago, but the actual life cycle has been learned only recently by controlled experiments in the laboratory, as well as observations in the natural habitats. The life cycle of hairworms is another evidence of the precision with which an individual parasite must follow a fixed schedule of life or perish. Production of great numbers is the safeguard of the species.

After mating, the females lay their eggs in strings usually twined about twigs submerged in the water. These are from 15 to 20 cm. long and contain an enormous number of minute eggs. Gordius lays more than half a million eggs and Paragordius about six million. Toward fall the adults die, the males before the females. The microscopic larva pierces the egg shell at a point that it softens with its own secretion. Within 24 hours after hatching it surrounds itself with a cyst wall and becomes inactive. If it is prevented from doing this on time, it loses its power to do so. Larvae may live for two months within cysts submerged in water, and for a month when they are in damp air.

The cysts are swallowed by aquatic insects or by land insects, such as grasshoppers and crickets, that forage on the grasses at the water's edge. As soon as the cyst walls are digested off, the larvae pierce the wall of the gut and burrow into fatty tissue from which they absorb abundant nourishment. There the young Gordius grows and changes to the mature form. If the host is an aquatic insect, the parasite escapes directly into the water. If it is a land insect, its successful escape must await the host's visit to the waterside. Most of these facts have been learned from experimental infections of insects.

It is noticeable that Gordius does not strictly specify its host. Well-grown worms have been found in various species of insects; larvae are probably swallowed and mature in several different aquatic invertebrates.

Phylum Acanthocephala

Spiny-headed Worms. Spiny-headed worms constitute a peculiar group of about 300 species ranging in length from six to 460 mm. (1½ ft.). All are parasites of vertebrates, from fishes to mammals. The name refers to their distinctive feature, a relatively short retractile proboscis armed with rows of stout recurved hooks (Fig. 26.8). The worm projects this proboscis in among the folds of the lining of the intestine of its host and holds its place with the hooks while it absorbs nourishment through the delicate porous cuticle that covers its body. Neither larva nor adult has a digestive tract, and no circulatory or respiratory organs. There are two primitive kidneys, and a roomy body cavity but, lacking a peritoneal lining, it is not a true coelom. The sexes are separate. The eggs are fertilized internally and the embryos well developed before they are extruded into the intestine of the host.

LIFE CYCLE. The life cycle includes an intermediate host, usually an arthropod: small crustaceans for those that are parasites of fishes and other aquatic vertebrates; cockroaches, larvae of June beetles and other terrestrial arthropods for those that are parasites of pigs, rats, and other land vertebrates.

Characteristics of Ecology and Form of Nematodes

Nematodes live everywhere that animals can exist. Great numbers of minute free-living ones stir and enrich the soil. In both soil and water they constitute links in the food chains that reach to higher animals. As parasites, large numbers of them are physiologically intimate with many species of plants and animals.

They are slender, cylindrical, and covered with a protective cuticle. They have a functional body cavity containing organs, but not a true coelom. The digestive tract is a canal with mouth and anal openings. The sexes are separate. Ectoderm, mesoderm, and endoderm are present.

The movements of nematodes are distinctive; swinging and thrashing due almost completely to the use of longitudinal muscles.

27

An Aquatic Miscellany

Ecological Intimacy. Ecologically, the animals described in this chapter are closely related and they have shared the welfare of water for untold generations. They have gradually fitted into one or another of the numberless niches in water, from ponds to oceans. They have many traits in common, also differences. The latter are the basis for their separation into several distinct groups.

Most of these animals are marine. As adults they creep, burrow, or are attached to rocks and plants, but in general the young swim about freely and are carried by the ever shifting currents of water. The free-swimming young of several of the groups resemble one another and are also similar to those of annelids and mollusks (Fig. 27.1). They are trochophores (Gr. *trochos,* wheel + *phorus,* to bear), the minute larvae which suggest that all of them used to resemble one another throughout their lives, though they do not now. Even the various adults meet over the same kinds of food. They consume bacteria and silica-coated diatoms, and themselves provide protein and minerals for their slightly larger neighbors. Rotifers, bryozoans, brachiopods and phoronids are food-sifters relying on the transporting power of water and their own equipment of tentacles and cilia to bring the harvest to their mouths.

The animals of this "miscellany" do not lack conflicts and contrasts, dramatic in their vigor and precision. Carnivorous rotifers hunt down the water-fleas with furious pounce. Arrow worms move up and down in the sea by the time clock of light. In the morning and evening twilights, millions of them swarm through the surface waters of the ocean. They arrive in them promptly, remain while the amount of light is precisely right for them, and departing sharply, spend other hours in the darkness of deep water. Also among the miscellany is the lamp shell, Lingula, so like the fossils of its ancestors of 400,000,000 or more years ago, that its nickname is "living fossil."

The classification of these groups has been rearranged several times and changes are still being made. Some groups have long been recognized as unique

533

enough to warrant their status as phyla. Others are named classes by certain zoologists and phyla by others. There are facts that stimulate arguments for both opinions. The latter one is followed here.

TROCHOPHORE LARVAE. The trochophore is a pear-shaped larva, the stem of the pear being the future posterior end of the animal (Fig. 27.1). A wheel of cilia encircles the body which also bears tufts of longer cilia, all of them used in swimming. The complete U- or L-shaped digestive tube is lined with cilia. The nervous system is relatively elaborate and there are various sense organs such as eyes and organs of balance that might be expected on an active animal. The trochophore larvae of several phyla of invertebrates have already been mentioned. In annelid worms and mollusks, the trochophores are very similar but the adult earthworm and clam into which they develop can hardly be confused. Immature animals show likenesses; mature ones show the differences.

Phylum Nemertinea—Ribbon Worms

Most ribbon worms live between the tide lines coiled among the rocks and seaweeds; a few live in fresh water or moist earth. All of them are slender, and their stretching ability is fantastic. The common *Cerebratulus lacteus* of muddy sands on Atlantic shores is three feet long when contracted and may be 35 feet outstretched, flat and only an inch wide. Its near relative (*Cerebrat-*

SIMILARITY OF YOUNG MARINE INVERTEBRATES

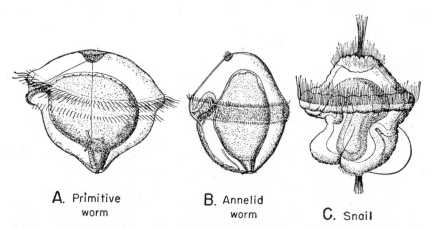

A. Primitive worm

B. Annelid worm

C. Snail

FIG. 27.1. Young stages of three marine invertebrates. *A,* Polygordius, a relative of annelid worms. *B,* Echiurus, a marine worm that as an adult (4 inches long) burrows in sandy bottoms. *C,* Patella, the limpet, a snail that clings to rocks. These animals are strikingly similar in their young stages but very different in habit and appearance when they are mature. As transparent, ciliated larvae they swim free in the sea making their own living; in the remote past they probably did so throughout their lives. (*A* and *B* after Hatschek. *C* after Patten. Courtesy, Hesse and Doflein: *Tierbau und Tierleben.* Leipzig, Teubner, 1910.)

ulus herculeus) of the Californian coast is 12 feet long contracted and an estimated 75 feet when expanded. The length of outstretched ribbon worms is
partly due to the extended proboscis that commonly reaches forward two or
more times the length of the body. Not all ribbon worms are so long; some are
minute and many measure but a few inches. Like flatworms, some are strongly
colored and patterned, many are pale and the species are difficult to identify.
The proboscis usually marks them as ribbon worms.

Unique Features. Proboscis. The ribbon worms' unique and surprising
feature is the protrusible proboscis that shoots rapidly forward, comes in contact with some hapless clamworm (Nereis), twines around it, and shortening
again, pulls the prey back to its mouth (Fig. 27.2). Then the proboscis and
the clamworm both disappear. It is as if an elephant could roll its trunk out

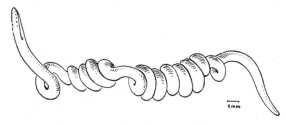

Fig. 27.2. Ribbon worm, *Lineus socialis*, 10 inches or more long, its body contracted in a characteristic close spiral. Ribbon worms prey upon clamworms that
live among the tide washed seaweeds. (From original of figure 1, Wesley R. Coe,
J. Exp. Zool., **54**:416.)

of a short upper lip, catch a peanut on it, and telescope it inside again. When
the wandering ribbon worm (*Paranemertes peregrina*) of the Pacific Coast
comes upon the tunnel of an annelid it extends its slender proboscis through
it, like a "plumber's snake," finally winds it about the annelid owner and pulls
the latter out. The proboscis is withdrawn by the shortening of a retractile
muscle and pushed out when the walls of its sheath are contracted upon the
fluid in the sheath.

Regeneration. Ribbon worms have exuberant powers of regeneration.
They break easily, but they more than make up for this in their mending.
Those of different species vary greatly in the freedom with which they fragment; some break into many pieces whenever they are touched. The hinder
parts of mature worms commonly break up spontaneously into pieces which
regenerate into perfect individuals, the regular method of asexual reproduction.
Many experiments in regeneration have been made upon ribbon worms by
W. R. Coe especially upon *Lineus socialis* of the Atlantic and *Lineus vegetus*
of the Pacific Coast (Figs. 27.3, 27.4). If a worm 100 mm. long is cut into
100 pieces, each one mm. long, they will develop into an equal number of
minute worms in four to five weeks. Regenerated worms like whole ones can

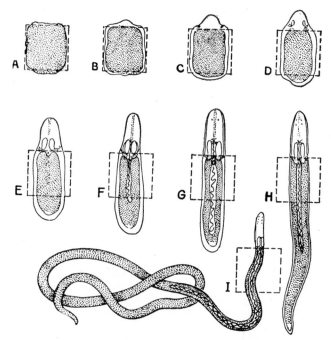

F. 27.3. Typical stages in the regeneration of ribbon worm, *Lineus socialis*, from a fragment (*I*) taken back of the mouth. (From original of figure 4, Wesley R. Coe, *J. Exp. Zool.*, **54**:426.)

go without food for a year or more during which they live upon their own constantly decreasing bodies.

Ribbon worms dwarfed by starving are commonly found in nature. Many dwarfs have been produced experimentally. When examined with the microscope they reveal a series of sacrifices. Some of the cells of the primitive middle layer, mesenchyme, become wandering phagocytes literally devouring the body cells, especially those of the digestive canal. Loaded with food these cells then disintegrate and their remains furnish food for surviving cells. As starving continues, this process is repeated over and over and the animal becomes smaller and smaller. In this way digestive tract, reproductive organs, and muscles gradually disappear.

CIRCULATORY SYSTEM. Ribbon worms are the simplest animals to have a circulatory system of the closed type with true blood vessels and spaces in the mesenchyme continuous with the vessels. The blood is usually a colorless fluid carrying blood cells but in various species it may be yellow, green, or red— the red color due to hemoglobin contained in the cells as in human blood. This system takes over the distribution of substances that in flatworms were carried by fluid in the gastrovascular cavity. There is no special pumping organ and the blood vessels have few branches.

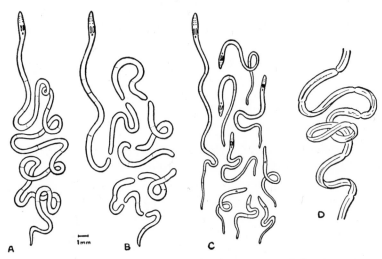

FIG. 27.4. Reproduction by natural division in *Lineus socialis*. *A,* mature worm; *B,* dividing; *C,* reconstruction of these pieces into nine complete worms; *D,* portion of body of mature worm showing zones of division. (Courtesy, Coe, *Physiol. Zool.,* **3:**299, 1930.)

Structures and Functions. The important structural advances in which ribbon worms have progressed beyond the flatworms are the digestive canal with mouth and anal openings present in all members of the phylum, and the circulatory system. The general plan of the body is otherwise similar to that of planarians. The body is completely covered with ciliated epithelium and beneath it are the circular and longitudinal muscles. There is no special respiratory organ. The excretory system consists of a pair of lateral canals with side branches ending in flame cells. The male and female systems are usually in separate individuals; a few species are hermaphroditic. Eggs and sperm are produced in many little sacs which open directly to the outside. The sex cells are strewn into the water where fertilization occurs and the free-swimming helmet-shaped larva (pilidium) develops (Fig. 27.1).

Ecology. HABITATS. Most marine ribbon worms are bottom dwellers in mucky sand, within holes lined with mucus; some live in parchmentlike tubes similar to those built by annelid worms.

FEEDING. Ribbon worms are carnivores—burrowers that feed chiefly on annelid worms, especially the abundant clamworms (Nereis), and they forage mostly at night when the latter are active. The proboscis is their chief burrowing tool.

WAY OF LIVING. Many nemerteans are free-living predators. Others are commensal, sharing "the bed and board" with a partner without affecting it. A smaller species (*Malacobdella grossa*) lives in the mantle cavity of various clams on the Atlantic coast, and in about 80 per cent of the razor-shell clams of the Pacific Coast. The currents of cilia that deliver the fragments of food to the clam's mouth at the same time serve it to the worms. Certain ribbon worms (Carcinonemertes) live on crabs, as larvae on the gills and as adults on the eggs. In the water as on land every cranny is a home niche for a plant or animal.

Phylum Rotifera—Trochelminthes

Their Place in Nature. Rotifers are minute animals that abound in fresh waters throughout the world. Only a few species live in salt water. Their forms and habits are in general similar, but in details they are varied and fit with durable nicety into the niches that their worldwide distribution supplies. They consume microscopic plants and animals, living or dead, and clean the water of its least debris. In turn they are eaten by their next sized neighbors, which are in turn eaten by larger animals and so on up to the fishes.

The body walls of rotifers are transparent, and their internal organs as easy to see as the works of a glass clock. Both inside and out their constant activity is visible. One of the early observers (Eichhorn 1761) wrote of Floscularia (Fig. 27.5), "Now I come to a very wonderful animal, which has very often rejoiced me in my observations: I call it the Catcher: extraordinarily artistic in its structure, wonderful in its actions, rapid in capturing its prey." Anton Leeuwenhoek, who first described rotifers in 1703, gave them their name meaning wheel-bearers and thought that he had discovered the principle of the rotating wheel in nature.

Rotifers are an old group with a very long evolution. They resemble flat-worms in having ciliated excretory organs called the flame cells. As in round-

FIG. 27.5. Representative rotifers selected from the great variety of form and habit in this typically fresh-water group. *Floscularia* (old name *Melicerta*), Rotifers of this group create tubes of a gelatinous secretion covered with meticulously fashioned pellets and attached to submerged plants. They are elegant but precise creations—minute, yet easily visible to the naked eye. *Asplanchna,* a predator on all kinds of minute animals including other rotifers. *Brachionus* is an omnivorous eater, dependent upon its crown of cilia to whirl particles of food into its grinding mastax. *Polyarthra,* a lake rotifer often in water that is poor in oxygen. It moves by jerks owing to the sudden beating movements of its long appendages. (Adapted from various sources. Courtesy, Needham and Needham: *Guide to the Study of Fresh Water Biology.* Ithaca, N.Y., Cornell University Press, 1941.)

worms, the body cavity has no special lining and hence is not a coelom. Rotifers are composed of relatively few cells, commonly a definite number characteristic of a species. Many of the adults are shaped like larval worms (trochophores).

Unique Features. The corona is unique and essential in the life of rotifers (Fig. 27.6). It is an irregular disk rimmed and banded with cilia whose beat creates the effect of rotation, the wheels that delighted Leeuwenhoek. The corona functions in locomotion, in gathering food, and in respiration. The mastax or chewing pharynx is unique. In other animals food is ground after it leaves the mouth, in the gizzard (part of the esophagus) of the grasshopper, and in the stomach of lobsters, but only the rotifers have a chewing-throat.

Structures and Functions. Various rotifers are excessively slender, almost spherical, turtle-shaped, and flowerlike; very many of them have figures with profiles like those of carrots and turnips (Fig. 27.5). The anterior end is topped by the corona. At the posterior end, the body narrows into the foot and one or two toes. Rotifers can poise and pirouette with sure stance because in each toe there is a cement gland that secretes a sticky temporary anchorage.

Numbers of Cells and Nuclei. There is probably an approximately constant number of cells in the bodies of various species of multicellular animals,

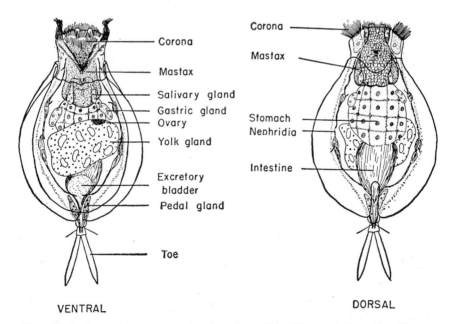

Corona

Mastax

Salivary gland
Gastric gland
Ovary

Yolk gland

Excretory
bladder

Pedal gland

Toe

Corona

Mastax

Stomach
Nephridia

Intestine

VENTRAL

DORSAL

Fig. 27.6. General structure of a female rotifer. The majority of rotifers are females; in many species males are unknown and reproduction is altogether parthenogenetic. Unique features of rotifers are the corona or rotating crown of cilia, and the mastax or chewing pharynx. (Courtesy, Robert W. Pennak: *Fresh-Water Invertebrates of the United States.* Copyright 1953, The Ronald Press Company.)

even of man. In rotifers, there is a definite number of cells according to the species, and so few that they can be easily counted. Adults are peculiar in that the whole body may be composed of incomplete cells (syncytia). In *Hydatina senta,* there are about 1000 nuclei in every adult and in embryos of the same species about 1000 complete cells are formed. Later, the cell membranes disappear but the number and locations of the nuclei remain definite and in the same relative position as in the embryo.

OTHER FUNCTIONS. The corona helps in locomotion, respiration, and getting food. Whether a rotifer is swimming or creeping, the strong backward strokes of the cilia on the corona drive it forward. Rotifers are delicately responsive to their surroundings and the activity of the cilia is quickened or slowed accordingly. Their beat continually bathes the animal with fresh water, provides oxygen and food, at the same time carrying away the carbon dioxide. Particles floating in the water are brought to the mouth at the center of the whirlpool (Fig. 27.7). The rotifer needs only to open its mouth.

Whatever the food may be, whole cells or fragments, plants or animals, it is whirled into the grinding mastax (Fig. 27.8). It then passes through the esophagus to the stomach where chemical digestion is carried on by the secretion from two large gastric glands. Digested food is absorbed through the walls of the stomach and intestine and on into other regions of the body. The undigested remains pass out through the anal opening. It is to be remembered that rotifers swallow great numbers of diatoms, all of them encased in silicious shells considerably harder than glass. In some species, the digestive canal does

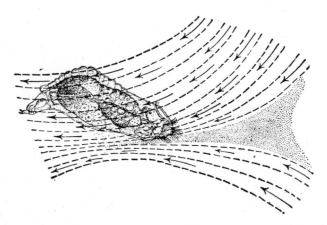

FIG. 27.7. Currents of water produced by the cilia of the corona of a rotifer, Proales. The fine dots represent particles drawn in a vortex toward the mouth as the animal moves toward the right. The cilia strike backward more strongly than forward and thus produce currents of water that pass backward from in front of the animal to its mouth and over the surface of its body. Thus, they bring food and a continual supply of oxygen to the surface of the body. (Courtesy, Ward and Whipple: *Fresh Water Biology.* New York, John Wiley and Sons, 1918.)

not extend beyond the stomach in either sex; in others, it is incomplete only in the males. Undigested remains are discharged from the mouth as they are in hydra.

Nitrogenous waste is removed by means of ciliated cells (flame cells) located at intervals along the two excretory tubes. These primitive kidneys that extend backward beside the digestive tube open into the contractile vesicle. The vesicle discharges relatively large amounts of water into the cloaca. Thus,

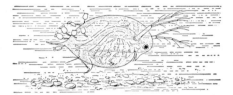

FIG. 27.8. *Left,* rotifers (Brachionus) holding on to Daphnia by their sticky toes, and collecting particles of food from the water as they ride. *Right,* a fierce carnivore (Dicranophorus) eating its way into one of its neighbor caldocerans. (Courtesy, Myers, "What is a Rotifer?" *Nat. Hist.* **25:**221, 1925.)

the excretory system is a water balancer just as the contractile vacuole is in the ameba and as the kidneys and urinary bladder are in the frog and higher animals.

The main part of the nervous system is the brain and from it nerves pass to various organs. There are several sense organs, usually one or two red eyespots, evidently strong tactile senses in the corona, and a pair of sensory tufts on the sides of the body. The sense of touch must be elaborate in Floscularia (*Melicerta ringens*) which builds its exquisite case with great precision of uniformly rounded microscopic pellets (Fig. 27.5).

Reproduction and Life Cycle. Female rotifers have a single ovary, a yolk gland that supplies the eggs with food, and a short oviduct that carries them to the cloaca in which they are fertilized (Fig. 27.6). Male rotifers are incompletely developed except for the reproductive system. In some species, there are no males. All eggs have the diploid or double number of chromosomes and develop without fertilization into females.

An annual succession of generations typical of many summer rotifers (having parthenogenetic generations in summer) is outlined in Figure 27.9. The chief peculiarities of rotifers are due to the presence of the diploid number of chromosomes in the eggs of the parthenogenetic female-producing females; and of the haploid or single number of chromosomes in the eggs of the sexual females. Parthenogenesis and diploid and haploid numbers are explained in Chapters 18 and 20. The reproductive cycle has a seasonal rhythm. A stem mother produces a generation of females, parthenogenetically. These are succeeded by several generations of females, an enormous population, all likewise

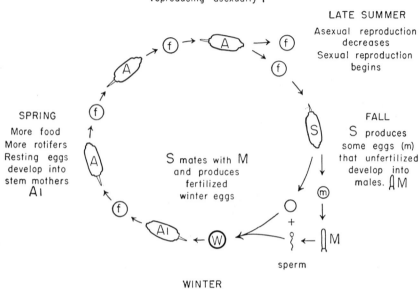

SUMMER

Much food. Great population
Every unit a female A
reproducing asexually f

LATE SUMMER

Asexual reproduction
decreases
Sexual reproduction
begins

SPRING

More food
More rotifers
Resting eggs
develop into
stem mothers
A I

S mates with M
and produces
fertilized
winter eggs

FALL

S produces
some eggs (m)
that unfertilized
develop into
males. M

sperm

WINTER

Food sparse. Population reduced
to fertilized resting eggs.

Fig. 27.9. Annual succession of generations typical of summer rotifers. Beginning with the stem mothers (*Al*) of spring there are successive generations that consist only of parthenogenetic females (*A*), all producing female young (eggs, *f*) an economical arrangement for great multiplication. Under changed conditions that occur in the fall a generation of sexual females (*S*) arises whose unfertilized eggs (*m*) develop into males (*M*). These males mate with the sexual females (*S*) of their mothers' generation and produce the fertilized resting or "winter" eggs (*W*) from which stem mothers (*Al*) develop. In the spring the stem mothers produce parthenogenetic females and the cycle begins again. (Based on data for *Lecane inermis* by H. R. Miller, *Biol. Bull.*, **60**:345–380, 1931.

produced from unfertilized eggs containing the diploid number of chromosomes. Then, with a change in the environment, such as temperature, or food, or others not fully understood, generations of sexual females appear that bear especially small eggs. They contain the haploid number of chromosomes and develop parthenogenetically into males. These males mate with the sexual females, actually the generation of their mothers. The fertilized eggs that result become the thick-shelled resting or "winter" eggs. They contain the haploid number of chromosomes from the male plus the haploid number from the sexual female, and thus carry a biparental inheritance. After a resting period they develop into the stem mothers.

Seasonal Differences in Reproductive Cycles. There are striking seasonal changes in rotifers, differences among species, and variations in the form and activities of individuals within the same species. In the perennial ones, parthenogenetic reproduction continues throughout the year although sexual reproduction may also occur in spring and fall. In the summer species, parthenogenetic reproduction occurs in summer, sexual reproduction in the fall and the species is carried over the winter in resting eggs (Fig. 27.9). In the winter species, there is a large parthenogenetic population in winter and the males appear in the spring.

CYCLES CHANGED EXPERIMENTALLY. The reproductive cycles are readily changed experimentally by food and temperature. When carefully cultured populations of rotifers (*Brachionus pola*) were kept on scanty food, parthenogenetic females were produced. When the food was adequate and plentiful, sexual females soon became superabundant. In other experiments, D. D. Whitney fed rotifers (Hydatina) on colorless flagellate protozoans (Polytoma) and obtained 289 successive parthenogenetic generations. By feeding them only chlorophyll-bearing flagellates, he could obtain sexual females at any time.

ECONOMIES. The reduction of male individuals enables rotifers to produce large populations with a minimum consumption of food. The only function of male rotifers is the fertilization of the resting eggs and their brief lives, with little need of food, are entirely adequate for this function. Parthenogenetic females eat far more than males, but every one of them produces more. Rabbit populations are scanty compared with those of parthenogenetic rotifers.

Phylum Gastrotricha

Some gastrotrichs are marine, but most of them live in fresh water and are often among the minute organisms swept up from the pond shallows with a fine collecting net. Beneath the microscope they can be seen swimming, creeping, even leaping rapidly about among the protozoans and rotifers with which they consort, and in some ways resemble. Unlike the rotifers, they have no crowns of cilia, but on their ventral sides they have bands of them which accounts for their gliding and explains the name Gastrotricha (Gr. *gaster,* belly + *trichos, hair*). On the dorsal side the cuticle is scaly or hairy (Fig. 27.10). The majority of fresh-water gastrotrichs have a pair of tubes at the end of the body, the outlets for the cement which forms their temporary holdfasts. In fresh-water gastrotrichs, all reproduction is parthenogenetic; no males have ever been discovered.

Phylum Bryozoa

Their Place in Nature. Bryozoans or moss animals are minute animals, nearly all of them living in colonies that look so much like moss that the name bryozoans has replaced their other name Polyzoa. All are aquatic and upwards of nearly 3000 species are marine; only about 35 live in fresh water. The marine species are widely distributed in coastal waters, between the tide lines. They grow on rocks and seaweeds, easy to see—but not to distinguish as animals. Most of the colonies seem to be only white, yellow, or brown patches of crust on the damp stones and seaweeds (Fig. 27.11). Other colonies might be delicate branching seaweeds, two to four inches high, rooted to rocks and kelp. The common fresh-water Plumatella resembles a dark vine with white-

FIG. 27.10. A typical gastrotrich, Chaetonotus. They are many-celled fresh-water animals of microscopic size, like their neighbor rotifers. They are so abundant, widely distributed, and striking in appearance that they demand attention even among hordes of other minute animals. (Courtesy, Robert W. Pennak, *Fresh-Water Invertebrates of the United States.* Copyright 1953, The Ronald Press Company.)

tipped branches, actually the folded tentacles of the animals. Colonies of the fresh-water *Pectinatella magnifica* live on the surface of great blobs of jelly which they secrete about submerged stems. Algae invade the jelly and the whole object might be a green pineapple floating in the midsummer pond. If they are taken from the water none of these colonies gives the slightest sign of life, but immersed in it, each animal puts forth its exquisite plumy crest on the regular business of gathering food.

Structures and Functions. The common bryozoan Bugula grows on the eastern and western coasts of North America in tufts two or three inches long, attached to seaweed. Although they are members of a colony, each individual lives independently of its neighbors (Fig. 27.12). In this type of bryozoan, each animal is protected within a horny tube; in others, every animal is in a limy cup or surrounded by jelly. The characteristic and, under a lens, conspicuous feature of each animal is the lophophore which bears hollow flexible tentacles astir with cilia that draw diatoms and protozoans into the mouth, whence they are passed along the digestive canal by more cilia.

Young Colony   Statoblasts

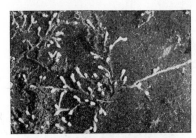

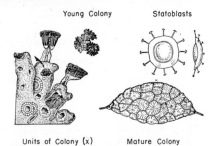

Units of Colony (x)   Mature Colony

FIG. 27.11. Bryozoan colonies. *Upper,* MARINE. Encrusting colonies that live in patches of their own limy deposits on rocks and seaweeds. The common *Bugula turrita* that at first glance seems to be a delicate seaweed growing in tufts but a few inches high. *Lower,* FRESH WATER. *Left,* Plumatella spreads like a dark vine over the stones in running water. Photograph of a living colony. The white tips are the crowns of the zooecia with the tentacles withdrawn. *Right, Pectinatella magnifica,* with its core of jelly, is a compound of many colonies. Floating in a pond it appears to be a great green pineapple, each of its colonies taking the place of the units of fruit. (*Upper,* courtesy, American Museum of Natural History, New York. *Lower right,* courtesy, Ward and Whipple: *Fresh Water Biology.* New York, John Wiley and Sons, 1918.)

Bugula and bryozoans of a similar type have a true coelom lined with a cellular peritoneum. The coelomic fluid contains corpuscles and is the main carrier of substances to and from the cells. There are no special organs of respiration, excretion, or circulation. In the smaller class Endoprocta, gelatinous mesenchyme fills the space occupied by the coelom in the ectoprocts such as Bugula. The ganglion or "brain" is connected by nerves with the tentacles and retractile muscles.

Many bryozoans have minute pincers scattered over their outer surfaces, believed to be very specialized individual animals rather than appendages.

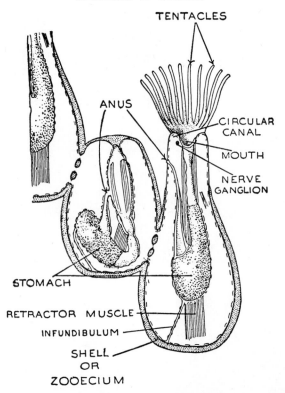

FIG. 27.12. Structure of one individual greatly enlarged of a bryozoan colony such as the common marine Bugula. (Courtesy, Miner: *Fieldbook of Seashore Life*. New York, G. P. Putnam's Sons, 1950.)

They are shaped like birds' heads, whence they are called avicularia. Under a lens they can be seen snapping their bills with every vibration in the water, and if any particle touches them they snap shut in a viselike hold. They catch and kill the microscopic organisms that continually settle on the bodies of the bryozoans and constitute private cleaning squads. Starfishes and sea urchins have similar mechanisms, but they are unknown in higher animals. No dog has pincers to trap his fleas.

Movements. A lophophore with all its tentacles can be instantly jerked out of sight by the bands of muscle in the body cavity. But, its emergence is slow and the tentacles spread forth seemingly with great caution, actually because each one is expanded by fluid flowing slowly into it (Fig. 27.13).

Reproduction. Bryozoans are hermaphroditic and ovaries and testes develop in the coelom in which the eggs are fertilized. The embryo develops in a brood pouch that opens out of the coelom (Fig. 27.12). In the marine species, the ciliated trochophore swims about freely for a short time, then becomes attached to seaweed or rock (Fig. 27.1).

Fresh-water bryozoans do not produce free-swimming larvae but bear internal buds or statoblasts that develop directly into colonies like the gemmules of sponges (Figs. 22.7, 27.13). Most bryozoans exist only as statoblasts during the winter. Many of these are banded with air cushions that buoy them up, and armed with circlets of hooks that catch on the feathers and feet of ducks. Statoblasts are carried far and wide by birds and currents of water. Occasionally, they are washed out along the shores of lakes and lie in countless numbers, long dark ribbons of them on the beaches.

Phylum Brachiopoda—Lamp Shells

Their Great Past. These animals were named brachiopods because somebody mistook their long lips for arms, and lamp shells because their shells suggested miniature Roman oil lamps.

Brachiopods have had a great past in numbers, diversity, wide distribution,

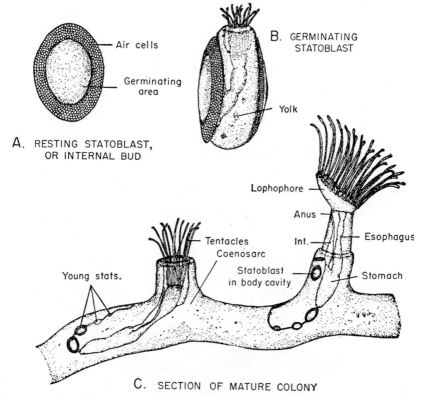

FIG. 27.13. Fresh-water bryozoan, *Plumatella repens.* Animals drawn greatly enlarged with their tentacles expanded, or withdrawn; both contain developing statoblasts. *A,* statoblast, about the size of a fig seed, with horny covering and band of air cells. *B,* in the germinating statoblast the young animal has split the shell revealing its body and yolky food. (After Brown, *Trans. Amer. Micr. Soc.* **53:**427, 1934.)

and an immensely long history all attested by their fossil remains. Undoubtedly, the adults were once free swimmers as their trochophore larvae are now. However, through millions of years the adults proved the success of their stalked food traps that contain a regulated collecting and filtering system for gleaning particles of food from the water (Fig. 27.14). The fossils show that their stalks extended from the posterior ends, as they do now, that the shells opened upward, and that the long-lipped mouths expanded like the petals of a flower. Their attached state and great abundance must have made them food for roving predators, annelid worms, crustaceans, starfishes, and sea snails. They constituted an important link in the food chain between the microorganisms they consumed and the carnivores that preyed upon them.

Fossils of over 2500 species have been discovered and a large number of these are known from Paleozoic rocks, the oldest rocks in which fossils of animals are found. The 225 living species are only a remnant of those that are now extinct. Of the living brachiopods, Lingula is scarcely changed from its ancient ancestors, an animal on which evolution paused (Fig. 27.15).

Structure and Relationships. An adult brachiopod is enclosed within a pair of shells resembling those of clams and oysters and like them, secreted by folds of a fleshy mantle (Fig. 27.14). But the shells differ from those of mollusks in that they cover the dorsal and ventral sides of the body, instead of the right and left, and they swing open on a hinge at the rear end from which the body stalk extends. In rock-dwelling brachiopods and most others, the shell is bent upon the stalk. However, when they are burrowing, brachiopods hold their bodies straight up, the original position with the tentacles and mouth facing upward.

Like bryozoans, a brachiopod has no real head, its place being taken by

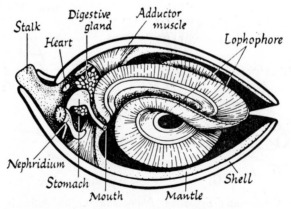

FIG. 27.14. Brachiopod, or lamp shell. A marine animal, about one inch long, that superficially resembles a giant bryozoan crowded into a clam shell. Its importance is in its antiquity, its residence on the ocean bottom over 400,000,000 years ago, and its pioneer development of kidneys (nephridia) and heart. (Courtesy, Pauli: *The World of Life*. Boston, Houghton Mifflin Co., 1949.)

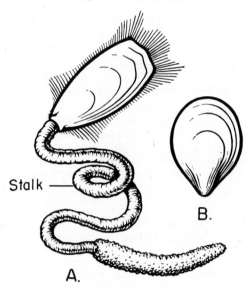

Modern (A) and Fossil (B) Brachiopods

FIG. 27.15. *A*, Lingula, so like its ancestors that it is called a "living fossil," still so abundant on the borders of the Indian Ocean that it is used for food. It lives in vertical burrows in the sand attached to the bottom by a stalk. *B*, a fossil brachiopod shell that displays marked likeness to living brachiopods. (After Pauli: *The World of Life.* Boston, Houghton Mifflin Co., 1949.)

enormous lips (lophophore), that surround the small mouth and bear rows of ciliated tentacles. When not in action, the lips or "arms" are coiled up on each side of the mouth. Their many tentacles have ciliated grooves through which food and water are drawn toward the mouth. The cavity within the shell is divided into a front chamber containing the lophophore and the lobes of the mantle, and a posterior one containing the coelom, branches of which extend into the mantle. It also contains the pairs of muscles by which the shell is opened or closed and turned on its stalk, also those that work the stalk of such burrowers as Lingula. The digestive canal usually lacks an anal opening. Any waste which remains after digestion must be exceedingly fine, probably dissolved and excreted by the two relatively large nephridia. The sexes are separate. Fertilization of the egg occurs outside the body. The free-swimming larva is ciliated and has a general resemblance to the trochophore larvae of annelid worms, rotifers, and mollusks (Fig. 27.1).

Phylum Chaetognatha—Arrow Worms

Their Vertical Migrations. In the morning and evening twilights, vast numbers of arrow worms join the plankton population of the sea. There they feed

for a brief time on microscopic organisms—crustaceans and larval fishes, and
then return to the dark deep water. They not only furnish food to animals a

FIG. 27.16. Arrow worms (*Sagitta hexaptera*) swarm in open seas suddenly
visiting the surface at certain times of the year and during morning and evening
twilights. This species (length 3 inches), among the largest of the arrow worms, is
abundant off Martha's Vineyard, Massachusetts, and occurs throughout the world.
(Courtesy, Miner: *Fieldbook of Seashore Life.* New York, G. P. Putnam's Sons,
1950.)

little larger than themselves, but a few billion of them make a tasty catch for
the whale-bone whale whose food sifter is as efficient for gallons as that of a
rotifer for droplets.

Structures and Functions. The phylum name refers to the bristly mouths
and that of the principal genus, Sagitta, to their habits of darting like arrows.

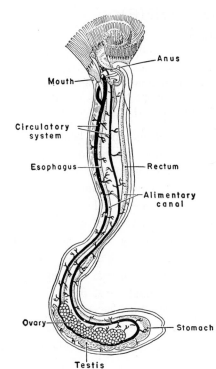

FIG. 27.17. Phoronis, a tube-dweller in
the mucky sand between the tide lines.
Diagram of its structure; the crown of
sticky tentacles is its all-important means
of getting a living. It is chiefly interesting
as a link suggesting relationships of various phyla of invertebrates and even a
remote one with the chordates because of
a notochord-like structure present in
them. (Courtesy, Hunter and Hunter:
College Zoology. Philadelphia, W. B.
Saunders Co., 1949.)

With their crystal transparency and cutting speed they are more like glass-
arrows than arrow worms. Dozens of them may swim about unseen in a glass
of water.

The bristles and hooks that surround the head of an arrow worm are instantly recognizable as the tools with which as a carnivore it seizes its prey (Fig. 27.16). The body cavity, a true coelom, is divided into compartments, all lined with peritoneum and filled with peritoneal fluid. Arrow worms are pioneers in the development of a coelom, and this possibly places them among the transitional forms from which the ancestors of the vertebrates finally emerged. There are no special respiratory, circulatory, or excretory organs but diffusion through the whole body carries on their work.

Arrow worms are hermaphroditic. The ovaries are in the coelomic cavities of the trunk, and the testes in coelomic cavities in the tail. At hatching, the young resemble the adult.

Phylum Phoronidea

The special features of phoronids are the food-catching organ, the body fluids, the coelom and the larva (Fig. 27.17). The food collector is a lophophore on a larger scale but similar to that of rotifers in its structure and importance to the welfare of the animal. There are two body fluids, a colorless one in the body cavity, and red blood circulating in blood vessels. Both fluids are very different from those of higher animals, the lymph and blood which they suggest.

28

Annelids—Pioneers in Segmentation

Annelids are extremists. The outside of an earthworm is monotonously austere; there are no decorations. But many among the marine worms bear plumy gills; those of the peacock and feather duster tribe are like miniature fountains shifting with iridescence (Fig. 28.1).

Annelids were pioneers in segmentation, the plan in which similar parts of the body are repeated over and over. It is conspicuous in only two groups of animals, the Phyla Annelida and Arthropoda, the latter known to everyone through the lobsters, flies, and grasshoppers. Although it is less obvious, segmentation is present in all higher animals, especially in the embryos but clearly traceable in their later life. The rings of an earthworm's body and the human vertebrae are evidences of segmentation. Both owe their origin to the segmentation established in the ancestors of annelid worms some 550 million and more years ago.

Annelids exist in variety—earthworms in sober colors and streamlined form, leeches with the parasite's appetite, marine worms of flowerlike beauty, delicacy and diversity. They are as significant in the economy of the sea and land as they have been in the evolution of the animal body. They are responsive to their environments to an extent and precision, ordinarily little credited to "worms." Examples of it are in: the burrowing habits of earthworms; their responses to the chemical and physical nature of the soil and their age-old plowing of the earth; the swarming of clamworms and the famous Palolo worms. Out of all the days of the year spent on the sea bottom, Palolo worms come to the surface only a few hours on nights appointed by the moon and tides, and by forces beyond our solar system. They answer to an environment that extends very far away.

Ecology. HABITATS OF ANNELIDS. Annelids are numerous, biologically suc-

FIG. 28.1. Tube-building annelids; peacock worm, *Sabella pavonia* (12 to 15 inches long). This and similar species live in British and North American tide waters. The feathery plumes are glorified breathing organs and food traps that emerge from the tubes and spread fanwise in the water like iridescent flowers. (Photograph courtesy, Douglas P. Wilson, Marine Biological Laboratory, Plymouth, England.)

cessful, and widespread over the world—some 6500 species in all. They live in soil and fresh water but are most numerous in the sea. There they live in the shallows and between the tide lines, at the surface, and on the bottom at great depths. Water is their natural home. Earthworms flourish in moist soil, and punctually come to the top in warm spring rains.

FOOD. Annelids feed heavily on bacteria and on decayed plants; among seaweeds, as well as inland gardens, they clear space by eating and fertilize it with their own bodies. There are predators among them, clamworms preying upon smaller worms, some leeches living on smaller invertebrates, others sucking blood. Annelids are in turn rich forage for larger predators in the water and on land—crabs, lobsters, and fishes that hunt over the coastal bottoms, gulls that pick the seaweeds, robins seizing earthworms at the surface of the soil, and ground moles catching them below it. By eating and being eaten, they help to check the unbalance of too few or too many.

WAYS OF LIVING. Burrowing annelids are successful animals but the tube-making ones far outdo them in variety of form and habit (Figs. 28.1, 28.2).

Fig. 28.2. *Amphitrite johnstoni* (8 to 10 inches long). The small scale worm *Gattyana cirrosa* lives in the tube as a partner and takes the food that escapes the larger worm. Various species of Amphitrite hide in sand-covered burrows but their filamentous crimson, or crimson and yellow gills wave freely in the water. Amphitrite, named for the Greek goddess of the sea, has a near relative named for Aphrodite, the goddess of beauty. (Photograph courtesy, Douglas P. Wilson, Marine Biological Laboratory, Plymouth, England.)

The developing young ones swim about freely, but the adults are nearly all rocking-chair travelers moving back and forth within their tubes. For various burrowers and most tube dwellers, the sticky mucus on a thrusting proboscis or waving gills is a means of collecting food. Many of them live alone in hard tubes of calcium carbonate fastened to rocks, to seaweeds and oyster shells. The majority of those in the larger, soft tubes have one or more guests, commensal worms and crabs that share the house and whatever board they can collect. On the Atlantic coast, a little crab (*Pinnixa chaetopterana*) lives with Chaetopterus and moves with the worm, keeping near its mouth for the extra "crumbs." Annelid scale worms are frequent guests. Some of these, like parasites, will live with only one kind of host; for others, almost any tube will do.

Characteristics. Annelids may be scarcely visible to the naked eye or several feet in length. A seaweed feeder (*Neathes brandti*) of the Pacific coast of North America is six feet long when relaxed and the giant earthworms of Australia reach 10 and 12 feet. The characteristic structures of annelids are the segmentation of the body before mentioned; a true coelom lined with a peritoneum; a central nervous system in which the brain (a pair of dorsal ganglia) is connected with a double ventral nerve chain expanded in each segment into a ganglion; and chitinous bristles or setae usually present on most segments. Whenever a larval stage is characteristic of the species, it is the trochophore type similar to those of many other aquatic invertebrates (Fig. 27.1). The ancestors of annelids lived in the Cambrian Period, the early part of the Age of Invertebrates.

Class Oligochaeta

The Earthworm

The earthworm, *Lumbricus terrestris,* is an immigrant from Europe that spread through the eastern part of North America and, at least, in laboratories has reached the west coast, a few years ago more conspicuously than now.

Ecology. These burrowers clear their way through the soil mainly by swallowing it. In spite of a long land residence and earthy contacts inside and out, the bodies of earthworms are excessively water hungry (Fig. 28.3). Their skins are too permeable for real land life. A worm that is transferred to water absorbs 15 per cent of its initial weight in 5 hours and then levels off, water-adapted. Conversely a water-adapted worm removed to moderately dry soil loses water for a few hours, then levels off, semi-land-adapted. As a consequence of their need for water, earthworms rarely live in dry climates and are active only in the rainy seasons. They benefit the soil by loosening and aerating it, swallowing and carrying top soil downward and deep soil upward. Thus, they have plowed the land for centuries. Charles Darwin brought out the importance of this in his "The Formation of Vegetable Mould, through the Action of Worms with Observations on their Habits"—his last book, published in 1881. It is the account of observations and experiments continued for over 20 years in his "earth worm field" close to Downe House, his home near London.

The Outer Tube—Protection, Locomotion, and Support. The earthworm's mouth is overhung by a supple grasping lip, the prostomium. The flattened rear end of the body is pressed against the inside of the burrow, a holdfast when the worm is extended on the surface (Fig. 28.4).

Earthworms are dark colored above and pale on the underside, embarrassingly good examples of counter-shading although they are strictly nocturnal. Such examples are thorns in the theory of counter-shading which is based on the presence of strong light from above. The conspicuous glandular swelling is the saddle or clitellum which secretes the cocoon that contains the developing eggs. On each segment except the first and last there are four pairs of minute chitinous setae. Each seta can be moved in several directions, also extended or withdrawn into the flesh, and the worms catch the ground with them as they crawl. On a quiet night the sound of moving earthworms can be heard among dry leaves, like sandpaper catching against the edge of paper.

There are numerous microscopic openings in the skin, those of the mucous

SUMMER   WINTER
Moist   Dry

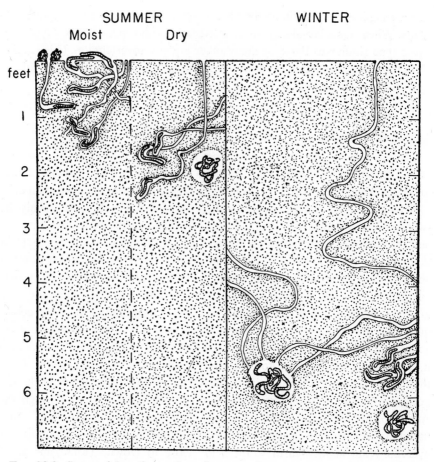

FIG. 28.3. Seasonal locations of earthworms. *Summer:* worms feed, mate and crawl about on the ground on moist nights; leave castings on the surface; burrow in the upper soil, the depth depending on moisture; cluster in dry soil. *Winter:* migrate below the frost line and hibernate; conserve moisture and heat by clustering. (Courtesy, Morgan: *Animals in Winter*. New York, G. P. Putnam's Sons, 1939.)

cells, of the dorsal pores from the body cavity to the outside, and above the sensory cells (Fig. 28.5). These and the outer openings of the nephridia (kidneys) are invisible except by microscopic examination. Other passageways are those of the two oviducts on the fourteenth segment; four minute openings of the seminal receptacles in the furrows between segments 9 and 10, and 10 and 11; and the sperm ducts on segment 15 (Fig. 28.11). The surface of the body is covered with layers of iridescent cuticle secreted by the outer cells of the skin. Cuticle and mucus compose the trail left on the sidewalks after a night's wandering. Earthworms are sensitive to touch especially at the ends of the body. Each contact cell has a hairlike tip that projects

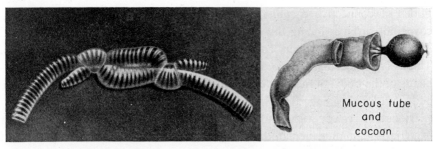

Mucous tube
and
cocoon

Fig. 28.4. Mating earthworms (anterior parts of bodies shown). Every earthworm has a fully developed male and female reproductive system. During mating each animal transfers sperm cells into the seminal receptacles of the other. The worms become bound together by mucous belts each secreted by a glandular swollen band, the clitellum, conspicuous in all mature worms. After mating, the mucous belts slip off over the heads of the worms, each one gathering up eggs and the transferred sperm cells. Each belt hardens and becomes the cocoon in which fertilization occurs and the embryos develop. The species figured *Allolobophora foetida* (or Eisenia) is smaller than the familiar *Lumbricus terrestris* and also very common especially in compost heaps. (Courtesy, Foot: "The Cocoons and Eggs of *Allolobophora foetida*," *Jour. of Morph.*, **14**:38, 1898.)

through a pore in the cuticle and its other end is in touch with the process of a nerve cell (Fig. 28.5). Light receptor cells are located on the front and rear segments.

The Inner Tube—Food and Digestion. The body consists of two tubes, an outer one, the body wall, and an inner digestive tube. The space between is the body cavity or coelom, divided into a succession of compartments by par-

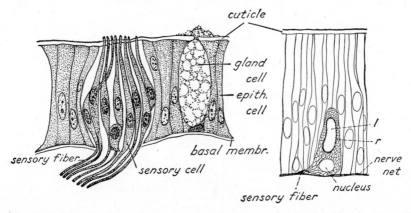

cuticle

gland
cell
epith.
cell

l
r

sensory fiber
basal membr.
sensory cell
nerve
net

nucleus
sensory fiber

Fig. 28.5. Gland cells and sense organs in the earthworm's skin. *Left,* section of the cuticle and skin. The large glands produce the cuticle, the substance that creates the iridescent trails left on sidewalks. Sensory cells receive stimuli and transmit nerve impulses to adjustor nerve cells in the ventral cord. *Right,* light-sensitive cell, containing a lens-like body (*l*) and surrounded by retina-like cytoplasm (*r*). (*Left,* courtesy, Curtis and Guthrie: *General Zoology,* ed. 4. New York, John Wiley and Sons, 1947. *Right,* courtesy, Hess, *Jour. Morph. & Physiol.,* **41**:68–93, 1925.)

titions of connective tissue. A layer of mesodermal cells, the peritoneum, covers all surfaces facing the cavity, including those of the organs within it. The cavity holds the watery coelomic fluid containing colorless ameboid cells. This is squeezed through pores in the septa and slowly circulated by movements of the body. Some of it oozes through the dorsal pores and moistens the body surface.

DIGESTIVE TRACT AND ITS FUNCTIONS. Earthworms consume quantities of bacteria and minute nematodes along with the soil that contains them. At the surface they feed largely on plant fragments. A worm can be caught by a spotlight and camera with a sheaf of broken leaves being sucked into its mouth. In the pharynx leaves are moistened by slippery saliva and further broken by squeezing (Fig. 28.6).

The food then passes through the relatively long esophagus where it receives a milky fluid from the calciferous organs located in segments 10, 11, and 12. All of these are outpocketings of the wall of the esophagus. The first

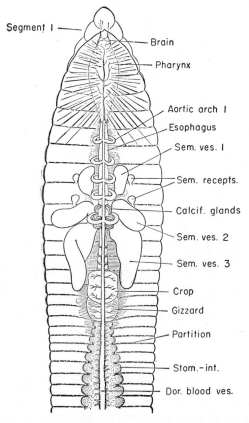

FIG. 28.6. Earthworm. The general structure of the anterior part of the body shown with the dorsal wall removed. The nephridia (kidneys) are not shown. (Courtesy, Calkins: *Biology*. New York, Henry Holt and Co., 1914.)

pair (10) are pouches; the second and third pairs (11, 12) are glands (Fig. 28.7). The glands produce the chalky secretion, evidently from an excess of calcium carbonate in the blood. From the glands it passes into the pouches, trickling forward through channels created by the infolding of the lining of the esophagus. The pouches act as storage sacs from which the secretion oozes into the food mass as it passes by their openings. The function of the calciferous bodies has been variously interpreted. Their secretion has been said to be a neutralizer that aids digestion. This was not borne out by the experiments of J. D. Robertson who concluded that the calciferous organs eliminate excess calcium that is absorbed from the food into the blood. The ways in which animals have dealt with extra calcium has had far-reaching effects upon them. Earthworms eliminate it and wriggle on with their soft, freely flexible bodies unaffected. Snails and clams use it in protective shells with which they are often weighed down in continual semicaptivity; vertebrates use it in their bones.

From the esophagus, food passes into the thin-walled and elastic crop, an expansion of the esophagus (Fig. 28.6). It opens into a muscular gizzard with a chitinous lining. This is essentially similar to the gizzards of grasshoppers and chickens and performs the same work of squeezing and grinding. The remainder of the food tube is the intestine where the main part of digestion and

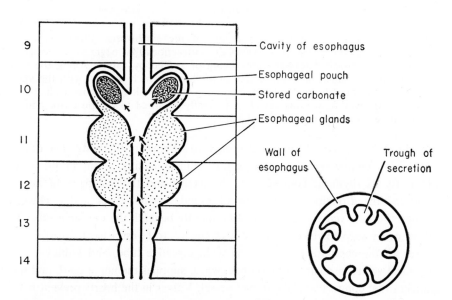

FIG. 28.7. Earthworms. Calciferous organs seen from the dorsal side. The glands, *11* and *12*, absorb calcium from the blood and produce a chalky secretion that trickles forward through the special channels in the lining of the esophagus visible in a cross section. It passes into the pouches (*10*) where it is temporarily stored before it oozes into the passing food masses. (After Robertson: "Calciferous Glands of Earthworms," *Brit. Jour. Exp. Biol.*, **13**:279–297, 1936.)

all of absorption occur. Its enzymes are cellulase that acts on the cellulose of plant tissues, amylase on carbohydrates, pepsin and trypsin on proteins and lipase on fats. Absorption of food takes place through the ciliated epithelium that lines the intestine. The absorptive surface is increased by the bulging out of the intestinal wall in separate segments and by an infolding of its dorsal wall—the typhlosole. The digested food is here either taken up by the blood into the numerous capillaries embedded in the intestinal wall, or directly into the coelomic fluid. A greenish layer of chloragog cells, important in excretion, covers the blood vessels and intestine.

Other Metabolic Processes. CIRCULATION. The body fluids are the watery coelomic fluid, the tissue fluid in direct contact with the cells, and the red blood. The red blood consists of the red plasma with the respiratory pigment hemoglobin in solution in it and the colorless ameboid cells. The blood circu-

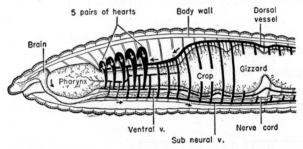

FIG. 28.8. Main vessels in the forepart of the earthworm. Blood is forced through the large dorsal vessel by waves of contractions that begin at its posterior end and pass forward, backward flow being prevented by valves. Along the way it is distributed to side branches, largely to the hearts which connect with the main ventral vessel. Small branches from this carry it to the kidneys (nephridia) and body wall. By way of various vessels it is finally returned to the posterior end of the dorsal vessel and carried forward again.

lates through a system of tubes that branch to all parts of the body. The dorsal vessel lying on the digestive tube is the main collecting vessel (Figs. 28.8, 28.9). By its rhythmic contractions, this vessel and the five pairs of hearts determine the direction of the flow of blood through them and backward through the long ventral vessel that lies directly beneath the digestive tube. In almost every segment blood flows out of the ventral vessel to the dorsal one by way of the capillaries in the body wall, digestive tube, and kidneys. The subneural vessel also carries blood backward, supplies the nerve cord, and has branches that connect with the dorsal vessel. Valves in the hearts prevent back flow as they do in the veins of higher animals.

There are special distributions of blood vessels to very vital structures: to the skin in which respiratory gases are exchanged; to the digestive tube with its food supply; to the kidneys concerned with water balance and excretion; to the muscles and to the nerves that depend upon abundant oxygen.

Respiration. Earthworms can breathe in air or water. Their wet skin functions essentially like a lung or a gill in spite of its cover of cuticle. It is well supplied with blood capillaries and under sufficient pressure oxygen passes into the blood and combines with the hemoglobin; in the outer skin cells it probably combines directly with the protoplasm as in the ameba. Although no exact measurements are available, it appears that earthworms can make use of oxygen in air or water with almost equal readiness. Experiments have shown that the oxygen-loading capacity of the earthworm's hemoglobin is low and inefficient as compared with the hemoglobin of higher animals.

Excretion. The nephridia (kidneys) of annelid worms are tubes associated with blood vessels and with the coelomic fluid (Fig. 28.9). Each one is a coiled tube with a ciliated funnel opening into the coelom, and a relatively long tube looped back and forth upon itself and ending in an enlarged bladderlike part

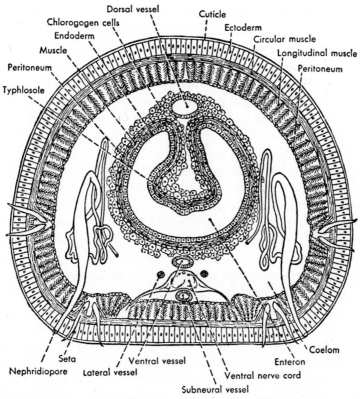

Fig. 28.9. Diagram of a cross section of an earthworm showing the intestine, one pair of nephridia, the chitinous setae which are aides in locomotion and the excretory chlorogogen (chloragog) cells. The inbent fold (typhlosole) extending nearly the whole length of the intestine is a means of increasing the area of absorption of digested food. None of the smaller blood vessels are shown; nets of them cover the coils of the nephridia. (Courtesy, Mavor: *General Biology,* ed. 3. New York, The Macmillan Co., 1947.)

that opens externally. At the inner end of the bladder, muscle cells prevent the excreted fluid from flowing back into the body. The essentials of structure in these kidneys are the tubes and their contact with blood capillaries, arrangements common to kidneys in general. Some waste substances are taken directly from the coelomic fluid through the ciliated funnel; other by-products are taken from the red blood. The kidney also helps to dispose of excess water.

Greenish chloragog cells surround the blood vessels and cover the intestine where they are in contact with microscopic capillaries (Fig. 28.9). They take up dissolved wastes from the coelomic fluid and these form the yellowish-green granules within them. When full of such granules they are sloughed off into the coelomic fluid. Some probably disintegrate and their substance passes out through the nephridia; others are taken up by the highly phagocytic ameboid cells. The latter wander into the tissues, disintegrate and their remains are deposited as pigment in the body wall.

Nervous System—Coordination. The two ganglia that constitute the brain are connected by nerves with another pair beneath the pharynx (Fig. 28.10). From these ganglia the double nerve cord, with a double ganglion in each segment, extends along the ventral floor of the coelom to the last segment. The removal of the brain has little effect upon the responses of an earthworm. However, after the subpharyngeal ganglia are removed, a worm neither burrows nor eats. The neurons in these ventral ganglia are evidently much more important than those in the brain. The ventral cord is the coordinating center of the body. The fibers of sensory neurons extend into it and those of motor neurons out of it as they do in the human dorsal nerve cord. Hundreds of both types of fibers pass through each of its branches (Fig. 28.10). Fibers from the receptor sensory cells connect with the cord. There the impulse on the sensory fiber passes over to an adjustor neuron and thence to a motor neuron which carries the impulse to the effector, in this case a muscle cell. Sensory and motor impulses pass one another on the same nerve but along separate cell fibers as in higher animals. Sensory and motor impulses are continually relayed along the cord over adjustor neurons.

The waves of muscular action which pass down the body as a worm crawls must be controlled by the ganglia in various parts of the cord since any moderate-sized piece of the body will crawl as well as a whole worm. If an earthworm is touched while outstretched from its burrow, it instantly snaps back, its longitudinal muscles contracting throughout their length. The nervous transmission is relatively rapid; it evidently passes over certain giant nerve cell fibers visible when specially prepared sections of the cord are examined microscopically. Experiments have shown that the speed of an impulse over these fibers is 1.5 yards per second. The speed of an impulse over the motor nerve cell fibers in man is about 100 yards per second.

Reproduction. The reproductive organs are located in the anterior part of

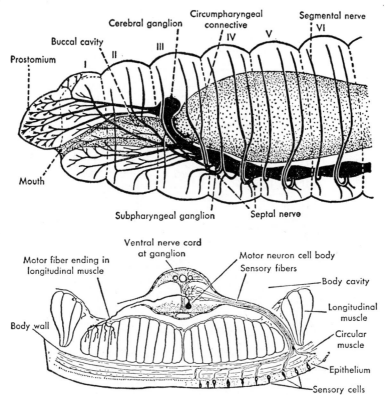

FIG. 28.10. *Upper,* forepart of an earthworm showing the nervous system with the ganglia repeated in each segment. *Lower,* diagram of the nerve cells involved in a simple reflex movement of the earthworm. (*A,* after Hess. *B,* after Parker. Courtesy, Mavor: *General Biology,* ed. 3. New York, The Macmillan Co., 1947.)

the worm, each organ in a particular segment (Fig. 28.11). The male cells originate in two pairs of minute testes. These are surrounded by conspicuous seminal vesicles, sacs in which the sperm cells mature. They finally pass into the ruffled sperm funnels and through slender sperm ducts to the two external openings on the ventral side of segment 15. Two pairs of small sacs, the seminal receptacles, open through pores, on the ventral surface of segments 9 and 10. During mating these receive sperm from the sperm ducts of the partner worm. The microscopic eggs are formed in a pair of translucent ovaries in segment 13. As the eggs mature they are shed into the funnels of the oviducts almost in touch with the ovaries. At the side of each oviduct is a minute pouch in which they collect. Behind the sex organs is the conspicuous clitellum (saddle) of gland cells. These secrete the mucous belt and cocoon that later protects the developing embryos.

The seminal vesicles very often contain large numbers of the parasitic protozoan, *Monocystis agilis,* in various stages of development. In one stage they

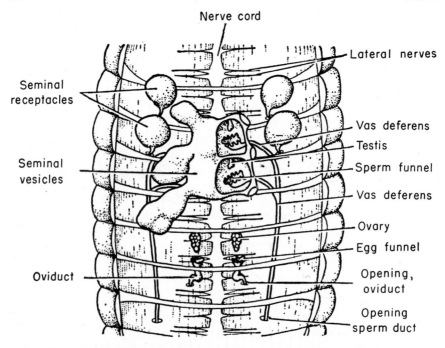

Nerve cord

Lateral nerves

Seminal receptacles

Vas deferens

Testis

Sperm funnel

Seminal vesicles

Vas deferens

Ovary

Egg funnel

Oviduct

Opening, oviduct

Opening sperm duct

FIG. 28.11. Earthworm. The hermaphrodite reproductive system composed of complete male and female organs. (After Vogt and Yung. Courtesy, Brown: *Selected Invertebrate Types.* New York, John Wiley and Sons, 1950.)

are ciliated and constantly moving; in another they are seedlike spores packed in a capsule.

The mating of earthworms is a complicated process, not simply the shedding of the sex cells into the water as in the aquatic annelids. Although earthworms are hermaphrodites they usually extend the forepart of their bodies and mate with worms of nearby burrows (Fig. 28.4). The heads of the worms are pointed in opposite directions with the ventral sides in contact. The clitellum of one worm is opposite to segments 9 to 11 of the other worm. Mucus is secreted until each worm is cloaked in a mucous tube that extends from segment 9 to the hind edge of the clitellum. As the sperm cells are discharged from the openings of the sperm ducts on segment 15, they are carried backward through two grooves to the sperm receptacles of the partner. This ends the mating process and the worms separate. The clitellum secretes a mucous belt which is shifted forward, along with the mucous tube, and finally over the head of one worm. As this elastic belt passes the openings of the oviducts, the mature eggs are evidently expelled into it. Farther forward, on segments 9 and 10, it apparently receives the sperm cells deposited there by the partner worm during mating. The sperm and eggs join and fertilization is completed within the mucous belt that in the meantime is slipping forward and finally off the worm. As this occurs the edges of the belt come together and a sealed capsule or cocoon results. Within this the young worms develop and in about three weeks, at least one or two of them emerge and make their way into the soil without going through a swimming stage such as the trochophore of the marine annelids. The cocoons of young earthworms, about the size of apple seeds, are numerous in moist compost heaps in spring and summer.

Regeneration. Adult earthworms can regenerate segments removed from the ends of the body, accidentally or by experiment. According to recent investigations of G. B. Moment (1953), the complete number of segments is present in the earthworm when it hatches and that number is not exceeded either by its usual growth or by regeneration. No more than five new segments will regenerate at the anterior end and no head will regenerate if 15 or more segments have been cut off. Various combinations can be made by grafting pieces together, fastening them by threads until they become united. It is doubtful whether regeneration contributes to their survival as it does to planarians and starfishes. In Tubifex, a common fresh-water oligochaete, the posterior end of the worm regenerated 31 new segments in 32 days. This is largely due to the totipotent cells (neoblasts) which migrate to the cut surface, multiply and differentiate into one or another kind of cells during the regeneration. Totipotent cells are those that have kept their embryonic character and have the power to multiply with great rapidity somewhat as cancer cells do. It is worth notice that such cells are killed by x-rays.

OTHER OLIGOCHAETES

Most of the 2400 species of oligochaetes are smaller than *Lumbricus terrestris*. The 10-foot giant earthworms of Australia are impressive exceptions. Two species of small earthworms are common all over North America; one of them (*Allolobophora caliginosa*) lives in the soil; the other (*Eisenia* [old name Allolobophora] *foetida*) lives in compost.

The majority of oligochaetes are aquatic. The young ones called naiads are transparent little bristle worms familiar to anybody who examines pond-sweepings under the microscope. Slender red worms, *Tubifex tubifex,* about an inch and a half long, live in tubes with their "tails" waving above the surface of mud, usually odorous from decaying organisms. Milk-white enchytraeids (*Enchytraeus albidus*) about half an inch long are sold at pet shops for turtle and fish foods.

Class Polychaeta

THE CLAMWORM

Ecology. Several species of clamworms live on sandy shores and clam flats on both Atlantic and Pacific coasts of North America. The large clamworm, *Nereis virens,* often a foot long, is one of the commonest annelids on the New

England coast, mainly in the low tide range. It is a ravenous hunter, swims at a good speed, and can grapple worms larger than itself. Clamworms construct loose flexible tubes on a base of sticky mucus that catches the sand and broken shells that disguise their chimneys. Like earthworms, they stretch out of their tubes at night but day and night they are preyed upon by birds and fishes.

The Outer Tube—Protection, Locomotion, and Support. The greenish skin is covered by iridescent cuticle like that of the earthworm. All of the segments are externally similar except the head (Fig. 28.12). On each side of the segments there is a flattened fleshy lobe the parapod or "side foot" bearing bundles of bristles.

Clamworms and earthworms greatly resemble one another but are products of unlike experience. For untold generations clamworms have lived in the sea, swimming after their prey and away from their enemies. For an equally long time streamlined earthworms have bored through the ground, swallowing

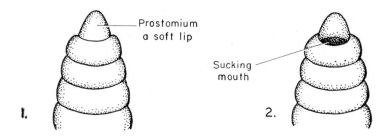

Head of earthworm, a herbivorous burrower: l. dorsal, 2. ventral view

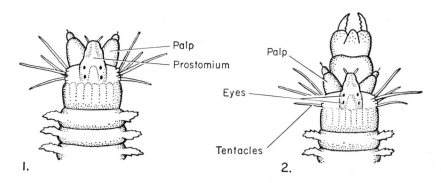

Head of clam worm, an active carnivore:
Dorsal views   l. Jaws withdrawn, 2. Grasping jaws extended

Fig. 28.12. *Upper,* head of the herbivorous burrowing earthworm with only primitive light and touch receptors and no oral armature. *Lower,* head of the active predatory clamworm equipped with clutching jaws and relatively complex eyes.

the inert soil. Clamworms and earthworms are illustrations of the saying that the outside of an animal tells where it has been, the inside what it is.

General Internal Structure. The internal structure of the clamworm is essentially the same as that of the earthworm. Behind the esophagus the coelom is divided into segments by partitions whose surfaces are covered with thin peritoneum; there is a pair of kidneys in nearly every segment; and the nerve chain is likewise branched.

The jaws and the protrusible pharynx which can be thrust out onto the prey are marks of the clamworm's predacious habit; withdrawing the pharynx is a part of swallowing the food into the esophagus into which a pair of digestive glands opens. From the esophagus, the digestive tube extends to the end of the body.

Reproduction. In Nereis and almost all polychaetes, the eggs and sperm develop in separate individuals from certain cells in the peritoneum of most of the segments. They are finally discharged into the water by way of the nephridia. The breeding habits of these, like many marine invertebrates, follow rhythms of the moon and the tides. In one of the smaller clamworms, *Nereis limbata,* each breeding period follows a cycle of the moon. In each one there are two peaks of abundance, also timed with phases of the moon. These clamworms that throughout the year have lived on the sea bottom come to the surface on certain days and hours, following a habit that probably began with the great tides of the Cambrian Period, half a billion years ago. At Woods Hole, Massachusetts, their swarming is a scheduled event of certain summer nights. By a light held over the water, the throngs of swimmers can be seen circling through the water as they shed eggs or sperm before they drop to the bottom again. Each run begins near the time of the full moon, increases to a maximum on successive nights, falls to a low point about the third quarter, then increases again, and finally shortly after the new moon no worms appear. The influences on the habits of these worms are examples of the many effects that originate far away in space and time.

OTHER POLYCHAETES

Illustrations of a few polychaete worms may give a slight notion of their variety and beauty. There is no hope of suggesting the translucence and play of color of the living animals. Those that are mentioned here, or their near relatives, live on both American sea coasts.

The sea mouse, *Aphrodite aculeata,* may be three to seven inches long. The under surface of the body is a flattened creeping sole like a snail's foot but is furrowed by segmentation. Along each side of the upper part there is a band of iridescent, hairlike setae. Between them the back is greenish gray bordered by green and gold setae and brown spines that hide the segmentation. At first glance, a sea mouse looks no more like a worm than it does like a mouse.

It lives on muddy sea-bottoms and, climaxing its peculiarities, commonly has one or more small guest clams, living in the furrows of its foot.

The parchment worm, Chaetopterus, is six inches long (Figs. 28.13, 28.14). Parchment worms secrete the tough substance of their U-shaped tubes whose chimneys project above the sand at low tide. As they lie in their tubes a steady

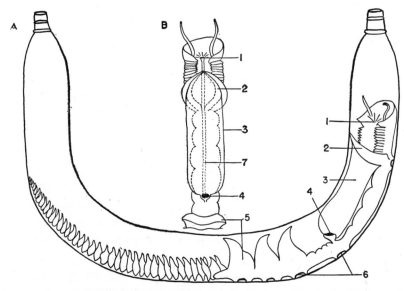

FIG. 28.13. Diagrams of Chaetopterus. *A,* animal feeding in its tube. *B,* dorsal surface of the anterior end. *1,* mouth; *2,* wing-like structure from the edge of which mucus is secreted; *3,* mucous sac; *4,* food ball, being rolled up in a ciliated cup; *5,* one of the main "fans" that with many smaller ones circulates the water within the tube; *6,* ventral suckers by which the worm holds itself to the sides of the tube; *7,* dorsal groove through which cilia carry the food ball toward the mouth. (Courtesy, MacGinitie and MacGinitie: *Natural History of Marine Animals.* New York, McGraw-Hill Book Co., 1949.)

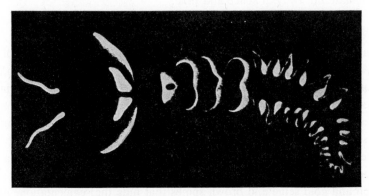

FIG. 28.14. Chaetopterus glowing in the dark. (After Panceri. Courtesy, Harvey: *Living Light.* New York, Academic Press, 1952.)

current of water goes in one end and out the other, kept in motion by the worm's rhythmic fanning of the broad flaps near the middle of its body. Oxygen and particles of food go in with the current. As before mentioned minute crabs (Pinnixa) often live in the tube and share the "crumbs." The daily life of Chaetopterus can be observed because it will live for long periods within a glass U-tube in a salt water aquarium. In the dark it is silvery from its bio-luminescence.

The plumed worm, *Diopatra cupraea,* is 10 to 12 inches long and is one of the most beautiful annelids of the Atlantic Coast. It constructs a tube large enough for the worm to turn around inside, with a chimney perfectly disguised by shells and seaweed. It is common in shallows below the low-tide line, from New England to South Carolina.

Palolo worms, *Eunice viridis,* and their near relatives are the classic examples of spawning associated with the tides and moon. The Atlantic palolo swarms a few hours before sunrise in June and July, shortly before the last quarter of the moon. The Pacific palolo swarms in October and November, near the last quarter. The Bermuda "fire worms" not only swarm but are luminescent while they do so. In Harvey's *Living Light* there is an account of their spectacular performance. A similar species (*Odontosyllis phosphorea*) swarms on the western coast of North America.

Class Hirudinea

LEECHES

Leeches are segmented worms that hold on by suckers. They get about by swimming and by looping over surfaces like measuring worms (caterpillars). Holding onto the surface with its rear sucker, the leech stretches out its body, attaches the front sucker to the surface and pulls the body forward. The rear sucker then releases its hold and is placed close behind the front one so that the body forms a loop (Fig. 28.15). The common name leech means to hang on and gain thereby. The class name, Hirudinea, comes from the hirudin that a leech injects into the wound as it bites and thus prevents the blood from coagulating.

Ecology. The majority of leeches live in fresh water; a few are marine; others abound in swamps and the forests of the humid tropics. Some of them feed on snails and worms; others are true bloodsuckers. As a group they are wavering on the edge of parasitism but not wholly committed to it. Most of them are predators, not more than 25 per cent are parasitic and many of these stay on their hosts only while they are feeding.

Leeches are acutely sensitive to vibrations and to extremely small amounts of substances dissolved in water. If you press your finger against the bottom of a dish containing leeches, they will at once begin to creep about, exploring the

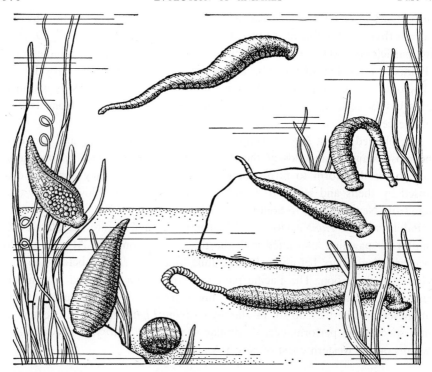

Fig. 28.15. *Right,* the common bloodsucker, American Medicinal leech (*Macrobdella decora*). Length, full grown, four inches or more. The general color is green, mottled and lined with black and orange; the underside is rich orange. This is one of the few leeches that regularly take human blood. It attaches itself by its rear sucker and explores the skin with its anterior end, then attaches the oral sucker and makes three fine painless cuts by a rotary motion of its jaws. *Left,* common brook leeches, *Glossiphonia complanata:* one with eggs attached. They live upon snails and are commonly called "snail leeches." A brook leech, two inches long, may have 40 or more young leeches attached to its underside, stretching out their bodies from beneath the parent as they ride.

whole surface and if they happen to pass over the fingerprint, their excitement shows that they detect it. In their native ponds, bloodsucking leeches are very responsive to movement of the water. They will gather from all directions even when one moves slowly and in high boots. They are also sharply responsive to light. Some have one or several pairs of eyes on the head as well as light perceptive organs on the segments.

Structure. There are 34 segments in the body of a leech but these are not clear-cut externally for each one is furrowed by two to five circular wrinkles or rings. Many structures of leeches are essentially similar to those of earthworms but their muscles are much stronger.

The bloodsucking leech (*Hirudo medicinalis*) has three sawlike teeth that make a Y-shaped cut in the flesh. Glands in the wall of the pharynx secrete the anticoagulant, hirudin, and the muscular pumplike pharynx draws out the blood (Fig. 28.16). The pharynx opens into an enormous crop extended by pairs of sacs, the last of which reaches nearly to the end of the body. This can hold enough blood for several months' food supply. Soon after a blood meal

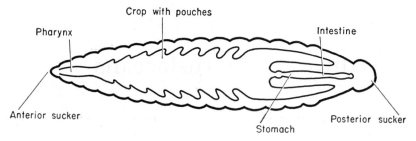

Capacity to take in much food at one time

FIG. 28.16. Leech. A general diagram of the digestive cavity. A leech sucks in enough blood at one time to increase its weight five times. When well inflated it loosens its hold voluntarily but the wound continues to bleed because of the anti-coagulant injected with its saliva.

much of the water is excreted and the concentrated blood is slowly digested in the small stomach into which the crop opens.

Leeches are hermaphrodites and, as in earthworms, there is a mutual transfer of sperm cells during mating. After mating, usually in summer, eggs and sperm pass into cocoons produced by a clitellum. The cocoons remain in water or earth except in one fresh-water family (Glossiphonidae) in which the cocoon and afterward the young leeches are attached to the underside of the parent (Fig. 28.15).

Leeches in Medical History. Leeching is an old medical treatment, so common that leech became the name for the physician as well as the treatment. The leeches, placed on the skin, carried on the real treatment that consisted of their sucking out a considerable amount of the "bad blood." During the early nineteenth century there was an enormous demand for "medical leeches." They were reared in ponds in many parts of Europe. Broussais (1772–1838), a French physician, was a leading advocate of "blood letting." During the year 1833 over 41 million leeches were imported into France for medical use and a good number into the United States.

Class Archiannelida

This is a small group of inconspicuous worms (e.g., Polygordius) of the seashore, that in the adult stage resemble the late larval stages of polychaetes. Internally the adults are segmented, but externally the segments are indistinct or missing. The larva is a typical trochophore. The class is merely mentioned here for completeness.

29

Arthropods—Crustaceans

There are more kinds of arthropods than of all other animals together (Fig. 29.1). They are a collection of multitudes: crustaceans, hosts of little ones as well as large lobsters and crabs; myriapods, the centipedes and millipedes; spiders and their allies, ticks and mites; and insects by millions. Their variety seems infinite but their basic pattern is the same, the tube within a tube plan of body and the segmentation inherited from annelid worms. Two leading

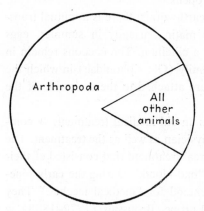

FIG. 29.1. The relative abundance of species of arthropods is estimated to be 80 per cent of all kinds of animals. (Courtesy, Frost: *General Entomology*. New York, McGraw-Hill Book Co., 1942.)

characteristics have developed upon this ground plan, an important and complex head, and jointed appendages the unique character of which has given the name Arthropoda (*arthros,* a joint + *pous,* a foot) to the phylum (Fig. 29.2).

Arthropods have complex and important relationships with plants and with other animals. Among them are the social organization of ants and bees, the most elaborate outside of human society, the effects of insects upon agriculture throughout the world, constructively by cross pollinating plants, destructively by feeding on plants and by carrying diseases from one to another plant, animal or man. Crustaceans provide the chief food for many fishes;

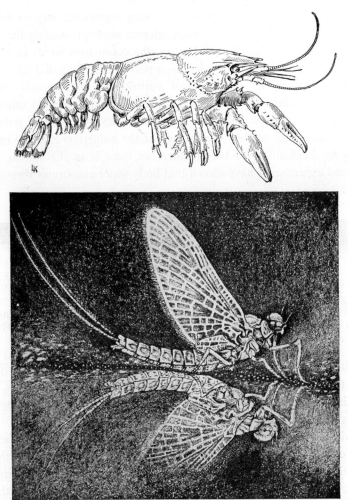

FIG. 29.2. A crayfish (*upper*) and a mayfly (*lower*) display the leading characteristic of all arthropods, segmented bodies combined with segmented appendages. The crayfish is an example of this plan in an arthropod that lives in the water, and the adult mayfly of an arthropod adjusted to the land. Arthropods have carried the basic plan into almost every corner of the earth.

small crustaceans are the main food of the great blue whale; the larger ones are human food throughout the world.

A Connecting Link. Peripatus is the only living animal that comes near being a common relative to annelid worms and to arthropods (Fig. 29.3). It is a couple of inches long, has a velvety skin and resembles a caterpillar. It belongs to a small group, the Onychophora ("claw bearing"), considered a phylum by some and a class by others. It lives in tropical forests in such separated regions as Australia and South and Central America, suggesting that it once may have been widely distributed and is now disappearing. It differs from both annelids and arthropods in being segmented only on the inside. There is a pair of stiff peglegs for each internal segment. Among the annelid-like structures are its thin cuticular cover, the continuous bands of muscle in the body wall, and the excretory organs, a pair of coiled ciliated tubes in each segment resembling the nephridia of earthworms. Arthropods lack cilia altogether. The arthropodlike structures are chiefly the tracheal tubes of the respiratory system carrying air directly to the tissues. A bundle of unbranched tracheae extends into the body from each of the numerous external openings. There is no mechanism for closing them as there is in the similar ones of insects, and experiments have shown that body water evaporates through them

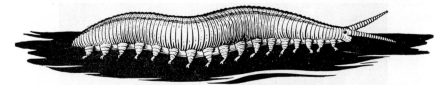

FIG. 29.3. Peripatus, a walking worm. Neither an annelid worm nor an arthropod yet resembling each, it has internal segments like the worms and air tubes like the insects and spiders. This connecting link is distributed in regions of the Southern Hemisphere. (Courtesy, Pauli: *The World of Life*. Boston, Houghton Mifflin Co., 1949.)

about 40 times more rapidly than in a caterpillar. The skin of Peripatus is adapted to moist land life and is restricted to it. The unguarded holes are unsafe against the evaporation of dry air. The advancement of Peripatus has doubtless been hindered by too much ventilation.

Trilobites—The Pioneer Arthropods. Over half the fossils that date from the first era of invertebrates are trilobites (Fig. 29.4). They were arthropods with 3-lobed bodies and many pairs of uniform 2-branched appendages, the latter probably for locomotion. In the course of time new types of arthropods developed from certain of the trilobites. The sea scorpions were among those that became the ancestors of the spider tribe (arachnids) and the horseshoe crabs (Limulus) which have survived into the present day. The trilobites, once the most numerous of invertebrates, now exist only as fossils but their descendants have more than taken their places (Fig. 29.1).

Class Crustacea

With but few exceptions, crustaceans are a great tribe of animals that breathe by gills. Some have pioneered into fresh water and a few live cautiously on land but, like their ancestors, most of them belong in the sea. There they exist in untold numbers and in great variety of shapes and sizes. Through all its variations the crustacean plan is evident—the segmented body bearing jointed appendages that typically have two branches (Figs. 29.5, 29.6). Crustaceans range in size from water fleas that are microsopic, and barnacles an

Fɪɢ. 29.4. Restoration of Silurian sea bottom, now the site of the city of Buffalo, New York. Made from a study of fossils found in the Niagara region, in that period some 400 million years ago when it was overspread by ocean. A large trilobite and several smaller ones creep upon the bottom showing the characteristic furrows and triple sections of the body. A cephalopod, and two crinoids, the once abundant stemmed echinoderms, are in the mid-ground of the scene. (Courtesy, The Buffalo Museum of Science.)

inch wide or less, to the American lobster that holds a record weight of 35 pounds, and the giant spider crabs of Japan that measure 20 feet from tip to tip of the first pair of legs.

Development. As in all higher animals, crustaceans pass through stages that suggest either the adult or the immature stages of simpler animals. Like most crustaceans, a shrimp (Penaeus) hatches into a larva called the nauplius stage that has three pairs of appendages and a single eye (Fig. 29.7). The nauplius transforms into a protozoea and the latter into a zoea in which the cephalothorax appears. The zoea develops into the mysis, a stage named after the common shrimp Mysis.

Cʀᴀʏꜰɪsʜᴇs ᴀɴᴅ Lᴏʙsᴛᴇʀs

Aristotle did well to call crayfishes "the small lobsters" of the rivers. Their habits of living are remarkably similar considering the differences in their

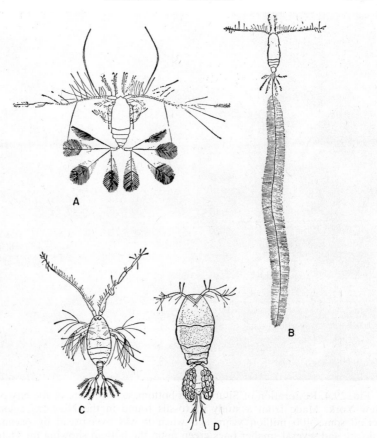

Fig. 29.5. Examples of the variety of small marine crustaceans. *A, B, C;* minute copepods of the surface waters of the open sea with appendages used in swimming and floating. *D,* an equally small copepod of the tide-pools which lacks any elaborate equipment for floating. Copepods compose an important part of the basic food supply of surface sea waters. (Courtesy, MacGinitie and MacGinitie: *Natural History of Marine Animals.* New York, McGraw-Hill Book Co., 1949.)

homes, lobsters in coastal sea waters and crayfishes in ponds and streams, most often in limy regions. As a representative crustacean either animal is attractive for study. Crayfishes offer the advantages of being widely distributed and in relatively small demand for food and in general structure they are but smaller editions of lobsters. In North America crayfishes of the genus Cambarus are common east of the Rocky Mountains and Potamobius (Astacus) west of them.

Ecology of the Crayfishes. Crayfishes hide in dark places and forage about on pool bottoms walking on their claws as if on tiptoes, their great pincers held out in front for instant attack, like hands in a reception line. Some species do not burrow, such as *Cambarus bartoni,* one of the common dwellers in small clear streams. *Cambarus diogenes* is a well-known burrower in swamps,

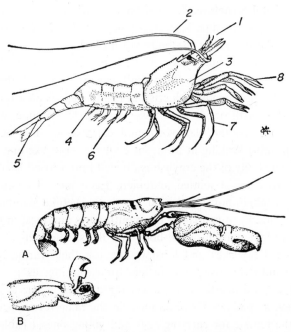

Fig. 29.6. *Upper,* Tidepool shrimp (Spirontocaris, length 1½ inches). *1,* antennule; *2,* antenna; *3,* carapace or "saddle"; *4,* abdomen; *5,* tail fan; *6,* swimmerets; *7,* walking legs; *8,* pincers. *Lower,* Pistol shrimp, *Crangon californiensis* (length, 2 inches) with pincers called pistol-hand closed. *B* shows the pistol-hand "cocked." The hand is the weapon of offense and defense as these shrimps forage in the tide pools where populations are dense and fiercely competitive. (Courtesy, MacGinitie and MacGinitie: *Natural History of Marine Animals.* New York, McGraw-Hill Book Co., 1949.)

where it digs long passages that extend away from the stream, and open above the ground surface through chimneys (Fig. 29.8). They are inactive in winter, eat and grow very little and molt seldom if at all. During droughts, burrowing crayfishes take to their tunnels, stop up the openings and retire into cisterns of ground water. In early spring they appear in the open water, usually in the shallows, leaving their tunnels—considerable numbers about the same time— as if they had precise appointments with the softening temperature.

A crayfish walks forward slowly with the stealth of a cat but a sudden stroke of the tail fin sends it streaking backward. They capture aquatic insects and fishes by lying in wait and seizing them with their claws. They notice moving objects but their other senses, touch, taste and smell, are more important to them (Chap. 17). Frogs, turtles, and herons feed upon little crayfishes. Pickerel and yellow perch take any size, tails in first, and stomachs of pickerel may hold four or five packed spoonwise. The shells of one or two may be completely dissolved off, while those of later arrivals have only thin spots in the shells where digestion has begun.

General External Structure. The exoskeleton of crustaceans is a secretion of the epidermis in which lime is gradually deposited (Fig. 29.9). Exoskeleton not only covers the outside of the body but lines the digestive tube except for the midgut. It will not stretch except while it is soft: neither is it enlarged by additions like the shells of clams. Periodically the crayfish sheds the old skeleton for a new one and this introduces a crisis in its life such as all arthropods share.

BODY REGIONS. Arthropods have fewer and far less regular segments than their annelid relatives, the clamworm and earthworm. The differences between them are most striking at the front end, far more exciting in a crayfish than a worm. The body of the crayfish is divided into a fused head and thorax, the cephalothorax, and a jointed abdomen. Each part is composed of segments. In the cephalothorax, covered by the jacketlike carapace, the segments are indicated by appendages, the mouth parts and legs; in the abdomen by the obvious segmentation of the body and the swimmerets.

APPENDAGES. Crayfishes and lobsters can use their variously specialized appendages in numerous ways: as feelers for exploring; as jaws for tearing and grinding; as food handlers; as bailers for dipping water; as pincer claws for seizing prey; as paddles for swimming; in the male for transferring sperm cells; and in the female for carrying eggs and young ones (Table 29.1). The

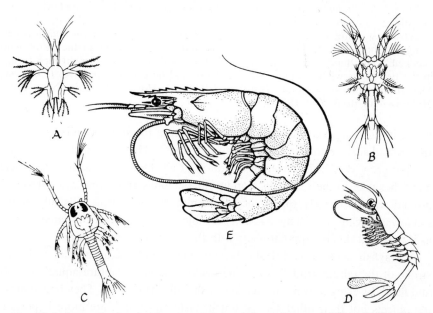

FIG. 29.7. Stages in the development of the shrimp, *Penaeus*. Like other animals, the higher crustaceans go through developmental stages that are in some respects similar to the adults of simpler ones. *A,* nauplius has three pairs of two-branched appendages as in certain simpler crustaceans; *B,* protozoea stage with six pairs of appendages; *C,* the zoea stage, with a distinct head and abdomen; *D,* mysis stage with more appendages on the cephalothorax; *E,* adult shrimp. (Courtesy, Pauli: *The World of Life.* Boston, Houghton Mifflin Co., 1949.)

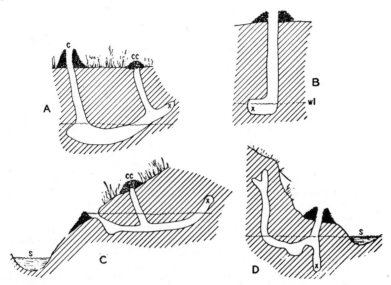

Fig. 29.8. Section of earth showing types of crayfish burrows. *c*, chimney and opening of burrow; *cc*, closed chimney; *s*, stream; *wl*, ground water level; *x*, place from which crayfish was taken. (After Ortman. Courtesy, Robert W. Pennak, *Fresh-Water Invertebrates of the United States*. Copyright 1953, The Ronald Press Company.)

jointed appendages of arthropods are among the most versatile of nature's inventions. The abdominal ones are built on the basic plan nearest the original pattern (Fig. 29.10).

Homology and Evolution of Appendages. The appendages of crayfishes and lobsters are homologous structures with like parts in similar relation to one another. They are striking examples of serial homology, all of them variables of a common pattern. In the developing young, the basic pattern is clear, especially in lobsters.

Internal Organs and Metabolism. DIGESTION. Food is cut, shredded and

Fig. 29.9. Female crayfish in a resting position. Eggs are carried glued to the swimmerets. After they are hatched the young ones hold on for a time with their pincers in the exact fashion of young lobsters.

Table 29.1

PAIRED APPENDAGES OF THE CRAYFISH (OR LOBSTER)—VARIATIONS OF FUNCTION ON THE THEME OF A 3-PIECE APPENDAGE*

Segment†	Appendage	Specialization
1	Antenna	A sensory filament (endo) and a shield for the eye (exo)
2	Mandible	Grinding jaw and a sensory feeler
3	1st maxilla	Food handling
4	2nd maxilla	Thin plates forming scoop to bail water over gills
5	1st maxilliped	Food handling, touch, taste
6	2nd maxilliped	" " " " (gill)‡
7	3rd maxilliped	" " " " "
8	1st walking leg	Pincer and great claw (chela)—grasping, touch (gill)
9	2nd walking leg	Walking and grasping (gill)
10	3rd " "	Walking and grasping, opening of oviduct (gill)
11	4th " "	Walking (gill)
12	5th " "	Walking, cleaning abdomen, opening of sperm duct (gill)
13	1st swimmeret	Reduced in female; in male, protopod and endopod fused forming organ for transferring sperm
14	2nd "	In female, creates currents of water, attachment of eggs and young; in male, takes part in transferring sperm
15	3rd "	Creates currents of water; attachment for eggs
16	4th "	As for 3rd swimmeret
17	5th "	" " " "
18	Uropod (Tail foot)	Swimming oarlike plates used in quick backward glide

* The fundamentals of the 3-piece appendage are a basal piece, protopodite, and two branches, an outer one or exopodite, and an inner one or endopodite. Some authorities list 20 and others 18 pairs of these appendages, depending on interpretations. The argument for 18 pairs is: that the antennules develop from a structure that is homologous with the prostomium ("upper lip") of annelids not considered a segment; and that the antennules and eyes are basically sense organs, not appendages. A gill is attached to certain of the appendages, is moved as they move and thus washed by more water.

† *Segment* indicates the segment of the body represented.

‡ (Gill) means that a gill is attached to the basal piece.

ground, the maxillae and maxillipeds holding it while it is crushed by the mandibles. It then passes through the short esophagus to the stomach. Cray-fishes can live in aquaria very well because being scavengers they do their own housekeeping. They seize earthworms and pieces of meat and their chewing competes with modern meat grinders; three pairs of tools hold, cut, shred and grind; all the motions are rapid, including the frequent spitting out of the rejects.

The stomach is partially divided into two chambers (Fig. 29.11). In the larger front, or cardiac, chamber there are three hard teeth that form a grinding mill moved by muscles attached to the carapace at one end and to the teeth at the other. When the food is crushed fine it enters the pyloric chamber through a strainer of hairlike setae which allow only liquids and fine particles to pass. There it is digested by the pancreaticlike secretion of the large digestive glands. In cooked lobsters these are always "liver," green quilted rolls that start arguments, to eat or not to eat. The digested food is absorbed

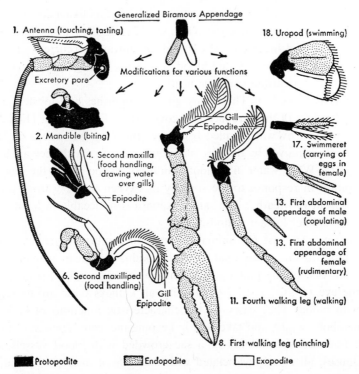

Generalized Biramous Appendage

1. Antenna (touching, tasting)   18. Uropod (swimming)

Modifications for various functions

Excretory pore

Gill
Epipodite

2. Mandible (biting)

17. Swimmeret
(carrying of
eggs in
female)

4. Second maxilla
(food handling,
drawing water
over gills)

Epipodite

13. First abdominal
appendage of male
(copulating)

13. First abdominal
appendage of
female
(rudimentary)

6. Second maxilliped
(food handling)

Gill
Epipodite

11. Fourth walking leg (walking)

8. First walking leg (pinching)

■ Protopodite   ▨ Endopodite   ☐ Exopodite

FIG. 29.10. Homology and the evolution of appendages. The appendages of the left side of a crayfish. All these special structures are believed to have been derived from a generalized two-branched appendage consisting of a basal piece, prodopodite; an inner branch, endopodite; and an outer one, exopodite as shown in the figures. These basic structures are adapted for the different uses noted. They are striking demonstrations of the changes that occur in evolution. (Courtesy, Hegner and Stiles: *College Zoology,* ed. 6. New York, The Macmillan Co., 1951.)

through the intestinal wall in the midgut, the part of the tract not lined with chitin. Only a small amount of waste passes through the straight insignificant-looking intestine. At certain times two limy bodies, the gastroliths, form in pouches in the lining of the cardiac chamber of the stomach. These are associated with molting to be discussed later.

BLOOD AND CIRCULATION. The blood plasma is a watery fluid that contains the bluish respiratory pigment hemocyanin composed of protein, copper, and sulfur. It is similar to the pigment that makes clam broth bluish. Suspended in it are numerous phagocytic cells. It clots very quickly and is probably a life saver every time a claw of a crayfish is bitten off. It distributes food through the body, carries respiratory gases to and from the gills, and waste products to the kidneys. As in all arthropods, the circulation is the open type in which blood vessels open into blood cavities, the sinuses or hemocoels. Blood flows from the heart into the arteries and from them is carried by capillaries to the various tissues, where it passes freely through minute open spaces and gradually accumulates in the large sternal sinus which appears like a coelom but is an unlined blood cavity (hemocoel) (Fig. 29.12). It then flows into the gills through thin walled incurrent vessels and out through excurrent ones. From the gills the now fully oxygenated blood flows back through vessels (branchio-cardiac) to the pericardium and the heart.

RESPIRATORY SYSTEM. The plumy gills of crayfishes and lobsters are pro-tected by the sides of the carapace that covers them like a jacket (Fig. 29.12). They are washed by water bailed back over them by the scoops on the 2nd maxillae and are moved by the legs and mouth parts to which they are attached (Table 29.1). When water in an aquarium becomes too warm, the scoop beats more rapidly. In response to the sparsity of oxygen in the warm water—the crayfish is "out of breath." The same response is noticeable in lobsters caged in tanks at summer lobster pounds.

EXCRETION. At least for animals beyond the embryonic stage, crayfishes and lobsters are unconventional in having kidneys, "green glands," in their heads, each one of the pair opening on a basal segment of an antenna just below the eye (Figs. 29.10, 29.11). Like all kidneys these are closely asso-ciated with blood. They carry on the characteristic functions of kidneys, re-move metabolic waste, and take part in keeping the water content of the body normal. Each consists mainly of a sac crowded with blood vessels, minute blood sinuses, all closely associated with the coils of microscopic kidney tu-

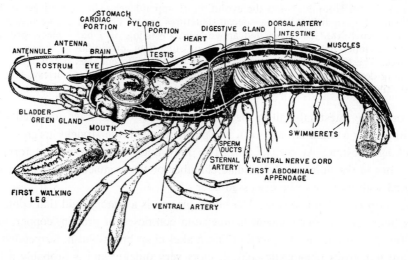

FIG. 29.11. Internal structure of the male crayfish (very similar to that of the lobster). The green gland is the secretory or working part of the kidney; the "bladder" of the diagram refers to the urinary bladder that opens externally below the eye. Note the sperm duct opening externally in the basal segment of the fifth walking leg. Sperm cells are placed in the seminal receptacle of the female by the slender first and second abdominal appendages here shown. These are easy recogni-tion marks of male crayfishes and lobsters. (Courtesy, MacDougall and Hegner: *Biology*. New York, McGraw-Hill Book Co., 1943.)

bules, and a canal that opens into the urinary bladder which in turn opens externally. The entire crustacean kidney is in principle comparable to one unit of the vertebrate kidney. Although crayfishes live in fresh water, they keep an adequately salt solution in their bodies by the water resistance of their body cover, by water loss from the kidneys, and by the absorption of salt by the gills. Like all fresh-water invertebrates they contain a higher percentage of salt than the surrounding water which would flood their bodies except for the special means of keeping it out.

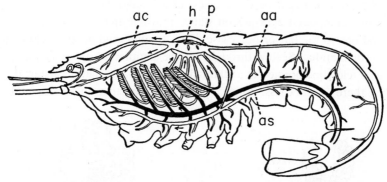

Fig. 29.12. Diagram of the respiratory and circulatory systems of the crayfish or lobster. Efferent blood vessels from gills to heart, and the arteries are unshaded; afferent vessels to the gills, and veins are black. Left side of heart with three openings; *p*, pericardium; *h*, heart; *aa*, abdominal aorta; *ac*, cephalic aorta; *as*, ventral abdominal artery. (After Claus. Courtesy, Conklin: *General Morphology*. Princeton, Princeton University Press, 1927.)

Coordination and Response. The central nervous system is similar to that of the earthworm but obviously further developed in the head and thorax corresponding with the more elaborate activities of the crayfish (Fig. 29.11).

In the embryo, each of the segments contains a pair of ganglia but in the adult crayfish members of the pairs and some of the pairs are fused. Numerous nerves penetrate throughout the body, all of them composed of the processes of nerve cells whose bodies are in the ganglia.

By means of sensory pits and bristles the surface of the body is more or less responsive, the pincers particularly to touch and the antennules to taste.

The organs of equilibrium by which the crayfish keeps its upright position are located in small chitin-lined sacs, the statocysts, one on the basal segment of each antennule (Fig. 29.11). Within the statocyst is a sensory cushion on which there are numerous sensory hairs innervated by a single nerve cell fiber. Large grains of sand (statoliths) are placed in the cup by the crayfish, an extraordinary habit. These adhere to hairs made sticky by a secretion produced below the sensory cushion. The contact of the sand with the sensory hairs is communicated by way of a nerve fiber to the central nervous system and thence to the muscles. The linings of the statocysts are molted with the rest of the skeleton and crayfishes cannot keep their balance until they have another supply of sand grains. An experiment made upon shrimps is easily repeated on crayfishes. Newly molted ones are placed in an aquarium of filtered water, clear except for a scattering of iron filings dropped into it. After exploring the bottom a while the crayfishes pick up the filings with their pincers and place them in the statocysts. If an electromagnet is then moved about in the water the crayfishes will follow it. According to the position of the magnet, they roll from side to side or lie on their backs and stab the air with their legs. The exercise might be the preview of a human dance.

The two compound eyes are on stalks, movable independently, one to the right and one to the left or otherwise. Each is composed of some 2500 simple eyes or ommatidia. Seeing through one or another of these is like seeing through a telescope pointed at a starry sky; through one there is a star; through another there is darkness. Many simple eyes together bring a picture put

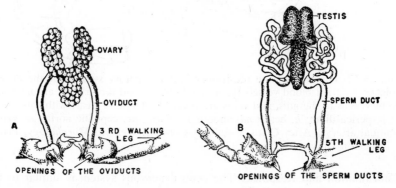

FIG. 29.13. *A*, female reproductive system of the crayfish. *B*, male reproductive system of the crayfish. (Courtesy, MacDougall and Hegner: *Biology*. New York, McGraw-Hill Book Co., 1943.)

together like a dissected puzzle as shown by photographs which have been taken through parts of the eyes of insects. With such movable eyes as those of crayfishes the pictures must be different in each one. Sight is essentially the same in crustaceans as in insects.

Reproduction and Life History. Crayfishes mate in September and through November of their first year. At that time, sperm are passed along the specialized appendages of the male to the seminal receptacle of the female, a cavity in a fold of cuticle on the mid-ventral line between the fourth and fifth pairs of legs (Fig. 29.13). The eggs are laid in April while the females are still within the burrows. Before spawning she cleans the underside of her abdomen, picking it over meticulously with her pincers. Then she lies on her back, with her abdomen curved so that it makes a bowl. Presently a gluey secretion flows out from the cement glands and over the bases of the swimmerets and tail pieces (uropods) coating every surface. Following this preparation eggs pour from the oviducts and pass backward across the seminal receptacle where they are fertilized. Further backward they spread out among the swimmerets, and stick fast to their fringes. Crayfishes and lobsters carrying eggs are said to be "in berry" (Fig. 29.9). The eggs of crayfishes hatch in five to eight weeks but the young ones, in Cambarus—diminutives of adults, are for some time fastened to the egg shells by delicate threads that act like "mother's apron strings." During their first year they molt about every 12 days and after that usually only twice a year, once in spring, and again in late summer.

Regeneration. Crayfishes can replace lost appendages but to a lesser extent than animals more simply organized. After a leg is lost, a new one appears partly formed at the next molt, and larger at each succeeding molt until it is complete.

Self-amputation—Autotomy. Crayfishes and other crustaceans, especially crabs, amputate their own thoracic legs. If a leg is injured or grasped it may be suddenly snapped off at a definite breaking place, on the basal segment of the great claw or at the third joint at the other legs. Across the inside of the leg on the proximal side of the breaking place there is a partition with a small hole in the center through which nerves and blood vessels extend to the tip of the leg. When the leg is cast off the hole is quickly stopped by a blood clot.

Molting and Hormones. A crayfish sheds a hard exoskeleton that fits tightly and will not stretch. It appears in a new one that is soft and elastic, and adjustable to increased size (Fig. 29.14). The old skeleton was brittle with calcium; the new one contains relatively little of it.

Molting is a laborious process during which every smallest spine and filament of the gill is pulled from its old cover. As it proceeds, the molting animal uses more and more oxygen until the shedding is over. Then, for a time, it is weak and helpless. There are profound adjustments in the metabolism of calcium in preparation for the discard of the old skeleton and the completion of the new one. For some time previous to the molt, a quantity of calcium from the old exoskeleton is absorbed and distributed by the blood especially to the stomach where it is deposited in the gastroliths (Fig. 29.14). Experiments prove that the formation of the gastrolith is under the control of an endocrine gland. After molting, the cuticle of the new exoskeleton is hardened by calcium brought from the gastroliths by the blood as well as from new supplies absorbed from the surrounding water. Most arthropods absorb unusual quantities of water before molting. This swells their bodies, helps to split the old exoskeleton and partly accounts for the sudden enlargement of the "soft-shelled" animal.

An endocrine secretion limits the number of molts. It is produced by the minute sinus glands, one in each eyestalk of crustaceans which have eye stalks;

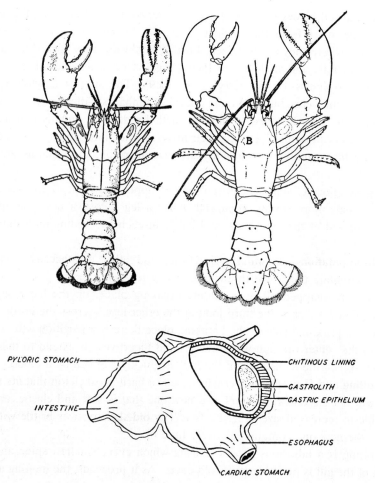

Fig. 29.14. *Upper, A,* the sudden increase in size of a lobster after molting. The skeleton that was shed has a crack in the thorax through which the lobster emerged. *B,* the "soft-shelled" lobster after the molt. The sudden increase in size is due to growth before molting and expansion afterward. *Lower,* diagram of the stomach of the crayfish with a part cut away to show the gastrolith in the wall of the cardiac chamber. For some time before molting calcium from the old exoskeleton is absorbed by the blood and is stored in the gastrolith. (*Upper,* after Herrick. Courtesy, Wolcott: *Animal Biology,* ed. 3. New York, McGraw-Hill Book Co., 1946. *Lower,* courtesy, Turner: *General Endocrinology,* ed. 2. Philadelphia, W. B. Saunders Co., 1955.)

in others they lie close to the brain. It is possible to remove the glands from the eye stalks of a crayfish without injuring other structures, and when this is done the animals form gastroliths, absorb extra water, consume more food and oxygen and molt repeatedly. This can be prevented, however, by grafting sinus glands of other crayfishes into those whose own glands have been removed.

OTHER EFFECTS OF HORMONES. The sinus glands of crayfishes in some way stimulate movement of the pigments in the retina of the eyes (Fig. 15.2). Experiments have shown that products of the sinus glands regulate shifting color changes in the skin once thought to be nerve controlled.

ENTOMOSTRACANS

Entomostracans are crustaceans, most of them small, even microscopic, and numerous beyond imagination. They feed upon the minute plants of fresh and salt waters and thus are the chief means of turning them into food for higher animals. They are themselves the main food of nearly all young fishes and the adults of several market fishes. There are three groups, the branchiopods, copepods, and ostracods.

Branchiopods

The gill-footed crustaceans, Branchiopoda, have thoracic feet that are expanded and function as gills. Most of them live in fresh water, among them the fairy shrimps (Eubranchipus), the largest and most colorful of entomostracans but not important food producers. The most common branchiopods, of the Order Cladocera, are the almost microscopic water fleas. The body, but not the head, is enclosed in a bivalve shell so transparent that the pulsating heart, the circulating blood, the contracting muscles, and vibrating gill feet can be clearly seen. Many water fleas swim by their antennae; Daphne and others with long antennae take slow strong strokes and go through the water in jumps; those that have short antennae make quicker strokes and progress evenly (Fig. 29.5).

The females carry the eggs and developing young in brood sacs. In summer they reproduce parthenogenetically. Their possible productivity is suggested by the calculation that, barring accident, the descendants of one female *Daphne pulex* might reach 13 billion in 60 days. Their populations create living soup.

Copepods

From springs to lakes, from tide pools to the open ocean hardly any body of water is without copepods. Those of one or another species are active in summer and winter, most abundant wherever there are diatoms, their main food. The great populations of glassily transparent copepods, a large part of the surface fauna of the ocean, are the main link in the food chain between microscopic plants and large animals. The blue whale, the largest of living animals, feeds chiefly upon Calenus. Two tons of this little copepod, believed to be one day's swallowing, have been taken from the stomach of a blue whale. Three simple eyes (ocelli) are often fused into one compound eye. The one-eyed jerky copepods, Cyclops, live as well in aquaria as they do in ponds. The developing eggs and sometimes the young ones (nauplii) are carried in brood sacs, one on each side of the tail. Copepods are prodigies in reproduction. *Tisbe furcata,* common in salt-water aquaria, goes through its life cycle from egg to reproducing adult in 9 to 10 days (Fig. 29.5).

Ostracods

Ostracods are minute crustaceans, about one millimeter long. An ostracod might be mistaken for a microscopic clam were it not for the appendages that kick out between the valves, neither in structure nor character like a clam. Ostracods live in fresh water and salt, usually creeping over plants, occasionally swimming out into surface waters. They range into new places during the free swimming nauplius stage.

CRUSTACEANS AS HUMAN FOOD

Of all the crustaceans, shrimps probably take first place as human food with crabs and lobsters close followers and crayfishes far behind.

Texas and other Gulf states furnish most of the shrimps for the American market. They are fished from South Carolina southward and to some extent on the northern Pacific coast. There are several "edible" species, one or another being more highly regarded in different regions. Those of the same species are called prawns or shrimps depending on their size, the shrimps being smaller. Shrimps have long been thought of as little shrunken lobsters and their name is derived from the Old English, scrimman, meaning shrink. Thus, somebody may be a "little shrimp." The main edible crab of the east coast of North America is the blue swimming crab (*Callinectes sapidus,* Cape Cod to Florida). On the west coast, the edible crabs include several species; in some of them the thorax of the adults is commonly nearly a foot wide.

The American lobster, *Homarus americana,* ranges from Labrador to South Carolina, along rocky coasts, in the shallows in summer, in deeper water in winter. The female lays her eggs in July and August, about 10,000 by a 10-inch lobster. The mating and egg laying are similar to those of crayfishes except that the lobster carries the eggs 10 to 11 months before they hatch and spawns only every other year. Lobster culturists claim that a modest crop of two adults from each 10,000 eggs is sufficient to maintain the species. The smaller spiny lobster (*Panulirus interruptus*) is the edible lobster of the Pacific Coast. Whether it has a quality of flavor equal to the New England lobster is difficult to discover, in New England.

30

Arthropods—Insects, Spiders, and Allies

Insects are small arthropods encased in lightweight, waterproof and flexible exoskeletons. Basic features of their success are—their ability to live on land, their economy of space and food, and their production of many offspring. Their exoskeleton protects them from the evaporation that would otherwise be inevitable with small size and life in dry air. Sense organs and sensory cells in abundance can be stimulated through the exoskeleton which thus becomes a means of contact and adjustment to the surroundings.

Insects have always lived with human beings; fleas have shared their blood; cockroaches, their food; and silkworms provided them with draperies. Insects have pressed upon humanity, hundreds of thousands of species to one of man. They have crowded over the earth for ages, far longer than man has existed. Many of them live together socially, ants, bees and others following inborn patterns that bear undeniable resemblances to those of human society. Not only are insects and man associated with one another, but among all animals they are the two paragons of social life.

Characteristics. Insects can fly. In this they are unique among invertebrates as birds are unique among the vertebrates. There are relatively few adult insects that cannot fly—primitive species and confirmed parasites such as lice and fleas. Immature insects do not fly except the mayflies and these do so only when they are in a subadult stage.

All insects are clothed in an integument, the living epidermis or "skin" and the nonliving exoskeleton or cuticle which it secretes (Figs. 30.1, 30.3). The exoskeleton of insects differs from that of crustaceans in the absence of lime and importance of chitin. The terms exoskeleton and cuticle are both used for the secreted layer but the latter suggests its chemical content and applies especially to insects. The best-known component of cuticle is chitin, a nitrogenous polysaccharide $(C_{32}H_{54}N_4O_{21})_x$ that is insoluble in water, dilute acids, and the digestive juices of many animals. Chitin is extremely resistant to decay and has been analyzed from the remains of beetles that lived in the Eocene Period of 25 million years ago. In addition to covering the body, the cuticle lines the fore- and hindgut, the air-tubes and the ducts of surface glands.

An insect is an air-breathing arthropod with a distinct head, thorax, and abdomen. The in-cut sharpness with which these parts are set off suggested

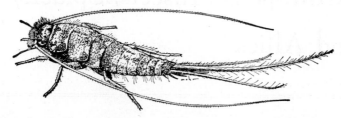

FIG. 30.1. Insects live almost everywhere and in unimagined places and ways. They represent perfection of adjustment and success. Silverfish, *Thermobia domestica,* a wingless insect about half an inch long, a rapid runner and skillful dodger. The various domestic species live in the warmest places in houses, eat glue, starch and paper, and are pests in libraries. Out of doors other species frequent moist fallen leaves. (Courtesy, Ross: *Entomology.* New York, John Wiley and Sons, 1948.)

the name insect. The head bears most of the sense organs, the thorax includes those of locomotion, and the abdomen those of reproduction. All adult insects have six legs, thus the name, Class Hexapoda. As adults, they usually have either one or two pairs of wings. The primitive wingless ones are the Thysanura, silverfish and firebrats and the Collembola, springtails (Fig. 30.1). Male and female organs are in separate individuals and fertilization is internal.

Abundance, Reproductive Capacity and Size. There are some six times as many species of insects as of all other animals (Fig. 30.4; Table 30.1). At least 685,900 have been described but there is no complete catalogue, and the estimates shift with many additions and changes due to duplications. Many new species are still being discovered, especially in the tropics. The number in any one locality is relatively small, varying greatly with the climate. Only 15,449 are given in "A List of the Insects of New York (state)" published in 1928 (Cornell University).

Individual insects are countless. The two or three hundred tent caterpillars in one web swell to enormous numbers when they are compounded with those in an unsprayed apple orchard. Mayflies emerge from the water by millions, fly for a brief period, then fall to the ground and mounds of them, accumulating under the lamps in lakeside parks, are cleared away by shovelfuls. In some pantries and kitchens, the supply of cockroaches is like a never-failing

Fig. 30.2. Termites. Buildings of the magnetic termites (*Hamitermes meridionalis*) or white ants near Darwin, Australia. They are slabs of peaty soil whose long axes lie almost exactly north and south. Within them millions of termites populate the passageways and the chambers are filled with grass collected in the wet season (November to April) and stored to last through the dry season (May to October). On a smaller scale termites in the milder climates of the United States build similar passageways in wood. (Photograph by W. Brindle. Courtesy, Australian National Information Bureau.)

spring. Warm damp evenings murmur with mosquitoes and a meadow lighted by fireflies tells more about their numbers than can be written. In autumn, ladybird beetles turn gregarious and pack together in protected spots for the winter. In northern California, ladybirds (*Hippodamia convergens*) go to the mountains in winter and hide under the pine needles in sunny slopes. Two persons working together can collect 50 to 100 pounds of them in a day and since each beetle weighs about 20 milligrams, a day's catch is estimated to be at least one to two and a half millions.

The reproductive capacity of insects depends upon the number of eggs laid and the length of time it takes for an egg to develop into an adult. "Seventeen year locusts" are 17 years old before they produce eggs, but most insects mature within a year or less. A grand climax is attained by aphids with 30 generations in a single season, nearly every one wholly made up of productive females and each generation a stepping stone to a larger generation. Aphids must be a pleasure to mathematicians. Herrick calculated the weight of cabbage aphids that produce 12 parthenogenetic generations between late March

FIG. 30.3. Carpenter ants (Camponotus), about half an inch long, and burnished black, in the corridors which they have cut. These ants are common in and out of houses. Their young are here shrouded in white cocoons. (Photograph by Lynwood Chace. Courtesy, National Audubon Society.)

and mid-August. At the end of that time, the progeny of the original female would weigh 800 million tons providing every one were living.

Insects are like old miniatures in their perfection within small size. Some are larger than the smallest vertebrate and others are smaller than the largest protozoan. The smallest North American beetles can scarcely be seen without a lens, yet their structure is as complex as any other insect. The Central American rhinoceros beetle (*Megasoma elephas*), a relative of our common June beetle, is five and a half inches long.

The large size of ancient animals was no more successful for insects than for the great reptiles. Only the fossils are left to tell the old story, too much body to feed and no place to hide. A fossil dragonfly (Meganeura) has a wing expanse of two feet; there are no such living ones (Fig. 30.5).

Habitats and Distribution. Although their remote ancestors came from the

Table 30.1

NUMBER OF DESCRIBED SPECIES OF INSECTS, TICKS, AND MITES AT THE END OF 1948*

Order	Common Names	World	North America, north of Mexico
Anoplura	Sucking lice (true lice)	250	62
Coleoptera	Beetles, weevils, twisted winged insects	277,000	26,676
Collembola	Springtails	2,000	314
Corrodentia	Booklice, barklice	1,100	120
Dermaptera	Earwigs	1,100	18
Diptera	Flies, mosquitoes, gnats	85,000	16,700
Embioptera	Embiids	149	8
Ephemeroptera	Mayflies	1,500	550
Hemiptera	True bugs and Homoptera (cicadas, leafhoppers, aphids, scale insects)	55,000	8,742
Hymenoptera	Ants, bees, wasps	103,000	14,528
Isoptera	Termites ("white ants")	1,717	41
Lepidoptera	Butterflies and moths	112,000	10,300
Mallophaga	Biting lice (bird lice)	2,675	318
Mecoptera	Scorpionflies	350	66
Neuroptera	Lacewings, ant lions, dobsonflies	4,670	338
Odonata	Dragonflies, damselflies	4,870	412
Orthoptera	Grasshoppers, crickets, roaches, mantids, katydids	22,500	1,015
Plecoptera	Stoneflies	1,490	340
Protura	....	90	29
Siphonaptera	Fleas	1,100	238
Thysanoptera	Thrips	3,170	606
Thysanura	Bristletails, "Silverfish"	700	50
Trichoptera	Caddisflies	4,450	921
Zoraptera†	....	19	2
Total	....	685,900	82,394
Acarina	Ticks	440	113
	Mites	8,700	2,500

* Source: *Insects,* U.S.D.A. Yearbook of Agriculture, 1952.

† Zoraptera includes Corrodentia or booklice, Embioptera—minute tropical species, and Protura—minute and rare species.

sea, insects have been land-adjusted for millions of years. In their immature stages, mosquitoes can thrive in brackish water but with rare exceptions, insects keep away from the sea. Those of several groups live in fresh water while they are immature and some others remain there as adults but all breathe air as adults and are essentially terrestrial.

Insects have spread almost all over the earth, in abundance in all tropical and temperate countries and as parasites living on the warm bodies of birds and mammals, in arctic and antarctic lands. One or another kind of insect makes a living in every conceivable location in and out of buildings, in every part of all kinds of plants, in forests and open fields. Insects are persistently active, feeding, and flying, constantly urged to shift their places by competition for food and space and changes in their microclimates. In general, they do not make long flights. The forays of migratory grasshoppers are exceptions; so are the seasonal migrations of butterflies (Fig. 30.6).

Insects are carried long distances by air currents. Newly hatched gypsy-moth larvae are buoyed up in the air by small air pockets on the hairs with

FIG. 30.4. Diagram representing the relative abundance of insects (Hexapoda) and other animals. (Courtesy, Frost: *Entomology.* New York, McGraw-Hill Book Co., 1942.)

which their bodies are covered. They have been captured 300 feet or more up in the air and on strong winds they may travel many miles a day. Insects travel far and wide on human beings and their vehicles—by water, by land, and by air.

Molting and Metamorphosis. MOLTING. The young insect grows larger but its cuticle does not. Relief comes to it only with a new and larger cuticle and escape from the old one, that is, by molting.

As before stated, the integument of insects consists of epidermal cells and the cuticle that they secrete. The cuticle includes two regions of different chemical content; the outer cuticle, mainly cuticulin, fats and waxes, is resistant to injury and has an outermost waxy layer; the inner cuticle is composed chiefly of chitin.

There are several steps in the preparation for molting. (1) The epidermal cells secrete a new outer cuticle which then lies between them and the old cuticle. (2) Specialized epidermal cells secrete molting fluid which passes outward through ducts in the new outer cuticle and spreads over its surface. In doing so it separates the new and the old outer cuticles. (3) Molting fluid gradually digests the old inner cuticle. (4) In the meantime, the epidermal cells are forming a new inner cuticle. The molting fluid does not digest this.

The digested substance of the old inner cuticle is absorbed back into the body. This has been shown by the absorption through the body wall of dye injected between the old and new cuticles. At this time the new cuticle is permeable to water. An insect sheds its old cuticle soon after the new one is completed. Some insects do this too quickly to be clearly observed; others

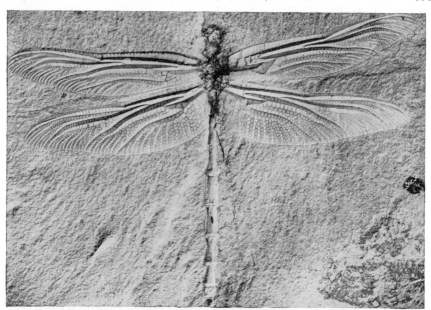

FIG. 30.5. A dragonfly is ancient history on wings. The form of this one was preserved in stone over 250 million years ago, long before there were birds to fly. Of three great steps in the evolution of insects, wings held straight out from the body came first; wings folded to the body when at rest was second; complete change of form in a single lifetime came third. (Courtesy, Frank M. Carpenter, Harvard University.)

take several minutes. The insect contracts the muscles of its legs and abdomen forcing blood into the thorax which swells accordingly. Young mayflies swallow air. The old cuticle cracks along the line on the head and thorax where the inner cuticle has never formed and the other one is weak. A molting insect bucks its thorax upward, wriggles its body free of the old cuticle, and contracts it spasmodically. This drives blood into the wings and legs which stiffen out as molting is completed. Forcing the blood here and there during molting stretches the cuticle to its utmost, leaving the softer parts in folds that are smoothed out only after further growth. The new cuticle hardens and darkens in a short time, but this is not due simply to exposure to air. If a part of the new cuticle is exposed by the removal of a piece of the old one 24 hours before molting, the new cuticle will neither harden nor darken.

METAMORPHOSIS. The young insect that crawls out of the eggshell is usually quite unlike the adult it will become. Between hatching and maturity insects increase in size mainly by steps at molting time. Most of them undergo a metamorphosis or change of form. The less the young and adult resemble one another, the greater are the structural changes inside and outside of the body.

There are three main types of metamorphosis (Fig. 30.7). (1) With slight change of form and no wings ever developed, e.g., the household silverfish

FIG. 30.6. Monarch butterflies (*Danaus menippe*) resting while on an autumn migration. They rest at night and whenever the wind is strong. (Photograph by Hugh Halliday. Courtesy, National Audubon Society.)

(Thysanura) and the springtails (Collembola). (2) With gradual or incomplete change of form or metamorphosis—the wings developing as external pads; in the immature stages the young are called nymphs. Grasshoppers, crickets, cockroaches, cicadas, squashbugs, dragonflies, mayflies and others develop in this way. Nymphs usually feed in the same manner and on the same food as the adults. (3) With complete change of form or metamorphosis, the wings

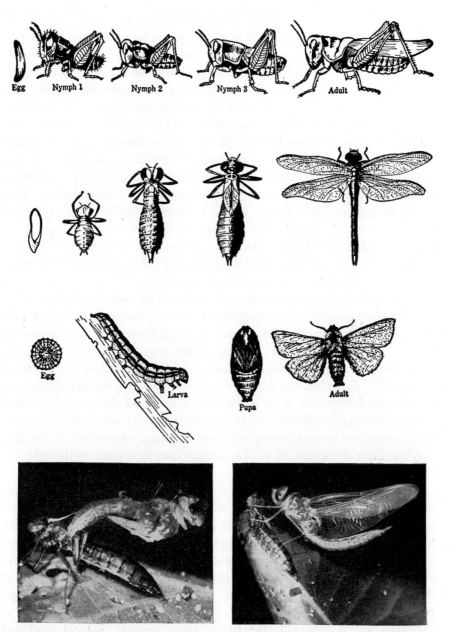

FIG. 30.7. *Upper,* types of life histories and metamorphoses: gradual metamorphosis of the grasshopper; incomplete metamorphosis of the dragonfly that
lives in water and breathes by internal tracheal gills during immaturity, and on
land as an adult; complete change of form in the army worm. *Lower,* transformation of a dragonfly. *Left,* the full-grown nymph has crawled onto a floating lily
pad. The adult has emerged through a crack in the nymphal skin, and is bent
backward still wet and soft, with wings tightly folded. *Right,* the adult rests with
stiffening wings unfurled. (*Upper,* courtesy, Strausbaugh and Weimer: *General
Biology.* New York, John Wiley and Sons, 1952. *Lower,* photographs by Lynwood
M. Chace. Courtesy, National Audubon Society.)

developing as internal pads; in the immature stages the young are called larvae and pupae. Bees, wasps and ants, moths and butterflies, beetles, and caddis-flies develop in this way. The larvae eat ravenously and increase greatly in size. At the end of several molts, the number depending upon the species, they transform into pupae. The pupa does not eat and moves little or none. It is a stage of transformation in which the outer form and the internal structures are changed; the digestive tube is reshaped; the reproductive organs are developed. Even the tissues are reorganized, and muscle is literally made over. The adult is the final mature stage. The larvae of moths and butterflies are caterpillars, strikingly different from the adult even in appetite. "Cabbage worms" have insatiable appetites for cabbage leaves; cabbage butterflies follow the scent of cabbage plants but only to lay their eggs on them, never to eat them.

Foods Habits and Mouth Parts. Insects of one sort or another eat all kinds of food. Many are very special but altogether they fall into four general groups, plant feeders, predators, scavengers, and parasites.

Nearly half of all insects feed upon living plants, the most reliable food there is. Most plant feeders prefer one group of plants or they may feed upon only one part of the plant, the leaf, stem, root, bud, flower and fruit. Plant lice (aphids) insert their slender, piercing mouth parts into the tissues of ten-der leaves and stems, dissolve the tissues with saliva and suck out the juices (Fig. 30.8). In spring, the garden cut-worms (larva of noctuid moths) are roused from hibernation in the soil and begin biting off the stems of seedling plants—tomatoes, cucumbers and others at the surface level of the soil. Gipsy-moth caterpillars eat oak leaves, veins and all; larvae of elm-leaf beetles take only one layer of the leaf. Most plant feeders take their meals in daylight, but there are some evening diners.

Predacious insects are less abundant than the plant eaters. Predators have dash and go, or stealth. Dragonflies with their arrowy flight, clutching fore-legs, and chewing jaws were built for predation 100 million years ago. The larva of the ant lion (Myrmeleon) digs a trap, an inverted cone in loose dry sand. Ants roll down the slopes of the cone and as they struggle, they are showered with sand by a twist of the ant lion's head whose jaws await them at the bottom. The majority of predatory insects depend upon less active vege-tarian insects for food.

Certain insects, especially the larvae, are scavengers that eat dead and decaying animal matter. Two familiar ones are houseflies and clothes moths. Both are typical scavengers but the clothes moth larvae have an insatiable craving for keratin, the hornlike substances in hair (fur, wool) and feathers. Many insects are parasites, living on other animals, and gradually consuming them while they are in the living state. Among them are the blood-sucking fleas, biting lice of birds, and the parasites of other insects.

The mouth parts of insects are often specialized and elaborate. The main

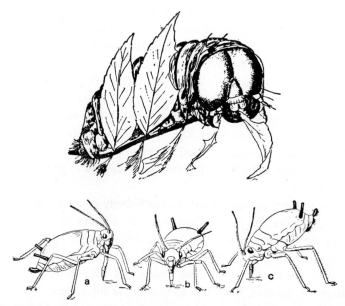

FIG. 30.8. Biting mouth parts in action. *Upper,* caterpillar shearing a leaf with its cutting jaws (mandibles). Its upper lip (labrum) and the attached piece (clypeus) hang downward at the center. The second pair of jaws (maxillae), the lower lip (labium) and the tongue are hidden. *Lower,* sucking mouth parts in action. Plant lice feeding. *a,* finding a place; *b,* needling in the slender tube, mainly composed of the mandibles and maxillae; *c,* sucking up the sap. The combination of piercing and sucking is the method of feeding in such successful insects as the plant lice, squash bugs, mosquitoes and bed bugs; and sucking is the way of the moths and butterflies. (Courtesy, Matheson: *Entomology*. Ithaca, N.Y., Comstock Publishing Co., 1944.)

biting tools are the mandibles hinged to the head at the sides of the mouth and operated by muscles that oppose or separate their tips, a sidewise bite. In the lapping and sucking equipments of insects the mandibles, maxillae, labrum and hypopharynx are stiletto-like blades combined into a beak used for sucking sap or blood and other fluids (Fig. 30.8). Houseflies lap up syrup. In stable flies (Stomoxys) the lapping organ has become needlelike and able to pierce the flesh. The long nectar-sucking tube of moths and butterflies consists only of maxillae that fit together and make a tube. Their mandibles and other parts have ceased to develop. No butterfly can bite.

Representative Insects—Grasshopper and Honeybee

THE GRASSHOPPER

Grasshoppers are generalized in structure and habits, less so than cockroaches, but outside of agriculture more attractive in human circles. Generalized insects are comparable to the crows that can both walk and fly, specialized ones to humming birds that can fly but scarcely walk. The ancestors of grasshoppers were pioneer insects in the warm dampness of the Carboniferous Period, when primeval forests were being slowly overspread and were turning to coal beds. Their fossils show that since then grasshoppers and cockroaches have changed far less than most insects.

Grasshopper. Grasshoppers belong to the family Locustidae, the locusts or short-horned grasshoppers with antennae shorter than the body. They include the common red-legged grasshopper (*Melanoplus femur-rubrum*), the "Carolina locust" (*Dissosteira carolina*), the "Rocky Mountain locust" (*Melanoplus mexicanus*), and the short-winged lubber grasshopper of the south, often studied in laboratories. The following discussion applies in general to any one of these.

The names grasshopper and locust are confusingly applied even to the same species. Grasshoppers are permanently resident, solitary species such as the common red-legged one. "Locusts" are migratory grasshoppers, such as the Rocky Mountain locusts that periodically produce enormous populations, completely exhaust the food in their own region and then move from one new feeding ground to another. In 1933 and before and since then, "Rocky Mountain locusts" have swarmed over the country from the Rocky Mountains eastward nearly to the Mississippi River, devastating corn and wheat fields and all ground vegetation before them.

Ecology. Grasshoppers flourish in sunlit fields of grass and grain. The young ones hatch in early spring, by July are usually abundant, and in August sprays of grasshoppers arise wherever long grass is disturbed.

FOOD AND RELATIONSHIPS. A great element of success in life is the habit of living on common food. The success of the tribes of grasshoppers is due to this habit. No other invertebrates consume grass and grains in such quantities.

Toads, frogs, owls, meadowlarks, chipmunks, and ground squirrels all feed upon grasshoppers. Parasites also beset them, young hair worms that bore into their bodies, red mites that hang from them like brilliant beads. Enough grasshoppers to produce a plague would appear every year were it not for the mishaps that befall the eggs, the attacks of parasites, winter freezing and thawing, spring floods, skunks and ground moles that nose them out of the ground, and their great enemies, the larvae of blister beetles. A nicety in seizing an opportunity is exemplified by certain small wasps (Lepidoscelio) which ride about on the females until they lay their eggs, and then deposit their own eggs beside them (Fig. 30.9).

External Structures and Functions. Like other agile animals, grasshoppers are bilaterally symmetrical. The body consists of three divisions, the head, the thorax, the abdomen (Fig. 30.10).

HEAD. The head is a hard capsule, composed of immovable plates or sclerites. The eyes and antennae, mandibles, maxillae and labium are believed to represent different segments in the wormlike ancestors. There are two kinds

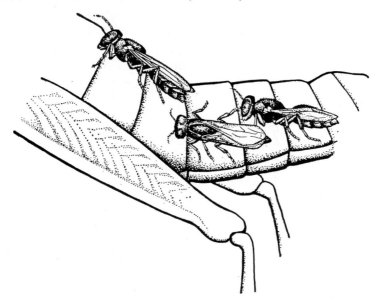

Fig. 30.9. Successful hitchhikers, quick transport and the right landing place. Females of wasp-like insects (Lepidoscelio) that ride about on grasshoppers until the latter lay their eggs. Then they dismount and lay their own eggs on those of the grasshopper in which their larvae develop. (After Brues: *Insect Dietary*. Cambridge, Mass., Harvard University Press, 1946.)

of eyes, simple (ocelli) and compound, the latter an assemblage of simple eyes. Insects never have but one pair of antennae; in grasshoppers they are primarily feelers. In other insects they may have auditory, olfactory, or respiratory functions.

Grasshoppers have the complete quota of mouth parts typical of insects (Fig. 30.11). Their comparative simplicity is a contrast to the specializations of the blood-sucking equipment of mosquitoes and the nectar-dippers of bees. The exact shape of the jaws of grasshoppers is also well fitted to bite particular plant tissues. Lubber grasshoppers feed upon leaves and have jagged "teeth" that tear and shred. Another species eats seeds that it cuts and chisels (Fig. 30.12). The mouth parts include: (1) the broad upper lip or labrum; (2) a median tonguelike hypopharynx; (3) two heavy biting jaws, the mandibles, so shaped that the teeth interlock; (4) two slender jaws, the maxillae whose several parts include jointed palpi with sensory organs on their tips; and (5) a broad median lower lip, the labium with two jointed palpi that bear sensory organs. The opening of the salivary glands is on the edge of the tongue or hypopharynx.

THORAX. The thorax, with the legs and wings, holds the chief muscles of locomotion and the nerve centers that control them (Fig. 30.10). It is divided into prothorax, mesothorax, and metathorax. On the dorsal side of the

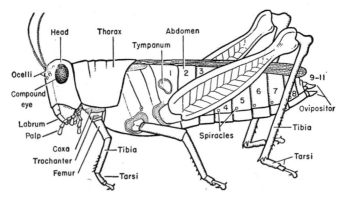

FIG. 30.10. Grasshopper. The tarsus of the hind foot is comparable to the sole of the human foot in relation to the surface. Foothold is strengthened by claws and non-skid pads. The hind legs are the powerful equipment for take-off in the jump of grasshoppers as they are in kangaroos.

prothorax there is a saddle-shaped sclerite that extends forward and protects the neck. Each of the other divisions bears one pair of spiracles and a pair of legs and wings; in the course of evolution the sclerites in these divisions have been greatly modified in accommodating the large muscles of locomotion.

Legs. In climbing plant stems grasshoppers pull with their front legs and push with the hind ones. Their take-off for a jump is a relatively enormous

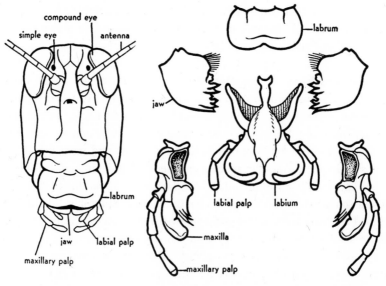

FIG. 30.11. Head and mouth parts of the grasshopper; outer surfaces of the jaws (mandibles) and upper lip (labrum); inner surfaces of the maxillae and lower lip (labium). (After Snodgrass. Reprinted from *Animals Without Backbones* by Buchsbaum, by permission of The University of Chicago Press. Copyright, 1948.)

push which would end in a crash-landing except for the flexiblity and spread of the middle and front legs and the jack-knife bend of the hind ones. As animals walk and run they alternately balance and move their bodies. The balance is a momentary rest on one, two, or three feet, depending on the type, whether human, horse, beetle, or others (Fig. 10.10). The movement, also momentary, is a falling forward of the body or a fall coupled with a pull. As an insect walks it balances by resting on a tripod, the first and last leg of one side, and the middle leg of the other. The balance quickly shifts into movement

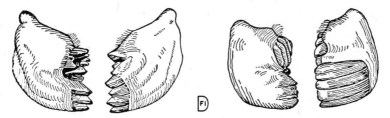

Fig. 30.12. Mouthparts of insects are precision tools, mandibles of two species of grasshoppers that eat different foods. *Left,* the lubber grasshopper (*Brachystola magna*) feeds on foliage. *Right,* another grasshopper (*Mermaria maculipennis*) feeds on seeds. (Redrawn from Isely. Courtesy, Brues: *Insect Dietary.* Cambridge, Mass., Harvard University Press, 1946.)

as the other three legs are swung forward. In this latter trio, the front leg pulls the body, the middle one lifts it, and the hind one pushes. The insect goes forward in such a slight zigzag that it seems to be a straight line.

Wings. Many invertebrates can walk and crawl but only the insects can fly. The wings of birds are highly modified front legs; those of insects have no relation to their legs. The wings of most insects are connected with the body by flexible joints to which the flight muscles are attached. In grasshoppers and other insects that gradually change form, wings are direct outgrowths of the posterior dorsal edges of the meso- and metathorax (Fig. 30.7). While it is developing, the wing pad contains tracheae, nerves, and blood. The arrangement of the tracheae usually determines the future pattern of the veins. By the time the wing is mature it is comparable to a flat envelope composed of chitin and the dead remains of cells. Within it the walls of the tracheae are thickened and transformed into solid rods, the veins. Although so much of the wings is chitinous, blood continues for a time to circulate slowly through it outward to the tip and back to the body by another route (Fig. 30.13).

The patterns of veins (wing venation) are important in showing relationships between species. All of them seem to have evolved from one or a few basic ones. The more primitive insects, mayflies, grasshoppers and others have many veins. Specialized insects such as bees have few veins. During the long history of insects the veins have been reduced in number but are better placed and mechanically more efficient.

ABDOMEN. Each typical segment has a dorsal and a ventral sclerite, connected at the sides by flexible membranes which allow the abdomen free breathing movements (Fig. 30.10). The first pair of abdominal spiracles is on the first segment, one in front of each eardrum; the others are in the same relative positions in the next seven segments.

In the female grasshopper, the terminal segments form the ovipositor. The ventral sclerite of the eighth segment is prolonged beyond its dorsal mate, and extends between the prongs of the ovipositor and into the genital opening and forms a trough, the egg guide. The most conspicuous parts of the ovipositor are the digging tools called valves. These are closed together like scissors, pushed into the ground and then opened, letting the eggs slip between them through the

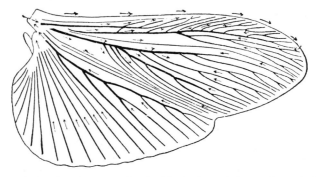

FIG. 30.13. Circulation of blood in the hind wing of the cockroach (*Periplaneta americana*). (From Wigglesworth. Courtesy, Ross: *Entomology*. New York, John Wiley and Sons, 1948.)

egg guide (Fig. 30.10). The ventral sclerites are lacking on the ninth and tenth segments. The eleventh is represented only by a triangular piece above the anal opening, and a pair of similar pieces, the cerci, one on either side of it. The latter are remnants of abdominal appendages present in the ancestors of grasshoppers when the bodies of insects were longer than now. In the male the sternum of the ninth segment forms a hoodlike cover over the copulatory organs.

Cuticle and Integument. Neither the outer nor inner surface of the cuticle is smooth. On the outer one there are ridges, spines and hairs. In butterflies and moths, there are numberless scales formed by secretions from cells in the epidermis. Certain cells build up flexible bristles (setae), and after the bristles are formed the cells usually die. On the inner surface of the cuticle there are knobs, hooks and ridges to which the muscles of the body are attached and thus it becomes a supporting framework.

Color. Insect colors are located in the epidermis, except for a few in the cuticle. They may be chemical colors, due to pigments, or structural ones due to the reflection and interference of light rays on the surfaces of cells and layers of cuticle as in the blue of butterflies; or pigment and structural effects may be combined in iridescence. The blackish pigment melanin and yellow carotin deposited in the secretion of the outer cuticle are responsible for practically all chemical colors. Following the intense muscular activity of their flights migratory grasshoppers, ordinarily light brown, turn dark brown with orange markings. If such grasshoppers are captured and kept quiet for a time their original color returns; if they are restless and continually fluttering, the dark background and orange marks remain.

Internal Structures and Functions. BODY CAVITY. The body cavity of insects lacks the epithelial lining of a true coelom as in the frog. It contains circulating blood and is correctly called a hemocoel.

MUSCLES. The muscles of insects are complicated and numerous. In man there are 792 distinct muscles, in a grasshopper over 900. The ends of insect muscles are attached by tendons to knobs on the inner surface of the cuticle.

DIGESTION AND ASSIMILATION OF FOOD. The digestive tube runs an almost straight course from mouth to anal opening (Fig. 30.14). In the head it is held

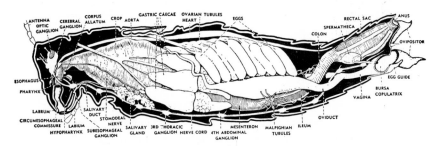

FIG. 30.14. Internal organs of the female grasshopper. The foregut extends from the mouth to the openings of the stomach pouches (gastric caeca); the midgut (stomach or mesenteron) from the gastric caeca to the Malpighian tubules; the hindgut from the tubules to the anal opening. (Courtesy, Matheson: *Entomology*, Ithaca, N.Y., Comstock Publishing Co., 1944.)

in place by muscles attached to the body wall, but elsewhere it is supported by the tracheae. The foregut is lined with cuticle continuous with the outer covering of the body; the hindgut is likewise lined; the midgut has no chitinous lining. The muscular action in the walls of each region results in the churning movements similar to those in other digestive tubes.

Foregut. The foregut begins with the mouth cavity which receives the saliva, continues into the curved pharynx and short esophagus that widens into the thin-walled crop, then narrows into the thicker-walled gizzard. The mandibles and maxillae cut and shred the food while the saliva is mixed with it. The brown "molasses" extruded from the mouth when a grasshopper is handled is at least partly a regurgitation from the crop mixed with fluid from the gastric caeca.

In herbivorous insects, the saliva contains a starch-splitting enzyme (amylase) whose action begins in the mouth. Plant lice inject such saliva into the plant tissues and digestion starts before the food is taken into the mouth. As it is swallowed it is evidently pushed backward onto the base of the tongue (hypopharynx). It then slips on into the crop, mainly a storage sac. The gizzard or proventriculus is equipped with chitinous teeth that thoroughly grind the food by a different method but with the same result as in birds.

Midgut. At the posterior end of the gizzard a valve keeps food from passing into the stomach before it is ground. The stomach is the main organ of chemical digestion and absorption. In the cockroach, its lining produces the sugar enzyme—maltase, the fat enzyme—lipase, and the protein splitter—trypsin. All of these enzymes are catalysts that speed digestive processes, much needed in animals with low body temperatures. Insects have no mucus to protect the lining of the stomach as the vertebrates do. In place of it certain epithelial cells produce an extremely thin sheath (peritrophic membrane) which in the stomach surrounds the food like a tube.

Hindgut (*intestine*). The excretory organs (Malpighian tubules) open into the digestive tube at the junction of the stomach and intestines (Fig. 30.14). The lining of the hindgut is permeable to water and, with the economy of water usual in insects, it is there absorbed back into the body. Waste substances are finally extruded from the body in dry pellets.

BLOOD AND CIRCULATION. Insect blood, like vertebrate blood, is a tissue fluid that distributes digested food to the tissues and carries away the waste products of their metabolism. Although it holds oxygen and carbon dioxide in solution it contains no such efficient oxygen carrier as the hemoglobin of vertebrates and its role in respiration is secondary. It contains proteins, glucose, salts, fats and an unusual amount of amino acids. With rare exceptions such as the larvae of chironomids (midges), it does not contain hemoglobin but absorbs oxygen and carbon dioxide in solution. As before mentioned, while an insect is molting, muscles in the legs and abdomen contract and fill the thorax with blood, swelling it till the outer cover cracks open along the midline of the back. As soon as the insect sheds the old cover it contracts the thorax and forces blood into the wings (Fig. 30.13).

Blood Cells. There are several different kinds of blood cells, but no red ones. They adhere to tissues and spread out often in star shapes and circulate with the fluid (Fig. 30.15). Here, as in other animals, blood cells are deeply involved in the experiences of the animal and their forms and functions change with conditions in the body.

Functions of Insect Blood. Three functions of insect blood are well established. The chief function of the blood cells is phagocytosis, the ingestion of minute particles and living bacteria. Blood carries digested food to the tissues and metabolic waste from them to the excretory organs (Malpighian tubules).

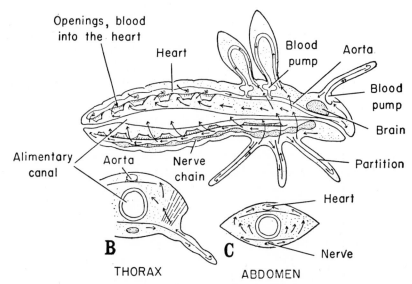

FIG. 30.15. *Upper,* diagram of the circulatory system of an insect. *B,* cross section of the thorax of the same. *C,* cross section of the abdomen. Arrows indicate the course of the circulation. The blood flows forward through the heart, a tube extending along the middle of the back. It pours out of the open front end of this and turns backward flowing through open spaces (sinuses) above and below the digestive tube. As it does this some of it turns toward the back and enters the heart through small openings. Some turns out into the legs and wings where it bathes the tissues directly.

It also transports hormones. Pressure upon the blood in one or another part of the body is a part of the mechanics of molting and of moving the air in the tracheae during breathing.

Circulation of the Blood. The only blood vessel is the heart, a tubelike succession of connecting chambers extending along the mid-dorsal line of the body, the heart proper in the abdomen, the aorta in the thorax (Fig. 30.15). Peristaltic contractions move in waves over the tube from rear to front. In many species, the movement is reversed in one or another phase of life, and the blood flows backward. As each chamber dilates, blood is sucked into the heart through slitlike openings along the sides. These close as a wave of contraction passes them and pushes the blood before it. At the open end of the aorta it floods out into an open space about the brain, circulates within the head and turns backward through the spaces (hemocoels) surrounding the internal organs, much of it passing into the wings and legs. Minute contractile pumps in the thorax draw it through the wings and legs. In the wings it passes outward beside the veins of the front part of the wing and inward again to the body beside other veins as it does in cockroaches (Fig. 30.13). With a microscope circulating blood can be clearly seen in the flattened legs of certain mayfly nymphs. The blood cells dally along the muscles, are moved toward the foot, then drift slowly back to the body and turn toward the heart.

RELEASE OF ENERGY—BREATHING AND RESPIRATION. Skin was the original respiratory organ of all multicellular animals but the skin of insects is covered with cuticle. In them its place is taken by a tubular ventilating system through which air is brought in and out by the muscular action of breathing (Fig. 30.16). The tracheal tubes open to the outside through spiracles. The structure of their walls is similar to that of the body wall and they originate by ingrowths of it during embryonic development. Tracheae carry oxygen directly to the cells and bring carbon dioxide away. Their walls are permeable to gases espe-

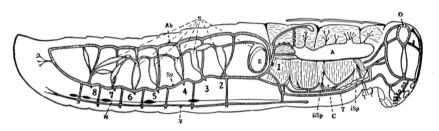

FIG. 30.16. Diagram of the tracheal system of the grasshopper by which oxygen is carried directly to the tissues. It finally reaches them through tracheoles, the minute ends of the tracheae not shown here. The main tracheae and air sacs of one side are shown with the digestive tube removed. *A,* main air sac; *O,* trachea surrounding the compound eye; *E,* inner surface of ear surrounded by trachea; *S,* abdominal air sacs; numbers indicate spiracles, the external openings of the system. (Courtesy, Matheson: *Entomology.* Ithaca, N.Y., Comstock Publishing Co., 1944.)

cially to carbon dioxide. The spiracles are opened and closed by valves that control the flow of air and evaporation. The chitinous lining of the tracheae is strengthened by spiral bands (taenidia) that with the aid of a microscope can be unwound like the spring of a curtain roller. Tracheae divide again and again, until they terminate in exceedingly minute tracheoles. Clusters of these, clearly visible with the great magnification of the electron microscope, extend from the tracheae to the cells of the body and end blindly within them or on their surfaces (Fig. 30.17). Tracheoles are the main functional part of the tracheal system. When oxygen is under high pressure in the tracheoles it passes into the cells where the pressure is lower; substances in the cell combine with the oxygen, energy is set free, and carbon dioxide diffuses into the tracheoles.

Tracheae are frequently enlarged into air sacs and muscles squeeze and release these like bellows thus aiding the intake and expulsion of air through the spiracles. Air sacs also lighten the body and must make it easier to jump and fly. There are also air sacs in birds.

BY-PRODUCTS OF METABOLISM—EXCRETION. The function of an excretory

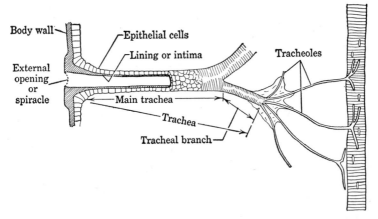

FIG. 30.17. A trachea, with its external opening, branches, and the tracheoles associated with muscle cells where the exchange of oxygen and carbon dioxide mainly occurs. (Courtesy, Ross: *Entomology*. New York, John Wiley and Sons, 1948.)

system is the maintenance of a good environment in the body, mainly by the elimination of unneeded substances from the blood.

The kidneys of the grasshopper are the thread-sized Malpighian tubes named after Marcello Malpighi (1628–1694), an Italian anatomist, who first described them in the silkworm. In the grasshopper, each one extends through the blood from its opening in the intestine to its free end, a blind pocket (Fig. 30.14). Metabolic wastes, destined to form uric acid, are diffused from the body cells into the blood. The walls of the Malpighian tubes gradually absorb the uric acid, discharge it in a watery solution into the tubes which in turn empty it into the intestine from whence excess water is absorbed back into the blood through the rectal wall. This is in line with the small animal's usual economy of water.

METABOLISM. Whether it is a grasshopper or a palm tree, the living organism is a result of chemical and physical reactions of which metabolism is the sum total. Digestion, respiration, excretion, and other processes are parts of metabolism. Grasshoppers become more active as surrounding temperatures rise. With increased activity their bodily temperature and the rate of metabolism also rise. Chemical reactions are increased. Heat is produced, and energy is liberated. When grasshoppers are warm they jump, fly, and eat more.

CHEMICAL REGULATION—HORMONES. The hormonelike substances in insects are briefly discussed with the endocrines (Chap. 15). One endocrine gland, the corpus allatum, is mentioned here because its endocrine nature was established largely by experiments on grasshoppers. It is a double body near the brain, often taken as two glands. During the growth of young grasshoppers its secretion, the "juvenile hormone," checks the differentiation of adult characters and stimulates the retention of nymphal ones. It gives the nymphs time to increase in size before they mature. In adults, its secretion partially controls the growth of the eggs. This has been discovered by removing the gland from young females in various stages of maturity. Its removal prevents the eggs from ripening. Evidently sex does not affect the corpus allatum since a transplant of one from an adult male into an adult female deprived of her own gland will bring on the maturity of her eggs.

COORDINATION AND SENSE ORGANS. The nervous system is highly developed and serves to coordinate the activities of the body with whatever is going on inside and outside it. The central nervous system consists of a pair of dorsal ganglia, the brain, and a series of pairs of ventral ganglia and nerves connecting and branching out from all of them (Fig. 30.18). From the subesophageal ganglia the ventral nerve cord extends posteriorly formed by a series of paired ganglia and connecting nerves. Each division of the thorax contains a pair of ganglia from which nerves extend to the legs, wings, and internal organs. There are only five pairs of abdominal ganglia, some of the once larger number having been fused during the evolution of grasshoppers. In addition to the central nervous system, insects have a visceral nervous system, ganglia and nerves concerned with the control of the purely involuntary activity of the salivary glands and parts of the digestive canal.

The Sensitivity of Insects. In spite of their armor, grasshoppers are highly sensitive to their surroundings. They have sense organs for the reception of tactile stimuli, hearing, taste, smell, and sight, all of these connected with the central nervous system.

TACTILE HAIRS. Their delicate sense of touch is due to many protruding hairs that are in contact with sensory nerve cells. In a simple type of such an organ three kinds of cells are concerned, the hair cell which secretes the hair, the

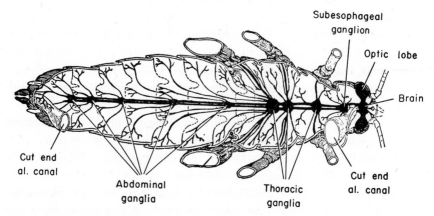

FIG. 30.18. Nervous systems of grasshopper. View after alimentary canal removed. The largest ganglia are those associated with greatest activity, e.g., with wings and legs. (After Hegner: *Invertebrate Zoology.* New York, The Macmillan Co., 1933.)

cell forming its socket, and the sensory nerve cell. The tip of this is in contact with the base of the hair exposed to the changes in pressure that it communicates to the nerve centers. Such tactile organs are abundant on the antennae and ovipositors of grasshoppers.

HEARING. In the red-legged, the lubber, and other common grasshoppers there is an eardrum on each side of the first abdominal segment (Fig. 30.10). In some species it is on the front legs. Comparatively few insects, among them grasshoppers, crickets, and cicadas have these eardrums. In the common short-horned grasshoppers, the eardrum is a thin cuticular drum fully exposed on the outside and closely associated with a group of peculiar sensory cells.

CHEMICAL SENSES—SMELL AND TASTE. Smell and taste are both chemical senses and not easy to distinguish. The chitin that covers these sensory cells is so thin that chemical substances can easily penetrate it. Chemical sense organs are often on minute knobs; others are in pits. Smell is located chiefly in the antennae and the palps. Grasshoppers are sensititve to temperature all over their bodies. They have sharp temperature preferences and as far as possible choose their own private climates in protected sunny nooks.

COMPOUND EYES. These eyes are immovable, set well over to the side of the head and a different object is seen through each one at the same time. They are composed of single eyes, usually thousands of them, through which pieces of an object appear in mosaic vision as in the similar eyes of crayfishes. Processes from the light sensitive cells of the eye continue through the optic nerve and are associated with nerve cells in the brain. As in all animals, the interpretation of vision occurs in the brain. That insects do interpret what they see is evident from experiments with honeybees. On the surface of a compound eye its units appear as many six-sided areas, each one a transparent lenslike cornea. Directly beneath this is the crystalline cone composed of crystal clear cells. This in turn rests upon the light receptors or retinal cells that are sensitive to light on the sides meeting in the center of a peculiar rosette (rhabdom). A process extends from each of the light receptor cells and together they form the optic nerve connecting the eye with the brain. A curtain of pigment cells keeps the light that falls on one unit from striking any other. As more or less light falls upon the eye, granules in the pigment cells move to different positions. This shuts out or lets in the light upon the retinal cells just as the iris of the human eye curtains the light sensitive retina.

REPRODUCTION. The sexes are separate in all insects. In most species they are readily distinguishable by the external sexual structures on the abdomen. There are two testes in which the sperm cells develop. The latter are discharged into two tubes (the vasa deferentia) which unite to form the ejaculatory duct extending through the penis, the organ by which the sperm cells are transferred into the female reproductive passage during mating. Each ovary consists of a group of egg tubules within which the eggs develop (Fig. 30.14).

Different stages of developing eggs fill each tubule of the ovary. They are supplied with nourishment from cells in the wall of the egg tubule, ultimately from the blood. As the oldest eggs mature they slip into the oviduct and in the egg-laying season this becomes distended with eggs. By that time each egg has a thin shell with a minute pore in it (micropyle) through which the sperm cell may enter. As the eggs pass into the vagina they come to the opening of the spermatheca which in a mated grasshopper is crowded with sperm cells. Pressure on this sac forces out the sperm cells and fertilization of the eggs follows.

Just before fertilization the number of chromosomes in the eggs is reduced to half their former number (Chap. 6). A comparable reduction in chromosome number also occurs in the sperm cells. Thus, after the male and female nuclei have joined, the fertilized egg begins as a new individual that will have the same number of chromosomes present in the body cells as in those of one or the other parent.

Egglaying and Winter Life. The grasshopper begins laying her eggs in late summer or fall several days after mating. She digs a short tunnel in dry ground and deposits the eggs shrouded in a sticky secretion. In common grasshoppers, development begins immediately and continues for about three weeks (Fig. 30.19). By that time the six legs, the antennae, eyes and the segments of the body all show clearly in the still unhatched embryo. It then enters a rest period (diapause); consumes little oxygen; growth stops and is not resumed until spring.

THE HONEYBEE—A FLOWER-INSECT

Honeybees are social insects, with each bee a team worker taking a particular part in the life of its colony—an organized society. Honeybees are wholly dependent upon flowers for nectar and pollen, their only food. Great numbers of plants, among them the fruit trees, are in turn dependent upon bees for cross pollination and the consequent continuance of their species.

Content of the Colony. Honeybees, *Apis mellifica,* were introduced into this country in colonial times and are now widely distributed in apiaries and as escaped wild bees that build their nests in hollow trees. The colony in a beehive has continued to be essentially a copy of the nest in the hollow tree. In summer, there may be 60,000 or more bees in a colony, but fewer in winter. There are three easily recognized castes, the females, workers and queen, and the males or drones (Fig. 30.20).

The workers constitute the great bulk of the colony—the honeybees that are usually seen on flowers and going in and out of their hives. They are sexually undeveloped females, highly specialized as workers for the general welfare of the colony. They rarely produce eggs and when they do the eggs are unfertilized and develop into males only. Workers are so called because

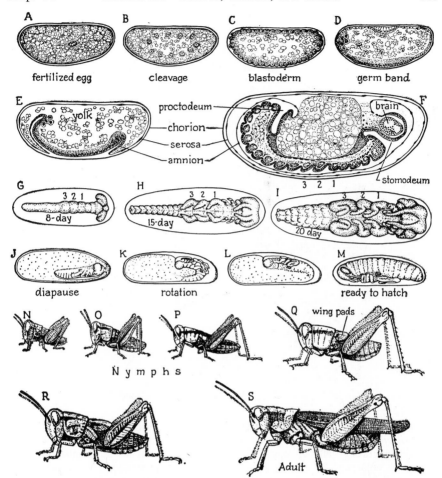

A fertilized egg B cleavage C blastoderm D germ band

E yolk proctodeum chorion serosa amnion brain F stomodeum

G 8-day H 15-day I 20-day

J diapause K L rotation M ready to hatch

N O P Nymphs Q wing pads

R S Adult

FIG. 30.19. Development of the grasshopper. Development begins in autumn immediately after fertilization, and continues two to three weeks till the embryo is well formed. Then there is a rest or diapause until spring when the nymphs hatch at the right time to feed on the young grass. *A, B, C, D;* nuclear division occurs and (*B*) nuclei are scattered through the yolk; they migrate to the outer surface of the embryo where each one is surrounded by a cell body. This (*C*) is the blastula stage. *D,* cells divide rapidly on one side forming the germ band which will be the embryo. *E, F, G, H, I;* continuous development *proceeding most rapidly on the ventral side* where the nerve chain will be located. Stomodeum is the layout for the mouth; proctodeum is the layout for the anal region. The serosa is the outer covering membrane of the embryo; the amnion is the inner one. *J,* development pauses for the winter (diapause). *K, L, M;* development begins again; the embryo turns about so that its head is at the larger end of the egg. It soon hatches, head first. Like other immature animals its head is relatively large. *N, O, P, Q, R;* five nymphal stages. *S,* adult. Legs came before wings in the evolutionary history of insects; they come first in young grasshoppers. (Adapted from various sources. Courtesy, Storer: *General Zoology,* ed. 2. New York, McGraw-Hill Book Co., 1951.)

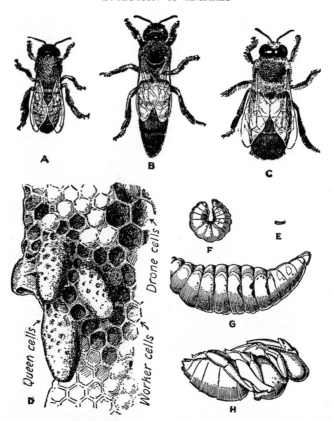

FIG. 30.20. Types of individuals in a colony of honeybees, and the life history of a honeybee. *A*, worker; *B*, queen; *C*, drone; *D*, portion of comb showing queen, worker and drone cells; *E*, egg; *F*, young larva; *G*, old larva; *H*, pupa. *A* to *C* somewhat enlarged; *D*, natural size; *E* to *H* much enlarged. In *D* several of the honey cells are capped. (Courtesy, Phillips: *Farmer's Bulletin 447*. Bur. Ent. and Plant Quar., U.S.D.A.)

they perform the labor. Young workers attend to the inside work, mold the wax into comb, feed the larvae, keep the hive clean, and guard the entrance. The older workers go into the field to collect nectar, pollen, and the mixture of plant gums called propolis. They live only a month or two except those that hatch out in the fall and live through the winter when the colony is smaller and the housework lighter. In the colony, workers are both governors and governed. Their treatment creates the queen; they kill unwanted queens; and they direct the outgoing swarm yet they are bewildered and often return to their hive if the queen is not with them.

There are few drones in a colony and they are present only in spring and summer until after swarming time. A small group of them follows the young queen on her mating flight and one of them mates with her. This is their only service to the colony.

The queen is the egg producer of the hive. At the height of the flower season she lays thousands of eggs per day with clocklike regularity, placing one in each cell. Most of the time she lays fertilized eggs, always placing them in the smaller brood cells; these develop into females (workers); if a queen cell is present she places the same kind of fertilized egg within it. Occasionally she lays unfertilized eggs, placing them in the larger brood cells; these develop into males. Thus, the eggs develop whether they are fertilized or not, but those with the double sets of chromosomes (32) become females, and those with the single sets (16) become males (Chap. 18). The queen is a generalized bee with wings and legs and an ovipositor but none of the specialities of the worker.

Special Structures and Functions of the Worker Bee. The mouth parts, legs (Fig. 30.21) and sting are the external parts especially concerned with the worker's activity; the digestive and respiratory systems and the wax glands are the internal ones. Workers use their mouth parts on building materials and food. The smooth-edged, scoop-shaped mandibles are adaptable to molding wax as well as biting off pollen. The nectaries of plants are located deep in the center of the flowers and reaching them is like licking syrup out of a bottle (Fig. 30.22). The bee does this with its combination sucking and lapping "tongue" that is folded back under the head when not in use. This remarkable instrument is composed of the modified maxilla and labium or lower lip, the central part of the latter forming the "tongue," actually a spoon with a tubular handle.

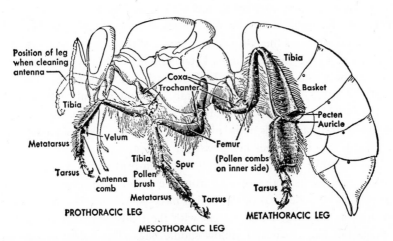

FIG. 30.21. The legs of the worker honeybee. Some part of each one is a tool used in collecting and manipulating pollen or wax. The wings have been removed and no hairs are shown on the head and body. Hairs are as abundant there as they are on the legs and the sticky pollen likewise clings to them. The pecten is a row of bristles on the hind leg; the auricle is a lobe used as a pusher; these parts are worked together in packing pollen into the basket. (Courtesy, Hegner and Stiles: *College Zoology*, ed. 6. New York, The Macmillan Co., 1951.)

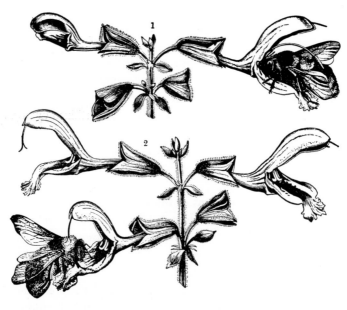

FIG. 30.22. Nectar is produced at the bottom of the flower and as the bees suck it up they come in contact with the pollen. Bees in flowers of Salvia: *1*, pollen-covered anther is striking the bee's back; *2*, the lower flower is being visited by a bee which carries on its back pollen from a younger flower and is rubbing it off on the deflected stigma. (Courtesy, Kerner and Oliver: *The Natural History of Plants*. London, Gresham Publishing Co., 1904.)

LEGS. There is some tool connected with pollen or wax on every leg of a worker bee; the rights and lefts match, are mirror images. As bees gather nectar from the flowers they also collect pollen that clings to the hairs on their eyes, legs and bodies. Workers must keep combing and brushing and the tools for this are built into their bodies. The eyebrush is a set of bristles on the first leg and just below it is the antenna-comb, a circular comb with a movable flap (Fig. 30.21). The bee raises its leg and draws the antenna through the comb while the flap holds it in place. A honeybee brushes an eye with a pollen brush as a cat curves her paw over one ear.

On each middle leg there is another pollen-brush and a wax-pick with which the bee plucks scales of wax from the under surface of the abdomen, and prys balls of pollen out of the pollen baskets. When a bee returns from a pollen trip, its hind legs hang straight with the loads of pollen in the baskets that bulge out like green and yellow saddle bags. The pollen combs on the inner surfaces of the tarsi serve to comb out the pollen entangled on the hairs of the body and transfer it to the pollen basket on the opposite leg. The tibia ends in a row of spines, the pecten (comb). The pecten of one leg is scraped across the pollen comb of the other and the pollen thus collected is packed into the pollen basket.

STING. The sting of a bee is an ovipositor modified into a weapon. Its external parts are two feelers that locate the point to be stung, and a needle, composed of two barbed shafts that slide within a shaft. Connected with this is the internal poison sac that receives the poison from adjoining glands. Bees sting to defend the colony; thus stinging is a social act. It often kills the bee because the shafts catch in the flesh and the whole stinging mechanism is pulled out of the bee.

DIGESTIVE SYSTEM. The special feature of the digestive system is the honey stomach, a modified crop used as a tank to carry nectar from the flowers to the honey cells in the comb (Fig. 30.23). A short tube (proventriculus) containing a valve connects the honey stomach with the true stomach (ventriculus). The valve is closed except when the bee takes some of the nectar for itself but what signals the opening of the valve is not known. The honey stomach is very distensible and when full of nectar, looks like a transparent balloon. Honeybees fly rapidly, distances of a mile or more, or make short trips—ones with quick stops and starts from flower to flower. The supply of oxygen in the air-sacs probably eases up on breathing during flight (Fig. 30.24).

NERVOUS SYSTEM—COORDINATION. As might be expected from their behavior, ants, wasps, and bees have the most highly developed nervous systems of any insects. In the bees the ventral nerve chain is characteristically shorter and more ganglia are fused than in the grasshopper (Fig. 30.18).

The Senses and Language of Honeybees. The statements that follow give

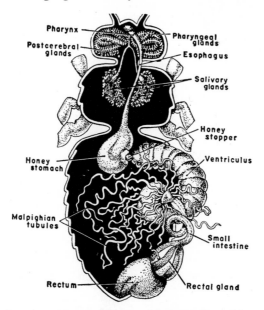

FIG. 30.23. The digestive system of the worker honeybee. (Courtesy, Hunter and Hunter: *College Zoology*. Philadelphia, W. B. Saunders Co., 1949.)

some of the results obtained by a famous student of animal behavior, Karl von Frisch, through years of experiment and observation. His book, *Bees, Their Vision, Chemical Senses and Language,* is largely made up of lectures given in American universities during 1949 with motion pictures of the dances of the bees. His conclusions have been termed "of basic importance to biological science and truly revolutionary in the special field of animal behavior" (Donald R. Griffin).

THE MATERIALS. In the course of the experiments, worker honeybees were marked with colored symbols by which each one of a large number could be

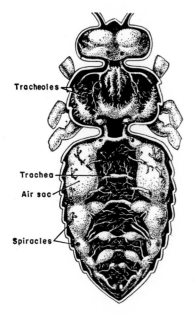

Tracheoles

Trachea

Air sac

Spiracles

FIG. 30.24. The respiratory system of the worker honeybee with the air sacs that hold an emergency supply of air. (Courtesy, Hunter and Hunter: *College Zoology.* Philadelphia, W. B. Saunders Co., 1949.)

identified. They were observed on combs among other bees in observation hives, and at feeding stations where dishes of sugar water and control dishes were placed on colored cards, and on flowers. The observation hives were in diffused light and in red light (black to the bees). Experiments and observations were repeated, and often varied many times. They have also been repeated by others.

ARE BEES COLOR BLIND? Bees can distinguish yellow, bluegreen, blue, and ultraviolet (Fig. 30.25). Red and black are the same to bees for they are red-blind. They and various other insects can distinguish certain red flowers, such as scarlet poppies because these flowers reflect ultraviolet light. Ultraviolet appears to be a distinct color for the bees (von Frisch). Color vision of man and the bee is different; the human eye responds to more colors but not to ultraviolet.

CAN BEES RECOGNIZE DIFFERENT SHAPES? They can distinguish solid objects from open ones, e.g., a solid triangle from three parallel lines (Fig.

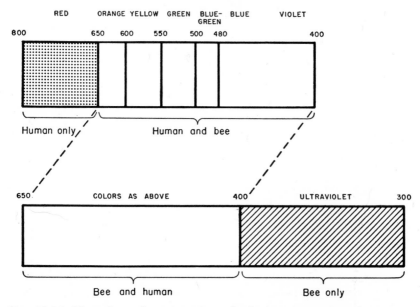

FIG. 30.25. The colors of a spectrum to the human eye and to the eye of the honeybee. For bees the visible spectrum is shortened in the red light but is extended in the ultraviolet. Apparently bees see only four qualities of color: yellow, blue-green, blue, and ultraviolet. The numbers indicate the wave length of light in millimicra (one micron = 1/25000 of an inch). (Based on data from von Frisch: *Bees*. Ithaca, N.Y., Cornell University Press, 1950.)

30.26). The criterion of visibility seems to be the amount of openness in the pattern. It apparently gives a flickering impression as the bee flies past it just as a picket fence looks to us as we ride past.

TASTE, SMELL, AND TOUCH. Honeybees can distinguish salt, sour, sweet, and bitter. There are some sense organs of taste on the mouth parts though it is not certain that they are all there. Butterflies have them on their feet. Honeybees are very sensitive to degrees of sweetness. They refused low percentages of sugar in the experimental sugar waters. Conditions modify their choices. In the spring blooming period they may refuse to collect nectar that is less than 40 per cent sugar, but in the fall when flowers are scarce, they will accept it with sugar content as low as 5 per cent. Honeybees are keenly responsive to odors. The sense organs of touch and smell are very close together on the first eight distal segments of the antenna (Fig. 30.27). As bees explore flowers they wave their antennae about and constantly touch certain parts of them. In bees, smell and touch may work together just as we handle something in order to see it better.

HONEYBEES BROADCAST NEWS OF FOOD. Workers perform the "round dance" after they have collected food near the hive (Fig. 30.28). The worker

FIG. 30.26. Bees distinguish between solid and broken patterns. They do not learn to distinguish between different shapes of solid patterns (upper row) or between those of different broken ones (lower row). (Courtesy, von Frisch: *Bees*. Ithaca, N.Y., Cornell University Press, 1950.)

sucks up the sugar water (placed there for the experiment), goes back to the hive and walks onto the comb among hundreds of bees. First, she delivers sugar water to some of them. After that she dances, turns a circle to the left, turns one to the right, repeats this in one spot for a half minute or more, then goes to another place and dances again. During the dances the nearby bees become more and more excited. They troop behind the dancer and extend their antennae toward her. Suddenly one of them turns away and leaves the hive; others follow and the watcher soon sees them at the feeding place.

Workers that have been collecting food at more distant places perform the wagging dance (Fig. 30.28). They run a little way straight forward wagging the abdomen then turn a circle to the left, retrace the straight line wagging

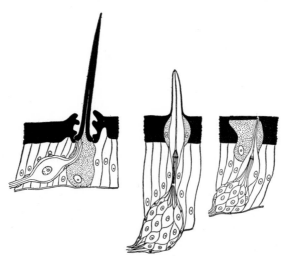

FIG. 30.27. Sense organs on one of the eight outer or distal segments of the antennae of honeybees. Sections through the chitinous body covering (black), the cells which produce it and the sense organs. *Left,* section through an organ of touch, highly magnified. *Center and right,* the organs of smell. Processes from nerve cells, in the cluster, end beneath a very thin part of the chitin and can be stimulated by scented substances diffusing through it. (Courtesy, von Frisch: *Bees*. Ithaca, N.Y., Cornell University Press, 1950.)

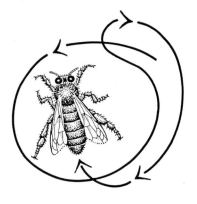 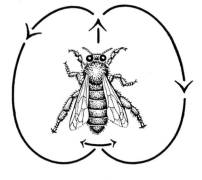

ROUND DANCE
Food near hive

WAGGING DANCE
Food distant from hive

FIG. 30.28. Honeybees broadcast the news of food by dancing on the comb after they return to the hive with nectar. *Left,* the round dance performed when the feeding place is *near* the hive (c. 10 meters). The bee turns around, once to right and once to the left, repeating the circles for about half a minute in one place. *Right,* the tail-wagging dance, performed when the feeding place is *far* from the hive. The bee runs a short distance in a straight line wagging the abdomen, then makes a complete 360-degree turn to the left, runs ahead once more and turns to the right, and repeats this over and over. (Courtesy, von Frisch: *Bees.* Ithaca, N.Y., Cornell University Press, 1950.)

again, turn a circle to the right, retrace the line and wag. In the wagging dance the number of turns in a given time indicates the distance more exactly, e.g., for 100 meters, nine or 10 complete circles. When sugar water was set out in nearby and in distant food stations at the same time the bees returning from them performed the appropriate dance for the station visited. If the farther food station was moved closer to the hive, the same bees which had been wagging, changed to the round dance.

The Diversity of Insects

Except in the Arctic and Antarctic, insects have occupied all lands. Their numbers have so intensified their struggle for existence that no place or way of living has been untried. Grasshoppers and honeybees meet their surroundings with complex and successful structures and activities that have been merely suggested in the brief descriptions in this chapter. Thus, insects have become of great importance to plants, to one another, to other animals and humanity. Observation and experiments upon them have brought great contributions to zoology and through it to agriculture, medicine, and sociology. In this book it is only possible to introduce these through the books in the Suggested Readings. Such subjects as insects and agriculture and forestry, insects and their food, insects and disease, and social insects are included there. Happily many of such books are readable and witty as well as informing.

A Review of Arthropod Relations

Again and again arthropods show their ancestral connections to annelid worms. Peripatus (Class Onychophora—"claw bearing") is the simplest living arthropod and with its segmentally arranged excretory organs and wormlike form most resembles the annelids. Centipedes (Class Chilopoda—lipfoot) and millipedes (Class Diplopoda—doubled feet) have mainly uniform segments. The voracious predatory centipedes are equipped with powerful mandibles each with an incurved hook from the tip of which a poison gland opens. In contrast to them the vegetarian millipedes have weak mandibles and no poison glands. A centipede is composed of flattened segments, each with one pair of long, jointed legs; a millipede is cylindrical and each segment is a fusion of two embryonic ones bearing two pairs of legs. When traveling these various legs are moved from front to rear rapidly like scales being played on a key-board. Crayfishes (Class Crustacea) are divided into a fused head and thorax, and abdomen and have gills, two pairs of antennae, and two-branched appendages. In grasshoppers (Class Insecta), the body is divided into head, thorax, and abdomen, and they have three pairs of legs, one pair of antennae and are usually winged. The bodies of spiders and their allies (Class Arachnoidea) are divided into a cephalothorax and abdomen; they are without antennae or mandibles, have four pairs of legs, and breathe by tracheae and book lungs.

Spiders and Their Relatives

Spiders are well named for the majority of the females are inveterate spinners and the word spider is a descendant of the Danish word *spinden,* to spin. For most spiders silk is the thread of life from the time they hatch from the shell. Spiders are air breathers, thoroughly land animals, yet inside of silken waterproofs a few of them live in water. Some occupy silk curtained holes in coral rocks that are immersed at high tide. The "water spider" (Argyroneta) of fresh waters of Europe and temperate Eurasia is a pioneer user of the diving bell. She collects her supplies of oxygen at the water surface raising her abdomen and capturing bubbles of air in addition to that caught on the covering of her body. Between repeated trips to the surface she weaves a canopy of silk attaching it to the submerged stems of plants that grow in the shallows of ponds and streams. After the canopy is made she continues to bring down air bubbles and to shed them beneath the canopy replenishing the supply as it is used. This airy chamber is the home of the female spider into which she brings her captured prey, and where she lays her eggs. The spiderlings that hatch there can also spin and swim and with their own silk soon repeat the performances of their mother. The males spin only small canopies sufficient for them to linger in the locality until they are mature. There are many spiders that frequent the margins of quiet inland waters, running about on the surface film foraging for water skaters and other insects. Spiders are predators that seize and crush their prey between the chelicerae or jaws and suck the juices. They are generally solitary with no hint of any such group organization as that of the social insects. In the instincts that guide female spiders in the architecture of their webs and the trapping of their prey, they are unsurpassed among invertebrates.

General Structure. Spiders are examples of the narrow-waisted arachnids, a contrast to the thick waisted harvestmen (Figs. 30.29, 30.30). They have neither antennae nor true mandibles. In front of the mouth are the two special jaws or chelicerae, each with a sharp fang through which a poison gland opens, and behind these is a pair of pedipalps. In the female each of the latter ends in a claw, often used in manipulating the silk. In the male the enlarged tip of each pedipalp is the organ by which sperms are transferred to the female. The four pairs of legs vary in size and function; some of them are important in

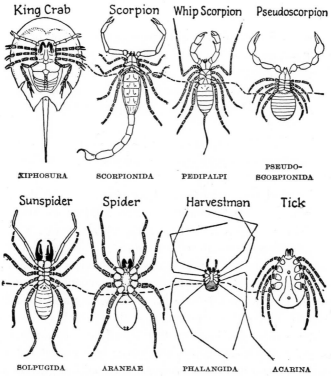

FIG. 30.29. Relatives in the Class Arachnoidea. King crab, a relative of the fossil trilobites; scorpions, the oldest of land arachnids, with fossils going back 400 million years; pseudoscorpions, the largest a quarter of an inch long and without the poisonous tail gland of the true scorpions; sunspiders of the American southwest, an inch long or more; spiders; harvestmen, long-legged, frequently in companies; ticks that push their heads through the skin and gorge themselves with blood. (Courtesy, Storer: *General Zoology,* ed. 2. New York, McGraw-Hill Book Co., 1951.)

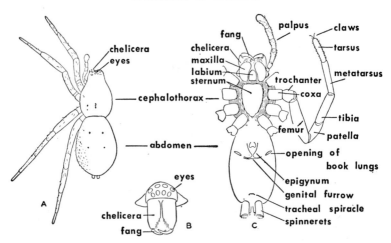

FIG. 30.30. External anatomy of a spider. (Courtesy, Gertsch: *American Spiders.* New York, D. Van Nostrand Co., 1949.)

constructing webs. Spines and other finer projections, many of them sensory, project from the surfaces of the body. Spiders usually have eight simple eyes, in some species fewer. The majority of spiders have poor eyesight, at its best in the runners and jumpers. Smell and taste are also weak. They know their environment through their extraordinary sensitiveness to touch and vibration. Near the posterior end of the abdomen are two or three pairs of spinnerets from the tips of which the silk glands open. Spinnerets are flexible fingers that a spider continually extends, withdraws and manipulates as the slender streams of silk pour from their tips.

The respiratory system also opens on the ventral side of the abdomen in front of the spinnerets. The openings of the two leaflike book lungs are located one on either side of the opening of the reproductive organs.

The short esophagus leads to the sucking stomach operated by powerful muscles that attach it to the skeleton of the cephalothorax (Fig. 30.31). These contract and enlarge the stomach thus creating the suction. It usually takes a spider about an hour to suck in the juice of a fly. Digested food is absorbed from a series of blind pouches extending from the stomach and from numerous glandular extensions of the intestine that branch and rebranch through the abdominal cavity. Waste substances accumulate in a pocket (stercoral) that opens from the hindgut and are afterward discharged from the anus.

The ovaries and the silk glands make great demands for food, the ovaries to build up a store of yolk in the eggs, and the silk glands to provide the substance, mainly protein, in the constantly expended silk. Wherever a spider goes it plays out a silken thread, the dragline. As a house spider drops from ceiling to floor, it descends gently on a dragline making it longer and longer as it drops. Before a spider jumps, it fastens a dragline down to some object and

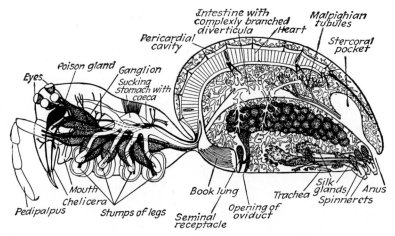

FIG. 30.31. Internal anatomy of a female spider. The nervous system highly developed in the head and thorax, is shown by dark stippling; the nerves in the abdomen are too small to be shown. The alimentary canal is white; note its branches (caeca) extending into the stumps of the legs; a network open into the intestine from a digestive gland which is packed around the abdominal organs. Note the prominent eggs in the ovary. The stercoral pocket, a sac in which waste products accumulate. The malpighian tubules are kidney-like in function as in insects. (From Comstock: *The Spider Book*. New York, Doubleday, Page and Co., 1913.)

then leaps spinning the line out as it goes through the air. Spiders spin forth yards of draglines that are carried by currents of air from tree to tree and across streams. Young spiders and the smaller species are lifted into the air and carried by draglines for miles over mountains and seas. The dragline is also the trapline which a spider holds until it vibrates from the touch of an insect caught in the web. Draglines are the outermost threads of orb webs, the fundamental lines in their construction (Fig. 30.33). There are seven kinds of silk glands in spiders but not all of these are present, even in any one family of spiders. The silk that is poured out through the minute holes in the tips of the spinnerets is of different sorts that are more or less elastic, but its final character depends largely upon the pull to which it is subjected. The viscid spiral lines of orb webs are two firm threads which are at first evenly covered with a fluid silk. As she spins, the spider holds the whole thread with her hind leg, stretching it a little but at regular intervals letting it snap back. On the shortened line drops of the sticky silk form at regular intervals. Dew gathered on them creates the shining beads of early morning (Fig. 30.33). An orb web is a triumph of symmetry and it takes a spider only an hour to build it.

Spiders always develop from the fusion of male and female sex cells but in most species the male individual is of no consequence except for the fertilization of the eggs. The females spin the egg sacs and give the young what care they receive. Male spiders have silk glands but spin little or none. They hunt

FIG. 30.32. The viscid lines of an orb web in close-up photograph. The viscid silk collects in droplets when the tension on the basal lines is loosened. Dew gathers on these and they are jeweled in morning sunlight. The web is a trap in which insects are ensnared. (Photograph by Lynwood Chace. Courtesy, National Audubon Society.)

alone and are inconspicuous because much smaller than the females. In their courtships the males of some species are stealthy; others are acrobatic. Many of them meet a tragic end since the female finally devours her mate.

Other Arachnids. Mites and ticks are small arachnids (Order Acarina) with the head, thorax, and abdomen closely fused and unsegmented (Fig. 30.34, 30.35). They hatch from the eggs as active six-legged larvae that feed and molt into eight-legged nymphs. These feed still more, molt and change into adults, also eight-legged. Ticks and mites are similar except for certain details of structure and size, ticks being much the larger. In both types, a dartlike structure (hypostome) below the mouth acts like an anchor when pushed into the flesh. In ticks the outer surface of the hypostome is armed with recurved teeth; in mites it is smooth.

Ticks are parasites of mammals, birds, reptiles, and some amphibians. A tick lays hundreds of eggs on the ground, in birds' nests and other homes of

FIG. 30.33. A complete orb web in early morning. The long trap leads to the retreat from which the spider emerges when the trap line is moved by the struggles of an insect caught in the web. (Photograph by Hugh Spencer. Courtesy, National Audubon Society.)

their hosts. After hatching, the larvae immediately seek their hosts and a blood meal. Unlucky larvae who do not find their hosts may survive eight months without food but they cannot molt or transform without a blood meal. When a tick bites, it cuts with its jaws, stabs with its hypostome and injects an anti-coagulating fluid into the blood. Its whole head is buried in the flesh and because of tearing by the reversed teeth, it should never be pulled out quickly.

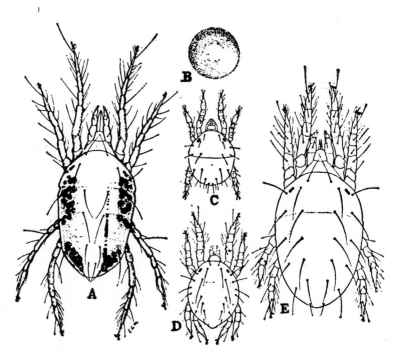

FIG. 30.34. The "red spider," *Tetranychus telarius*, of plants is a mite that covers the leaves with silk and sucks out the sap. *A*, the mature female; *B*, the egg; *C* and *D*, larva and nymph; *E*, the fully developed nymph just before its last molt and maturity. (Courtesy, Matheson: *Entomology*. Ithaca, N.Y., Cornell University Press, 1944.)

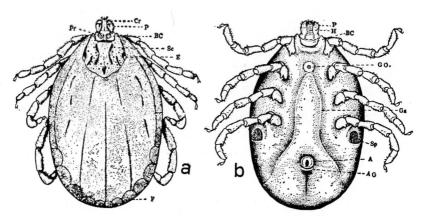

FIG. 30.35. The spotted fever tick, *Dermacentor andersoni*. In its immature stage it is a parasite of rabbits, squirrels, and other rodents—as an adult, a willing parasite of man. (Courtesy, Matheson: *Entomology*. Ithaca, N.Y., Cornell University Press, 1944.)

It will drop off when surfeited with blood. The danger from ticks is in the organisms they may carry from an infected animal to an uninfected one. Some of the resultant diseases are: relapsing fevers of certain western states, due to a species of spirochaete; Rocky Mountain spotted fever of rodents and man caused by Rickettsia organisms; and tularemia, a disease of rabbits, squirrels, rats and certain game birds, caused by a bacterium (*Pasturella tularemia*) carried by the tick (*Dermacentor andersoni*). Tularemia is highly infectious to man since the organisms pass through slight breaks in the skin when infected game is handled.

Mites live on plants and animals and cause great damage to both. Among those of plants are the destructive stored grain mites, the citrus bud mite of the lemon trees of California, the mites on peas, clover, and the "red spiders" of junipers (Fig. 30.34). The parasitic mites of animals include the "southern chiggers" or "red bugs" whose larvae burrow just under the skin as a ground mole burrows just under the surface of a lawn.

31

Mollusks—Specialists in Security

Most people know that clams and oysters make shells; that oysters belong in stew, clams in chowder, and that scallops are fried. Many know the pleasant softness of oysters on the half shell. When the novelist Thackeray ate his first raw oyster he is said to have exclaimed that he felt as if he had "swallowed a little baby." For the majority of mollusks, these impressions are correct. Most of them bear shells, provide abundant food for man and other animals, and have such soft bodies that the phylum is named Mollusca.

The group includes an enormous number of animals whose lives are deeply affected by their shells. It contains animals of such different forms and activity as snails and slugs, clams and oysters, swift darting squids, slow creeping chitons, and the storied paper sailor and chambered nautilus (Fig. 31.1). Mollusks are scattered over the lands and through the seas and fresh waters of the world. There are over 80,000 known species. Fossils of the ancestral mollusks are abundant in Lower Cambrian rock laid down 600 million years ago. The free-swimming ciliated larvae of mollusks and annelid worms are so similar that they suggest a common ancestry.

General Characteristics. The dominant structures of mollusks are the mantle, the foot, and the spiral form. The fleshy cloaklike mantle produces the myriad kinds of shells, takes part in forming the gills and the lung sacs of air-breathing snails, and in many species bears cilia. The foot is the organ of locomotion (Fig. 31.5), the traveling platform of snails, the digging tool of clams, the head-foot from which tentacles originate in squids. Spirals or some hint of spirality appear in many mollusks; laterally developed spirals are prominent in the majority of snails; the symmetrical spiral is equally prominent in the chambered nautilus; and an oblique slant in the hinges of clam and oyster shells is noticeable. Mollusks have a true coelom but lack several prominent features of other higher invertebrates. Although they can swim, crawl, climb, dig and bore, they have no legs. The body is not divided into segments, and only in the chitons is the shell segmented (Fig. 31.1).

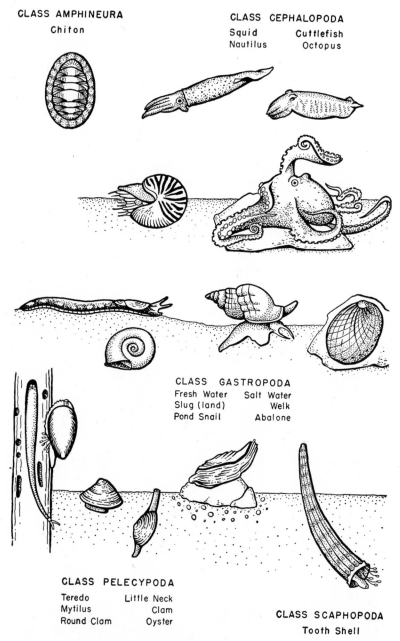

CLASS AMPHINEURA
Chiton

CLASS CEPHALOPODA
Squid   Cuttlefish
Nautilus   Octopus

CLASS GASTROPODA
Fresh Water   Salt Water
Slug (land)   Welk
Pond Snail   Abalone

CLASS PELECYPODA
Teredo   Little Neck
Mytilus   Clam
Round Clam   Oyster

CLASS SCAPHOPODA
Tooth Shell

FIG. 31.1. Mollusks, the shelled animals. They are predominantly marine, except for the snails and mussels, many of which live in fresh water, or on land. In persistence, distribution and numbers Mollusks are highly successful. The majority of them are hindered as well as helped by the safety of their shells. Except in the cephalopods the nervous and sensory structures are only moderately developed.

Ecological and Economic Importance. Marine mollusks are far more numerous than terrestrial ones. Their free-swimming ciliated larvae abound in the surface plankton that forms the basic food supply of the sea. Myriads of pteropods often crowd the surface waters. They are snails, many no longer than cloves, with lobes of flesh that give them their name sea butterflies and enable them to flit and glide on the surface as their namesakes do in air (Fig. 31.2). Vast schools of them swim among the icebergs around Greenland and are strained from the water by the whalebone whales.

Hosts of small snails live on the seaweeds between the tide lines and rasp off the tissue with their filelike tongues. Each incoming tide brings more seaweeds, inhabited by more snails and with each ebb tide leaves a new harvest for the gulls and sandpipers. In ponds and lake shallows, snails forage chiefly on the plants but from any submerged surface they scrape bacteria, protozoans, and algae. Benefiting by this food they eventually furnish their own bodies to the frogs and water birds.

The majority of mollusks are hampered by their shells and do not travel far

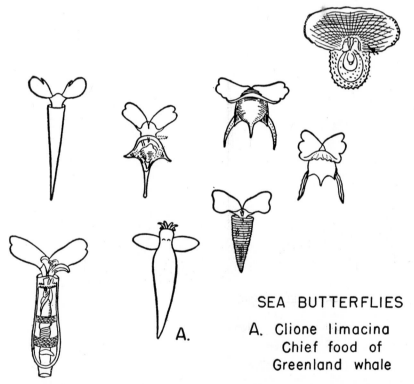

SEA BUTTERFLIES

A. Clione limacina
Chief food of
Greenland whale

FIG. 31.2. Pteropods, the sea butterflies, are winged snails, many of them but little longer than cloves. Each side of the foot is extended into a wing and they skip and sail in vast schools on the surface of the sea. One of them (*Clione limacina*) is the chief food of the Greenland whalebone whales. (Courtesy, Miner: *Fieldbook of Seashore Life*. New York, G. P. Putnam's Sons, 1950.)

except as they cling to boats, driftwood, and floating plants, to the bodies of fishes, seals, and whales; and on land to the feet of birds. The striking exceptions are the free-swimming squids that range the seas. Sense organs are not highly developed in mollusks, the tactile sense, and the eyes of land snails, scallops, squids and octopuses excepted. Great aggregations of marine snails and mussels are common. On land, slugs and snails congregate in moist places and about decaying tissues, but there is no such variety of responses and social relationships as in arthropods. The periwinkles and blue black mussels that cling to rocks between the tide lines are expressive of the monotony of relative safety and endurance that accompanies their survival. Security is expensive.

Oysters feed upon microorganisms from the muck and water of the bottom and in turn are consumed by starfishes, oyster borers and mankind. In open sea, enormous numbers of squids follow and feed up on schools of herring and other fishes. Toothed whales attack the giant squids. Part of a giant squid's arm, eighteen feet long, was once taken from a whale's stomach.

Mussels, clams, scallops, oysters, and various kinds of snails including abalones, are all used for human food. In North America, the "American oyster," *Crassostrea virginica,* that is cultured along the eastern coast, brings an annual income of millions of dollars. The native oyster (*Ostrea lurida*) of the Pacific coast is commercially less important. It is small and when shucked there may be 1600 to 2000 in a packed gallon. In late years, Japanese and eastern American oysters have been introduced on the Pacific coast and are thriving especially in the northwest. Scallops are harvested on both coasts but to no such extent as the common oyster. Abalone steaks familiar in California markets, though little known outside the state, are slices of the muscular foot of this large marine snail whose iridescent shell figures in many collections. Formerly great numbers of pearl buttons were cut from the shells of large mussels of the Ohio-Mississippi River system. That industry has almost disappeared since synthetic substances have captured the market.

The Classes. The five classes of mollusks have Greek names, all but one referring to the shape or location of the foot (Fig. 31.3). These names are: Amphineura meaning double nerve—the chitons; Scaphopoda meaning plow foot—the tooth shells; Pelecypoda meaning hatchet foot—the clams, mussels, and oysters; Gastropoda meaning stomach foot—the snails, conchs, slugs; Cephalopoda meaning head foot—squids, nautiluses, and octopuses.

Class Amphineura—Chitons

Chitons are widely distributed mollusks of the many seashores. Their eight overlapping shells are flexibly attached to one another and when a chiton is not clinging to rock it usually rolls up in a ball like an armadillo (Fig. 31.4). There are fossil chitons at least 400 million years old. These also have the typical eight shells, a sign that chitons have survived long and changed little.

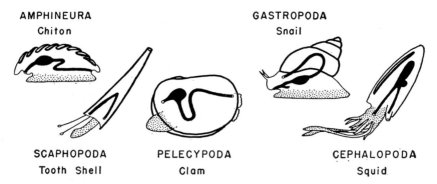

FIG. 31.3. Comparison of three important structures in the members of the five classes of mollusks, the shell (heavy line), the digestive tract (solid black) and the foot (stippled).

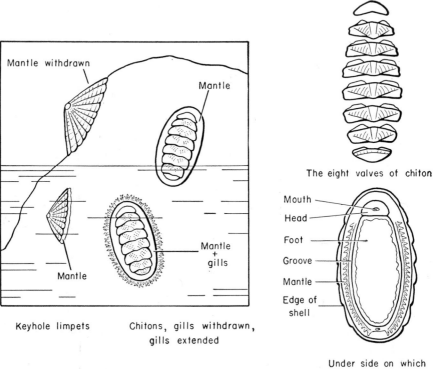

FIG. 31.4. Chiton and keyhole limpets (snails) clamped to a rock lying between the tide lines. Each chiton shows the ancient pattern of overlapping shells that form a flexible roof over its body. When a chiton is turned ventral side up, the foot is exposed, and the borders of the mantle roll up, giving it the common name, sea cradle.

Commonly chitons are about four inches long. They are generally drab-colored, frequent shaded rocks and seaweed, and are neither dangerous, strikingly beautiful, nor edible. They are plant feeders that scrape fine bits from the rocks and seaweeds and the small ones furnish picking for shore birds. Chitons are chiefly interesting as pieces of living history.

Chitons are bilaterally symmetrical outside and inside. The shells and a fold of the mantle project over deep grooves, one extending along each side of the under surface of the body. These are parts of the mantle cavity with gills located in them as they are in the larger mantle cavity of clams. The surface of the tongue is a file, in function a replica of those on the tongues of snails. The relatively large fleshy foot has a ciliated surface and strong muscles. Chitons move like drifting sailboats.

Class Scaphopoda—Tooth Shells

This is a small and little known class of mollusks, with single shells usually less than two inches, but in some species even six inches long (Fig. 31.1). They live in sand beyond the low tide mark, some of them at great depths. Their shells are open at both ends, larger at the head end which is pointed forward as they burrow.

Class Pelecypoda—Bivalves

These are the clams, oysters, scallops, and other two-shelled mollusks. The majority of fresh-water bivalves, both large and small, are widely distributed in lakes and streams (Fig. 31.5). All bivalves are essentially similar and the following outline of the fresh-water mussel applies in general to common marine species such as the round clam, Venus, and the soft shell, Mya. Fresh-water mussels practically all belong to one family. Over 500 species have been found in the United States, but many are impossible to distinguish except by special students of this group.

Fresh-water Mussel

Skin and Mantle. The mantle makes the shell; the shell protects the mantle and together they are the main contributors to security which is the prime achievement of mollusks (Figs. 31.6 and 31.7). The mantle is the soft covering of the body extended into folds on the ventral side, opposite the hinge of the shell. It covers the back of the clam and folds of it hang free in front as an open topcoat hangs free on the human body. It is different in that the mantle of the mussel also fits close to the body even though the folds hang free. There is a space between the open coatsides and the human body. The comparable space in the clam is the mantle cavity in which the gills are suspended. The borders of the mantle contain many glandular cells, are supersensitive to touch,

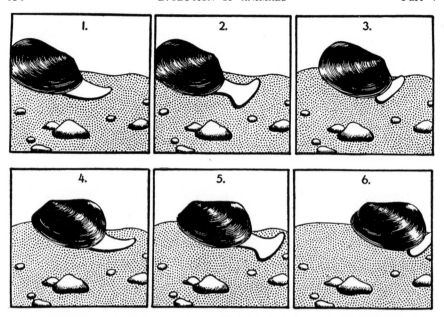

Fig. 31.5. Locomotion of the fresh-water clam is slow as in most clams excepting the razor shells. Blood is forced into the foot and it reaches forward. This takes time. Finally, the muscles of the foot contract and pull the body forward. Thus, the clam takes a step. (Reprinted from *Animals Without Backbones* by Buchsbaum by permission of The University of Chicago Press. Copyright 1948.)

and freely movable for a short distance back to the pallial or fence line where the mantle is attached to the shell. In the soft-shell clam (Mya), the borders of the right and left folds of the mantle are grown together and form the band of flesh prominent in steamed clams. At the rear, usually recognizable by the more pointed end of the shell, the flaps of the mantle are joined and form a tube with fleshy walls. This contains the siphons. In some clams, there are two tubes but if single, the tube is divided within by a partition. Drawn in by the cilia on the mantle and gills, water passes into the incurrent or ventral siphon carrying microorganisms and other particles of food with it (Fig. 31.7). Part of the water is carried toward the mouth and part of it enters the gills. After passing through the gills it passes out the excurrent or dorsal siphon taking away metabolic waste. Although always at the rear end, the siphon is commonly called the neck, long neck for the soft shelled Mya, little necks for the round clams. The tips of siphons are heavily pigmented and black, removed as inedible for indoor meals, eaten with relish at outdoor parties (Fig. 31.8).

Shell. The shell is composed of three layers; the outermost or periostracum is thin, often horny; the middle one contains prisms of lime (calcium carbonate), and the innermost pearly layer is composed of crystals of lime lying irregularly parallel to the surface so that they break up the rays of light and create iridescence (Fig. 31.6). The pearly layer is secreted by cells in the whole surface of the mantle. The other two layers are formed only by cells in the border which at intervals add to the edge of the shell and thus produce the lines of growth. The main function of the shell is protection but it also neutralizes acid. Clams flourish where the mud abounds in organic matter, much of it decayed. Oxygen is scarce; carbon dioxide and sulfur abound and acidity is high. Under these conditions the calcareous shell is an important source of neutralizer of the acid. In clams (Venus) kept out of water experimentally, oxygen is depleted and carbon dioxide accumulates. Under these conditions

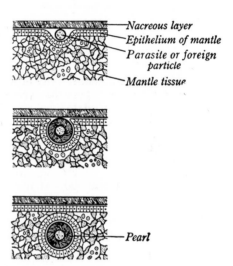

Fig. 31.6. In the innermost, pearly or nacreous layer of the shell the crystals of lime are irregularly parallel and rays of light are broken upon them. This is the cause of iridescence.

If a sand grain or minute animal gets between the shell and the mantle the latter forms a pocket around it and then a pearly cover. Many a natural pearl is the casket of a worm. (Courtesy, Fasten: *Introduction to General Zoology.* Boston, Ginn and Co., 1941.)

Nacreous layer
Epithelium of mantle
Parasite or foreign particle
Mantle tissue

Pearl

some of the shell is dissolved by the mantle and the calcium content of the fluid in the mantle cavity is this increased with the necessary neutralizer.

Respiration. If one shell and flap of the mantle are removed the gills are conspicuously displayed hanging into the mantle cavity with their ventral edges free. The dorsal edges of each pair are so attached that a chamber above the gills (suprabranchial) is shut off from the large mantle cavity below (Fig. 31.8). The incurrent siphon opens into the chamber containing the gills; the excurrent siphon opens out of the chamber above them. The fold of each gill is divided by partitions into narrow water tubes. Minute holes open into these from the mantle cavity and the tubes extending from these open into the suprabranchial chamber. Urged on by cilia, water continually enters the holes in the gills and passes through the water tubes close to blood vessels comparable to arteries and veins (Fig. 31.8). When breathing, a clam always extends the siphons. It gets little or no oxygen when its shells are closed. This is the time when it draws on the calcium carbonate of the shell to neutralize the acidity produced by the excess carbon dioxide.

Circulation. Oxygen diffused from water in the gills, and digested food absorbed from the stomach and intestine are distributed over the body by the

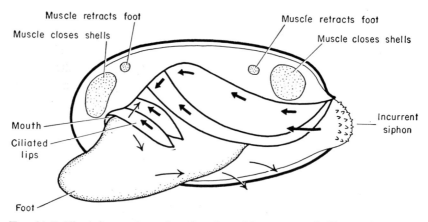

FIG. 31.7. The left mantle cavity of a clam. Movements of cilia on the gills and surfaces of the mantle cause the currents (marked by heavy arrows) that carry particles of food toward the mouth. Other cilia create currents (marked by lighter arrows) that carry rejected particles outward over the folds of the mantle as the clam lies with shells partly open when feeding. This occurs likewise in the right mantle cavity.

slightly bluish watery blood. At the same time metabolic waste is collected from the tissues. The heart composed of two auricles and one ventricle is in the pericardium near the hinge of the shell (Fig. 31.9). When the ventricle contracts it forces blood forward through the anterior aorta and backward through the posterior one each leading to the intestine and other organs of the body. It is finally returned to the auricles. All the blood except that reach-

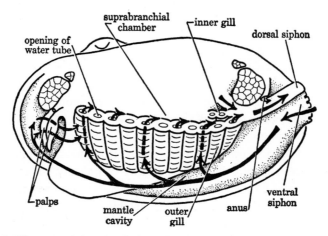

FIG. 31.8. Diagram of the circulation of water through the gills of a fresh-water clam. Movements of cilia cause continual currents of water to pass into the hundreds of pores in the gills, through the water tubes, and finally out of the dorsal or excurrent siphon. (Courtesy, Brown: *Selected Invertebrate Types.* New York, John Wiley and Sons, 1950.)

ing the mantle returns through the kidneys and gills where waste substances are eliminated and oxygen received. Many animals must hunt for their food; clams are relaxed receivers lying quiet while cilia-driven currents of water serve them. Most of the water coming into the mantle cavity enters the gills. The smaller particles of food become entangled in mucus on the outer surfaces of gills and are propelled by cilia to the lips (labial palps). These are remarkable sorting mechanisms that separate out the usable particles which are turned into a groove between the lips and from thence go directly to the mouth.

Food and Digestion. As before stated, clams feed upon bacteria and microscopic plants and animals. Ciliated lips surround the mouth which opens into a short passageway leading to the stomach that is surrounded by a greenish black gland, the so-called liver, whose ducts empty a digestive secretion into it. The intestine extends from the stomach into the foot where it is coiled about the ovary or the testis as the case may be, then turns toward the dorsal side of the body, extends through the heart and opens into the excurrent siphon. This curious route is necessitated by the close quarters of the shell (Fig. 31.9). Food is digested by secretions such as the enzyme amylase of the liver and also within cells. Throughout the digestive canal ameboid cells are common. From microscopic examinations it is believed that such cells make their way through the walls of the canal, ingulf food and digest it, then leave the intestine and return into the spaces between the tissues. Similar intracellular digestion occurs in hydra and other invertebrates including starfishes.

Excretion. The two kidneys are close to the heart (Fig. 31.9). They are difficult to understand without special study but two important facts can be made out. They are tubular and they are closely associated with the blood vessels. Thus they conform in essentials with other kidneys.

Coordination. The nervous system is mainly composed of three pairs of ganglia and their connectives: one pair, the brain or cerebropleural ganglia, is above the mouth, the usual location of a brain; the pedal ganglia are in the foot; and the visceral ganglia just below the posterior adductor muscle (Fig. 31.9). The different ganglia of each side and the members of each pair are joined by nerves. Small branches extend from the ganglia to muscles and sense organs.

Sense organs are few and their functions uncertain, as might be expected of an animal living in unusual security. A minute structure near the pedal ganglia is a typical organ of balance, a cavity containing a bit of lime surrounded by sensory cells. The edges of the mantle contain cells peculiarly sensitive to touch, those of the siphon to touch and light.

Reproduction and Development. In some bivalves, male and female organs are in the same individual; in fresh-water clams, they are in separate ones. The reproductive organs are in the foot packed between the coils of the intestine. The sperm cells are shed into the excurrent siphon and carried into the open

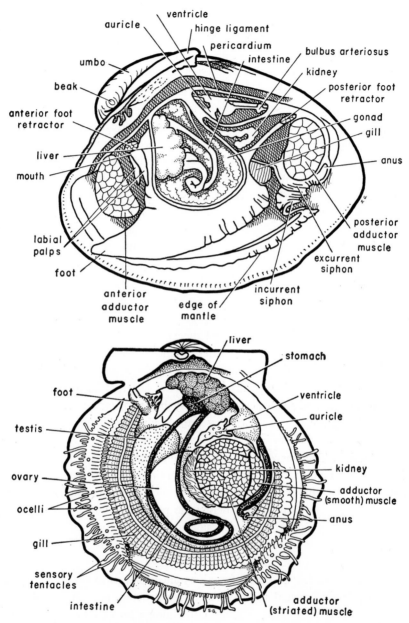

FIG. 31.9. *Upper,* general structure of the salt water littleneck or quahog (*Venus mercenaria*). The left shell, part of the mantle and the gills are cut away. *Lower,* general structure of the scallop (oyster), Pecten. The adductor muscle that pulls the shells together is familiar as fried scallop. The brilliant blue eyes are located along the borders of the mantle. A scallop jumps through the water by clapping its shells together, forcing out the water between them and flying forth, hinge forward, actually jet propelled.

water from whence they are usually drawn into the incurrent siphons. Sperm and eggs ripen at the same time and the latter are shed into the mantle cavity. Both sperm and eggs are drawn through the microscopic holes into the water tubes of the outer gills where fertilization occurs. There millions of embryos develop. The outer gills become swollen brood pouches, and the young clams thrive until they are easily visible to the naked eye. They are then definitely clam-shaped animals called glochidia. They are discharged from the excurrent siphon and scattered on the bottom with their valves open and a sticky thread trailing out between them. For a time they are gamblers for their existence, and then for several months they are parasites (Fig. 31.10). The edges of the shells are smooth in some species; armed with hooks in others. From time to time glochidia snap their valves together, bounce upward, then drop back with valves open. If there is any disturbing motion of the water their snaps and bounces increase. Fish or anything savoring of fish creates the wildest excitement. All of this can be seen with glochidia in a glass of water and a bit of fish meat or blood. It is easy to remove glochidia from a ripe brood pouch—a slight cut in it and they pour out like sand.

All of this happens in nature when fishes are near except that the glochidium

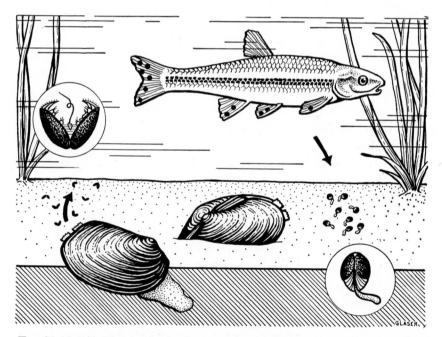

FIG. 31.10. Life history of a fresh-water clam. The embryos develop in the outer gill. Later they are shed through the excurrent siphon (nearer the hinge), as minute clams with one strong muscle connecting the valves and a sticky thread dangling from them. They clap their shells at every fish that approaches and some among the millions are able to hook themselves into the fins and gills where they live for weeks as parasites. Finally they drop off into the mud.

snaps its shells permanently into the skin of the fish and is gradually enclosed in a fleshy case. Through the next weeks or months the glochidium is a parasite receiving nourishment and protection from the fish. Finally it breaks out of the case and falls to the bottom, now formed like its parents but still small. During its life in the fish, it may have traveled many miles; after that it becomes independent and for a time at least a local resident.

OTHER BIVALVES

The bivalves are all aquatic, mainly dwellers on the bottom, most of them marine, and commonest between the tide lines. Among the rare climbing ones are the little fingernail clams (Family Sphaeridae), many of them less than half an inch long. A fingernail clam forages over the bottom of ponds. It also curves its supple foot around the stems of water weeds like a pole climber with one leg. Meanwhile, its split siphon is extended and apparently it is drawing in some of the minute organisms which it must disturb as it climbs.

The razor-shells (Ensis), 4 to 7 inches long, are both agile and strong burrowers that can outspeed a human shoveler. They also jump with a steel-spring action of the foot. The common scallop (*Pecten irradians*) is another lively bivalve that makes zigzag jumps by opening and forcibly closing its valves (Fig. 31.9). One clap expels the water from the mantle cavity and drives the scallop, hinge first, a yard or more in a straight line through the water—sometimes out of it like a flying fish. Another clap drives it in a different direction. It is as difficult to catch as a clothes moth when it performs the familiar zigzag trick in the air. The scallop closes its valves by its one powerful adductor or cross muscle, and the springy hinge-ligament opens them. The adductor muscles are the tasty fried scallops. Tons of scallops are harvested annually along the Atlantic Coast and only one muscle from each animal is used. Deep sea scallops (*Pecten grandis*), five inches or more wide, are most abundant off the coast of Maine and most expensive in restaurants.

Oysters undergo rhythmical changes of sex during the individual's lifetime. There are two similar types of these changes; one type occurs in the European oyster (*Ostrea edulis*), and in the Pacific oyster (*O. lurida*), a species native to Japan; the second type occurs in the American oyster, *Crassostrea virginica* (formerly *Ostrea virginica*), and others. In the American oyster, the majority of the young are males and during the first spawning season they function as males and produce sperm cells that are extruded into the water. Before they become sexually mature however, these young oysters may present all gradations from true males in which there are developing sperm cells to other individuals that have complete ovaries. After the second spawning season, the number of individuals of each sex is almost equal. The adults usually function permanently as one or the other sex. American oysters begin to spawn soon after the temperature of the water passes 63° F., usually at higher temperatures in the south. In Long Island Sound, the season is late June to September; in Chesapeake Bay, May to October; in Puget Sound, May to October.

Class Gastropoda—Snails and Slugs

Gastropods are distributed in almost every part of the earth—land and fresh-water snails, great numbers of marine snails including the huge whelks and conchs and the limpets. The soft naked land slugs are limited to moist places; the equally naked nudibranchs are marine. There are some 30,000 living species of gastropods and many more that exist only as fossils, among them limpets of millions of years ago.

Structure. The common edible garden snail (*Helix aspersa*) is often taken as a type (Fig. 31.11). This snail moves about on its fleshy foot leaving a trail of mucus from the gland within it. On the prominent head there are two pairs of tentacles, the shorter pair sensitive to smells, the longer one to light. The single coiled shell is secreted by a mantle as in other mollusks. The organs of the body are crowded within it, a complicated mass of twisted viscera including a complete male and female reproductive system, and a digestive tube begin-ning at the mouth, twisting upward into the spire and turning back toward the head to end in the anal opening (Fig. 31.3). One section of the mantle is an air sac whose walls are supplied with blood vessels and blood pumped by the heart; thus it functions as a lung. Most fresh-water snails come to the sur-face and take air into the air sac or breathe through their skin; the majority of marine snails breathe by gills.

Activities and Functions. The snail's shell is a house into which it retreats.

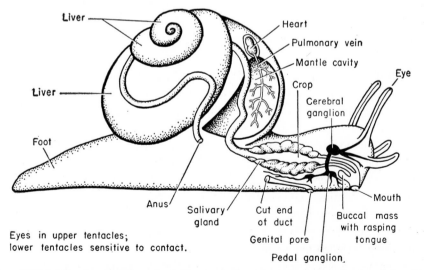

FIG. 31.11. The form and part of the general anatomy of a snail; the right side with the shell removed; the reproductive systems, male and female, are not shown.

In most species, there is a hard plate on the upper surface of the foot that is last to be drawn into the shell. This is the operculum that acts as a stopper to evaporation and keeps out intruders. The small opercula of snails were the original eyestones passed between the eyelid and eye to bring out foreign bodies.

Feeding. Snails scrape surfaces with the rasping tongue or radula; when a garden snail is rasping cabbage the sound can be heard several feet away (Fig. 31.11). The radula is a horny ribbon with ridges and teeth on its upper surface and beneath it is a cartilage which can be pushed forward against whatever the snail is feeding upon. The radula is then pulled back and forth over the cartilage to rasp a green leaf, the skin of a tadpole, seaweed, or films of algae and bacteria depending upon the snail's habits. A great many snails are carnivorous and in these the radula is at the end of a proboscis which can be extended through a hole bored in a shell. The familiar and unpopular "drills" are snails that rasp holes in the shells of edible clams and oysters and other bivalves whose pierced shells are common on many beaches (Fig. 31.12). Sea slugs, beautiful though too soft, feed upon sea anemones likewise soft (Fig. 31.13).

Relationships. Snails are the hosts of immature worms, including the highly injurious flukes that as adults are parasites in birds and mammals. Both fresh- and salt-water snails are eaten in great numbers by fishes and shore birds. Any one who examines the stomachs of common fresh-water fishes known as suckers will find plenty of small snails swallowed whole, with shells being slowly dissolved by the powerful digestive juices. In the stomach of a mullet (a name given to many small bottom-feeding fishes in fresh and salt waters), one investigator found 35,000 little marine snails. Snails are generally unimportant among human foods, but at European shore resorts roasted periwinkles are sold in bags like peanuts; and steaks from the foot of abalones are sold in California markets.

Reproduction. In about half the species of snails there is a fully functioning male and female reproductive system in each individual, but even so, these snails mate and cross fertilization occurs as it does in a similar situation in earthworms. Fresh-water snails produce relatively few eggs in blobs of crystal clear jelly deposited on submerged stones and on the undersides of floating leaves. Marine snails produce great numbers of eggs. The sea hares (or sea slugs, *Tethys californicus*) of the California coast lay their eggs in gelatinous strings. By counting and computing them, the MacGinities of the Kerckhoff Marine Laboratory, California, found that one of these sea hares produced 478 millions of eggs in four months and one week. The animal, obviously kept in captivity, weighed five pounds and 12 ounces.

In many mollusks, sex variations occur in the same individual. Young marine snails of the genus Crepidula, commonly called boat shells, function at

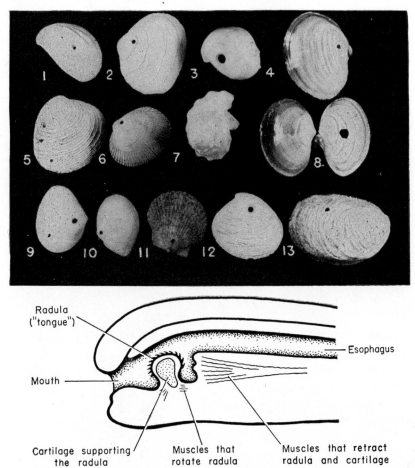

FIG. 31.12. *Upper,* holes bored by snails whose rasping tongue (radula) is on the end of a proboscis that is finally pushed into the soft body. They suggest the number of animals consumed by snails and by boring sponges which bore holes by dissolving the shells. *Lower,* proboscis of marine snail cut lengthwise to show the rasping tongue. (*Upper,* courtesy, MacGinitie and MacGinitie: *Natural History of Marine Animals.* New York, McGraw-Hill Book Co., 1949.)

first as males but later transform into females. This sexual transformation is hereditary, normally occurring in all individuals.

Class Cephalopoda—Squids and Octopuses

Characteristics. These are the most highly developed and swiftest of all mollusks (Figs. 31.14, 31.15, 31.16). The head-foot is used equally as a head and a supporting foot. The digestive tract turns back upon itself as it does in snails so that the mouth and anal opening are close together, but there is no such coiling as in snails (Fig. 31.3). In cephalopods, the foot and head with its remarkable eyes are most highly developed and the shell most

Fig. 31.13. The gray sea-slug feeds on sea anemones such as the one on the left; another one at the upper right has its tentacles withdrawn. Sea-slugs are mollusks that lose their shells in early life and commonly bear gill-like filaments brightly colored, translucent and continually moved by the currents of water. Length of slug 4 inches. (Photograph courtesy, Douglas P. Wilson, Marine Biological Laboratory, Plymouth, England.)

unevenly so. The shell of a squid is a horny quill pen embedded in flesh; that of a nautilus is a many-chambered dwelling. All of the tribe are marine. No other mollusks approach them in travel, the drifting of the female paper sailor, the darting of the squids and sepias (Figs. 31.15, 31.16). Clam and snail shells have great beauty of color, but no other mollusks can display the

FIG. 31.14. Common octopus or devilfish, *Octopus vulgaris*. When they are extended the arms of this species may have a span of over six feet though they are usually much shorter. The arms of an *Octopus apollyn* of the western coast of the U. S. may have a span of 20 feet. (Photograph courtesy, Douglas P. Wilson, Marine Biological Laboratory, Plymouth, England.)

mauve and rose, and the yellows and browns that shift over the body of an excited squid. Some species have bioluminescence to add to their beauty of daytime color (Fig. 31.17). In the squids and sepias, an ink gland secretes a dark fluid that is stored in the ink sac. When the owner is disturbed it shoots jets of ink from the siphon, creating a cloud in the water that hides its escape.

Living cephalopods are a small group, but their ancestors once swarmed the seas and fossils of some 10,000 different species are known. The pearly nautilus (*Nautilus pompilius*) is the only living relic of great numbers of predecessors which also had spiral shells, divided into compartments by septa. As a nautilus grows, it enlarges its shell and secretes a partition behind it so that the whole shell comes to be a series of chambers empty except for the cord of living tissue connecting the body to the first small chamber (Fig. 31.15). Among the ancestors of the pearly nautilus was one whose fossil shell is 15 feet long. The shell of the living nautilus measures about 10 inches.

THE SQUID—LOLIGO

The common squid, *Loligo pealii,* of the Atlantic, is about 10 inches long; that of the Pacific is a little more than half that. Squids range from those that are less than two inches long to the giant squids of the deep sea some of them probably having an over-all length of over 50 feet—by far the largest living invertebrates. All of them are fierce carnivores that follow and attack schools

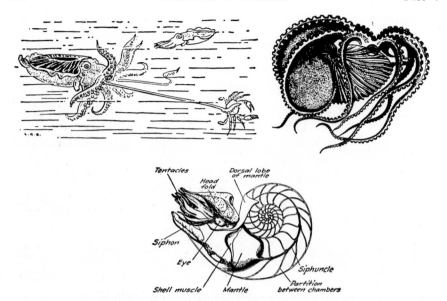

FIG. 31.15. Cephalopods, the swiftest of all mollusks. *Upper left,* sepia, the cuttlefish with one tentacle stretched forward gripping a crab with its vacuum disks. The white "cuttlebone" fed to canaries for lime is the shell of the cuttle-fish. The name sepia is due to the brown inklike secretion that the cuttlefish throws off when disturbed. *Upper right,* paper sailor (Argonauta). Female in floating position. Paper sailors float on the surface of the warmer waters of the Atlantic and Pacific oceans, occasionally in coastal waters. The thin papery shell is secreted by the flattened arms. It is not attached to the body, has no partitions and is mainly a carrier for the eggs. The female is eight inches long, the male about one inch long. *Lower,* chambered nautilus (Nautilus) cut open to show the successive chambers that have been occupied as the animal has grown. A cord of living tissue extends from the animal's body to the first chamber that it occupied. (*Upper left* after Boulenger. *Upper right* after Claus and Sedgwick. *Lower* after Ludwig and Leunis.)

of fishes. They are themselves in turn the prey of fishes, but they are swift dodgers. They are actually jet propelled, darting with sudden speed when water gathered in the mantle cavity is spurted out of the siphon with great force (Fig. 31.16). They swim by undulating movements of the fins, actually flaps of the mantle, not at all like the fins of fishes.

Structure. Squids have 10 arms, including one pair with grasping tentacles much longer than the others. When a squid is swimming it holds the arms close together and uses them as rudders for steering. A squid darts at its prey arms foremost and when almost upon it spreads them like the rays of a daisy, stretches out the tentacles, grips the prey, pulls it back against the sharp beak in the meantime clasping it with the other arms. Next to the arms, the eyes are the most prominent features of the head. Although entirely different in their development, they are the camera type like those of vertebrates. The squid is an example of the association of the active hunting habits of a carnivore

FIG. 31.16. The common squid (*Loligo pealii*) photographed in an aquarium at Marine Biological Laboratory, Woods Hole, Massachusetts. Length, about ten inches. (Courtesy, General Biological Supply House, Chicago, Ill.)

FIG. 31.17. A school of bioluminescent deep-sea squids (*Watasenia scintillans*) as it might appear in the darkness of the deep sea. An actual observer said of one tropical species of squid that the eyes shone blue, the sides of the body with pearly sheen, and the underside of the body crimson. The common squid (*Loligo pealii*) is *not* bioluminescent. (Courtesy, American Museum of Natural History, New York.)

coupled with the development of an acute sense of sight, a contrast to the lack of vision in the lethargic clams.

The mantle is a conical envelope from which the head and siphon protrude, the latter structure representing the front and rear of the body; the digestive tube is bent double like a jackknife (Fig. 31.3). The shell is a quill feather-shaped plate of chitin buried under the skin on the dorsal side of the body.

The jaws resemble a parrot's beak and with them a squid can kill a fish by a single bite through the spinal cord or head. The ink sac is a relatively large pear-shaped organ. It consists of a gland which secretes the ink, a sac for storage, and a duct leading to the anal chamber from which the ink is expelled.

The sexes are separate, each with one gonad opening toward the siphon. When mating a sperm packet is transferred by the specialized right arm of the male to the mantle cavity of the female where fertilization eventually occurs. The eggs are laid in long capsules of jelly from which the young ones emerge, minute but in perfect squid form (Fig. 31.18).

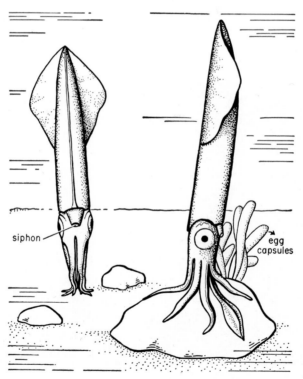

siphon

egg capsules

Fig. 31.18. Common squid (*Loligo pealii*). Squids stand on their heads when laying eggs. The gelatinous egg capsules, about three inches long, are discharged through the opening of the siphon and attached by one end to seaweeds and rocks, usually in clusters. They are commonly washed in upon the shore all along our coasts.

32

Echinoderms—Forerunners of the Vertebrates

Their Relatives. The starfishes and their relatives are animals whose body plan, except in the developing young ones, is utterly different from that of any other animals. A clue to their possible kinship comes from the resemblance of the larvae to those of certain primitive chordates clearly related to the vertebrates. Because of this the echinoderms have been promoted, by general but by no means unanimous opinion, to a position near the chordates. Although mollusks and insects have reached high peaks of invertebrate specialization and would seem to belong in that place, their larvae resemble those of annelid worms more than those of any chordate. And young animals are tell-tales of the origins of their parents.

Characteristics. As the name of the Phylum Echinodermata, spiny-skinned, implies, many of these animals are armed with hard, chalky and in some species very heavy spines. Except in the larvae, they are radially symmetrical on a plan of five or multiples of five that is unique (Figs. 32.1, 32.2). Even in adults, however, they show signs of bilateral symmetry such as the position of the sieve plate in the starfish through which a line may be drawn separating the body into right and left halves. The bilateral symmetry of the free-swimming larva (Fig. 32.8) is generally regarded as the fundamental plan upon which the radial one has been overlaid during a long evolution.

All echinoderms live in salt water and are thoroughly and curiously adjusted to this existence. Their bodies are continually drenched with sea water, inside and out. Their blood is practically sea water. A starfish cannot take one step unless its watery blood flows into its foot. Oxygen diffuses into the blood and carbon dioxide diffuses out of it through the thin walls of hundreds of skin-gills.

There are no special excretory organs but slowly circulating fluid is continually washing the tissues and carrying away their by-products. Cilia are

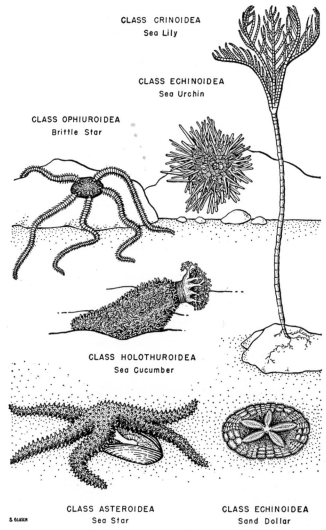

CLASS CRINOIDEA
Sea Lily

CLASS ECHINOIDEA
Sea Urchin

CLASS OPHIUROIDEA
Brittle Star

CLASS HOLOTHUROIDEA
Sea Cucumber

CLASS ASTEROIDEA
Sea Star

CLASS ECHINOIDEA
Sand Dollar

S. GLASER

Fig. 32.1. Echinoderms. Animals of this group are built upon a plan of five. Details of the plan vary greatly, but five and multiples of five appear as insistent and clear as the theme of a symphony. Of those shown in this figure, the five is least apparent in the sea urchin and sea cucumber. If the sea urchin were moving however, its five rows of tube-feet would reach out to the rock; and if the sea cucumber were active five pairs of respiratory gills would be expanded in the water. The starfish has so stretched its stomach into the clam that the five lobes are pulled out of their regular shape during this meal time.

numerous on the internal organs as well as on the outer surfaces of the body, the latter a proof of complete limitation to life in the water. With the rare exceptions of certain feather stars, only the larvae can swim. Nearly all echinoderms live on the bottom and minute organisms and particles are always falling upon them. Suffocation from these is prevented by a remarkable skin-cleaning and trapping equipment consisting of great numbers of minute pincers distributed over the outer surface of the body (Fig. 32.3). The smallest adult echinoderm is half an inch in diameter. The largest starfish is 32 inches or more across and a slender worm-shaped sea-cucumber may be six feet long.

Class Crinoidea—Sea Lilies

In ancient times crinoids (*crinon* meaning lily) stood like waving lilies attached to primeval sea bottoms (Fig. 29.4). Some of those sea bottoms were long ago lifted and now constitute inland highlands. In upper New York

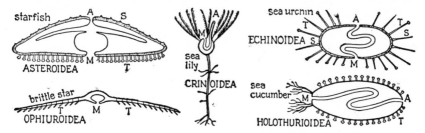

FIG. 32.2. Schematic representation of the relations of important structures in five classes of echinoderms. *T*, tube feet; *S*, spines; *M*, mouth; *A*, anus. (Courtesy, Storer: *General Zoology*, ed. 2. New York, McGraw-Hill Book Co., 1951.)

State, slabs of stone have been found with dozens of fossil sea lilies pressed into it as if they had been outspread by falling earth. The majority of fossil echinoderms are crinoids but there are relatively few living species. These are the stalked sea lilies attached on the bottom in deep waters and the feather stars that can swim feebly on the surface. All crinoids are attached when young (Fig. 32.1). Each arm and its branches bear central grooves through which cilia propel particles of food toward the upturned mouth.

Class Asteroidea—Sea Stars or Starfishes

These echinoderms have flat bodies with five conspicuous arms or variations of this number. The central part of the body is relatively broad and high and the arms short. In all starfishes, the arms are broad as compared with those of brittle stars.

Class Ophiuroidea—Brittle or Serpent Stars, Basket Stars

The body is flattened with a very definite central disk from the under side of which the slender, flexible, jointed arms are sharply marked off. These are provided with strong muscles and are bent and lashed like rapidly moving serpents. There are no tube feet, but structures comparable to them all help to pass food toward the mouth. Brittle stars are the most agile of echinoderms, crowding together in narrow crevices and scuttling rapidly when disturbed.

Their arms are easily snapped off and in turn easily regrown (Figs. 32.1, 32.9).

Class Echinoidea—Sea Urchins, Sand Dollars

Sea urchins are generally biscuit-shaped with more or less prominent spines for which the class is named. Sand dollars are flat, cooky-shaped, with very short usually fine spines. Instead of the separate pieces of skeleton being

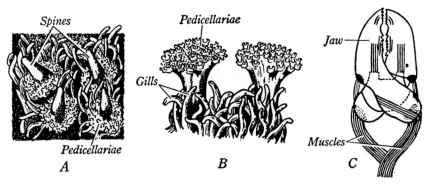

FIG. 32.3. *A* and *B*, small portion of the surface of a star fish showing the large spines and finger-shaped skin gills through whose thin walls gases are diffused, oxygen into the tissue fluid which they contain and carbon dioxide from tissue fluid into the surrounding water. The minute pincers or pedicellariae cooperate in keeping the surface clean aided by cilia which create currents of water. *C*, a single pedicellaria. These pincers are very responsive to touch. Hundreds of them will snap and clamp if a hair is drawn across the body. (After Jennings. Courtesy, Fasten: *Introduction to General Zoology*. Boston, Ginn and Co., 1941.)

embedded in a muscular body wall as in starfishes, these skeletons are inflexible cases formed of limy plates lightly fused together (Fig. 32.1). The spines are attached by ball-and-socket joints and sea urchins walk on them as if on stilts. Colonies of sea urchins cling to wave-washed rocks. Sand dollars commonly lie half burrowed in sand rich in organic matter. Relatively few tube feet touch the surface when a sea urchin walks over flat places, but it uses feet from every surface of the body when it climbs (Fig. 32.1). The crystal clear eggs and developing embryos of sea urchins and sand dollars are among the most famous subjects of embryological investigations.

Class Holothuroidea—Sea Cucumbers

Some sea cucumbers are replicas of pickled cucumbers; others are long and slender, translucent and beautiful (Fig. 32.1). They have no skeletal frame. What skeleton there is consists of small limy plates, helplessly isolated and embedded in the thin muscular body wall. Sea cucumbers rest and travel on their sides mouth forward; all other echinoderms except the crinoids travel mouth down. Superficially sea cucumbers seem bilaterally symmetrical, and

do not display the five-point plan that is evident enough when they are carefully examined.

The Starfish—An Example of the Echinoderms

The following general description applies to the common American starfishes such as *Asterias forbesi* of the eastern coast south of Maine and the
Pacific starfish, *Pisaster ochraceus*.

Appearance. The mouth and feet of a starfish are on the down or more
correctly oral side upon which it rests and travels (Fig. 32.4). The rear or
aboral surface is up. On that side, between the bases of two of the arms is the
ciliated sieve plate through which water is continually drawn into the body
(Fig. 32.5). Its position is one of the indications of bilateral symmetry present
even in adult starfishes. The entire surface of the body is rough with the
blunt spines fastened to the units of the skeleton in the body wall. Hundreds of
these units, the ossicles, are set close together in the soft middle layer of cells
(mesoderm) that formed them (Figs. 32.6, 32.7). Covering the whole surface
of the body including the spines and pincers (pedicellariae) is a delicate skin

FIG. 32.4. Starfish. A detail of the oral surface. Rows of tube feet radiate
from the central mouth region. Most of the tube feet are extended by the
pressure of the watery body fluid; some have been retracted by the strap-shaped
muscle within each one. The tip of each foot is enlarged by a suction disk or
foot hold. (Reprinted from *Animals without Backbones* by Ralph Buchsbaum
by permission of The University of Chicago Press. Copyright 1948.)

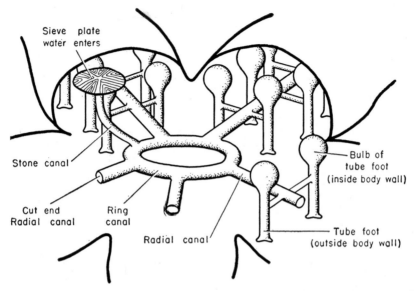

Fig. 32.5. Diagram of a part of the water-vascular (circulatory) system of a starfish; three of the radial canals are cut near the base. This system takes part in all movements. It is to the starfish what the circulation of blood is to the human body and more—a waterway constantly receiving water through the sieve plate and constantly expending water carrying other substances with it. Water takes part in every movement of the starfish and in every phase of its living. Tiedemann vesicles are not shown.

clothed with cilia, whose rapid whipping keeps currents of water moving over the surface. Some of the pincers work like forceps, others like scissors, but all are traps that pinch and hold until they are stimulated by some other contact such as the touch of a neighboring pincer or a falling particle. Multitudes of minute skin gills which freely open from the body cavity are filled with the coelomic fluid that oozes slowly about in any open place (Fig. 32.3).

Locomotion, Circulation of the Blood, and the Water Vascular System. Starfishes move by manipulating the fluid in the versatile water vascular system. This contains the circulating fluid that, although largely sea water, may still be called blood since it contains cells and is concerned with respiration. The structures that belong especially to this system are the sieve plate, many canals, the tube feet, and the skin gills. The ciliated stone canal leads from the sieve plate to the circular canal around the mouth. Opening into the latter are nine small sacs (Tiedemann vesicles) in which the ameboid blood cells originate. Also opening from the circular canal are five radial canals, one to each arm (Fig. 32.5). These connect with each tube foot by a short canal. All the tubes are passageways for the water that enters through the sieve plate and, picking up various substances in the body, becomes the blood.

The tube feet are so coordinated through the central nervous system that they are able to work together and the starfish can move in one direction. Progress is slow and often begins only after a period of seeming disagreement among the feet as to which direction they will go. In order to take a step, a tube foot must receive a signal from the nervous system and be stimulated by contact with a surface. First the internal bulb (or ampulla) contracts and forces fluid into the external tubular part of the foot which is extended (Fig. 32.4). In the meantime, a valve prevents the fluid from instantly flowing back into the bulb. The extended foot makes a contact with the surface, muscles in the disk or sole of the foot contract, suction is produced, and a foothold established. Longitudinal muscles in the tube then contract and pull. This is the pull that moves the body of the starfish when many tube feet are working. Following this, the longitudinal muscles of the tube relax, and circular ones contract and force fluid back into the bulb. The foot is now ready for a refill and another step. Water continually diffuses from the water vascular system into the body cavity and this diffuses through the gills and body wall. With every step some water is lost from each tube foot.

Nervous System. The central nervous system consists of a nerve ring surrounding the mouth and connected with five radial nerves, one in each arm (Fig. 32.6). At the tip of the arm a radial nerve gives off fine branches. This region is highly sensitive to touch and to light through the eyespot. The cen-

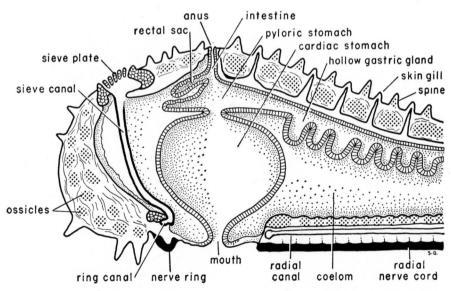

FIG. 32.6. Diagram of a vertical section, tube feet omitted, through the central disk and base of one arm of a starfish, Asterias. A few pedicellariae are shown to indicate their presence; actually gills and pedicellariae are abundant. The cardiac stomach is the part that the starfish extends out through its mouth and spreads over the soft body of a clam or oyster. (After Brown: *Selected Invertebrate Types.* New York, John Wiley and Sons, 1950.)

tral system is associated with a network of nerves spread out below the surface of the body.

Feeding and Digestion. Most starfishes are carnivorous, feeding principally upon clams, oysters, scallops, and mussels. If a starfish is placed in an aquarium with one or two clams the sensitive tube feet at the ends of the arms soon wave excitedly in their direction. Very soon, the starfish proceeds toward them and attacks one of them. It climbs over the clam, its body tentwise above it with its arms so placed that the tube feet finally pull on the opposite shells. Many tube feet pull but not all of them at the same time so that there is a relay of continuous pulling that fatigues the muscles of the clam which eventually opens its shells. Immediately, the arms of the starfish contract pressing fluid against the pouched part of the stomach which is everted through the mouth and lowered between the shells. It envelops the clam's body and digestion

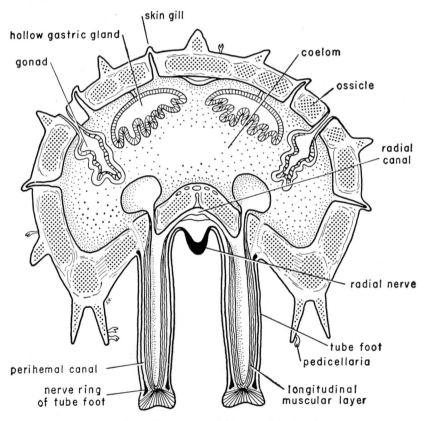

Fig. 32.7. Cross section of an arm of the starfish. It shows the separateness of the ossicles; the free passage ways between the roomy body cavity (coelom) and the skin gills, between the radial canal and the whole extent of the tube feet; and the openings of the gonads, the ovaries or testes whichever the sex may be. (After Brown: *Selected Invertebrate Types.* New York, John Wiley and Sons, 1950.)

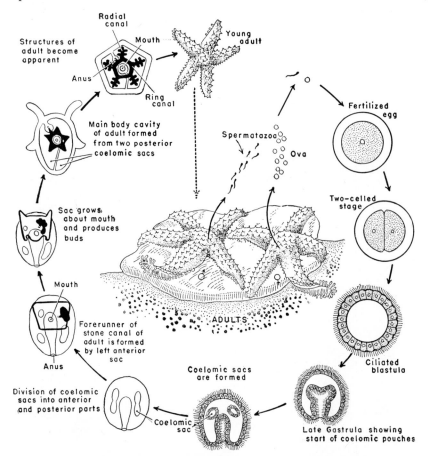

FIG. 32.8. Diagrams to show the development of the starfish. This is one more example of the similarity of the early processes of development among animals that are later as different as worms and echinoderms. It is clearly shown here in the blastula and gastrula stages. The diagrams of the later stages can probably mean little without a special study of the embryology of starfishes. Even in these stages it is clear that the starfish has a two-sided symmetry before it attains the five-sided one. (Courtesy, Hunter and Hunter: *College Zoology*. Philadelphia, W. B. Saunders Co., 1949.)

is begun. The partly digested food is sucked into the posterior or pyloric part of the stomach into which five pairs of conspicuous digestive glands open. They are hollow so that food passes into them freely, and their linings are provided with cilia that keep the contents astir. Their surfaces are greatly increased by infoldings and their cells produce powerful protein-splitting enzymes which complete the digestion of the food eventually absorbed through their walls (Fig. 32.6). Free-moving ameboid cells are abundant in the digestive tract and they digest food just as similar ones do in hydra and in the clam. Practically no indigestible food is consumed by common starfishes

(Asterias). There are certain species that feed on small snails, taking them into the stomach in the regular way. After the soft parts are digested these starfishes spit out the shells, following the custom that has persisted from ameba to man. An intestine and anal opening are practically nonfunctional.

Excretion. Many ameboid blood cells are drawn into the skin gills by the cilia which line them. Such phagocytic cells, usually carrying waste matter, gradually work their way through the thin membranes of the gills into the open

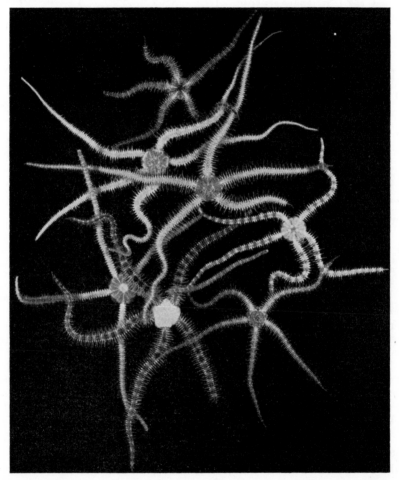

FIG. 32.9. Brittle-stars (*Ophiothrix fragilis*), the most agile of the echinoderms. They are named for their ability to snap off their arms. This species is common in Great Britain; others with similar habits live on rocky coasts of North America. They are usually wedged in between rocks, tangled with seaweeds or one another. When scattered on the bottom of a large aquarium without rocks or seaweed brittle-stars will clump together within ten minutes and twine their arms about one another. This and others of his experiments with brittle-stars are mentioned by W. C. Allee in his book *The Social Life of Animals*. (Photograph courtesy, Douglas P. Wilson, Marine Biological Laboratory, Plymouth, England.)

water. Other waste is probably carried away by escaping body fluid. There are no kidneys.

Reproduction. With few exceptions, the sexes are separate in starfishes. There are two ovaries or two testes in each arm with a minute opening in each organ near the base of the arm (Fig. 32.7). In most species, the eggs and sperm are discharged into the open water; fertilization occurs there, and there is no trace of parental care (Fig. 32.8). Certain of the West Coast starfishes brood their eggs. In one very small species, the female carries her eggs in clusters fastened to her mouth. Others arch the center of the body and draw the arms together making a kind of brood pouch in which they hold the eggs.

33

Introduction to the Vertebrates— Lower Chordates and Fishes

Higher and Lower Chordates. The higher chordates are the vertebrates, the most highly developed of all animals—fishes, amphibians, reptiles, birds, and mammals. They are to a certain degree familiar and commonly known as animals. The lower chordates such as the worm-shaped Balanoglossus and the tunicates formed on the same basic plan are unfamiliar, unrecognized as animals, and altogether unsuspected as relatives of the vertebrates (Fig. 33.1). Dozens of tunicates firmly attached to a wharf pile suggest miniature hot water bottles rather than living relatives of man. Yet they have three fundamental characteristics that occur in every chordate including man, and in no other animals.

Three Unique Characteristics of Chordates

1. All have at one time or another a strong flexible notochord that extends through a part or the whole length of the body. In lower chordates, unless lost by retrogressive evolution, it is present throughout life. In higher chordates, it is fully present only during embryonic stages and is replaced by the vertebral column.

2. The central hollow nerve cord is dorsal to the digestive canal and enlarged at the anterior end as the brain.

3. Paired gill pouches which open as gill slits, or traces of them are present in the pharynx at some time in the life of all chordates. Up to and including the fishes, gills on the arches between the slits serve for respiration throughout life. In higher vertebrates, gill slits or traces of them are generally present only in larval or embryonic stages. In mammals, the gill slits never open and only in amphibians do they function in breathing.

The presence or absence of a notochord, and the dorsal or ventral position

662

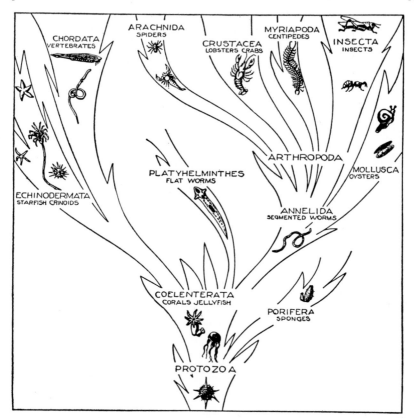

Fig. 33.1. A simplified family tree of the animal kingdom suggesting the probable relationships of vertebrates. Studies generally agree that coelenterates, such as jellyfishes, sea-anemones, and corals are the basic stock of all animals above the protozoans and sponges. Clues to any ancestral relationship between invertebrates and vertebrates are still unsatisfactory. Certain similarities between vertebrates and, strangely enough, the echinoderms have been discovered. They are claimed to establish some affinity between the two groups though by no means placing the echinoderms as ancestors of vertebrates. (Reprinted from *Man and the Vertebrates* by A. S. Romer by permission of The University of Chicago Press. Copyright 1933.)

of a central nerve cord and heart are invariable differences between vertebrate and invertebrate animals (Fig. 33.4).

Lower Chordates

These constitute three subphyla of little-known animals, but they are significant because of their relationship to echinoderms on one hand and to vertebrates on the other (Fig. 33.2).

Hemichorda. In the Hemichorda, represented by the acorn worm *Balanoglossus* the so-called notochord is a short tubular outgrowth that extends forward from the mouth into the proboscis (Fig. 33.3). It stiffens this muscular burrowing organ and thus performs a skeletal function. Acorn worms are common on muddy bottoms along both east and west coasts. The pharynx is divided into a dorsal region, containing many pairs of gill slits, and a ventral food passage.

Urochorda. Members of the Urochorda are called tunicates because of their tunic-like covering and sea squirts because they squirt water from the pores

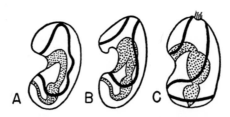

FIG. 33.2. Diagrammatic side views of the larvae of *A*, an acorn worm (a hemichordate); *B*, a starfish; and *C*, a sea cucumber—all of them minute, nearly microscopic. The black lines represent bands of cilia. In life the digestive tract (stippled) is clearly seen through the translucent body. Until the life history of the acorn worm was known the larvae of acorn worms were taken for starfishes. This is an example of certain similarities between chordates and echinoderms that has led to the theory that the two groups have a common ancestry in some minute bilaterally symmetrical animals of the ancient oceans. There is also a striking biochemical resemblance. The amino acid, creatine occurs in all vertebrates; among invertebrates it is known only in echinoderms. (Courtesy, Romer: *The Vertebrate Body*, ed. 2. Philadelphia, W. B. Saunders Co., 1955.)

of the mantle when disturbed. The larvae, but a few millimeters long, are tadpole-shaped with a notochord in the tail. Appropriately for their free living, they are equipped with eyes. As they go on developing, they settle front end down on submerged seaweeds and rocks and become permanently attached. The tail and notochord waste away and the eyes disappear. These animals are striking examples of evolution gone backward, but their abundance shows that they have fitted into a niche in which they have survived with great success.

Cephalochorda. The Cephalochorda includes the lancelet Amphioxus, the fish-shaped burrowers, two to four inches long, that live in limited zones of sea bottoms all over the world (Fig. 33.3). The basic pattern of these lancelets resembles that of the vertebrates. The development of the embryo is also a ground plan of vertebrate development and certain studies of it are classics in embryology (Chap. 19).

Higher Chordates

SUBPHYLUM VERTEBRATA

The animals that attract human interest are most often the vertebrates. Insects are their chief competitors for attention—the only group that equals

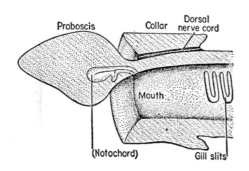

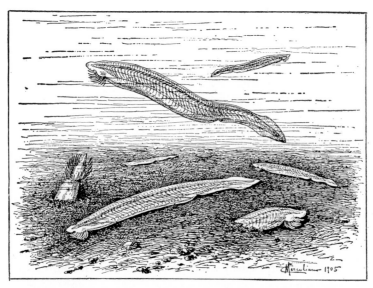

FIG. 33.3. Representative lower chordates. A notochord is present at some time in every chordate; in man only in the embryo. *Upper,* acorn "worm," Balanoglossus (adult worm), a burrower in sand, between the tides and deeper. *Middle,* a sagittal section of the anterior end of the adult. If the notochord were prolonged backward it would lie between the nerve cord and the alimentary canal as it does in all chordates. *Lower,* Amphioxus—*Branchiostoma lanceolatus.* About 2 inches long, a burrower along the coasts of warmer seas. (*Upper,* after Bateson. Courtesy, Rand: *The Chordates.* Philadelphia, The Blakiston Co., 1950. *Middle,* courtesy, Romer: *The Vertebrate Body,* ed. 2. Philadelphia, W. B. Saunders Co., 1955. *Lower,* after Hesse-Doflein: *Tierbau und Tierleben.* Leipzig, B. G. Teubner, 1910.)

them in prominence. On no other group of animals has the human race depended so much for food, work, transport, and companionship. Vertebrates have a bewildering capacity for adaptability in form, size, and habit; mouse and whale, ground mole and eagle, flying fish and antelope, flounder on the sea bottom and squirrel on the tree trunk, penguins grand marching on the ice and dancers in the ballroom. Differences in size do not alter the basic pattern. Learn the anatomy of a mouse and you can understand that of an elephant. An elephant's trunk is still a nose.

Animals in the Subphylum Vertebrata fall into 7 groups:

Class Cyclostomata. Lamprey eels.

Class Chondrichthyes. Cartilaginous fishes. Skeleton cartilaginous, dogfish, shark.

Class Osteichthyes. Bony fishes. Skeleton more or less bony; trout, perch, true eels.

Class Amphibia. Salamanders, frogs, and toads. Skin moist and glandular; gills temporary or permanent, rarely lacking; five-fingered and four-toed limbs.

Class Reptilia. Turtles, lizards, and snakes. Cold-blooded; embryo developing in a sac (amnion); dry skin with outer horny layer of scales.

Class Aves. Birds. Feathers.

Class Mammalia. Mammals, including man. Hair and milk glands.

In addition to the three unique characteristics of all chordates the leading ones of the vertebrates are: an internal skeleton of cartilage or bone; a vertebral column, replacing the notochord of lower chordates; usually two pairs of appendages, fins or jointed limbs; a ventral heart with two or more chambers; a closed circulatory system; a large coelom or body cavity containing essential organs.

Lamprey Eels

The lamprey eels are usually a foot or two long with round, sucking mouths without jaws, numerous gill clefts, no paired fins, a poorly developed skull, and no scales in the mucous skin. Lampreys are neither eels nor true fishes, although they have some resemblance to both. Almost every feature of a lamprey eel is peculiar. Its most striking one is the large suction disk that surrounds the mouth and bears circlets of horny teeth upon its surface. The adult lamprey fastens this disk to the side of a fish, rasps the teeth against the flesh and sucks out the blood while the fish carries its rider about as long as it can swim (Fig. 33.5).

Most species of lampreys pass part of their lives in salt water but some are land-locked in fresh water and all of them breed there. The lake lamprey eel, *Petromyzon marinus,* is generally considered the same species as the great sea

INVERTEBRATE

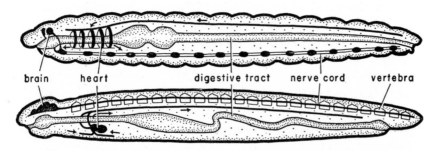

brain   heart   digestive tract   nerve cord   vertebra

VERTEBRATE

Fig. 33.4. Diagrams to show the difference in body plan between an invertebrate (an annelid worm) and a vertebrate. In the latter, the inner ends of the vertebrae (centra) are in the area occupied by the notochord in the embryo.

lamprey that became land-locked in ancient times. Lampreys are abundant in the Finger Lakes of New York and tributary streams and it is estimated that tons of fish are killed by them every year. Before the breeding season, when lampreys are hungriest, the upturned body of a dead fish with its quota of lamprey holes is a common sight in Cayuga and the other Finger Lakes.

In spring, these lampreys go up the creeks to make their nests and breed. Like many fishes, they clear the bottom of gravel by fanning with their tails. They pick up stones with their sucking mouths, which during this season are turned from blood-sucking to domestic work.

Fishes

Fishes are the dominant aquatic animals, more numerous than any other vertebrates except birds. Various kinds live in fresh, brackish and salt water —in clean water and on mucky bottoms. Some stay near the surface, others live at great depths where there is no light except from the light organs of

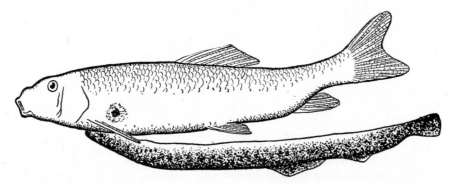

Fig. 33.5. Lake lamprey eel, *Petromyzon marinus,* attached to a fish. Above the pectoral fin is a scar where another lamprey made a ragged opening with its rasping tongue.

animals. Their sizes are various. The whale shark grows to be 40 feet long; the pygmy fish (Pandeka) of the Philippines is less than half an inch long.

All fishes, except the sturgeons and lung fishes, have a more or less well-developed vertebral column. The nervous system has essentially the same arrangement as the frog. The sense organs differ from those of the latter mainly in degree of development. In the skin, fishes have chemical senses similar to taste and smell; they also have organs of smell in the nostrils. The lateral line organs are rows of pits containing cells that are very sensitive to changes in pressure and to any commotion in the water—even a fish passing by. To a large extent fishes can find their way by means of their skins.

Fishes are classified according to the condition of their skeletons. At one extreme, in general the most primitive, are the sharks and rays, the elasmobranchs (Class Chondrichthyes), whose endoskeletons are cartilaginous except for whatever beads of notochord still persist (Figs. 33.6, 33.7). At the other extreme is the great group of teleosts or bony fishes (Class Osteichthyes), true eels, catfishes, swordfishes, trout, perch, mackerel and scores of others, that are familiar at least in books and the fish market. Their skeletons are the most completely bony of any fishes. Between these two extremes are fishes whose skeletons are partly cartilage and partly bone in various proportions.

Bony Fishes. There are more than 12,000 species of bony fishes, one or

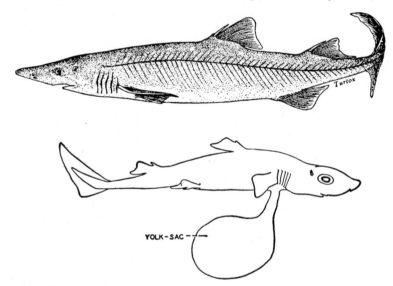

FIG. 33.6. *Upper,* dogfish (spiny dogfish or shark) (*Squalus acanthias*). A bottom feeder, commonly 2 to 3 feet long. *Lower,* dogfish shortly before birth. The yolk sac containing the still unused yolk protrudes from the body wall for some time after birth, but becomes gradually smaller. (*Upper,* courtesy, General Biological Supply House, Chicago, Ill. *Lower,* courtesy, Rand: *The Chordates.* Philadelphia, The Blakiston Co., 1950.)

another kind distributed through salt and fresh waters everywhere (Fig. 33.8). They are the main food fishes. Seagoing fishermen catch more than 10,000,-000,000 herrings annually to be salted, smoked, and packed. The 1947–1948 catch of sardines off the coast of Calfornia was 10,237 tons. Haddock, mackerel, flounders, and salmon are standards of the market among many other

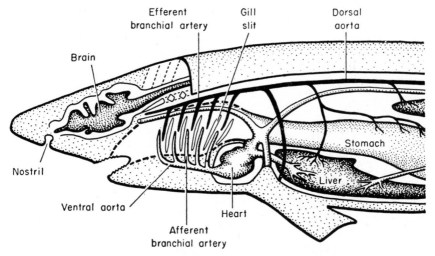

Fig. 33.7. The arrangement of the internal organs of a dogfish shark is near to being a living diagram of a generalized vertebrate.

fishes including those of fresh waters. Fishes are even more important as food for other fishes than for man. From greatest to least, larger fishes eat smaller ones. The great sport fishes are bony fishes—mackerel, tuna, and swordfishes; in clear streams, the golden trout of the west, the rainbow trout, the eastern brook trout and the hardier brown one (Fig. 33.9).

SKIN AND SCALES. In bony fishes, the outermost layer of the skin is a living layer. Except for a coating of slime, the skin is constantly in contact with a world of water. Fishes have no eyelids and no tears, but water is always washing their eyes.

The skin secretes the first defense of the body, a slimy covering that permits the fish to slide more easily through the water and protects the cells against fungus and bacteria. With the skin, kidneys, and gills this helps to keep an excess of water from passing in or out of the body. In the ocean, such structures hinder the weaker salt solution of the body fluid from passing into the stronger salt solution of sea water, thus shrinking the body. In lakes and streams, they likewise hinder the fresh water from passing into the weak saltiness of the blood, thus bloating the body.

The skin produces scales, the second defense of the body, by the division of dermal cells in its inner layer. Scales, like fingernails, are composed mainly

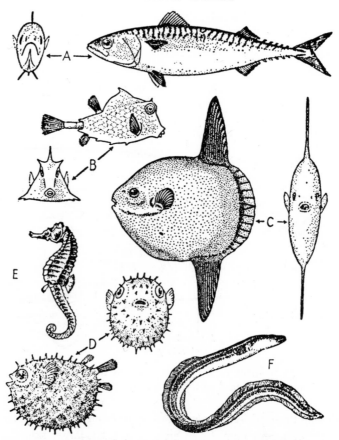

FIG. 33.8. The streamlined bodies of fishes and the variations that are usually associated with a reduction in the efficiency of swimming and the development of some protective mechanism. *A,* mackerel, a streamlined fish known to travel more than twenty miles an hour. *B,* trunk fish (Ostracion) whose scales form a rigid box; it lives in coral pools browsing on the polyps. *C,* sunfish (Mola), may have a length of 5 feet or more and, whatever the advantages may be, has managed to inhabit all temperate and warm oceans. *D,* globe fish (Chilomycterus) is slow moving but has heavy armor. *E,* sea horse (Hippocampus) has no caudal fin but anchors itself by its prehensile tail. *F,* common eel (Anguilla) that can squirm over barriers between bodies of water. (Courtesy, Young: *The Life of the Vertebrates.* Oxford, England, The Clarendon Press, 1950.)

of dead cells and like them have a growing part or quick. In most fishes, the scales are covered by a layer of skin, so thin it is invisible, and usually worn off at their tips. In others such as in the various species of trout, they appear only when the surface of the body is rubbed lightly; in eels, they are deeply hidden and it is commonly thought that there are none. In bony fishes, the scales overlap one another like shingles. The visible part of each one is smaller than the hidden part and always points away from the head. In black bass and others, the scales are ctenoid, i.e., comblike with toothed edges; in salmon, trout, and others, they are cycloid, more or less circular and smooth-edged.

As the fish grows, scales increase in size but not in number. Within close range, each individual has the same number as others of the same species. Each scale enlarges by the addition of many bands or rings per year (Fig. 33.10). The width of a ring signifies the rate of growth and is based on the metabolic activity of the fish. In summer, when food is abundant, the bands are broad and the lines farther apart. In winter, food is sparse and growth is slow; the lines are close together. The age of many, though not all, bony fishes can be told by the number of summers and winters recorded. It is believed that most fishes grow as long as they live and usually obtain enough food to have something extra beyond routine upkeep.

The color of skin is due to saclike cells, the chromatophores, that contain pigment. They are distributed in great numbers through the deeper layer (dermis) of the skin. Each contains only one color, usually red, orange, yellow, or black and these pigments may be spread out in the cells or contracted to pinpoints. White, blue, and green are due mainly to the break up of light rays on the surfaces of crystals of guanin that are colorless metabolic

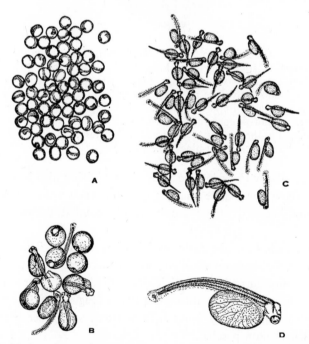

FIG. 33.9. Early stages of eastern brook trout, *Salvelinus fontinalis. A,* eyed eggs showing the embryos through the egg envelopes; *B,* hatching; *C,* a group of free swimming fry; and *D,* a recently hatched fry with its blood vessels outspread through the yolk-sac (enlarged about five times). (Courtesy, Needham: *Trout Streams.* Ithaca, N. Y., Comstock Publishing Co., 1940.)

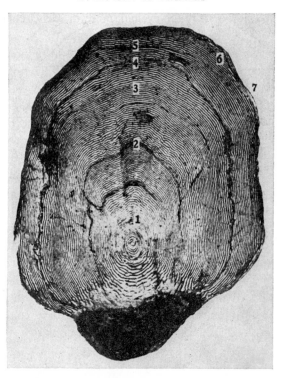

Fig. 33.10. A scale from a seven pound female rainbow trout (*Salvelinus gairdnerii*) taken at spawning time, May 20, in Paul Creek, British Columbia. The age is indicated by winter rings (*1–7*) showing slowed growth in such periods of low food supply. The ring at *4* is a typical example of a spawning mark, when feeding stops and life is strenuous. This fish probably did not spawn in its fifth (*5*) year, but did so again in its sixth (*6*). The dark part of the scale without rings is embedded in the flesh. (After Mottley. Courtesy, Needham: *Trout Streams.* Ithaca, N. Y., Comstock Publishing Co., 1940.)

products. The silvery sheen on the undersides of fishes also is due to guanin. Some fishes show remarkable changes of color when against different backgrounds. Sunfishes and others are brilliantly colored during the breeding season.

Skeleton. Fishes are the early models of vertebrates. The main parts of the skeleton are the skull, vertebral column, the pectoral and pelvic girdles, and the pair of pectoral fins with the pelvic fins behind them. There are other fins but these are the most important to the skeleton (Fig. 33.8). The pairs are far apart in most primitive bony fishes such as trout, and closer together in the more specialized yellow perch.

The great feature of the skeleton is the strength and flexibility of the chain of vertebrae that form the backbone (Fig. 33.11). Its weakness is with the paired fins and their girdles that are not attached to the backbone, but are only embedded in the flesh. This arrangement is adequate for the fishes that do not depend upon paired fins to pull or push greatly, or to carry weight. Its faults are in its use by other animals. It started a pattern in evolution and millions of years later, the human shoulder blades (scapulas) and collar bones (clavicles) slip about, or break too easily and often.

MUSCLE. The important muscles of a fish are arranged on each side of the body in the V-shaped blocks that are familiar on the dinner plate. The body muscles are wholly responsible for the alternate swimming movements, contraction and bending to the right and to the left, repeated over and over. In fishes, each group of muscles acts locally within a small area. The muscles that control the fins are concerned with piloting, the tactics of locomotion.

Fishes can cut straight down or straight up through the water; they can hang motionless, as if suspended in it; and they can maintain themselves facing into a current with the merest flicker of their pectoral fins. Most of this is due to the lift of water, to its density which makes it a support. A fish that in air would weigh about 20 pounds is estimated to have a pressure or equivalent weight of about one pound in salt water.

DIGESTIVE SYSTEM. The majority of fishes have a large mouth and numerous teeth on the jaws, on the roof of the mouth, the pharynx, and on the almost immovable tongue (Fig. 33.11). All of these are used for gripping and straining food; fishes do not chew and they have no salivary glands. Most of them are carnivorous and their prey is swallowed undamaged until it reaches the stomach. There are great variations from the typical teeth. Some vegetarians like the carp have no teeth in their mouths; in the parrot fish the front teeth are fused into a beak with which it nibbles seaweeds; but both of these fishes grind their food with their pharyngeal teeth.

The sac-shaped stomach is highly extensible and provided with gastric juice that dissolves bones and shells. As in other animals, the intestines of carnivo-

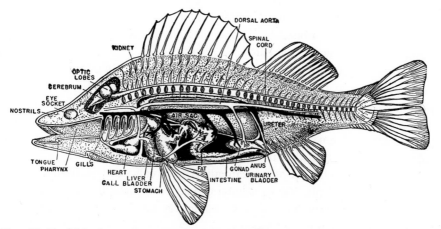

FIG. 33.11. Main internal structures of a bony fish. (Courtesy, MacDougall and Hegner: *Biology.* New York, McGraw-Hill Book Co., 1943.)

rous fishes have a relatively small absorptive surface and those of herbivorous ones a very large one. In many bony fishes, the blind pouches or caeca which open off the intestine just behind the stomach increase the digestive and absorptive surface. Such caeca as these are found in no vertebrates above the fishes. A catfish has none, a sunfish has seven, and the king salmon of the Pacific has over 200. Fishes have an extensive liver, in some so stocked with oil that it helps them float. The pancreas is in small pieces, not easy to identify; they contain the islets of cells that secrete insulin. Fishes are peculiar in having the anal opening anterior, instead of posterior, to the urino-genital ones as it is in other vertebrates.

BREATHING. Fishes breathe through their mouths and by means of gills. The breathing mechanisms are shown in Figure 33.12 and are described further in Chapter 13. Two arrangements prevent undue confusion of food and water. The esophagus is tightly closed by circular muscles except when food is swallowed. The arches supporting the gills bear inward-projecting rakers that keep food from lodging on the gills. It is not always remembered that the oxygen mainly available to aquatic animals is originally absorbed from the atmosphere. Oxygen in the composition of water, H_2O, is not available.

The amount of water in the goldfish bowl is of little help if its surface exposure is too small. Trout keeping close to the brook bottom on a warm day remind one that cold water sinks and that it holds more oxygen than warm water.

WATER CONTENT AND EXCRETION. The gills are the main breathing organs, but they are also excretory organs that control the salt and the water content of the body and eliminate waste products. An important difference between fresh- and salt-water fishes is in their water income and outgo.

Fresh-water fishes continually absorb water mainly through the gills. It passes through the semipermeable membranes and into the salty body fluids according to the law of osmosis (Chap. 2). Fresh-water fishes must have the income of water controlled or their bodies swell. Much of the nitrogenous waste diffuses out across the gills.

Salt-water fishes drink water and their stomachs are often found full of it. Their gills excrete salt. Their kidneys eliminate ammonia and urea, but very little water. They must conserve water because their body fluid is less salt than the ocean water and in very small amounts water leaches through the semipermeable membranes wherever it can. Salt-water fishes must have their outgo of water controlled or their bodies shrivel.

Shad, salmon, eels, and others can adjust from salt water to fresh and vice versa, but not suddenly. Young salmon cannot be dumped into salt water any time; only when they have silvery guanin crystals (nitrogenous excretory products) in the skin is the change safe.

THE AIR BLADDER AND THE SOUNDS OF FISHES. The majority of fishes

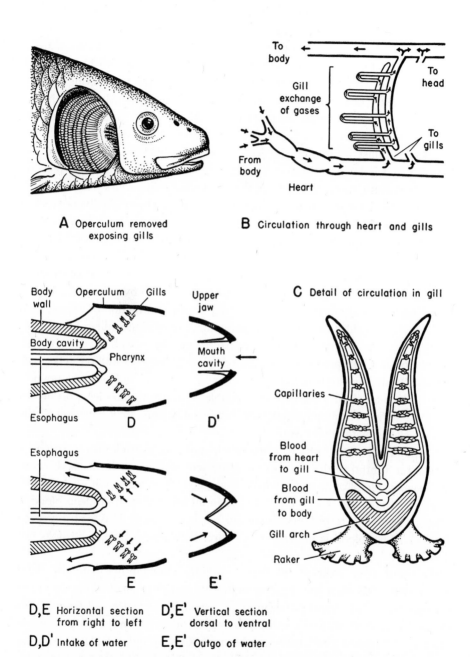

A Operculum removed exposing gills

B Circulation through heart and gills

C Detail of circulation in gill

D,E Horizontal section from right to left

D',E' Vertical section dorsal to ventral

D,D' Intake of water

E,E' Outgo of water

FIG. 33.12. Respiratory organs and breathing action of a bony fish. The circulation of blood is shown in one gill; the structures in diagram (B) are shown in the same position that they would be in the fish (A). The diagrams (D, D[1] and E, E[1]) represent the intake and outgo of water in one complete "breath."

have a conspicuous air or gas bladder that lies in the dorsal part of the body cavity parallel to the backbone. In some species, it is connected with the pharynx by an open duct; in others, as in the perch, by a solid strand of tissue (Fig. 33.11). Its transparent walls are plentifully supplied with blood vessels and it is filled with oxygen, nitrogen, and carbon dioxide in varying proportions, evidently originating from the blood. African lung fishes use the air bladder as a lung. In certain deep-sea fishes, the unusually large proportion of oxygen that has been identified in the bladder has been taken to be an extra insurance against its sparsity in deep water. The bladder also aids the fish in lifting and holding its body at one or another level of water as a pickerel hangs in ambush, motionless among the pond weeds. The sharks lack air bladders, but they have the lifting capacity of relatively enormous livers stocked with oil (Fig. 33.7).

Fishes make sounds with their air bladders. Undersea noises were heard in full strength by a hydrophone during World War II. Certain regions, one of them the Chesapeake Bay, were at that time a bedlam of racket obstructing any other sounds. The croaker (Micropogon) listened to by means of a hydrophone proved to be guilty of the noise, made by the contraction of a muscle on the capacious bladder that acted as a resonator. Croakers are edible fishes common along our southern Atlantic coast. It has been estimated that their population in Chesapeake Bay was at one time about 300 million. The male weakfish (squeteague) can set its bladder in vibration and produce sounds. The fresh-water drum or sheepshead is able to grunt by muscles working on the gas bladder. Although fishes lack true vocal organs, they have joined the world's chorus with what means they have.

CIRCULATION. The heart with its auricle and one ventricle lies in the pericardial sac ventral to the pharynx. It is located far forward in the body, contains venous blood only, and pumps it to the gills, from whence it goes directly to other parts of the body (Fig. 33.12). In all other vertebrates, the blood is returned from the respiratory organs to the heart before it is distributed to the body. Fish blood is under low pressure, is relatively thick, and does not flow easily.

REPRODUCTION. Almost all fishes multiply abundantly, many of them enormously. The sexes are separate and in the majority fertilization occurs in the open water. Mackerel gather in great assemblies of males and females and the water swarms with sex cells. Herring do likewise and a single female produces 30,000 to 2,500,000 eggs per year. Counts and calculations by the U. S. Bureau of Fisheries credit the halibut with 2,000,000 eggs per year and a codfish with 9,000,000.

In central New York state, brook trout (Salvelinus fontinalis) begin to ascend to the spring-fed headwaters of streams in September. There the males and females first congregate in the deeper pools below the spawning grounds.

By late October, the female prepares the nest. It is a basin a foot or two in diameter, if possible placed near a spring, swept in the gravelly bottom by vigorous brushing with the body and tail. The male takes no part in the preparations but is always nearby. After some hours of courtship, the two fishes vibrate their bodies above the basin and spawning occurs. The pair then separates and the female swims a short distance upstream from the nest and stirs up sand and gravel which the water carries over the eggs. The average nest contains nearly 200 eggs about 70 per cent of which hatch in the spring.

The herring and the brook trout, sunfish and other nest makers represent extremes in deposition of the sex cells and the numbers of eggs. There are hundreds of variations in spawning habits. The eggs of fresh-water fishes are relatively large, fewer, and usually sink to the bottom. The newly hatched young (fry) of a one pound brook trout is half an inch long. The newly hatched fry of a 300-pound swordfish is one quarter of an inch long.

NERVOUS SYSTEM AND SPECIAL SENSES. The discussion of the nervous system is given in Chapter 16. Whatever is said about the special senses will mean more if Chapter 17, Sense Organs, is read with it.

Vision. Most of us know a fish's eye as the hard white ball in the head of a baked fish. That ball is the crystalline lens, the gatherer of light rays that has lost its translucence but is a perfect sphere as it was when the fish was alive. The shape of the fish's lens cannot be changed like that of the human eye. It can only be moved backward and forward to get a little better focus (Fig. 33.13). Fishes have no true eyelids and no lachrymal glands. The living cells of the cornea are washed by the waters of lakes or oceans, not by tears. With some exceptions, e.g., shark, there appears to be practically no control of the amount of light that enters the pupil. An iris is present but immovable.

When the human eye is focused on objects that are close by, the lens is nearest to spherical. The lens of the fish's eye is always spherical, always adjusted to close vision. Many fishes are naturally nearsighted. On the other hand, sharks that pursue rapidly fleeing prey have lenses that are peculiarly set for distance. The fish's eyes are on opposite sides of its face; they look in opposite directions and see different things but only a little of what is in front of them. If the headlights of automobiles were moved even a little distance to the sides of the hood the front view would be greatly foreshortened. Something comparable to that has happened to the fish.

When a light ray passes from air into water its direction is changed. This occurs when rays pass from air into the watery interior of the eye. The human eye is adjusted to this and vision is clear, but under water human vision is blurred. The direction of light rays is not changed as they enter the eye of a fish because they pass from water into wet cells and a watery interior. Such facts have been learned by experimentation and repeated observations. On the basis of certain trials, it appears that a fish can tell a blue fly from a red one when either one is submerged, but not when they are on the surface. One version of what a fish may be able to see above the surface is set forth in *The Story of the Fish,* by Curtis Brian (Suggested Reading).

Hearing. Bony fishes must hear better than sharks and others with cartilaginous skulls since bone is a better resonator than cartilage and because fishes

A.   B.

ACCOMMODATION IN EYE
OF A BONY FISH
A. Position for near sight
B. Limited far sight

Fig. 33.13. Eye of a blenny. *A,* usual resting position for near sight. *B,* the lens pulled backward, in the position for limited far sight. Fish are nearsighted and probably their eyes and the condition in water do not allow vision to extend more than fifty feet. As any trout fisherman knows the trout can see above the water surface. Blennies (Blennius) live among the mussel beds on reefs of the Pacific coast. (After Walls: *The Vertebrate Eye.* Bloomfield Hills, Mich., Cranbrook Institute of Science, 1942.)

lack eardrums and middle ears. They have parts of the inner ear (utricle and sacculus), but they do not have the cochlear duct so important in the human ear (Fig. 17.9). Experiments have led to the conclusion that goldfishes can hear, although within a very small range of sound. Care must be taken that responses to vibrations received by the skin cells are not mistaken for hearing. The sounds used to test the goldfishes were produced by a telephone inside a submerged balloon.

Pressure. The lateral line is a tube that lies just below the skin and runs along each side of the body from the gill openings to the tail. It often continues with several branches onto the head. The tube is filled with mucus and at frequent intervals opens by a pore over a group of sensory cells in its floor (Fig. 33.14). Slightly deeper in the body wall is a long branch of the tenth cranial nerve which supplies a branch to each lateral line organ. These organs are extremely sensitive to changes of pressure. They react to the slight changes of pressure that come from a passing fish and they doubtless initiate the shifting of position that can be seen so often in a school of fishes idling in a slow stream.

Touch. Sense organs of touch essentially like our own are spread over the surface of the skin.

Chemical Senses—Taste and Smell. There are organs of taste on the tongues of certain fishes and experiments have indicated that those fishes can taste salt and bitter. Catfishes have taste organs on their whiskerlike barbels and organs of chemical sense are distributed all through their skins. In aquatic animals especially, taste and smell are so similar that it is hard to separate them. The behavior of some fishes does not seem to leave the slightest doubt that they can smell. Sharks have a keen sense of smell, or taste, but when catching its prey a bony fish such as the trout seems to depend entirely upon its eyes.

Great Migrators. Salmons and eels are true migrators to distant places.

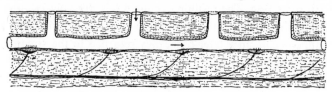

Fɪɢ. 33.14. Long section of the body wall of a fish showing the lateral line sensory system. A branch of the lateral nerve runs to each sensory organ which opens into the minute openings in the body wall and allows water to enter the canal. By means of the lateral line organs fishes taste the water that washes their sides. (Courtesy, Romer: *The Vertebrate Body,* ed. 2. Philadelphia, W. B. Saunders Co., 1955.)

Under certain conditions in themselves and their surroundings, they journey from their native homes to other places where they live for a time and then in full maturity return to their native waters to spawn. The great migrations of Atlantic salmon have become history. Salmon are now known mainly from the Pacific Ocean and its watershed. They are hatched from the eggs, high up in the rivers away from the sea and spend the first months of their lives there. When they are five or six inches long, in answer to an age-old inherited habit and state of body, they turn downstream. They feed and loiter but finally reach the Pacific Ocean. They remain in the ocean about four years and then as mature fishes ready to spawn, they collect near the mouth of a river. The mouth of the Columbia in the state of Washington is a famous gathering place; the mouth of the Fraser in British Columbia is another. The Chinook, blueback, and silver salmon enter the Columbia in early and late summer and begin their ascent, an army of animals that cannot stop pushing against currents and waterfalls. They swim upstream for hundreds of miles, without taking food, often mounting 19-foot falls, until they reach their native tributary stream. There the female lays her 10,000 or more eggs, the male sheds the milt (sperm cells) over them, and the female covers them with sand. Within a brief time, the exhausted fishes float downstream, dead or dying. The eggs hatch, the young grow, and the story begins over again.

The change from fresh to salt water demands a period of adjustment. A young salmon can be killed by being dropped into fresh water at the wrong age. There once were and still are Atlantic salmon. Thousands of them once went up the Connecticut River to spawn. Now when a few swim up the river it is an event for the newspapers. The New Englanders took too many fishes from an easy catch.

Two federal dams now span the Columbia River, the Bonneville dam, 152 miles from the sea, and the Grand Coulee, 552 miles from it. They are in the direct way of the salmon. Bonneville supplies fish ladders. The Federal Government tried education on the offspring of salmon headed for the Grand Coulee. Eggs and sperm were collected from the migrating fishes and mixed together for fertilization. The resulting young fishes were placed in streams that entered the Columbia below the Coulee. In time, these fishes left the stream and entered the ocean. In a later time, they returned to the streams below the Coulee, known to them but not to their parents or grandparents. As an experiment, at least, it was successful.

The journeyings of the eels (Anguilla), true bony fishes of the east coast of North America and west coast of Europe, are directly opposite those of salmon. They are hatched in the Sargasso Sea, northeast of the West Indies where seaweeds (Sargassum) float in the relatively calm water. Here the spawning grounds of American and European species are near together, yet separate, and the young eels take their own routes to their respective continents. The larvae are slender and thin, so different from their parents that their relation was for a long time unknown. On the first part of their journey, the young eels ride on the great ocean currents, the American ones chiefly in the Gulf Stream. They are one-quarter of an inch long when they leave the Sargasso Sea. A year later, when they reach the mouths of the North American rivers, they are 3 inches long. There they are transformed into elvers, that look and act like little eels. In the Gulf Stream as larvae they were carried; in the rivers as elvers they swim upstream into tributary streams and into lakes. There they live for five years or more until they are fully mature. Then they swim downstream to the river mouths and as silver eels probably colored from guanin crystals, they pass out into the ocean.

The eels, true bony fishes, of the Pacific live in the coastal waters and do not migrate to fresh water. Salmon, trout, and other fishes that go upstream to spawn are termed anadromous, meaning up the river and eels are catadromous, meaning down the river. Next to birds, fishes are the great travelers. These migrations are examples of much coming and going, to and from deeper water, in winter and summer, in daylight and dark.

34

Amphibians—The Frog,
An Example of the Vertebrates

Salamanders, frogs and toads, and the little-known wormlike caecilians live partly in water and partly on land; hence the name, Class Amphibia, from *amphibios* meaning double living. All of them spend part of their life span in the water. A very rare and specialized few stay in it all their lives. From the fossils that picture their early history, it appears that amphibians originated from fishes, that some of those pioneers of ancient times lost their scaliness and became the ancestors of modern frogs while others kept their scales and gave rise to reptiles. Amphibians are the oldest four-footed backboned animals, once dominant in the swamps of the early Mesozoic Period 200 or more million years ago. In times long before paddles were transformed into legs, the air-breathing lobe-fin fishes must have been stranded in muddy water full of gas from decaying vegetation. A few were mired in the clay and became fossils. Others wriggled into fresh pools and shady places. After millions of years of natural selection their descendants managed to walk on their weak legs shifting their bodies from side to side, as salamanders still do (Fig. 34.2).

Characteristics. Amphibians are vertebrates with moist glandular skins and no external scales. Except for the limbless caecilians, they have two pairs of limbs used in walking or swimming (Fig. 34.1). The two nostrils connected with the mouth cavity have valves to shut out the water. The heart has two auricles and one ventricle. Respiration is by gills, lungs, skin, the lining of the mouth, or combinations of these. There are gills at some phase of the life span, e.g., in the tadpoles of frogs. The eggs are fertilized externally in frogs and toads, internally in salamanders. No membranes are formed around the embryo (Chap. 19).

2. Loud speaker
One inch long,
heard one mile.

1. With sticky toe pads,
climbs a tree
or window pane.

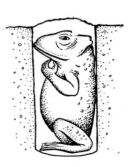

3. Shell headed toad
lives in burrow,
its head the stopper.

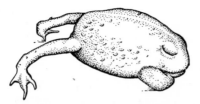

4. Defense stand of toads and frogs:
head low, eyes flat, body puffed.

5. Burrowing toads
wedge headed, barrel bodied.

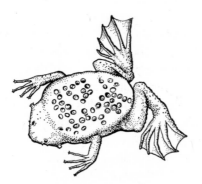

6. Each egg hatches
in a pool of fluid in skin

7. An amphibian of over
two million years ago.

FIG. 34.1. Shapes and ways of frogs and toads. *1,* the common "tree toad," *Hyla versicolor* (length 2 inches). *2,* spring peeper, *Hyla crucifer* (length, one inch); its resonating vocal sac is a third the size of its body. *3,* shell-headed toad, *Bufo empusus* of Cuba, whose head fits perfectly as a stopper in a tubular burrow. *4,* the defense, fright reaction of a toad, *Bufo calamita. 5,* some burrowing toads have sharp narrow, often bony snouts, others have blunt bony heads. *6,* the Surinam toad, *Pipa pipa,* of South America is a purely aquatic toad as its webbed hind feet testify. Its eggs are spread over the spongy skin of its back and the young ones develop there in individual pouches till they are minute toads. *7,* an ancient amphibian (eryops) of North America, a partial restoration from the fossil. These animals dragged their bodies after the fashion of present day alligators.

Class Amphibia

There are some 2500 species of living amphibians; at least 1500 of them are frogs and toads. This smallest of the classes of vertebrates is usually divided into 3 groups: Caudata or Urodela (tailed); Anura (tailless); and Apoda (limbless).

Order Urodela—Salamanders

The Urodele's body is long and slender, carried or dragged on puny legs as if it belonged to a pigmy dachshund (Fig. 34.2). All larvae and some adults have gills. Among the gilled adults are the common mud-puppies (Necturus) of the eastern United States and Canada that live in rivers and creeks, crawling over the bottoms, mostly at night. It is easy to see why they are called puppies. The "ears" are the very beautiful gills that swing rhythmically as the puppy breathes (Fig. 34.3).

The majority of tailed amphibians are without gills in adult life. They include the better-known and generally smaller salamanders. There is no sharp distinction between salamanders and newts or efts except that the latter are smaller and more delicate. Newt, eft, and asker with varied spelling are old names for salamanders, commonly taken for lizards. Like frogs and toads, they are bound up with superstition, often with witchcraft (Fig. 34.26).

Many salamanders are abundant and some of them such as the spotted salamander (*Ambystoma maculatum*) and the newts (Triturus) are subjects of important experimental studies. The tiger salamanders (*Ambystoma tigrinum*) widely distributed in the United States resemble the spotted salamanders. They start life as typical aquatic larvae, breathing by gills. In most regions, the

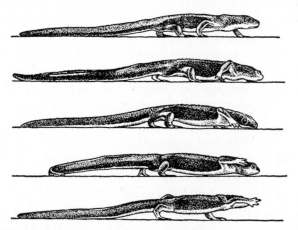

Fig. 34.2. Newt (Triturus) walks on its 4 weak legs at the same time weaving its body like a fish. Drawings from photographs of slow locomotion. (After Evans. Courtesy, Young: *The Life of the Vertebrates*. Oxford, England, The Clarendon Press, 1950.)

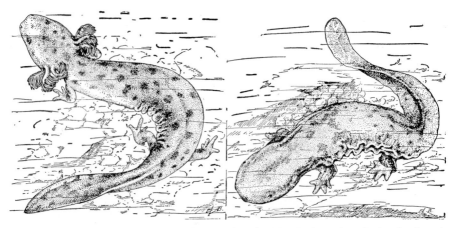

FIG. 34.3. Two of the largest salamanders in North America. *Left,* the "mud puppy" (Necturus), one foot long, has gills throughout life. Common in eastern rivers of United States and Canada. *Right,* the hell-bender (Cryptobranchus), about a foot and a half long; the adult has no external gills but makes up for this by loose folds of skin that function as gills. Hell-benders are usually in the shallows of streams and are secretive, but once seen are not forgotten.

larvae transform and climb on land as air breathers. But in some localities, such as Mexico, western Texas, the southwest, and Colorado, and under certain special conditions, they continue to grow to full size in the water, become sexually mature but do not change their form or lose their gills (Fig. 34.4). In such a phase they are known as axolotls.

The best-known North American newts are the "water dog" (*Triturus torosus*), eight inches long, of the Pacific drainage, and the spotted newt (*Triturus viridescens*), half as long, of the Atlantic drainage. The "red eft" or "red lizard" of the woods and the spotted newt of the ponds are the same animal in different color phases (Fig. 34.5). Adult spotted newts live in ponds and meandering streams from September or October to the next summer, perhaps longer. The breeding season is in the spring, when an elaborate courtship precedes the egg-laying and lasts from several hours to a day or more, as readily in aquaria as in a pond. After the pair separates, the male deposits white jellied spermatophores containing spermatozoa, on submerged leaves and sticks. As he moves away from a spermatophore, the female creeps over it and takes it into the cloaca, the cavity through which the eggs must pass to be fertilized and laid. Upwards of a hundred are deposited separately here and there, usually on submerged plants. The larvae live in the water until toward fall. Then their gills gradually shrink; they acquire lungs, their skin becomes firmer; and their color changes from green to orange-red. They climb out of the pond and spend at least one winter and summer on land, during which they are the red newts of the woodland carpet. In some localities, they return to the water in the fall, as nearly mature animals, their backs turning olive green with

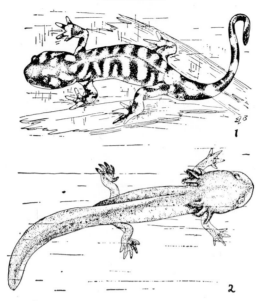

Fig. 34.4. Tiger salamander (*Ambystoma tigrinum*). *1,* adult and *2,* larva, adult 7 inches long. Under particular conditions and in certain parts of the country the larva (axolotl) grows to full size and sexual maturity without transforming.

red spots along the sides, the adult coloration. These are the animals that will reproduce the next spring. In some parts of their range, certain ponds on Long Island and Cape Cod, spotted newts retain their gills and do not leave the water for a long time, if at all. If such newts are kept in cages, with little water except that in damp moss, their gills shrink away and their skin changes in texture to the land type. This is an example of the easy adjustment of which amphibians are capable.

ORDER ANURA—FROGS AND TOADS

Frogs and toads hop and leap with an always ready kick-off by the massive muscles of the thighs and calves that snap the bent hindlegs into action. When salamanders walk, their body muscles work, pull and swing the body. When frogs hop, the leg muscles work, but the weak body muscles take little part. Frogs have the shortest backs and smallest number of presacral vertebrae of any land-living vertebrate. Correlating with this they have very long hip bones (ilia) extended to meet the fanlike extensions of the sacral vertebra. The meeting place is the conspicuous hump on a frog's back, the outward sign of a peculiar evolution.

Frogs and toads are more specialized than salamanders. Their metamorphosis includes not only the change from gills to lungs, but from the digestive tube of a herbivore to that of a carnivore, and from a mouth fitted for scraping

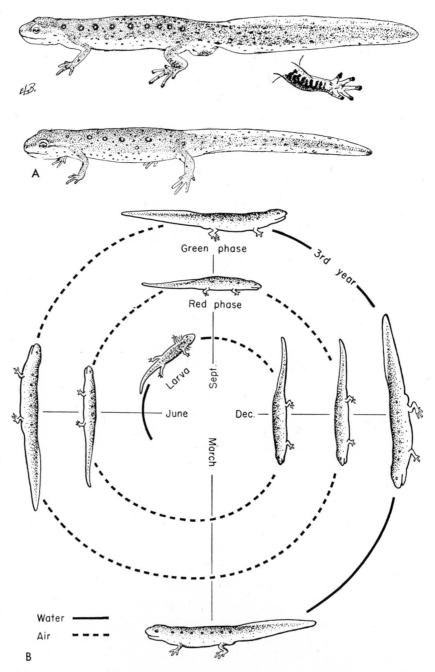

Water ———
Air - - - -

FIG. 34.5. *A*, adult spotted newts (*Triturus viridescens*). The male (*upper*) has a fin on the tail especially prominent during the breeding season and horny pads on the hind legs. Length of male, 3½ inches. It is easily recognized by the row of scarlet spots ringed with black on each side of the body. *B*, diagram of the typical life history of the spotted newt indicating its first summer in the water, its winter and second year of residence on land when it is known as the red eft, and the return to water in autumn in the adult green phase.

algae to one adapted to catching insects. They also change from fishlike swimmers to expert jumpers. A description of the essentials of the biology of frogs is included later in this chapter.

ORDER APODA—CAECILIANS

At first glance caecilians might be mistaken for earthworms instead of vertebrates. Except for a few that are aquatic, they live underground, burrowing in moist places in Mexico, South America, and other tropical countries. Their amphibian characteristics are unmistakable. They have gilled larvae and go through the typical metamorphosis. The adults have well-developed lungs and their skin is smooth and glandular.

The Frog—An Example of the Vertebrates

Frogs are nature's gift to laboratory study and experiment. They are abundant, widely distributed, and live well in captivity. Hundreds of papers and books have been written about them and important facts have been discovered by means of them. The frogs most frequently used are: the leopard frog, *Rana pipiens* (Fig. 34.6), distributed from the east coast through the western states except California; and the bullfrog, *Rana catesbiana,* the largest North American species, with a natural range through the eastern half of the United States and an introduced range in the west.

Ecology and Life History. Frogs are limited to lands where there is enough moisture. They do not live in deserts, in frigid climates, or salt water. In temperate climates, they commonly leave the water after their spring breeding

FIG. 34.6. Leopard frog, *Rana pipiens,* the frog of the laboratories. It is also the mainstay of the edible frog business that supplies hotels and markets for which an average expert can dress 1000 frogs per hour.

season, scatter off by themselves, and spend the summer in meadows and moist woods. Their haunts vary with the species, but all are moisture seekers.

Food. Adult frogs eat any animal they can get, of any size that they can swallow whole, mostly invertebrates—insects, spiders, earthworms, snails, fish fry, and their own tadpoles. The latter are strict herbivores that rasp and comb soft water plants (Fig. 34.7).

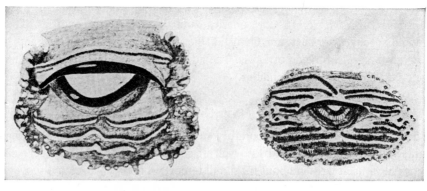

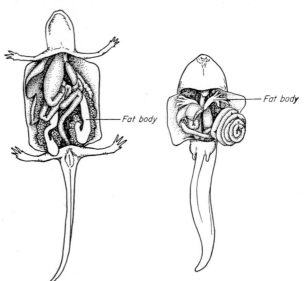

Fig. 34.7. *Upper,* mouths of tadpoles. *Left,* green frog, *Rana clamitans; right,* spade foot toad, *Scaphiopus holbrooki.* Tadpoles of frogs and toads live on soft plant food collecting it with the chitinous scrapers and combs that surround their mouths. Different species have such different patterns of scrapers that they are used as recognition marks. *Lower,* the relatively short intestine of a carnivorous adult newt (*left*) and the long watchspring coil of the intestine of the herbivorous tadpole of a bullfrog (*right*). The adult newt, Triturus, length 4 inches, lives on aquatic worms, crustaceans and insects. The tadpole, length 2 to 4 inches, feeds exclusively on algae and other soft plants of which it requires a large amount. (*Upper,* courtesy, Wright: *Life Histories of the Frogs of the Okefenokee Swamp, Georgia.* New York, The Macmillan Co., 1931.)

Frogs have little or no defense against predators. Diving beetles suck out the body juices of the tadpoles and catfishes swallow a hundred of them at a gulp. Turtles, snakes, herons, raccoons, and man all prey upon them. They are used in hotels, markets, and laboratories, a total that goes into billions per year, chiefly leopard frogs.

PARASITES AND DISEASES. Leeches clamp to their bodies and suck out their blood; molds and bacteria invade their moist skin; flukes, roundworms, and protozoans flourish within their bodies. One of the worst calamities is their wholesale destruction due to the drying out of swamp lands by dams and irrigation.

SEASONAL LIFE (FIG. 34.8). Frogs and toads are like rabbits: in front they stand; behind, they sit in continual readiness for a take-off. In the ponds, frogs lounge with their nostrils, valves open, just above the surface. The hippopotamus, also semi-aquatic, does the same thing. In winter, when they are under water they depend upon skin breathing and the lungs are nearly emptied of air. This is adequate for long periods when the metabolism of the body is low and the demand for oxygen decreased.

In temperate climates, frogs spend the winter in damp protected places, mainly in the muddy bottoms of ponds and in swamps. About mid-winter, preparation for the early breeding period begins in the reproductive organs, supported by food stored in the fat bodies. As spring approaches, the former increase in size and maturity. Secondary sex characters, the horny thumb pads of the males and the vocal sacs, are prominent during the breeding season. At its height, even the most solitary frogs become social as they gather in the ponds in full croak. The male leopard frog and to a lesser degree the female inflate the vocal sacs, one over each shoulder, swelling them larger and larger by drawing air across the vocal cords as the croak is repeated. Then the air is suddenly drawn into the lungs and the sacs collapse. The breeding season reaches its climax in mating, and the release and fertilization of the eggs. A leopard frog produces up to 5000 eggs per season deposited in the water in masses of about 500 each.

After the breeding period, great changes take place in these frogs that for months have taken no food and for weeks have been congregated in their ancestral home in water. Promptly they leave the ponds and scatter, each a solitary land animal. This is the beginning of the summer-feeding period when fat is accumulated in the fat bodies and glycogen is stored in the liver and muscles. With the chill nights of autumn they stop feeding, and seek winter quarters in the swamps, crowded together by dozens, even hundreds. For the second period of the year they are social animals, urged by sex at one time and by cold weather at the other.

LIFE HISTORY. For the development of the embryo, and the transformation of the tadpole into the frog, see Figure 34.8 and Chapter 19.

Structure and Function. FORM, COVERING, AND COLOR. The flattened head of a frog still suggests that of its ancient ancestors. A frog's neck is short, and like those of other aquatic animals, the fishes and whales, is not marked off from the rest of the body. The body is short. Its complete lack of external tail is rare among lower vertebrates. As in all vertebrates, the skin consists of an outer epidermis and inner dermis (Fig. 34.9). Throughout their lives frogs molt the outermost dead part of the epidermis, casting it off in a whole piece every few weeks except in winter when living processes are slowed and molting is almost or entirely absent. The shed skin is pulled over the head like a sweater and swallowed. The comparable layer of human skin is constantly shed, but less dramatically in scalelike bits. Numerous mucous and poison glands originate in the epidermis but project down into the dermis where they are nourished by the blood. Mucus becomes a lifesaver by moistening the skin and slowing evaporation. The deeper-lying dermis includes blood vessels that function in skin respiration, many small nerves, smooth muscle cells, connective tissue and pigment cells.

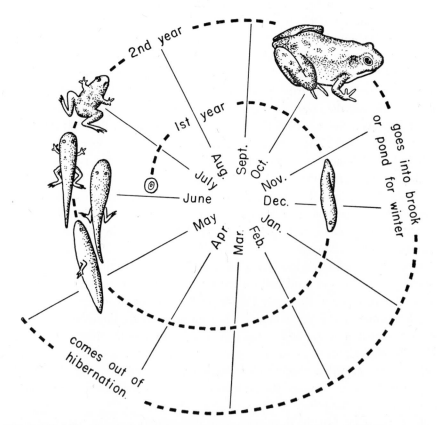

FIG. 34.8. Life history of the green frog, *Rana clamitans*, that transforms and goes onto the land in its second year.

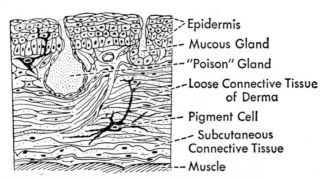

FIG. 34.9. Section of the frog's skin. (After Haller. Courtesy, Walter and Sayles: *Biology of Vertebrates,* ed. 3. New York, The Macmillan Co., 1949.)

Frogs are prevailingly green and brown, with light underparts, usually white, often yellow. They may be paler or darker depending on the physiological condition of the frog and its response to the environment. Although melanin or black pigment occurs in the epidermis, the shifts of color in amphibians are primarily due to changes in certain dermal cells called chromatophores. In these cells, the pigment may be dispersed throughout the cell or concentrated in its center (Fig. 34.10). There are three kinds of chromatophores arranged from without inward in the following order: lipophores with yellow or reddish pigment, the carotene like that in carrots; guanophores holding guanin crystals (allied to uric acid) that reflect blue when against a dark background; and melanophores containing brown or black pigment and always lying deepest in the dermis. By their contraction or expansion, chromatophores hide others from the light or expose them to it. The skin is green when the expanded black pigment gives the guanin crystals the dark background against which they reflect blue and the yellow pigment is expanded (Fig. 34.11). The blue and

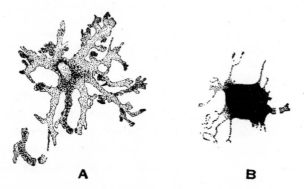

A   **B**

FIG. 34.10. Black pigment cells (melanophores) of frog skin. *A,* with pigment dispersed. *B,* with pigment concentrated in the body of the cell and the processes appearing shrunken. (After Hewer. Courtesy, Noble: *Biology of the Amphibia.* New York, McGraw-Hill Book Co., 1931.)

Light

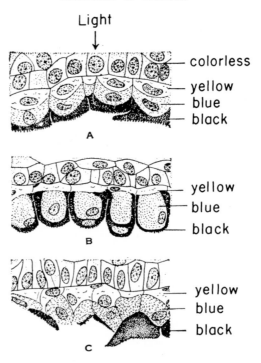

— colorless
— yellow
— blue
— black

A

— yellow
— blue
— black

B

— yellow
— blue
— black

C

SECTIONS OF SKIN. TREE FROG

FIG. 34.11. Sections of skin cells of a tree frog (Hyla), showing the relations of the pigments and blue-reflecting crystals when the skin is bright green, dark green, and yellow. Yellow pigment is contained in the cells next to the outer skin cells or epidermis. In the next layer inward the cells contain blue-reflecting crystals (guanin). The cells below these contain black pigment. *A*, bright green. The yellow pigment is expanded. The cells with the blue-reflecting crystals are covered by black pigment on one side. *B*, dark green. The yellow pigment is only slightly expanded. The black pigment covers much of the cells that contain crystals. *C*, yellow. Black pigment is greatly contracted. Yellow pigment is expanded and blue-reflecting crystals are irregularly arranged. In brown, not shown here, the crystals are almost covered and black and yellow are expanded, with black dominant. (After Noble: *The Biology of Amphibia.* New York, McGraw-Hill Book Co., 1931.)

yellow produce the green. The skin is yellow when light is reflected only from yellow pigment; the black pigment is then contracted and fails to give the guanin crystals the dark background. Brown color occurs when black pigment covers the guanin crystals; black and yellow are reflected and mixed. The association of endocrine secretions and color changes is discussed in Chapter 15.

SKELETON. The skull is roughly triangular with bones firmly joined except the loose attachments of the lower jaw. The cranium, a narrow bony box that holds the brain, is similar in shape to the fish's cranium and a contrast to the high-domed human one (Fig. 34.12). Between the cranium and upper jaw are the capsules that hold the sense organs for smell, hearing, and sight. The relatively enormous cavities for the eyes have no bony floor and, when the eyelids are closed, the eyeballs bulge down into the mouth cavity, seeming about to be swallowed. An opening in the posterior end of the cranium (foramen magnum) makes the cranial cavity continuous with the canal (neural canal) in the vertebral column. The skull can be revolved only slightly on the first and only vertebra of the neck.

The vertebral column consists of nine vertebrae and the urostyle which functions as a balance rod swung in the crotch of the pelvic girdle. It represents a number of tail vertebrae now fused together and unrecognizable, but believed to be the fused remains of the vertebrae of external tails in ancient amphibians. The human skeleton also carries the remains of a once external tail that still shows in the fused vertebrae of the coccyx.

The pectoral girdle forms attachment places of the forelimbs and an almost complete circlet of the body over the heart, lungs, and liver. It supports part of the body's weight but is fastened to the vertebral column only by muscles and ligaments which allow it to slide and act as a shock absorber in jump landings. Dorsally, it consists of the flat shoulder blades (suprascapulas) that

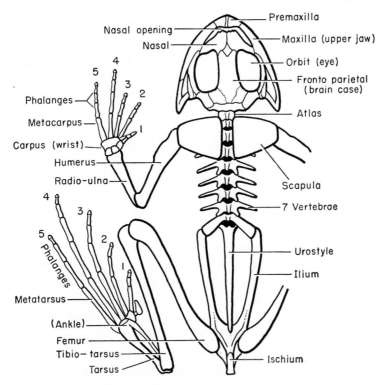

FIG. 34.12. Skeleton of the frog.

cover the second, third, and fourth vertebrae. Joined to these are the coracoids and clavicles; the latter known in man as the collarbones, in chickens as the wishbone. The upper bone (humerus) of the foreleg fits into a cavity where the coracoid and clavicle come together. The pelvic girdle is formed by the long innominate bones each composed of three pieces, the ilium, pubis, and ischium, that are joined together to form the sockets for the femurs of the hind legs. The spread of the anterior end of the girdle accounts for the hump back of the resting frog. The solitary sacral vertebra is the only anchor for the frog's pelvic girdle and appended hind legs. This arrangement provides for the rebound needed in the rear of a jumping animal. It does not support weight like the human pelvic girdle with its attachment to the fused sacral vertebrae (Fig. 34.12).

The arrangement and in general the number of the bones of the fore and hindlimbs of the frog are similar to those of human limbs. In the forelimb, however, the radius and ulna are permanently crossed. A frog cannot turn its forefoot, "palm up."

MUSCLES. The main kinds of muscular tissues and arrangements of muscles are discussed in Chapter 10.

BODY CAVITIES. Body cavities are bounded by the body wall, by mesentery or other membranes, or by combinations of these. In the frog, the main ones are the pericardial cavity containing the heart and the pleuroperitoneal cavity. The latter is called pleura from the membrane that covers the lungs and lines the spaces surrounding them, combined with peritoneum, the lining of the abdominal walls (Fig. 34.13). The peritoneum is a transparent, moist, shimmering membrane that continues, as part of the mesenteries, around the stomach, intestines, and other abdominal organs and forms a partial capsule about each kidney (Fig. 34.14). It is so thin that tissue fluid filters through it and, becoming the coelomic fluid, keeps the surfaces of the organs wet and slippery. Folds of the intestine and lobes of the liver slide upon one another. The internal organs of a breathing animal are slightly but continually moved.

FOOD AND DIGESTION. With its tongue, a frog jerks small animals into its mouth and throws them down its throat (Fig. 34.15). It clutches larger ones by its maxillary teeth and by vomerine teeth on the roof of the mouth. The movement of material through one or another part of the alimentary canal is aided by contraction of muscles (peristalsis), lubrication by mucus, and downward lashing of cilia. The pharynx begins where the mouth region narrows backward at the level of the internal nares, and ends by gradually merging into the esophagus. Its lining bears constantly lashing cilia. If powdered chalk or small bits of cork are scattered on the roof of the pharynx they will instantly begin moving into the esophagus. The latter is short, capable of great extension, with strong muscular walls that contract peristaltically and urge the food over the slippery lining.

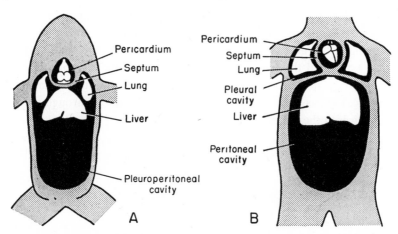

FIG. 34.13. Outlines of the body cavities of frog and man. *A,* in the frog, the pericardial cavity contains the heart; the pleuroperitoneal cavity contains lungs, alimentary canal and associated glands, and reproductive organs. There is no diaphragm. *B,* in man; the pericardium contains the heart; the thoracic cavity is divided into two pleural cavities, each holding a lung; the abdominal cavity is separated from the pleural cavities by the diaphragm.

Storage, digestion, and absorption of food are carried on by the stomach and intestine (Fig. 34.16). The stomach is a pouch for temporary storage. Muscles in its walls squeeze and mix the food, and cells in the lining secrete the gastric juice, which begins the chemical break-up of proteins. Stomachs are not essential to life, but wild animals must eat when food is available and temporary storage in the stomach is important. Frogs may find a pond swarming with mosquitoes on one day and none the next. While food is being mixed

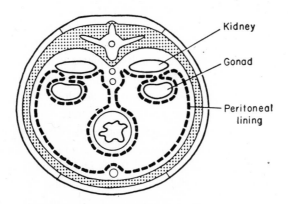

RELATION OF PERITONEAL LINING
TO ABDOMINAL ORGANS

FIG. 34.14. Cross section of the body of a male frog taken through the abdomen showing the peritoneal cavity and the kidneys. The peritoneum covers them as it does the other abdominal organs.

by the muscles of the stomach, the cardiac valve at the upper end and pyloric valve at the lower end keep its contents from escaping in either direction. In the meantime, the gastric juice flows into it. This contains acid that softens shell and bone, and the enzyme pepsin which begins the digestion of proteins, converting them into proteoses and peptones. When a sufficient stage of softness and acidity has been attained, the food mass is passed through the relaxed pyloric ring into the intestine.

This is divided into the relatively long small intestine, in which digestion is completed and digested food absorbed, and the shorter large intestine, in which

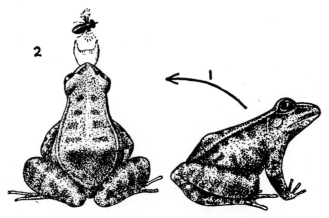

FIG. 34.15. Action of the tongue when a frog catches a fly. (Courtesy, Tinbergen: *Study of Instinct*. London, England, Oxford University Press, 1951.)

water is absorbed from the residue of indigestible matter. Like other parts of the alimentary canal, both intestines are attached to the dorsal wall by mesentery. The acid food mass entering the small intestine immediately stimulates glandular cells in the lining to produce the hormone, secretin. This soon enters the circulation, reaches the pancreas and stimulates it to produce its digestive secretion, the pancreatic juice. The pancreas and liver pour their secretions through the common bile duct opening into the first loop of the small intestine, the duodenum. The pancreas performs two functions; the bulk of it produces the digestive fluid called pancreatic juice, and islets of cells within it form the hormone, insulin. The pancreatic juice, able to act in the alkaline conditions within the intestine, affects all classes of foods and virtually completes digestion. It does this mainly by three enzymes; trypsin that breaks proteins into peptones; amylase that changes starches into sugars; and lipase that separates fats into fatty acids and glycerol. Cells in the intestinal lining also secrete digestive enzymes, the most important of these (erepsin) breaks peptones to amino acids, the basic constituents of proteins.

In all these processes, molecules of the food substances become smaller and

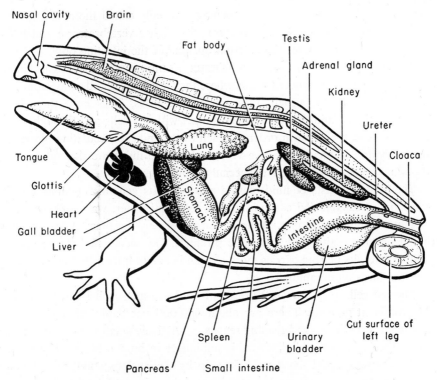

Nasal cavity   Brain   Fat body   Testis   Adrenal gland   Kidney   Ureter   Cloaca   Lung   Tongue   Glottis   Heart   Gall bladder   Liver   Stomach   Intestine   Cut surface of left leg   Spleen   Urinary bladder   Pancreas   Small intestine

FIG. 34.16. Frog showing the relative positions of systems.

able to pass through cell membranes as they could not have done before. Finally simple sugars, fatty acids, glycerol and amino acids are absorbed through cells in the intestinal lining. The fats are taken up by the lymph, the sugars and amino acids by the blood plasma, and all are distributed by these fluids. The vertebrate liver is only indirectly a digestive gland (Fig. 34.16). It is an excretory organ that picks waste substances from the blood and prepares them for elimination, the nitrogenous waste into urea and the pigment of worn-out red blood cells into bile pigments. It is a storage place for an emergency food (glycogen). It produces bile that carries away waste pigments and certain other waste products and performs important functions in the intestine connected with the digestion and absorption of fat. Bile aids digestion indirectly because it stimulates the enzymes of the pancreatic juice by creating the alkaline environment necessary for them to act. It is a lubricator and easy slipping is essential. Excess bile is stored in the gall bladder. The liver is in short a strainer and balancer of the blood content, having also an indirect but essential part in digestion.

Peristaltic contractions gradually move the undigested residue of the food into the large intestine. Its walls absorb water from this, contract upon it, and eventually force it into the cloacal chamber and out of the body through the external or cloacal opening. This opening is usually called the anus, but this term does not homologize the structure with higher vertebrates in which the term anus always signifies the external opening of the intestine only.

COOPERATING FLUIDS—BLOOD, TISSUE FLUID AND LYMPH. Circulating blood transports substances to cells where they are needed and away from cells to which they are a burden. Like other vertebrates, frogs have three body fluids; the tissue fluid that is in direct contact with the cells and through which all substances must pass in order to reach them; and the circulating blood and related lymph in their respective vessels. All three fluids are dependent upon the water content of the body, especially so in frogs.

The blood consists of fluid plasma and cells. Its general functions are the transport of oxygen and carbon dioxide, food and water, waste substances of metabolism, and hormones. Although largely water, the plasma also includes blood proteins, salts, and metabolic products. On account of the frog's low temperature, its plasma carries more oxygen in solution than that of the warm-blooded birds and mammals.

The red cells (erythrocytes) are relatively large and each is bulged out by its prominent nucleus. There are about 400,000 per cubic millimeter, most abundant just before the breeding season, a relatively small number compared to the four to five millions per cubic millimeter in human blood. Their small surface exposure and the space taken up by the nucleus combine to reduce their efficiency in carrying oxygen. In certain salamanders (*Batrachoseps*) many red cells lose their nuclei as they mature just as mammalian red cells do, but this is very rare in amphibians. Red blood cells ordinarily develop in the spleen. Only when metabolism of frogs is at its height in spring do red cells arise in the red marrow of bone as in mammals. The white cells (leucocytes) are colorless and nucleated, about 7000 per cubic millimeter of blood. Spindle cells (thrombocytes) are nearly twice as numerous as the white cells and extremely minute, disappearing from blood which has been shed for any length of time.

BLOOD VESSELS AND CIRCULATION. In the frog and with few exceptions in the vertebrates in general, blood circulates within a system of vessels, the heart, arteries, capillaries, and veins. Lymph flowing through tubes and open spaces provides fluid with a return route to the heart, an alternative to that of the veins. In the frog, the characteristics and functions of the three types of blood vessels are similar to those of other vertebrates. The reader is referred to the discussion of these in Chapter 12 and to figures 34.17, 34.18, and 34.19.

Heart. The frog's heart is a muscular pump that pushes the blood through blood vessels, but does not affect it in any other way. It is enclosed in a thin but strong membranous sac, the pericardium, containing just enough fluid to let the heart slip easily as it beats.

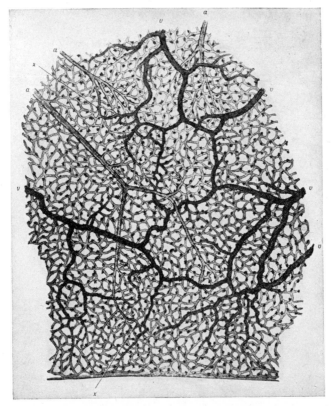

FIG. 34.17. Networks of blood vessels in the web of a frog's foot. *a,* the arterioles; *v,* venules and the capillaries between them; *x,* direct connections between arterioles and venules; pigment spots are scattered along the capillaries. (Courtesy, Maximow and Bloom: *Histology,* ed. 6. Philadelphia, W. B. Saunders Co., 1952.)

The frog is midway between fishes and higher vertebrates and its heart is midway between the two-chambered heart of fishes and the four-chambered hearts of reptiles, birds, and mammals. It contains two auricles and a single ventricle (Figs. 34.18, 34.19). On its dorsal side is an important entrance chamber, the sinus venosus, to which three great veins bring blood from all parts of the body except the lungs. The auricles have thin, elastic walls strengthened by narrow bands of muscle. The right one, larger than the left, is separated from it by a partition. The ventricle has a relatively very thick wall containing interlacing muscles. It is separated from the auricles by a partition whose location is indicated on the outside by a prominent constriction. On the ventral side a great artery, the truncus arteriosus, is the only exit for the blood. It runs forward a short distance and divides into two trunks, the right and left aortic arches, each of which splits into three branches that supply the entire body.

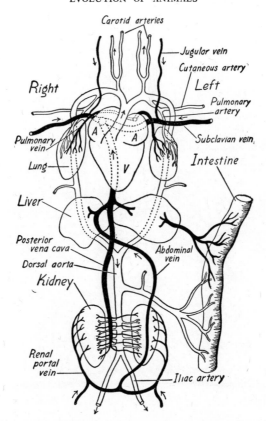

FIG. 34.18. Circulation of blood in the bullfrog. Veins in black. (Courtesy, Wolcott: *Animal Biology,* ed. 3. New York, McGraw-Hill Book Co., 1946.)

Circulation of Blood. Blood containing various substances from the body is poured into the sinus venosus which opens into the right auricle. At the same time, well-oxygenated blood flows through the pulmonary veins into the left auricle. Both auricles then contract and force their contents onward into the ventricle. Blood is kept from going back into the sinus by blood behind it, which pours in from the veins, and from going into the pulmonary veins by the pressure of the distended wall of the auricles against their openings. Well-oxygenated blood fills the left side and sparsely oxygenated blood the right side of the ventricle with blended blood between. The ventricle then contracts. With the valves into the auricles closed behind it, the blood takes the only free road, into the truncus arteriosus. As it does so it passes the semi-lunar valves, three soft cups, and the current approaches from beneath and completely flattens them. Muscles in the truncus contract upon the blood and it fills the cups behind it bringing their soft edges together. This creates a backstop. Muscular contraction continues in a wave over the arteries of the body.

Blood with a low-oxygen content enters the truncus from the right side of the ventricle. It takes the path of least resistance and enters the pulmocutaneous arches to the lungs and skin (Figs. 34.18, 34.19). The next to enter is the partially mixed blood from the central part of the ventricle and this goes into the systemic arches, the pair that offers next least resistance. The carotid arches that supply the head region receive the remainder, the blood from the left side of the ventricle, that carries the best supply of oxygen. The twisted ribbon of tissue (longitudinal or spiral valve) in the truncus has been held

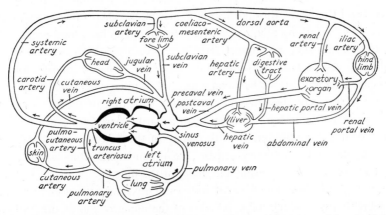

Fig. 34.19. Circulation of the blood in a vertebrate with two auricles (atria) and one ventricle as in the frog. (Courtesy, Curtis and Guthrie: *General Zoology*, ed. 4. New York, John Wiley and Sons, 1947.)

important in keeping the blood rich in oxygen from that less well supplied with it. This has not been supported by some recent experiments.

The circulating blood of the frog makes two partially separated circuits, each one passing through the heart. In one of these (pulmonary), the blood flows from the heart to the lungs and back to the heart. In the other (systemic circulation), the blood flows to all parts of the body, except the lungs, and returns to the heart. Since it is constantly shifting, all of the blood is able to go through each route very often.

Lymph and Lymphatics. Lymph is a watery fluid similar to the blood plasma. It contains colorless cells, the lymphocytes, but no red blood cells. Several fluids contribute to its content—the plasma of the blood, tissue fluid, and, in the frog, extra large quantities of water. It is contained in tubes, in spaces between the tissues (lymph sinuses), and in lymph hearts. In frogs, the lymphatic system is especially important and conspicuous. The smallest lymph vessels have blind ends. They form networks of capillaries which join larger and larger vessels and finally one or more main trunks that open into the veins. Some lymph vessels are broken by lymph sacs in which the lymph is in direct contact with the tissues. Such sacs are located directly beneath the skin, almost surround the body and sometimes become pillowed out by abnormal accumulations of the fluid (Fig. 34.20). In the common species of Rana, there are four lymph hearts, each of them a two-chambered pump which forces lymph into the blood stream through openings in the vessels.

RESPIRATION, BREATHING, AND VOICE. Properly speaking, breathing is external respiration and the chemical changes in the cells constitute an internal respiration.

Breathing. Floating with only its nostrils above the surface, a frog breathes air and takes oxygen from it by way of its mouth and lungs. It also takes oxygen from the water through its skin. In winter, when there is less oxygen demand, skin breathing alone is sufficient for life. The breathing organs of the adult frog, lungs, skin, and lining of the mouth cavity, are abundantly supplied with blood vessels. The lungs are thin elastic sacs with low internal folds that greatly increase the surface between which the capillaries extend (Figs. 34.16, 13.9). The lining of the lungs is continuous with that of the larynx into the alimentary canal. The lungs branch from a hardly perceptible trachea. Their outer covering is continuous with the lining of the body cavity. Nerves, connective tissue, and pulmonary arteries, veins, and connecting capillaries are outspread between the covering and lining of the lungs.

As a frog breathes, the floor of its mouth rhythmically rises and falls, a throat-breathing in which the capillaries of the lining of the mouth and throat

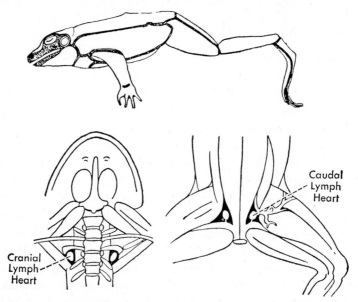

FIG. 34.20. Frog's lymphatic system. Sacs for the lymph which creates a fluid coat about the frog's body. The skin has been removed from this frog. The dark lines represent the boundaries of lymph sacs. *Lower,* lymph hearts in the frog (Rana); these are pulsating lymph pumps which keep the lymph moving. (Courtesy, Walter and Sayles: *Biology of Vertebrates,* ed. 3. New York, The Macmillan Co., 1949.)

are exposed to air. Now and then, the frog seems to swallow—a sign of lung-breathing. Actually it pulls the floor of its mouth downward creating a partial vacuum and air comes into this through the open nostrils. The flaps over the nostrils are then pulled down, the floor of the mouth lifted, the glottis opens and the air escapes the pressure by going into the lungs. At the same time, an exchange of gases has been going on between air and blood, through the lining of the mouth. As it exhales, the frog contracts its abdominal wall and squeezes the lungs. The glottis is pushed open; the flaps over the nostrils are lifted; and the air escapes. Usually, the skin is moist enough for an exchange of gases. Experiments have indicated that more carbon dioxide is given off by the skin than by the lungs.

Voice. Frogs and toads may have been the first animals to use vocal cords. The sound of their spring choruses still seems to come from ancient marshes. The vocal cords are two folds of the lining of the larynx, below and parallel to the glottis. When a frog croaks, it keeps its mouth and nostrils tightly closed and squeezes air back and forth between the lungs and mouth. During this performance air escapes through slits in the floor of the mouth into the air sacs and dilates them into balloon-like resonating organs (Fig. 34.1).

EXCRETION. Along with essential products, metabolism produces harmful ones, usually accompanied with water. The waste products may be gases, solids, or liquids. Carbon dioxide, from the oxidation of carbohydrate and fatty foods, is eliminated through the lungs of frogs, the gills of the tadpoles, and the skins of both. The undigested residue of food is not a metabolic product, except as it contains bile excreted by the liver.

It is important to any animal that a standard amount of water be maintained in its body, especially so in frogs. The skin, urinary bladder, and kidneys maintain this. Frogs constantly absorb water from the air and soil, as well as from the ponds. A relatively large amount passes into the lymph, blood, and other tissues, and from the kidneys into the urinary bladder. The latter is actually a water reservoir.

Like those of all vertebrates, the kidneys of the frog are composed of micro-scopic tubules bound together by connective tissue, supplied with nerves and closely associated with the blood (Fig. 34.16). The ureter of each kidney lies along its outer edge and receives the urine from minute collecting tubes which cross the dorsal side of it. These collecting tubes in turn receive urine from the kidney tubules which have completed it from urea brought by the blood from the liver.

ENDOCRINE GLANDS. The frog's body is under the elaborate chemical control of the endocrine glands that produce secretions which pass directly into the blood. Some of these influence another gland or structure; others affect the whole organism, its behavior, rate of growth, and symmetry. The endocrine glands of vertebrates are discussed in Chapter 15.

NERVOUS SYSTEM—CELLULAR CONTROL, PERCEPTION. Nervous and endocrine systems cooperate, with the nervous system taking the lead in quick actions. The nervous system is divided into three closely associated divisions: the cerebrospinal, brain and spinal cord; the peripheral, all the nerves which extend to and from the brain and cord and connect them with the sense organs, muscles and outer parts of the body; and the autonomic (involuntary) division, the nerves that carry messages to and from the digestive, respiratory, and circulatory systems and the glands (Fig. 34.21). All three divisions work together to make a unified animal.

Cerebrospinal Division. The narrow cranium and the bony tube made by the vertebrae form a first line of defense for the brain and cord. Within this are other covers, the meninges. The colorless cerebrospinal fluid circulates slowly about the cord, within its central canal, and through the ventricles of the brain. Oxygen is supplied from this fluid as well as from the blood.

Spinal Cord. The spinal cord is a tube with relatively thick walls and a minute central canal which continues into the brain where it widens into the

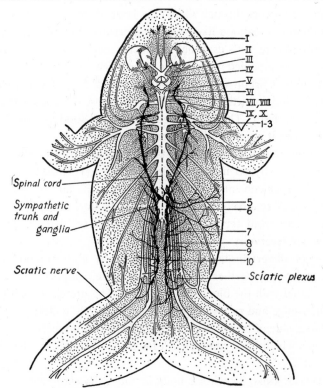

FIG. 34.21. Nervous system of the frog, ventral view; the brain and cord and their branches; the sympathetic nerve trunks (part of the autonomic system) lie on either side of the cord and the branches join the spinal nerves. Cranial nerves, Roman; spinal nerves, Arabic. (Courtesy, Wolcott: *Animal Biology,* ed. 3. New York, McGraw-Hill Book Co., 1946.)

ventricles (Fig. 34.22). The outer part of the tube wall contains long processes of nerve cells (white matter), whose fatty sheaths cause the whiteness. The inner part, like a letter H surrounding the central canal, contains the bodies of nerve cells and looks pearly gray (gray matter). The central canal is a remnant of the open groove which was present in the brain and cord during the early development of the nervous system (Chap. 19). The cord extends backward from the opening in the cranium (foramen magnum) to the seventh vertebra where it tapers into a fine thread of non-nervous tissue, the filum terminale (Fig. 34.21). Like the nerve chain of the bee, the frog's nerve cord is in an evolutionary process of shortening. At the levels of the front and hind legs, it is enlarged by the large number of nerve cells and nerve cell fibers involved in the movement of the legs. There are similar arrangments in other animals—the ganglia near the bases of the wings and legs of the grasshopper are also extra large because of the many nerve cells involved with movement.

Brain. During its development, the brain (encephalon) at first forms three and then five enlargements with constrictions between them. These five divisions are found in all vertebrates. The divisions and the structures they contain are as follows:

TELENCEPHALON. This is composed of the olfactory and cerebral lobes, chiefly the latter (Fig. 34.22). To the former, nerves pass from the sensory epithelium of the nostrils. Each cerebral lobe contains a cavity (first and second or lateral ventricles). These are continued forward into the olfactory lobes

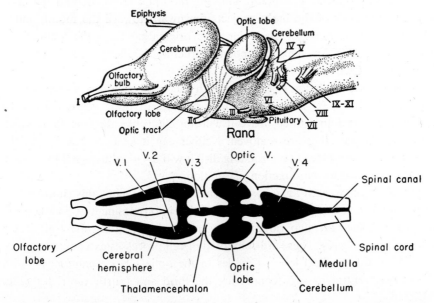

Fig. 34.22. *Upper,* brain of frog, side view. *Lower,* diagram of ventricles of the frog's brain—*V.1, V.2, V.3, Optic V.,* and *V.4.* (*Upper,* courtesy, Romer: *The Vertebrate Body,* ed. 2. Philadelphia, W. B. Saunders Co., 1955.)

and backward through a small hole (foramen of Munro) which opens into the third ventricle. They are finally continuous with the central canal of the cord. Thus, all of them are open to the circulation of the cerebrospinal fluid and there is a serious disturbance if the passage becomes closed.

In frogs, the nerve cells of the cerebral lobes seem to function mostly in the conduction of nerve impulses from the olfactory lobes to a more posterior region (thalamus). If the olfactory and cerebral lobes are removed the frog sits, jumps, and eats as usual, a contrast to the result even of a minor injury to the cerebrum of a mammal.

BETWEEN BRAIN, DIENCEPHALON (OR THALAMENCEPHALON). Directly behind the cerebral lobes is a folded membrane, the anterior choroid plexus that forms the roof of the median third ventricle. Its large blood supply is important to the brain which, like the human brain, has work to do. The pineal stalk, a delicate stemlike process, reaches up to the cranium and, in the skin above it, is marked by the brow spot. These structures are remains of a third eye present in the ancestral amphibians. The optic nerves from the eyes reach the diencephalon just below the third ventricle. All the processes from nerve cells in the right eye cross over to the left side of the brain, and those from the left eye cross to the right side thus forming the optic cross or chiasma. There are theories regarding it but the reason for this crossing is not known; in higher vertebrates, it is only partial (Chap. 17). The sides of the diencephalon are thickened and form the thalami over which the cell processes of the optic nerves spread out fan-wise before entering the optic lobes. Behind the optic chiasma, the floor of the brain projects downward toward the mouth and is joined to a little mass of glandular cells originating from the wall of the mouth (Fig. 34.22). This compound structure is the pituitary gland or hypophysis (Chap. 15).

After the diencephalon is removed with the cerebral lobes, a frog seldom moves voluntarily. It is completely blind because its optic nerves have been cut. When placed on a tilted board it will not climb like the frog from which only the cerebral lobes are removed. Neither can it keep its balance on the edge of the board. Placed on a rotating disk it will try to adjust itself by turning its head opposite to the direction of rotation.

MIDBRAIN OR MESENCEPHALON. In fishes and amphibians, this short section of the brain stem is expanded on its dorsal side into prominent optic lobes. On its under surface are two ridges, the crura cerebri, literally the legs of the cerebral hemispheres. These are composed of cell processes extending from the medulla to the cerebral lobes. Cavities in the optic lobes communicate with the slender central passage connecting the third and fourth ventricles (Fig. 34.22).

In lower vertebrates, the midbrain is a coordinating center and impulses enter it through the nerves from the eyes, ears, and certain other parts of the body. Frogs with all of the brain removed except the cerebellum and medulla can still move about more or less normally, will croak when properly stimulated and can breathe regularly.

METENCEPHALON. This very short section is here roofed by the narrow cerebellum; it is relatively large in higher vertebrates. Experiments show that it is a center of muscular coordination.

MYELENCEPHALON. The sides and floor of the myelencephalon make up the medulla oblongata which is composed of nerve cell processes extending to and from the spinal cord and parts of the brain. Processes of its cell bodies extend to the autonomic nervous system (parasympathetic) that controls breathing movements and the action of the heart. It contains the fourth ventricle which tapers posteriorly into the central canal of the cord. The former is covered by the posterior choroid plexus, and in freshly killed frogs it is colored red by its abundant capillaries.

After all of the brain except the medulla has been removed, a frog is inactive apparently with comfort. It will swallow food placed well down its throat and, properly cared for, may live for some time. Removal of the whole medulla kills the animal since this region controls the breathing movements, contraction of the walls of the blood vessels and the action of the heart.

Spinal and Cranial Nerves. The spinal and cranial nerves are the roadways over which pass all the countless messages of the frog's awareness of and adjustment to its surroundings. Ten pairs of spinal nerves branch from the sides of the cord and extend out through openings between the vertebrae (Fig. 34.21). Each nerve has two roots. The dorsal or sensory root contains nerve cell processes (afferent) over which nerve impulses from sensory cells such as touch pass into and up the cord. The bodies of the cells over which the impulses go are grouped together in a ganglion on the dorsal root. These ganglia are covered by white chalky deposits, the calciferous bodies, pouches of the dura mater filled with granules of calcium carbonate. The ventral or motor root of the same nerve contains processes over which impulses, initiated in the brain or cord, pass from cells in the cord to the muscles and direct their movement. Processes of sensory cells and motor cells lie side by side in the same spinal nerve, but impulses from the skin always come in on the sensory ones and impulses from the cord to the muscle always go out over the motor ones. It is a strictly one way system, like messages passing one another on different telephone wires. Impulses go over the complete sensory-motor circuit when something touches a frog's foot and it moves away.

Ten pairs of cranial nerves branch from the brain of the frog. Some are sensory, like the olfactory nerves, others are motor such as the oculomotors through which the movements of the eyeballs are controlled (Figs. 16.13, 34.22). Most of the cranial nerves have single roots and do not occur at such regular intervals as the spinal nerves.

Autonomic Nerves. The autonomic nerves regulate involuntary action, routine functions such as those of muscles in the alimentary canal, blood vessels, and glands. Fibers of the autonomic nerve cells enter and leave the cord and brain in the cranial and spinal nerves.

The whole autonomic system was formerly called the sympathetic system. That term is now commonly used for the chains of nerves and ganglia which serve the viscera. They lie on either side of the thoracic and lumbar vertebrae. Autonomic is the word used for the entire system with reference to its involuntary nature (Chap. 16).

SENSE ORGANS. The sense organs are described in Chapter 17 and only particular applications to frogs will be given here.

Sense organs or receptors are cells or groups of cells whose content is changed or stimulated by particular conditions in the environment. Familiar ones are the eye and ear; less known are the receptors of cold and heat in the skin.

The frog's skin is sensitive to touch, to cold and heat, to pain, to acids and other irritants in each case through different sensory cells. To some degree, frogs taste through their skins. They can also detect odors under water as well as in the air. The lateral line organs of balance that are well developed in tadpoles are absent in most species of adult frogs.

The frog's eye has some markedly fishlike characters. It will not accommodate, that is, the shape of the lens cannot be changed nor can it be moved nearer and farther from the retina to any such degree as the human lens. In the air, frogs are nearsighted; in the water, they are farsighted; in either medium they see moving objects best. Because their eyes are located so far to the sides of the head, frogs cannot easily use both eyes on an object directly in front of them.

Frogs have a well-developed sense of hearing. They respond to croaks heard in the distance, also to simulated croaks. Anyone who has disturbed a populous spring frog pond knows the sudden silence that falls upon it. Then after a waiting time of complete quiet, one frog raises a solitary voice and, as if that were a signal, other frogs one after another begin to call. One of the sure proofs that a frog hears is the quickening of its throat movements when a bell is rung in a nearby room.

Frogs have a sense of balance. This is located in the semicircular canals associated with the inner ear (Chapter 17).

REPRODUCTION. *Female Organs.* In winter, the ovaries are the most conspicuous objects in the body cavity. The eggs are then absorbing food from the blood and approaching full size. Beneath the membrane of each egg a layer of black pigment partially surrounds the yolk. After the breeding season, the ovaries are a small fraction of their former size with the eggs of another season hardly visible.

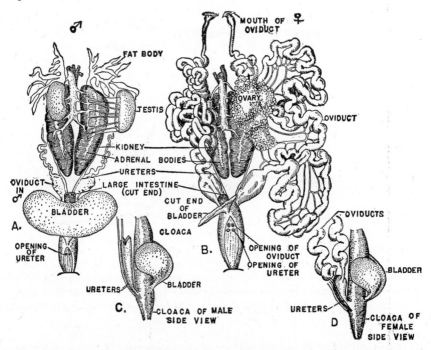

Fig. 34.23. Excretory and reproductive organs of the frog. Male and female. Note the vestigial oviduct in the male. (Courtesy, MacDougall and Hegner: *Biology*. New York, McGraw-Hill Book Co., 1943.)

Each ovary is a lobed sac, with its interior divided by partitions into chambers which are more or less filled with fluid (Fig. 34.23). It is covered with epithelium continuous with the peritoneum of the mesentery (mesovarium) that suspends the ovary from the body wall. Blood and lymph vessels and nerves extend into it by way of the mesentery. The eggs originate from certain cells in the lining of the ovary; certain others produce endocrine secretions. As the eggs are enlarged with yolk, they project into the cavity of the ovary. Cells in the lining of the ovary multiply and form a sac around each growing egg (Fig. 34.24). Each follicular sac fits about the egg like a grape skin around the pulp becoming a tighter fit as the egg reaches full size. Finally, the egg is squeezed out of the sac, through the covering of the ovary and into the body cavity. This process of ovulation occurs at about the same time for the hundreds of eggs that mature in one season and leave the ovary within a short interval. There are several factors which bring this about, among them the secretion of endocrine glands chiefly of the anterior lobe of the pituitary (Chap. 15).

After ovulation, eggs fill the body cavity but only briefly for they begin one by one to pass into the funnels of the oviducts in a steady procession (Fig. 34.25). The funnels are small and are located on each side of the esophagus.

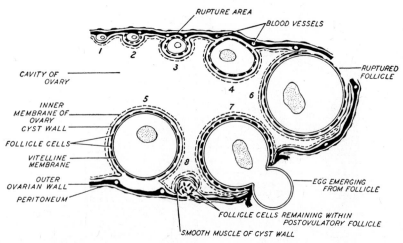

FIG. 34.24. Diagrammatic section through a lobe of the frog's ovary. *1, 2, 3, 4,* and *5* represent stages in the growth of an ovarian follicle (ovum and sac); *6,* the break of the peritoneum, the ovarian wall and the follicular sac; *7,* the emergence of the egg from the ruptured follicle; *8,* the follicle after ovulation. (Courtesy, Turner: *General Endocrinology,* ed. 2. Philadelphia, W. B. Saunders Co., 1948.)

The peritoneal lining, the outer surface of the ovary, the liver, and the funnels themselves all bear cilia, each of which waves its microscopic lash toward the destination of the eggs in the oviducts. Motion pictures of the funnel region in anesthetized frogs show the eggs carried inevitably as on a moving stair, coming to the funnels of the oviducts and toppling into them. The eggs are pushed through the oviducts by the contraction of their walls. At the same time, each one is covered with crystalline jelly, just as hens' eggs are coated with the "white" or albumen. They gradually collect in the expanded part of each oviduct, the uterus. Eventually the whole mass from each uterus is expelled at one time, usually while mating. The size and numbers of eggs vary with the species. In the family Ranidae to which leopard frogs belong, there is a range from about 350 eggs in certain species to 20,000 in the bullfrog. The size of the frog does not determine the size of the egg.

Male Organs. The testes are two relatively small bean-shaped bodies (Fig. 34.23). Like all organs in the body cavity their outer covering is continuous with the peritoneal lining. Its extension out over each testis forms a mesentery (mesorchium) by which it is attached to the dorsal wall. Each testis is a compact bundle of microscopic, coiled seminiferous tubules. The spermatozoa develop from cells in their linings, when mature, a sum total of many millions. They pass out of the testes through threadlike tubes, the vasa efferentia that extend into the collecting tubes of the kidney which in turn join the ureter. They finally lodge in an expanded part of the ureter (seminal vesicle) where a great number of them accumulate for some time before mating.

Fig. 34.25. Photograph of the body cavity and ovary of the frog, *Rana pipiens,* at the height of ovulation. (Courtesy, Rugh: *The Frog.* Philadelphia, The Blakiston Co., 1951.)

The finger-shaped fat bodies, present in both sexes, provide extra food for the gonads when the sex cells are growing. The secondary sex characters of male frogs are stouter arm and pectoral muscles and swollen, roughened nuptial pads on their "thumbs."

Mating is preceded by springtime assemblies and congregational singing, mostly by the males. The females come to these assemblies a little later than the males and mating begins immediately. The male rests on the back of the female with his forelegs around her body and mating pairs float with their heads just above water. When the female finally expels the eggs, the male discharges the seminal fluid over them. Fertilization occurs at once, and with this process the first cell of a new individual comes into existence (Chap. 19).

FROGS IN FOLKLORE

Frogs have played a prominent part in folk tales and legends. They appear on tribal crests and in designs wrought on dishes and clothing (Fig. 34.26).

The Indians of western British Columbia carved them on totem poles believing that they would prevent the destruction of the poles. They held frogs wise and helpful to man and beast. The great Thunderbird of the Haida Indians had two large frogs in his celestial kingdom whose duty it was to croak loudly, to give warning of the approach of strangers. The Thunderbird tops the totem pole and the frog gazes upward from below. Humanity's use of totems, very often animals, began before history and still flourishes, with the American eagle and the British lion among them.

FIG. 34.26. Blanket border of frogs from a drawing by Chief Charlie Edensaw, Haida Indian. Masset, Queen Charlotte Islands, B.C. (From *Amphibians of British Columbia* by C. C. Carl. Victoria, British Columbia, Provincial Museum, 1950.)

35

Reptiles—First Land Vertebrates

The first land animals were reptiles. They were the ancestors of modern turtles, lizards, snakes, and crocodilians, a small remnant compared with those that once overspread the earth during the "Age of Reptiles," at least 150 million years ago. In the early part of that era, certain reptiles developed structures and habits the like of which would eventually be those of birds and mammals.

The name of the Class Reptilia refers to the creeping habits of many of the group (Fig. 35.1). Reptiles originated from primitive amphibians that then and ever since have been bound to water by their unprotected eggs that develop only in watery surroundings. Unlike amphibians, the reptiles made permanent homes on land and laid their eggs there. In the course of time, the eggs became truly land eggs with fluid held within them by their shells. Inside the shell the young reptile was surrounded by membranes that had various uses. One of these was the amnion, a sac of fluid, the private pond in which every reptile, bird, and mammal now goes through its early stage of life (Fig. 35.2).

In addition to the all important eggs, there were three other main keys to reptilian success on land—their skins, respiratory organs, and means of locomotion. Necessity of being near a body of water and dependence upon warm climate are like chains limiting the distribution of land animals. Reptiles broke the first, but not the second chain. With their low rate of basic bodily activity and "cold blood" they have continued heavily dependent upon a warm climate. Only warm-blooded birds and mammals can live on the polar ice.

Three Key Adjustments to Land Life. SKIN. The skins of reptiles and amphibians are essentially similar except for one great difference. A snake's skin resists drying; a frog's skin does not. The difference is in the outermost horny layer of the epidermis (stratum corneum) that in frogs is soft and permeable to water and in lizards is tough and waterproof (Fig. 35.3).

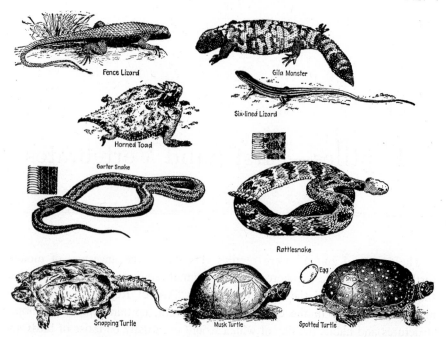

FIG. 35.1. Types of North American reptiles. *Fence Lizard* (Sceloporus). Length, 5 to 6 inches. Gray brown to green. A dozen and a half species ranging throughout south-central United States and in the west north to Oregon. A common pet. *Horned Lizard* or *Toad* (Phrynosoma). Length 5 inches. Several species in western United States only. Unlike most lizards they give birth to living young. *Six-lined Lizard*. Race runner (Cnemidophorus). Length to 10 inches of which 7 inches is tail. Easily identified by the prominent yellow lines in a brown background. Allied species common in south to south-central regions across the continent. *Gila Monster* (Heloderma). Length to 24 inches. Beautifully colored gray with rose patches and beading. The only poisonous lizard in the United States. It lives in desert places in the southwest, especially Arizona. *Common Garter Snakes* (*Entema sirtalis*) live in every part of America where snakes exist, the first to come out of hibernation in spring, the last to go into it in autumn. With several related species it ranges the north and north-central United States. *Rattlesnakes*. There are 15 species of rattlesnakes in the United States and with one or another of them their range extends over all but the northernmost part of the country. They are all dangerously poisonous. *Snapping Turtle* (Chelydra). Less protected by shell than most turtles, snappers are demons for fighting and will snap even as they are hatching. Found in ponds. Common snapper grows to 50 pounds or more. (Courtesy, Palmer: *Fieldbook of Natural History*. New York, McGraw-Hill Book Co., 1949.)

RESPIRATION. Reptiles cannot breathe through their skins and they have no gills. They do have lungs, however, with greater capacity than the most elaborate amphibian ones. In most reptiles, the heart is incompletely four-chambered; in crocodilians, it is completely so insuring a supply of better oxygenated blood.

LOCOMOTION. Reptiles long ago developed legs and speed such as never

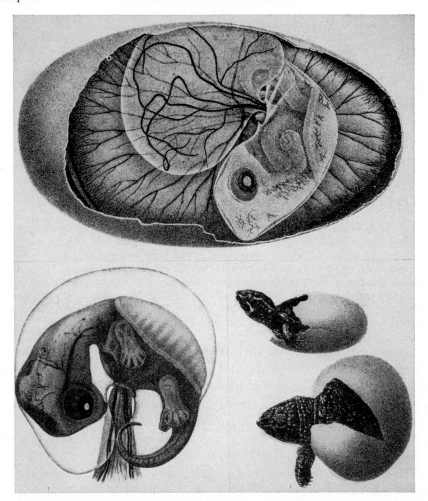

FIG. 35.2. *Upper,* embryo of the painted turtle, *Chrysemys picta,* enlarged about 3 times. *Lower left,* embryo of the snapping turtle, *Chelydra serpentina,* surrounded by the amnion. *Lower right,* snapping turtles at hatching, about natural size. Reptiles were the first land animals. Before them all animals had been bound to the water. Their young could not and cannot now develop without it but now they have it in a sac. The shelled egg and the amnion, the sac of fluid that contains the embryo, were the keys to land life for the reptiles. Shelled eggs are all important to the birds, and the amniotic sac of fluid has continued important in birds and mammals. Every human being spends his early months in a pond. (After Agassiz: "Embryology of the Turtle," in *Contributions to Natural History of U.S.A.,* vol. II, pt. III. Boston, Little, Brown, and Co., 1857.)

had been achieved by any animals before them. Many of the ancient dinosaurs could run on their hind legs, and dig up roots, pick fruit and fight with their forefeet (Fig. 35.15). Most snakes can travel rapidly and although they have no appendages they can climb and swim.

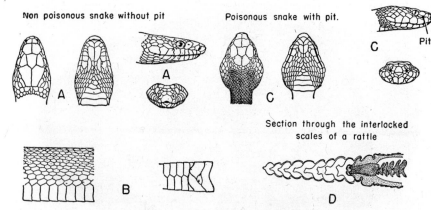

Non poisonous snake without pit   Poisonous snake with pit.

A

C   Pit

Section through the interlocked
scales of a rattle

B

D

FIG. 35.3. Scales of snake. *A*, head of a non-poisonous pilot snake. *B*, side of the body of a snake with smooth scales; the anal region and tail showing the large ventral scales. *C*, head of poisonous copperhead snake. The pit between the eye and opening of the nostril is characteristic of poisonous snakes. *D*, section through the tip of the tail of a rattlesnake showing the loosely interlocked scales which are rattled. (*A, B,* and *C,* courtesy, Surface: *Serpents of Pennsylvania.* Harrisburg, Penna. State Dept. of Agric., 1906. *D,* courtesy, Weichert: *Anatomy of the Chordates.* New York, McGraw-Hill Book Co., 1951.)

Characteristics of Reptiles. The outer layer of skin is dry and horny, usually with small scales in lizards and snakes and very large ones (scutes) in turtles and crocodilians. The ancient reptiles and the modern lizards, alligators, and others have two pairs of limbs, typically with five toes that end in horny claws (Fig. 35.5). Their bodies are low slung, adapted to running close to the ground, to climbing in many lizards, and to crawling in alligators. Limbs are reduced or absent in some lizards and in all snakes.

The reptilian skeleton is relatively heavy, and contains more calcium than that of fishes or amphibians. Except in turtles and snakes, the ribs are moved during breathing much as they are in birds and mammals. Reptiles have a distinct neck region, and were the first vertebrates that could turn their heads sidewise. Even the sea turtles breathe chiefly by means of lungs. Eyes and other sense organs are adapted to life on land, always protected from exposure to air. The temperature of the body, always the expression of its metabolism, is low and varies with that of its surroundings. This has limited reptiles to long hibernations or to life in subtropical regions. For example, Louisiana has over 70 species of reptiles; northern Alberta has one, a garter snake.

Fertilization is internal, a protection of the sex cells from drying. The eggs are large with abundant yolk, and in leathery or limy shells. The majority of reptiles are oviparous, and their eggs are incubated and hatch outside the body. Some lizards and snakes are ovoviviparous; the eggs, fertilized and later supplied with shells, are incubated and hatched within the oviducts from which the shells are later expelled. In essentials, this process is intermediate between

FIG. 35.4. Tuatera (*Sphenodon punctatum*) has features of the early ancestral reptiles (Cotylosaurs). A relic from a remote past, existing now only on the islands near New Zealand. Length, 30 inches. (After Blanchard. Courtesy, Rand: *The Chordates*. Philadelphia, The Blakiston Co., 1950.)

the development and hatching of the eggs of birds and development and birth in practically all mammals (Fig. 19.14).

Like other land animals, reptiles do not go through an aquatic or larval stage. Living upon the yolk and with the help of the other membranes the reptile embryo like the bird embryo grows to relatively large size and independence before it hatches (Fig. 35.2). As soon as they hatch, snakes take care of themselves, much better than do chickens.

Orders of Living Reptiles

Modern reptiles are usually classified in either four or five orders, variously arranged and named by different workers. In contrast to this small number are the 14 or more orders of ancient ones known only by their fossil remains. Modern reptiles include:

Order Rhynchocephalia. Only one representative, Sphenodon, a lizard-like connecting link between ancient and modern reptiles (Fig. 35.4).

Order Squamata. Lizards and snakes.
Order Crocodilia. Crocodiles and alligators.
Order Chelonia. Turtles and tortoises.

ORDER SQUAMATA—LIZARDS AND SNAKES

These reptiles have certain distinguishing structures not intelligible without special study. The two suborders are easy to separate, since lizards have legs and snakes do not. However, there are a few limbless lizards which cannot be distinguished from snakes except by internal structures.

Lizards. In general, lizards are clean vigorous carnivores that earn their way in the living web of their community. All are interesting. Many are beautiful. The little geckos, numerous in hot countries, run about at night often on the walls of houses, even on the ceilings to which they hold tightly by their sticky toe pads (Fig. 35.5). In the flying dragons of the East Indies, the ribs are

FIG. 35.5. Common wall gecko (*Tarentola mauritanicus*) of southern Europe. Length, 6 inches. Geckos are a large group of lizards, four of them native to the southern United States. Their sticky toe pads enable them to walk on ceilings. (Courtesy, *Guide to the Reptile Gallery, British Museum.*)

extended beyond the sides of the body and covered by folds of skin that serve as wings enabling their owners to take gliding flights from branch to branch (Fig. 35.6). The wings are gorgeously colored and flying dragons are suggestive of brilliant butterflies.

Chameleon is the common name of one of the most remarkable of the families of lizards (Fig. 35.7). Because of their ability to change color the same name is also applied to the chameleons (Anolis) of the southern United States. The true chameleon however is found in Africa, Arabia, and southern India. In it, the toes are joined together in two bundles; with these and its prehensile tail it is a truly non-slip climber of extraordinary agility. It can thrust out its tongue more than the length of its body, aim with accuracy and bring back a fly on the sticky tip, all in motions too fast for the eye to follow clearly. Its ability to change color receives more than its share of fame for it is equaled or surpassed in this by other species. The lizards found in the United States include the horned lizard or "horned toad" (Phrynosoma) of the Great Plains and Rocky Mountains (Fig. 35.1); and one of the only two lizards known to be poisonous, the Gila monster (Heloderma) of the Texas and Arizona deserts, marked with alternate rings of black and coral pink

FIG. 35.6. An unusual display of ribs. In the "flying dragons" (Draco) of Malaya the ribs support wing-shaped sheets of skin, folded when the lizard is running, spread when it parachutes. In the hooded cobras (Naja), the ribs support the hood spread when the snake is excited (Fig. 35.8). (Courtesy, *Guide to the Reptile Gallery, British Museum.*)

(Fig. 35.1). It has a row of poison glands along the inside of its lower lip, holds on like a bulldog when it bites, and chews in the poison. It has a bad reputation but is so conspicuous that human beings are rarely bitten by it.

Caught by the tail a lizard immediately escapes leaving the captured piece

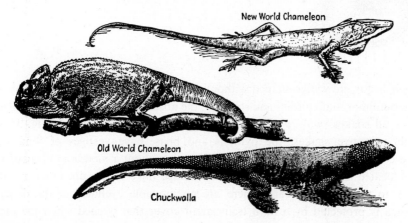

New World Chameleon

Old World Chameleon

Chuckwalla

FIG. 35.7. Three well-known lizards. The *new world chameleon* (Anolis), about 6 inches long, common in southern United States, varies in color from gray to green. The *old world chameleon* (Chameleon) may be a foot long including its prehensile tail and is famous for its changes of color. The *chuckwalla* (Sauromalus), one foot long, is locally known in southwestern United States. (Courtesy, Palmer: *Fieldbook of Natural History.* New York, McGraw-Hill Book Co., 1949.)

behind it. Such breaks occur in definite cleavage planes through the middle of a vertebra. The lost part of the tail is replaced on a simpler plan without true vertebrae and often with a different kind of scales.

Snakes. Snakes travel on the ground. They also climb trees and the "flying snake" of India is a glider. Snakes work their way into crevices and holes made by other animals and the "earth snakes" of southern India are blind burrowers. They swim easily and a few tropical ones spend most of their lives in the water. Nevertheless, the real home of the great majority is the surface of the ground, in touch with earth and plants. There they hunt their prey, waiting for it or silently slithering after it.

Snakes are superlatively streamlined examples of an efficiency of omission.

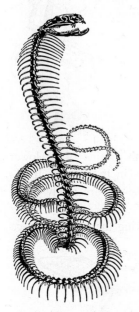

FIG. 35.8. Skeleton of cobra. The skeletons of nearly all snakes are without limbs, limb girdles and sternum. Pythons are among the exceptions. (Courtesy, Rand: *The Chordates.* Philadelphia, The Blakiston Co., 1950.)

Their heads are wedge-shaped without extensions of ears or feelers. They are without limbs, limb girdles and sternum, the absence of the latter a convenience since all snakes swallow whole animals, mice, rabbits, or sheep (Fig. 35.9). Only primitive snakes, the pythons and boas, have vestiges of hind legs. The complexity of the middle ear is reduced, without a membranous eardrum and located far back on the head, an advantage since snakes open their mouths back to their internal ears. There are no movable eyelids, but the delicate cornea is protected by a hard transparent cover that is shed when the outer skin is molted. The eye is never left unprotected. There are no vocal cords and no voice. There is no urinary bladder; metabolic waste is semisolid and water is conserved as it is in birds.

In spite of all these omissions, snakes have all the essential structures of such wide-bodied relatives as the turtles. The pairs of lungs, kidneys, and

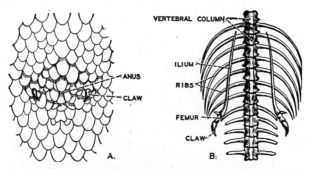

FIG. 35.9. Remnants of hind legs and pelvic girdle of a python, indicating that the ancestors of snakes once traveled on legs. *A*, ventral external region where claws extend out between the scales. *B*, skeleton in the same region. The hip girdle is represented only by a slender ilium, embedded in the flesh on each side. The limbs are vigorously moved and the claws are capable of inflicting deep cuts. Pythons and boas are constricting snakes, some of them 30 feet long, with jaws capable of opening widely enough to take in a sheep. (Courtesy, Rand: *The Chordates*. Philadelphia, The Blakiston Co., 1950.)

ovaries or testes are present, but one lung is in front of the other, one kidney in front of its mate and so on. It is a tandem series.

Ribs play various parts in the activities of snakes. They stiffen the spreading hoods of cobras (Fig. 35.8), and urged by the muscles that control them, they squeeze the still-living animal that the snake has swallowed. Contractions of muscles in the body wall, contractions of rib muscles, and of those that lift the ventral scales all take part in locomotion. This is either a glide straight forward or a curving slither alternately from side to side like a swimming eel. A snake seems to slide without effort. It is not surprising that Solomon found "the way of a serpent upon a rock" one of the things that baffled his mind.

Snakes are pure carnivores. Common garter snakes prey upon insects and other animals up to the size of frogs. Rattlesnakes do likewise and can swallow small rabbits. The bones of the lower jaw have elastic joints allowing the necessary great stretch. The snake hooks its teeth into the victim, first on one side, then the other gradually pulling its mouth over the rabbit. Teeth, especially the poison fangs, are often broken but partly developed ones behind them immediately take their places (Fig. 35.10). A snake travels by its tongue as a dog travels by its nose. Slipping leisurely along with its mouth tightly closed it explores every object with this ominous, flashing, black and red, but entirely harmless organ. It is lodged in a sheath in the floor of the mouth and extended through the small opening formed by a notch in each jaw.

POISONOUS SNAKES. Of some 2500 living species of snakes about 600 are more or less poisonous. The venom is secreted by modified salivary glands in the upper jaw and injected into the wound by the fangs which are grooved or tubular teeth. The venom contains poisonous proteins whose proportions vary

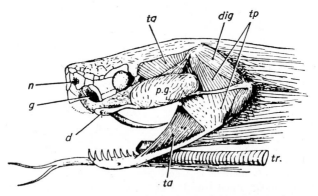

Fig. 35.10. One side of the head of a poisonous snake, with the skin and cheek muscle removed to show the duct connecting the poison gland with the tubular fang. When the jaws are opened the fangs drop downward; when they clutch the contraction of cheek muscles pushes poison into the fangs, *ta, dig, tp, ta,* muscles; *pg,* poison gland; *d,* duct; *g,* sensory groove; *n,* nostril. (Courtesy, Gadow: "Amphibia and Reptiles," in *Cambridge Natural History,* vol. 3. London, The Macmillan Co., 1909.)

with the type of snake. Venoms produce two main effects. In one, the venom breaks up the blood cells and injures the linings of blood vessels. In the other, it attacks the nerve centers especially those of the respiratory system. Anti-venins are available in certain countries but are in no wise so accessible as they should be. First aid treatment, however, is described in almost all recent books about snakes. Anti-venins are prepared by immunizing horses against a particular poison by gradually increasing injected doses of the venom. The clear serum of the horse's blood with its antitoxins is then ready to be used to inoculate patients. Snake venom is one of the most complex poisons produced by animals and it has not been possible to prepare a general antitoxin for it. In some cases, an antitoxin works against the venom of only one species, in others against those of two or more. Snakes of the United States that produce the most serious poisons are: the western diamond-backed rattlesnake, eastern diamond-backed rattlesnake, prairie and Pacific rattlesnake, timber rattlesnake, and water moccasin. If frequency of the bite, not strength of poison and danger, is considered the copperheads would top this list.

HIBERNATION. Large numbers of snakes commonly of one species, sometimes of two or three, hibernate in one locality, in various protected holes in the ground where the temperature stays above freezing. They congregate in autumn, always in warm places, mate and finally retire for the winter, sometimes dozens intertwined in clumps in which heat and moisture are conserved.

ORDER CROCODILIA—ALLIGATORS AND CROCODILES

Crocodilians are the giants among reptiles. They are ponderous, lizardlike and clothed with exceedingly tough skin and an armor of bony plates overlaid by horny scales. They are seemingly dull and slow but are capable of lightning quick attacks (Fig. 35.11). In past ages, they were widely distributed into the cooler regions. Now they are restricted to the tropics and semitropics. In relatively few years excess hunting for eggs, young animals, and skins valued for leather have dangerously decreased the alligators and crocodiles in Florida and other southeastern states.

Crocodilians are without exception amphibious. They float partly submerged in quiet, warm waters, but true to the habit of their group they lay their eggs on land. They are all carnivorous, the young ones feeding upon fishes, the older ones upon water birds and mammals. They have pointed teeth and under jaws with a spring like a steel trap, capable of easily crunching the bones of a dog. The feet are little used in swimming but the side-swinging of its powerful tail sends an alligator rapidly through the water. The heart is four-chambered, the right and left ventricles being separated in crocodilians, but in no other reptiles. The urinary bladder is absent as it is in birds.

Alligators and crocodiles are essentially similar but the differences between them are sufficient to place them in separate genera, the two American ones being Alligator and Crocodilus. The most obvious difference in these two is in the shape of the head: in alligators broad with a blunt snout; in crocodiles narrow with a pointed snout (Fig. 35.11). Alligators are hardier, can live farther north than crocodiles, and are able to hibernate under water as turtles do. Crocodiles are practically helpless in water at 45° F. and soon drown.

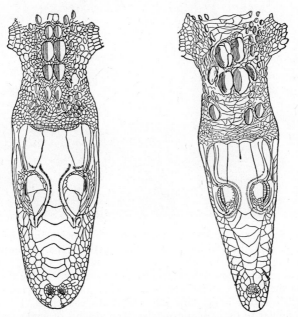

FIG. 35.11. *Left,* head of alligator, blunt snout. *Right,* head of crocodile, pointed snout. (Courtesy, Rand: *The Chordates.* Philadelphia, The Blakiston Co., 1950.)

ORDER CHELONIA—TURTLES

Turtles can be instantly distinguished from all other animals by the shell, a fortress so large in many of them that they can withdraw into it, head, legs, and tail (Fig. 35.12). The order consists of over 200 species that breathe air and lay their eggs on land with some, such as the sea turtles, that spend most of their lives in water. In general usage, chelonians are called turtles or tortoises with little regard for meanings. The most common three types are:

Turtles—Semiaquatic in fresh or salt water, e.g., painted and loggerhead turtles (Fig. 35.12).
Tortoises—Mainly or entirely land dwellers, e.g., wood turtles.
Terrapins—Edible with market value, e.g., diamondback terrapin.

In Britain, tortoise is applied to land and fresh-water species and turtle to marine ones.

Ancestry. In the early part of the Age of Reptiles certain ones developed horny, toothless beaks and bony casings about the body. Their descendants are the turtles of today.

Shell. This consists of an upper carapace and lower plastron united on each

FIG. 35.12. Sea turtles probably originated from ancient marsh-inhabiting ancestors. They live in the warmer seas encircling the globe. Atlantic green turtle (*Chelonia mydas mydas*). For the food market the most valuable reptiles in the world, they have been exterminated from many areas by hunting them in the sea, and collecting their eggs on land. They are still a staple food in some Caribbean ports and a delicacy in large American and European cities. The Pacific green turtle is very similar to the Atlantic species. The weights of green turtles now captured are from 25 to 200 pounds, formerly 500 pounds was common. (Photograph by Isabelle Hunt Conant.)

side by a bridge of cartilage or bone (Fig. 35.13). The two are usually composed of plates of bone overlaid by a mosaic of flat horny scales. In soft-shelled turtles the carapace and plastron are partly bone and covered by a leathery skin (Fig. 35.14). The thoracic vertebrae and ribs are fused to the bony carapace outside the pectoral girdle. It is as if our shoulder blades and collarbones were inside our ribs. Since only the vertebrae of the neck and tail can be moved, the muscles of the body are greatly reduced. Only those of the neck, legs, and tail are well developed.

The form of the shell varies with the habits of the animal. In land turtles, it is usually high domed and permits the head and appendages to be completely protected as in box turtles; in aquatic species it is low, in the snapping turtle, so small that the head and soft parts are unprotected. The protection afforded by the shell seems to be correlated with the disposition. Most turtles are inoffensive, being structurally set up for retirement to their shells under disagreeable circumstances. On the other hand, those with small or soft shells snap and bite at the slightest excuse. Snappers are ferocious and will strike with the speed and fury of a rattlesnake, without the poison.

BREATHING. The respiratory system is typical of air-breathing vertebrates, with nostrils, pharynx, glottis, larynx, trachea, and lungs—the latter containing

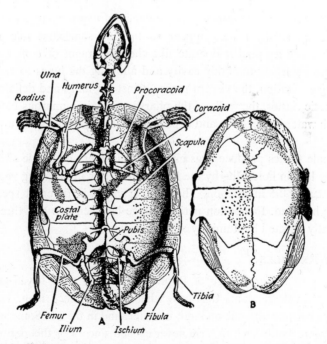

FIG. 35.13. Skeleton of a turtle (Cestudo). The living epidermis outside the bony plates produces the horny shell. During the embryonic development the processes of the vertebrae and the ribs are fused with the bony plates. (Courtesy, Wolcott: *Animal Biology,* ed. 3. McGraw-Hill Book Co., 1946.)

Fig. 35.14. Florida soft-shelled turtles (Trionyx) are highly active aquatic turtles in which bony plates are reduced or absent, and the outer covering is a leathery skin. (Photograph by Isabelle Hunt Conant.)

enough air chambers to furnish an abundance of exposure to air. In spite of the unyielding shells, turtles appear to breathe somewhat like mammals. Muscles in each leg-pocket operate like the diaphragm of a mammal, their contractions enlarging the body cavity and allowing the lungs to expand with air. During expiration, the viscera press against the lungs and deflate them. In many aquatic turtles, the walls of the pharynx contain numerous blood vessels over which water is sucked in and expelled so that the whole structure acts as a gill.

All female turtles produce eggs either with leathery or brittle shells. These are usually laid in holes dug by the female in soil or in decaying vegetation in which heat aids the incubation. The number varies in different species up to about one hundred. Incubation periods range between two and three months, being greatly affected by humidity and temperature.

ANCIENT REPTILES

The story of the great Age of Reptiles is told by their fossilized remains and by certain descendants that have changed little since then. During that age reptiles became at home on land, in water, and in the air. Some were small, but many were giants such as have never existed since. For this period of some 140 million years reptiles dominated the earth, but in spite of them birds, small mammals, insects, and flowering plants were becoming established. The reptilian promise of bird life seems to have been dramatic and convincing while the promise of mammalian life was still hidden in small meat-thirsty carnivores that ate the large yolk-filled eggs of the reptiles (Fig. 35.2).

Among the earliest reptiles were three types from which a varied host of animals originated. One side line of those (Cotylosauria) with sprawling legs, heavy bodies and remarkable armor were the ancestors of turtles. In another side line were the mammal-like reptiles (Synapsida) that ultimately gave rise

FIG. 35.15. *Upper,* a small dinosaur, the bird catcher (Ornitholestes), 5 or 6 feet in length, that lived 200,000,000 years ago, here represented in the act of catching the first known bird (Archaeopteryx). In such agile animals the two footed pose was finally established along with a carnivorous diet. *Lower,* a contemporary dinosaur, the four-footed Tyrannosaurus, of 50 feet total length, and a weight 8 to 10 tons. So far as fossil remains show, this is one of the largest animals that ever lived. Restorations from fossils, painted by C. R. Knight and in the American Museum of Natural History. (Courtesy, Colbert: *The Dinosaur Book.* New York, American Museum of Natural History, 1945.)

to egg-laying mammals (e.g., duckbill), marsupial mammals (e.g., kangaroos), and placental mammals (e.g., man). The central reptilian stock (Archosauria) were the seemingly insignificant progenitors of the midgets as well as the giants of the Reptilian Age. The amphibious dinosaurs were plant feeders that moved heavily on four legs in their marshy homes. Certain of them were only 30 to 40 feet long, but the fossil skeleton of one measures about 80 feet. The carnivorous dinosaurs ran upright on their hind legs, as do some modern lizards, pricked into speed by hunger and fighting (Figs. 35.15, 35.16). They became increasingly large and the fossil of Tyrannosaurus shows a monster that reared upward 19 feet, no doubt using its great teeth and front claws on the unarmed

FIG. 35.16. Drawings of three frilled lizards. (Chlamydosaurus) and another species (Grammatophora) at right showing the bipedal habit in living reptiles. Drawings made from photographs of exhilarated lizards running at full speed. Millions of years ago reptiles walked on two legs. In succeeding ages nearly all the reptiles abandoned the habit but in the birds that originated from them, walking was continued with success. An ostrich can run. (Courtesy, Young: *The Life of the Vertebrates.* Oxford, England, The Clarendon Press, 1950.)

plant feeders. Some small reptiles were no larger than chickens and squirrels. A little dinosaur whose fossilized skeleton was about one foot long was discovered a few years ago near South Hadley, Massachusetts, in a region where footprints of giant dinosaurs are found in the sandstone. Some flying reptiles were the size of sparrows; some had wingspreads of 20 feet.

After some 140 million years, the Age of Reptiles came to an end and the hordes of these ruling animals gradually disappeared. A cataclysm or a gradual change of climate or great competition for food and space between the reptiles and other animals may have brought about their disappearance. By that time there was a host of active, warm-blooded mammals with appetites for reptilian eggs and meat. These mammals originated from one or more strains of reptiles. From the reptiles also had come the shelled egg which could be incubated in a dry place, yet the developing embryo would be surrounded by fluid. The shelled egg and the embryonic membranes were the great contributions of the reptiles to the evolution of vertebrates.

36

Birds—Conquest of the Air

Mastery of the Air. Birds are the only animals that have mastered the air. Human flight is a mastery of machines. Compared with the flights of birds those of insects are little and near the earth—cautious, fair weather travels; even those of bats with their sure piloting by supersonic echoes are specialized and limited. Birds swing into the air with certainty. The golden plover takes off on an over-sea journey of 2000 miles; geese have been seen flying at a height of 9000 feet; by slight turns of body and wings hawks ride on the air currents; bobolinks sing as they fly skyward, then drop, tumbling almost to the earth with the showmanship of an aviator. Birds travel by day and by night, in soft weather and through wind above rough seas. They are the world's greatest migrators (Fig. 36.1).

Birds are animals that have feathers. Their power and skill in flight, their steering and balancing all depend upon feathers. They are protected from cold and water by feathers dressed with oil; the ear openings of diving birds, American loons and Antarctic penguins swimming under water, are roofed with mats of oily feathers (Fig. 36.2).

Birds are the warmest of all animals. They have a usual temperature of 100° F to 110° F; that of mammals rarely exceeds 98° F to 100° F except under special conditions. In accord with the body temperature, the rate of their metabolism is high. The bodily activity of birds is rapid; their metabolic build-up and use-up is swift. They eat relatively enormous amounts of food, digest it quickly, and eliminate the waste frequently. The prompt use of digested food is aided by oxygen from the air in the air sacs as well as in the lungs.

The largest living birds are the ostriches (*Struthis camelus*) that may be 7 feet tall and weigh 300 pounds. The condors (vultures) of North and South America have a wingspread of 10 feet. The smallest bird is Helena's humming-bird of Cuba; it weighs one-tenth of an ounce. The bodies of birds are wedges

FIG. 36.1. Flying geese. Drawing by Peter Scott. (Courtesy of Peter Scott: *Wild Chorus*. London, Country Life Ltd., 1950.)

thrust into the air in flight, streamlined, and slipping forward with no outriggers to hinder. Walking birds, quail, pheasants, chickens, fold their wings and slip through underbrush. The diving sea birds do likewise, driving down through the water with arrowy velocity.

Feathers

Their covering of feathers provides birds with a light, water resistant insulation from cold, a matchless equipment for flight, and a clothing whose beauty has brought them admiration and relentless killing.

A feather is a complex, exquisitely wrought, yet durable structure composed of the horny remains of dead cells. Its growth begins, like the scale of a bird's leg or reptile's body, as a nipple-shaped upgrowth of the skin that soon sinks into a depression, the future follicle or sac that holds the feather in place. The

Fig. 36.2. King penguins. A penguin is a bird that swims with great speed usually below the surface of the sea, and dives often and swiftly. A land animal, it is also superbly aquatic. It is the result of an evolution of animals that swam the sea with fins, that clambered onto the land and lived there for long ages, climbed trees, and eventually could fly. Sometime in the succeeding millions of years they returned to the water and now their wings work only like flippers. Penguins cannot fly. (Photograph courtesy, New York Zoological Society.)

development of a feather is described with other outgrowths of the skin in Chapter 8. Pinfeathers, the common name for developing ones, are a source of vitamin requirement. They are enclosed in a horny, pointed sheath, the "pin" which breaks as the feather grows. The sheath and other castoff bits of feathers are eaten during the bird's frequent oiling and cleaning of plumage. These oiled fragments have usually been exposed to sunshine. Thus, while preening their feathers birds treat themselves to irradiated oil containing the fat soluble vitamin D.

Feathers do not develop equally on all parts of the body. Except in a few primitive species including the penguins and ostriches they grow in tracts separated by bare skin (Fig. 36.3). It is likely that in the early ancestors of birds the feathers were small and covered the whole body like those of penguins.

Types and Functions. The contour feathers are the larger ones that contribute most to the form of the bird. The outer ones covering the body and limbs are the flight feathers of wings and tail (Fig. 36.4). The bases of the contour feathers of wings and tail are usually protected by smaller covert feathers. The tail is primarily a rudder for steering, but it has many forms and uses. A peacock's so-called tail is a gorgeous display of overgrown covert feathers and the real tail is inconspicuous. The male turkey displays a fan of tail feathers but, when they are folded, the tail is a rudder.

At hatching, chickens, ducklings, and many other birds are covered with small fluffy down feathers that shut in the heat of the young animals. Each one consists of filaments that spring from the tip of a very short quill. Down is often abundant under the contour feathers especially in ducks and geese. Filoplumes or thread feathers are the hairlike ones that remain after all the others are plucked and are removed when a chicken is singed. In the course of evolution these feathers have lost the spreading vane or web and only a weakened shaft is left. Whippoorwills, flycatchers and others have stiff bristles near the base of the beak. A bristle has a short quill, and a slender shaft with a few barbs at its base.

Colors. White and the colors of feathers including iridescence are due to structure and pigment. There is no pigment in white feathers. Reflected light rays strike obliquely against the dried cell membranes and when there is no pigment, no rays are absorbed—all are shattered and the surface appears white. The microscopic bubbles in well-beaten albumen or "white of egg" are white for the same reason; in this respect a white feather and meringue are nearly related. A blue feather is like the white one except that the cells contain the dark pigment melanin (Fig. 36.5). Rays of reflected light strike obliquely

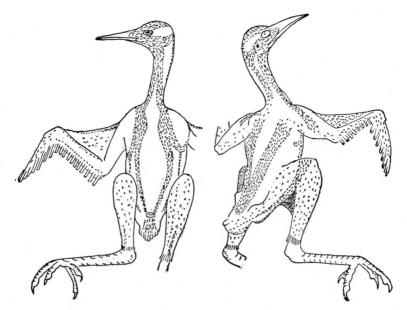

FIG. 36.3. Feather tracts of a cuckoo (*Geococcyx californicus*). Feathers do not develop equally on all parts of the body except in primitive birds such as penguins. (After Shufeldt. Courtesy, Rand: *The Chordates*. Philadelphia, The Blakiston Co., 1950.)

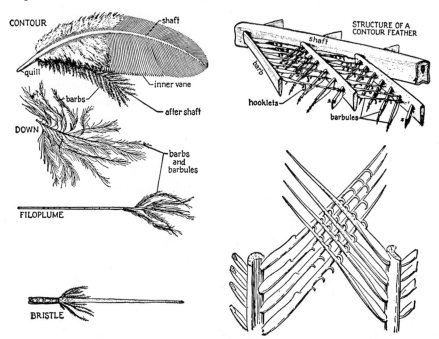

Fɪɢ. 36.4. Types of feathers. *Left,* the contour feathers provide the main covering of the bird, establish the outlines of its figure, and are the flight feathers of wings and tail. Down feathers are air traps that provide insulation for nestling birds and for older ones of certain kinds, notably the water birds. Filoplumes or thread feathers are down feathers without the loose barbs that create the down, the feathers that are singed off the chicken before cooking. Bristles are wiry feathers about the mouths of the phoebe and other flycatchers. *Right,* detail of a contour feather. Strength is secured by barbs interlocked by barbules. (*Left* and *upper right,* courtesy, Storer: *General Zoology,* ed. 2. New York, McGraw-Hill Book Co., 1951. *Lower right,* courtesy, Rand: *The Chordates.* Philadelphia, The Blakiston Co., 1950.)

against the dried cell membranes; some are absorbed by the pigment; others are shattered and the surface appears blue. The same feather appears dark gray in direct light because the rays pass through the dark pigment and the black is predominant. In reflected light the physical effect of structure is predominant.

There are two general kinds of pigment: melanin—blacks, browns to dull reddish, all in minute granules soluble in acid; and lipochromes—pure yellow and pure red, soluble in alcohol or ether. Combinations of different melanins give the blue gray of the chickadee; those of lipochromes the orange of the Baltimore oriole. The iridescence in the neck feathers of pigeons is due to the pigment granules in the feather tips being perfectly spherical so that light striking against them is broken up and rainbow tints produced.

Molting. This is a gradual, systematic process during which no part of the body is left bare of feathers. Its details vary in different species and within one species with age, sex, and other physiological conditions. The molt of a feather is the stimulus to the growth of another in its place, but the succeeding one may be different from its predecessor. In its first winter plumage, the male scarlet tanager is olive with brown wings and tail. In the following spring, these feathers are replaced by scarlet and black ones. All adults of the smaller land birds undergo at least one annual molt at the end of the breeding season when their plumage is entirely renewed. The large and important wing feathers

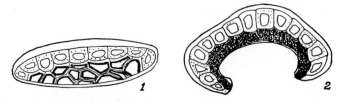

Fɪɢ. 36.5. Cross sections of a barb from a blue feather of an Ant Thrush (*1*) and Cotinga (*2*), greatly magnified. A layer of reflecting cells on the upper surface of the barb is backed by cells containing black pigment. Whether shades of blue are light or dark depends upon the amount of black pigment that is present and how it is distributed in the cells. (Courtesy, Allen: *Birds and Their Attributes.* Boston, Marshall Jones Co., 1925.)

are molted less often than any others. Those of the wings and tail are typically molted in symmetrical pairs making the least disturbance to flight. Molting is mainly under the influence of the thyroid and pituitary glands.

Special Adjustments

Bill and Food. A bird's bill is its mouth, lips, teeth, and nose, and in use takes the place of hands. With it birds get their own food, feed their young, preen and oil their feathers, defend themselves and build their nests (Fig. 36.9).

Of all uses of bills, feeding is the most important. Birds are high-geared engines running at a rate that in mammals would be fever heat and only plenty of the most nutritious foods is adequate for them. These are mainly seeds and animal tissues. Seeds are stored with oil and starch. The meat is of many sorts, worms and insects, fish, mice and other small mammals, all of it high in protein.

Bills tell what birds eat and where they find it (Figs. 36.6, 36.7). A crow's bill is an all-round tool for miscellaneous food. Crows dig up corn, crack nuts, break eggs, and pick and tear at various refuse. With the same kind of bills, starlings are also markedly successful in getting a living.

Many of the carnivorous birds are fish eaters. The American bittern of the watery bogs spears both frogs and fishes. The edges of the bill of the fish-eating merganser duck are deeply saw-toothed, once in its grip the most slippery fish is helpless. The pelican scoops fishes into its great pouch as into an aquarium, lets the water strain away, then tosses the fish in the air to come down headfirst into its gullet. Other meat eaters, the hawks, eagles, and owls seize small animals with their feet and tear the flesh with the hooked end of the upper mandible. Bills may be insect traps, hedged at the base with stiff hairs as in the phoebe and other flycatchers, widely opened as well as hedged in the night-flying whippoorwills. Delicacy of sensation is remarkable in the bills of birds that search muddy pond bottoms with their bills or that probe for worms in moist earth. The upper mandible of the woodcock is extremely sensitive and so flexible that it can be moved without opening the angle of the jaw. With its bill driven deep into the soil it feels about and seizes the worm. In the meantime, its eyes set well back in the head have a clear lookout for danger, though they are of little use in hunting wrigglers on the ground. The seed-eating birds, sparrows, goldfinches, cardinals, grosbeaks, pigeons, and domestic fowls, usually have simple pointed bills, that are strong at the base. Crossbills pick the seeds from pine cones with special nutpicks, their crossed mandibles.

The tongue is also a food-collecting tool. That of a sapsucker ends in a brush but in the insect-eating woodpeckers it bears spines and teeth. The tubular tongue of hummingbirds ends in two brushes suited for nectar dipping. In fish-eating birds such as pelicans, the tongue is very small and well out of the way of the fishes slipping down the throat.

Relatively few birds are pure vegetarians. As fledglings almost all are fed on bits of animals or animal products. Both young and adults of many species live upon a miscellany of small animals in summer and revert to buds and

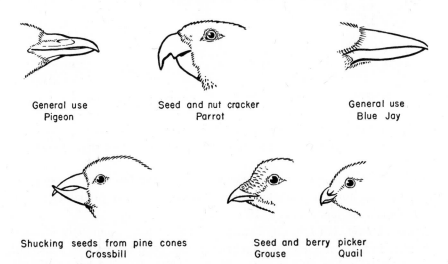

General use   Seed and nut cracker   General use
Pigeon   Parrot   Blue Jay

Shucking seeds from pine cones   Seed and berry picker
Crossbill   Grouse   Quail

FIG. 36.6. Beaks of birds that live on mixed or on purely plant diet. (Not drawn to scale.)

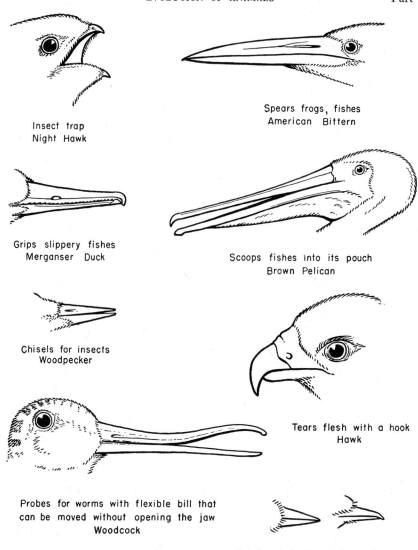

Insect trap
Night Hawk

Spears frogs, fishes
American Bittern

Grips slippery fishes
Merganser Duck

Scoops fishes into its pouch
Brown Pelican

Chisels for insects
Woodpecker

Tears flesh with a hook
Hawk

Probes for worms with flexible bill that
can be moved without opening the jaw
Woodcock

Bristles help to catch small insects
Phoebe

FIG. 36.7. Beaks of birds that feed upon animals, insects to small mammals; the structures are more specialized and striking than those of plant feeders.

seeds in winter, the only food on which they can live through the winters of temperate and northern climates. Owls, hawks, and other predators live on small animals the year round.

Types of Feet. No birds have more than four toes, commonly arranged with three in front and one corresponding to our great toe pointed backward. From this oldest pattern, feet vary with the habits of the birds and the toes may be four, three or two. From hummingbirds to ostriches the legs and feet of birds are covered with strikingly reptilian scales. The heel is the first back-ward bending joint above the part of the foot that rests upon the ground. The forward-bending knee is covered with feathers (Fig. 36.10).

Perching birds are the crows, thrushes, warblers, swallows, larks, and others, numbering more than half of the group. All of them have muscles so arranged that sitting on a perch is automatic with holding to it with the feet. This efficiency is due to the remarkable strength in the tendons which run through each toe and enable it to clasp and to hold and balance the bird on its branch. In all this, the hind toe is essential (Fig. 36.14). There are specialists among the perchers. With the same arrangement of toes, American wood-peckers clutch the surface of a tree trunk, lean back on their tails and hammer with their bills.

A nuthatch climbs down and around tree trunks as easily as up, with stops to pick up insects, and no help from its tail. Swallows have little feet and telephone wires are their favorite perches. The feet of chimney swifts are still smaller, yet weak as its feet may be, a young swift can cling fast to the vertical face of a brick chimney. Owls are as flexible as many human "liberals," being able to move their outer toes backward or forward and perch like a robin or to put two toes before and two behind like a parrot.

A bird's feet tell where it lives (Figs. 36.8, 36.9). Herons that wade about the shallow margins of ponds and streams have long legs that lift their bodies

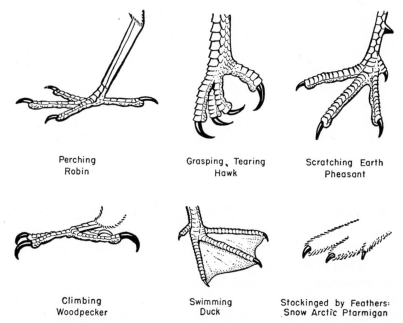

Perching
Robin

Grasping, Tearing
Hawk

Scratching Earth
Pheasant

Climbing
Woodpecker

Swimming
Duck

Stockinged by Feathers:
Snow Arctic Ptarmigan

FIG. 36.8. The shapes of birds' feet are correlated with their habits and sur-roundings. Their feet and beaks are often used like hands in finding food and building nests.

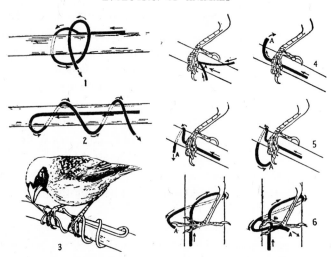

FIG. 36.9. Process of nest-building by a weaverbird (Quelea). The arrows show the direction in which the string is pulled. *A,* the points of holding by the beak. *4, 5,* and *6* show stages of cooperative work by foot and beak. Weaverbirds are relatives of house sparrows that range through Europe, Africa, and Australia. Birds follow a set pattern of nest building. Weaverbirds raised by hand for four generations made perfect nests of a type they had never seen. (After Friedman. Courtesy, Young: *The Life of the Vertebrates.* Oxford, England, Oxford University Press, 1950.)

above the water surface, and four long toes that distribute the weight on the mud. The plover runs along the beach, swims into the waves, then scurries onto the sand again on front toes that are partly webbed but still flexible for running. In ducks, geese, swans, and other water birds, the three front toes are joined together by a web of skin that is outspread against the water in the backstroke. When pulled forward the foot slips through the water, with toes drawn together and webs folded. An ostrich runs on its third toe, the large powerful one which supports most of its weight. The fourth or outer toe is the small helper with a toenail only as large as the claw of a chicken.

Internal Structure

Modifications for Flight. SKELETON AND MUSCLES. The skeleton of a bird is modified for flight, for walking and running, for perching and for laying eggs with hard shells (Figs. 36.10, 36.12, 36.13, 36.14). It bears several reminders of the skeletons of reptiles.

The skeleton is light yet rigid. Except in running birds, the bones of the skull unite early making it strong against shocks, such as those from a woodpecker's hammering. The importance of vision in birds is emphasized by the large eye sockets. The neck is commonly long, 14 vertebrae in a pigeon, 25 in a swan, with peculiar joints that allow the bird to turn it freely when watching for danger, feeding, and nest building. The remainder of the vertebral chain is rigid except for four or five caudal vertebrae which allow the tail to act as a rudder during flight. The terminal bone, called the ploughshare or pygostyle, is composed of fused vertebrae supporting the tail. It is a great contrast to the long tail (20 vertebrae) of the earliest known bird, Archaeopteryx (Fig. 36.20).

The shoulder girdle supplies the sockets for the wings and with the keeled

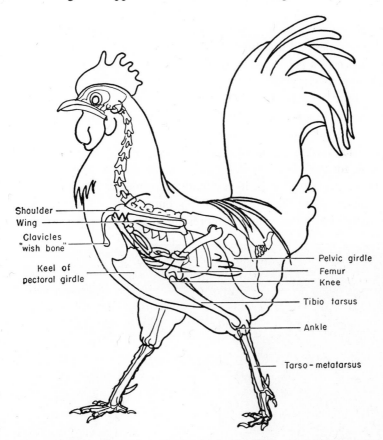

Fig. 36.10. Skeleton of a bird (domestic fowl). The main skeleton of birds is built for locomotion in the air and on land (or water). No other animals are so perfectly adapted to travel in such different surroundings. The flexibility of the vertebral column is almost solely limited to the neck whose turning makes it possible for a bird to see in every direction, and the tail which is a rudder. The pectoral girdle, chiefly its keel, is concerned with air travel. The keel serves for the attachment of the flight muscles, the "white meat" of domestic fowl, the relatively huge pectoralis major muscle that lifts the wings, and the smaller pectoralis minor that lowers them. The pelvic girdle or saddle is concerned with land travel. Its irregular plates (pelvis in the figure) serve for the attachment of the leg muscles; those of the "drumsticks" (dark meat) are as important to walking as the pectoralis muscles are to flying. (Courtesy, Putnam: *Animal X-Rays*. New York, G. P. Putnam's Sons, 1947.)

breastbone furnishes the attachment for the great flight muscles. The wing socket is formed at the junction of the shoulder blade or scapula, the coracoid that connects with the sternum, and the spread ends of the collarbones or wishbone. The spread of the wishbone helps to keep the shoulders sprung apart when the wings are raised. The keel of the breastbone, familar to anybody who has carved a chicken, is the attachment for the great flight muscles (pectorals). In ostriches, as in other flightless birds, the breastbone is a simple shield without a keel.

A bird's hips are mainly broad plates that form attachment places for the great leg muscles and a saddle above the otherwise unprotected vital organs. The presence of a pelvic saddle of bones fused together and to the vertebrae instead of a pelvic girdle allows the passage of the large hard-shelled egg (Fig. 36.18).

WINGS AND FLIGHT (FIGS. 36.11, 36.12). When a bird folds its wings the elbows point backward like human elbows. At the same time, a bird folds its "hands" backward in a jackknife bend with the wrists in a sharp point forward, impossible for the human wrist. A bird's "hand" is small and rigid, reduced to three fingers from the five of its reptilian ancestors. The inner stub next to the ulna corresponds to the index finger, the outer stub and the bones fused together at the tip of the wing also represent fingers. In reptiles, the fingers end

FIG. 36.11. The take-off of an American egret. The bird leaps into the air, raises its wings and stretches out its neck, thrusts the feet down. In the air as in this picture it draws the head back; the legs balance the neck; the wings go into the down stroke. (Photograph by Allan D. Cruickshank. Courtesy, National Audubon Society.)

FIG. 36.12. Pigeons (Columba) photographed during a take-off for flight with exposures of 1/825 second. *A*, front and *B*, rear view with wings together. *C*, nearly, and *D*, at the bottom of the downstroke; note the slight rotation and forward movement of the wing. *E* and *F*, wings during the upstroke; in *F* the feathers have opened and the wings move backward, their motions faster than on the downward stroke. (After Aymar. Courtesy, Young: *The Life of the Vertebrates*. Oxford, England, The Clarendon Press, 1950.)

in claws; so do the first and second fingers of the ostrich. Ancient birds had such claws and used them in climbing. After making several downward and forward strokes birds often hold their wings motionless and glide. Before a high wind a bird can flex its wings and glide with the wind. Usually, at high elevations, it rises through the air and soars in circles without moving the wings,

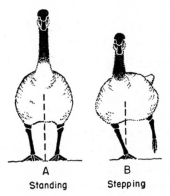

A   B
Standing   Stepping

FIG. 36.13. Standing and stepping. Drawings from photographs of a goose. *A*, standing; *B*, stepping. In stepping the center of gravity is brought over the foot on the ground by a rotation of the femur on the tibia (Fig. 36.10, knee). The tail is shifted to the left. A similar human gait is associated with weight and certain moods. (After Heinroth.)

taking advantage of upward rushing air currents. A bird hovers, even poises in the air over some object, a hummingbird over a flower, a gull above the water. Birds do other things with their wings; penguins swim with them; geese, broody hens, and fighting cocks strike with them; and birds in general spread them over their eggs and young.

Special Features of Digestion. Various birds obtain the same kind of food in different ways: an osprey hovers and drops, catching the fish in its claws;

Flexor
muscles

Flexor
tendons

FIG. 36.14. Mechanism of perching in birds. Leg of crow. The flexor muscles end in tendons that pass behind the joints, beneath a strap of ligaments at the base of the toes, and are distributed to the toes. As a bird flexes its legs and sits on the perch, the flexor muscles contract, pull on the tendons and the toes automatically grip the perch. (Courtesy, Wolcott: *Animal Biology,* ed. 3. New York, McGraw-Hill Book Co., 1946.)

herring gulls swoop down and grip it with their bills; a heron stalks or stands motionless till a fish swims by; the kingfisher makes a sudden plunge; penguins swim rapidly under water and grip the fishes in their bills.

Cormorants, pelicans and others that eat large fishes have small tongues. In sparrows, warblers, small seed- and insect-eaters the tongues are horny, often with inward pointing spines along the sides that catch in the bits of food. The hummingbird has a long cleft tongue with an inrolled membrane on each half which is worked back and forth in the flower to take up nectar. Saliva figures prominently in some birds; in woodpeckers, its stickiness picks up insects; chimney swifts use it as glue in nest building. In all birds, digestion and its associated processes are rapid.

The esophagus is simply a passageway, or a passageway with an expansion, the saclike crop, which provides for quick filling when food happens to be plentiful (Fig. 36.15). Chickens, pigeons, and other grain and miscellaneous feeders have well-developed crops. In pigeons, the lining secretes "pigeon's milk." This is the first food of young pigeons and they reach down their parent's gullet to collect it. An air-filled crop is the pout of the pouter pigeon. Some birds quickly empty their crops when they are frightened into sudden flight. This is a bird's involuntary reaction against extra weight. There are two divisions in the stomach, the first and smaller one (proventriculus) has thin glandular walls which secrete the gastric fluid. In grain-eating birds—pigeons, chickens, and turkeys, in insect eaters, and some others, the second section of the stomach is a well-developed gizzard. Its walls are composed of two great muscles whose tendons are brilliantly iridescent. Its inner layer of cells produces a fluid that hardens into the tough lining that is peeled out when the gizzard is prepared for cooking. Grain-eating birds swallow small stones and gravel that grind against the food, without which their gizzards are useless. The great muscles contract again and again grinding the gravel against the already softened food. Birds such as owls, hawks, gulls, and ducks that eat flesh and plants, have poorly developed gizzards or none. In flying birds, the large intestine is relatively short. It is kept almost clear of waste, another way of decreasing the flight load.

Circulation of Blood. In birds, the circulation of blood differs from that of reptiles in one very important respect. In most reptiles, the oxygen-rich blood

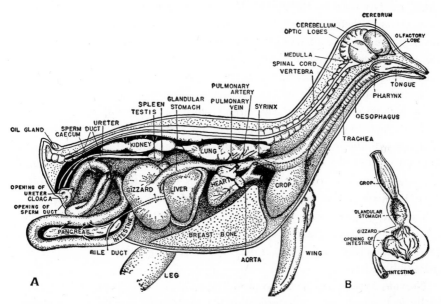

Fig. 36.15. Diagram of the general structure of a bird (except the air sacs), the domestic fowl. The crop is a storage pouch formed by an enlargement of the esophagus. It is highly developed in seed eaters and practically absent in fish eaters. The stomach includes two sections, the proventiculus whose walls secrete the digestive juices and the heavily muscular gizzard where grinding occurs. (Courtesy, MacDougall and Hegner: *Biology*. New York, McGraw-Hill Book Co., 1943.)

from the lungs received in the left auricle of the heart is mixed with the oxygen-poor blood from the right auricle in the incompletely separated ventricles. For the slow metabolism of the cold-blooded reptiles, this is enough oxygen to supply the needs. This is not true in birds. The bird's heart is completely four-chambered and the two kinds of blood are entirely separated. Except for those that go to the lungs, all arteries carry highly oxygenated blood. Only a rapid and generous supply is adequate for the oxygen-hungry body of a bird. The heartbeat of birds is incredibly rapid. The basal rates of the heartbeat of an English sparrow, a canary, and a hummingbird have been recorded respectively as 350, 500, and 1000 per minute. The adult human heart beats about 70 times per minute. The red blood cells of birds are nucleated like those of lower vertebrates; there are more of them per unit of blood than in any other animal.

Respiration. The vocal organ or syrinx is ordinarily located where the windpipe forks into the bronchial tubes, one to each lung (Fig. 36.15). The lowermost rings of the windpipe fuse to form a tube within which are the membranes and muscles whose vibrations produce the voice. Because of their intense activity and high temperature, birds have the highest oxygen consumption of all animals. This is satisfied by fast breathing, the rapid passage of air through the small compact lungs, and the extremely swift flow of blood through them. The lungs are expanded by the pull of the ribs to which they are closely fitted. Air goes through them and enters the internally ciliated air sacs by way of the bronchial tubes. The air sacs extend along the neck, beneath the wishbone, and far back among the viscera (Fig. 36.16). Air spaces connected with them reach into the larger bones. Air is forced out of the air sacs by the pressure of muscles; this time, it enters the lungs directly from the sacs. It rushes through them past the blood capillaries from which carbon dioxide is collected and to which oxygen is contributed. The air sacs constitute a cooling system that combats the intense heat of the bird's body produced by the muscles and kept within it by the feathers. When a bird's air sacs are opened experimentally it continues to live, but its temperature rises higher than the usual 100° to 110° F. In swimming birds the air sacs are helpful floats.

Excretion. Birds conserve water and excrete salts. The completed urine of a bird is a semisolid mass of uric acid crystals cast out of the body as whitish material adhering to the darker waste from the digestive tract. There is no urinary bladder.

Nervous System and Sense Organs. The cerebellum and optic lobes are relatively well developed. This indicates that birds have good coordination and sight. The olfactory lobes are small and even buzzards suspect dead flesh by sight rather than smell. As might be expected birds taste very little. They are sensitive to touch in particular places. Woodcocks probe soft earth and feel for worms with the tips of their bills; various ducks have sensitive sifting plates

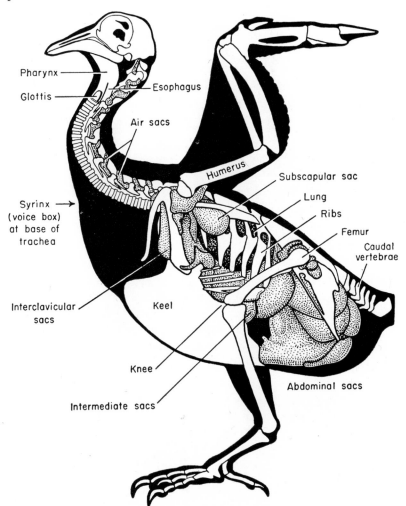

FIG. 36.16. The respiratory organs of a pigeon. The lungs fit closely to the ribs and do not dilate. The air sacs are extensions of the lungs. Their thin transparent walls are freely expansible and they communicate with one another directly or by way of the lung cavities. Air sacs constitute a ventilating system which moderates the high body temperature of the bird. The syrinx, the unique voice box, is located at the junction of the bronchial tubes close to the lungs. In this figure it is hidden by the air sacs. (Redrawn and modified from Muller: *The Air Sacs of the Pigeon.*)

along the sides of the bills between which particles of food are strained from the water; bristles about the mouths of the fly-catching phoebes are responsive to contact with small insects. Next to sight, hearing is the most important sense. Birds have no external ears, but near their peculiar bony eardrums the feathers are especially open to currents of air. Barn owls have folds of skin near the eardrums that they can lower or raise to make catch cups for sounds.

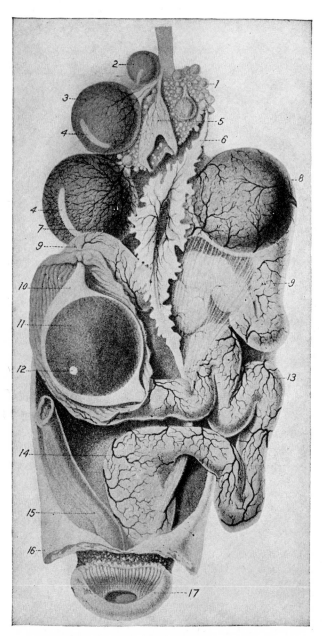

Fig. 36.17. Reproductive organs of the hen. (After Duval.) The organs fully develop only on the left side; those of the right are rudimentary. Two eggs are shown in the oviduct at different levels; normally but one is in the oviduct at one time. *1*, ovary showing many young follicles each containing an egg; *2* and *3*, successively larger follicles containing the enlarging eggs; the dark lines are blood vessels in the walls of the follicular sacs; the white band, *4*, is the line where the follicular sac breaks and releases the egg; *5*, empty follicular sac; *6* and *7*, lip and funnel of the oviduct; *8*, egg in the upper part of the oviduct; *9*, region of the oviduct in which the albumen is secreted; *10*, the oviduct cut open to show the albumen surrounding (*11*) the egg; *12*, the germinal disk where the chicken be-

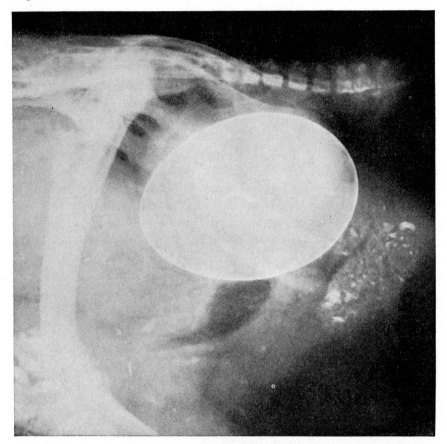

FIG. 36.18. An x-ray photograph of a living hen showing an egg about to be laid, 25½ hours after the last one was laid. Note that there are no bones below the egg. The skeleton is strikingly open at the rear, a reminder that birds are the only animals that produce such large hard-shelled eggs. Actually birds have a pelvic saddle, not a pelvic girdle. (Courtesy, J. A. F. Fezzard: Series (1) of Medical and Biological Illustration. Cambridge, England, Cambridge University, 1951.)

The eyesight of birds is exceptionally keen. They can see to dart through trees without striking a twig and to alight on one branch out of a thousand others. This means constant shifts from far to near vision and reverse—great power of accommodation. A sparrow hawk can drop down upon a beetle after hovering 200 feet above it; by rapid peering this way and that chickadees and warblers catch even the smallest insects on rough bark. The eyes of

gins to develop; *13* and *14,* lower regions of the oviduct; the latter is the part where the shell is secreted; *15,* the alimentary canal (cut off); *16,* reflected body wall; *17,* external opening of the cloaca. (Fertilization of the egg occurs before it is coated with albumen.) (From Hamilton: *Lillie's Development of the Chick.* Copyrighted 1952 by Henry Holt and Co. Reprinted with their permission.)

birds are relatively large, often enormous, and set in exposed positions. The eyeballs are protected by bony plates embedded in the outermost coat. The pecten, a peculiar structure shaped like a half-folded fan, is suspended in the vitreous humor. It is crowded with blood capillaries and nerves. Although its function is not proven it may be connected with nutrition.

Reproduction. Courtship and mating reflect the bird's generally rapid activity. Courtships may include brief darting flights, social gatherings and ceremonies such as those of prairie fowls, dances dignified or tempestuous (Fig. 36.19). Reproduction in birds is similar to that in reptiles. All young birds hatch from hard-shelled eggs. Paralleling the essentially complete land life of birds fertilization is always internal. Sperm cells developed in the testes pass through coiled sperm ducts that open into the cloaca, and are ejected into the cloaca of the female in the extremely brief mating contact. In the cloaca of very young male chicks there is a small process, the rudiment of a copulatory organ similar to one that is well developed in some reptiles. This structure is the means by which the sex of downy chicks is determined in hatcheries.

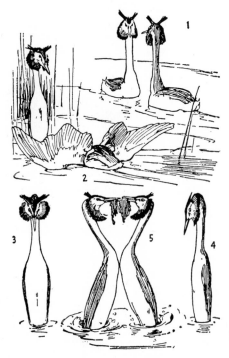

FIG. 36.19. Incidents in the mutual courtship of the great crested grebes, marine diving birds in which the two sexes are strikingly similar in color and form. *1,* mutual head shaking; *2,* the female is displaying her plumage before the male; *3* and *4,* further views of the male rising from the water after various dives; *5,* both birds have dived and brought up weeds. Then, they meet together and go through a period of head swaying. (Courtesy, Young: *The Life of the Vertebrates.* Oxford, England, The Clarendon Press, 1950.)

The female organs usually develop to maturity only on the left side, but hawks and some others are exceptions (Fig. 36.17). During the laying season the ovary of an ostrich may weigh three pounds or more and the egg is equal in volume to about a dozen and a half chicken eggs. When an egg reaches full size in the ovary it breaks out of its enclosing sac, is grasped in the soft funnel of the oviduct and begins its travel through the tube. Fertilization occurs in the upper part of the tube. The albumen or white is laid over the yolk by glands in the middle region of the tube and the shell membranes, the so-called skin, and finally the shell are added in the latter part. Eggs are usually deposited soon after the shell is completed. For comparison of the reproductive processes of other animals see Chapter 18.

Distribution

Birds live on all continents, on most islands, and in all seas. They live in all climates, and are abundant in the tropics and through the temperate zone. They penetrate well into the Arctic and penguins thrive in the antarctic cold that mammals cannot endure. One or another species is at home from sea level to heights of 20,000 feet on the slopes of the Himalaya Mountains. Although flight has given birds the vast space of the air, they still conform to the laws of animal distribution, and each species has its own geographic range and particular habitat. Woodpeckers range all over North America below the Arctic, but they hunt insects on tree trunks wherever they are. Emperor penguins endure the storms, cold, and darkness of antarctic winters because they can secure food. Owls and woodpeckers nest in holes in trees and bank swallows and others in the ground, but no birds are subterranean like the woodchucks and ground squirrels. In polar regions, there are few species and many individuals; in temperate regions, many species are resident and many more come and go in different seasons. There are also many species in the tropics, among them various and resplendent parrots and birds of paradise.

Migration

Birds outdo all land animals in the distance and regularity of their migrations. Not all species are far travelers; chickadees, downy woodpeckers, and blue jays are semipermanent residents in many localities. Yet, individual birds move from one place to another, and bird banding has shown many migrants even among so-called winter residents. Except poor-wills and certain swallows no birds hibernate. They remain in their own locality in full activity, or they leave it and return in a later season. The general trend of migrations is north and south. In the Northern Hemisphere, birds move toward the north where food and nesting places are available during the warmer months, and toward the south to warmth and food in winter. In the Southern Hemisphere where the seasons are reversed, migrations are less general and occur in opposite directions.

The times and general migration routes of North American birds are now fairly well known. Most of the insect eating birds, flycatchers and warblers, retire to the southern states, many of them to South America. The majority of species either cross the Gulf of Mexico, or follow its western shore and settle in Central and South America. Ducks and other waterfowl have definite routes, several of them over the ocean. Certain birds migrate by day and others by night. This was long ago discovered by pointing a telescope at the moon and observing the silhouettes of the birds that cross it.

Many migrants follow river valleys, mountain chains and coast lines; others launch off over the ocean, or across country where there seem to be no guide marks. The urge to migrate is to a considerable degree affected by changes in amount of light and other features of the environment, also by the endocrine secretions of the reproductive organs.

Ancestors

In 1860, on a slab of limestone taken from a quarry in Bavaria, an imprint was discovered that appeared to be the fossilized imprint of a feather. Its identity was established a year later when in the same locality another fossil was found, an almost complete skeleton of a vertebrate animal with feathers. About 16 years later, a still better fossil of a feathered animal was found in the same locality. The fossil record of birds is sparse. No other similar fossils

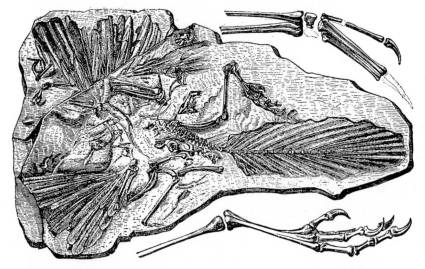

FIG. 36.20. Fossil remains of an ancient reptilian bird (Archaeopteryx) embedded in a slab of limestone—as they were discovered. Above the slab is a partial reconstruction of the distal part of the wing and below the foot is represented. In life, the bird was about the size of a crow. (After Zittel. Courtesy, Rand: *The Chordates*. Philadelphia, The Blakiston Co., 1950.)

have been found in Bavaria and none anywhere so perfect as the now famous Archaeopteryx (Fig. 36.20). The skeleton is similar to that of the flying reptiles of the same era. As a bird, Archaeopteryx is certified only by its feathers. It was about the size of a large crow but more heavily built than a modern bird. The skeleton is lizardlike; the vertebrae of the pelvic region are separate, not fused as in birds and freely movable ones formed a long tail. Each tail vertebra supports a pair of long feathers all of them forming an expanse that was probably spread fan-wise in the air. The wings had free movable "fingers," each with a claw, and on the jaws there were true teeth set in sockets. Ages must have elapsed between the scaly flying reptiles and a feathered Archaeopteryx, but there is no fossil record of a development of birds in that long period. In fossil birds of the far later Tertiary Period (Eocene), the teeth are missing and the tail is short.

37

Mammals and Mankind

Characteristics and Reptilian Origin. Mammals are animals that have hair. No others, except birds, are warm-blooded, and no others, except birds, have coverings that so well conserve the heat of their bodies. Mammals have lungs; their breathing is always aided by the diaphragm, a muscle that works like a bellows. Their red blood cells, without nuclei when mature, are uniquely efficient oxygen carriers. The brain is relatively large due to the great development of the cerebral hemispheres.

Except in the two egg-laying species the eggs are minute, are without shells, and contain scarcely any yolk. Fertilization is always internal. The young develop within the body of the mother, are born alive and are fed milk produced by the mammary glands for which the class is named. While the embryo is developing, it is surrounded by membranes formed on the basic patterns inherited from reptiles (Fig. 35.2). In the higher mammals, the placenta, a modification of the chorion and allantois, is unique among all animals in its provision for the developing young.

Birds and mammals arose from different branches of reptiles early in the Reptilian Age. Mammals increased in number slowly through that long period of 70 million years or more. Towards its end, however, one of the most consequential developments in the history of life was quietly appearing, the rise of flowering plants. After that, there were flowering trees, with edible leaves, seeds, nuts, and fruits. Times of good feeding had come. The flowering plants spread, especially the grasses, as lands were lifted, and through seasonal changes many climates became more livable. Swamps dried and became grazing lands. The Great Plains of North America were coming into existence, and grass-eating hoofed animals spread over them. The evolution of mammals quickened and broadened following that of the plants. The great Age of Mammals had begun (Figs. 37.1, 37.2, 37.3).

Mammalian Structures and Functions. For the structure and physiology of

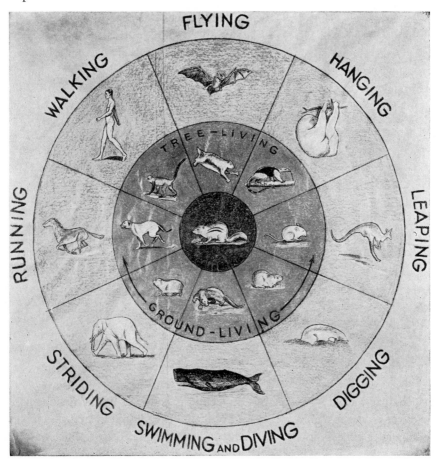

FIG. 37.1. The spread of mammals in environments and habits. Mammals probably first lived in trees, climbing and leaping. From there they gradually radiated into other habitats and activities. (Courtesy, American Museum of Natural History.)

mammals accounts such as Movement and Muscles (Chap. 10), Foods and Nutrition (Chap. 11), and The Release of Energy—Respiration (Chap. 13) and others should be consulted. These are units of The Internal Environment of the Body discussed in Part 3.

The Domestic Cat—A Representative Mammal

The cat is regularly studied as a mammal and an introduction to the human body. The discussions of organs and systems in Part 3 were prepared with those two ends in view, especially the latter. It will be of help and interest if they are consulted as suggested.

The study of organs should always be lifted by acquaintance with the grace of the living animal (Figs. 10.1, 37.4). A cat is a natural carnivore and hunter. It prowls in the grass, waits, and pounces. If not too hungry, it brings the mouse home still alive, sets it free to take a crippled run, then pounces again. Cats catch and clutch and climb—the play of their foreshoulders is something to see and remember. Their muscles are surpassingly supple, elaborately developed on head, neck and shoulders. Their facial expressions

FIG. 37.2. The flexibility of a mammal. Gibbon, the acrobat of mammals. At home in southeastern Asia these long-armed apes leap and swing through the treetops always depending greatly upon their arms. (After Clark: *History of the Primates.* Courtesy, *British Museum Guide,* 1949.)

change. Their night "eyeshine" is momentarily reflected by the headlights as the car approaches within twenty feet of them. Then it glitters and disappears. The angle of reflection is limited as it is in the wayside signs. Cats walk on their toes; the hind foot is bent at the heel with a downward sag, not upright as it is in dogs, and their step is more elastic. They are famous for turning in the air and landing "on all fours" when dropped.

About 3000 B.C., the Egyptians tamed a certain variety of African wild cats so that they might hunt and protect their grain. The cats did this so well that they were for a time believed to represent one of the gods. Later, they were exported and introduced into other countries. It is a comment on the cat's subtlety that where a dog and cat are pets, the dog follows the owner, and the owner follows the cat.

Chief Types of Mammals

Based on the provisions for the developing young, there are three types of mammals: those which lay eggs; those which carry the young in a brood pouch after a short period of internal development; and those in which the developing young are attached by a placenta to the uterus of the mother.

Egg-laying Mammals—Subclass 1, Monotremata. Monotremes are so called because the single opening (*L. monotrema,* one opening) of the cloaca re-

CITATION

FIG. 37.3. The speed of a mammal—portrait of Citation. The thoroughbred horse is developed for speed. The world's record for one mile was made by Citation of Calumet Farms, Lexington, Kentucky, who ran at Golden Gate Fields, Albany, California in one minute and 33 and three fifths seconds, June 3, 1950. For a human run the fastest mile to this date is three minutes and 58 seconds, by John Landy of Australia, June, 1954. (Portrait of Citation, by Allen F. Brewer, Jr., equine artist, Lexington, Ky.)

ceives the urinogenital and digestive tubes, as it does in the amphibians, reptiles and birds. Only two species have survived, the duckbill (Ornithorhynchus)—a semiaquatic animal with soft fur, and the spiny anteater or Echidna with coarse hair and spines that lives in dry country (Fig. 37.5). The duckbill deposits its two leathery-shelled eggs in its burrow and crouches on them during incubation. The anteater carries her one egg in a fold of abdominal skin warmed by her body until it hatches. The membranes of the embryo (amnion, chorion, allantois and yolk sac) are essentially like those of reptiles. The mammary glands produce the milk which the young ones lick from the skin; monotremes have no nipples.

Marsupials—Subclass 2, Marsupialia. These are mammals with a brood pouch or marsupium on the outer surface of the body, as in koalas and well known in the kangaroos (Figs. 37.6, 37.7). Most marsupials live in Australia,

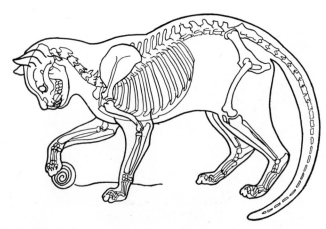

FIG. 37.4. The joints of cats allow them great flexibility and grace of movement. The turns of a cat's forefoot and leg during a face washing rivals those of a human hand and arm in the same exercise. (Courtesy, Putnam: *Animal X-Rays*. New York, G. P. Putnam's Sons, 1947.)

New Guinea and Tasmania, but not in New Zealand as might be expected. Marsupial moles (Notoryctes) and others inhabit South America; and the opossum (*Didelphis virginiana*) is well known in our southern states (Fig. 37.8). The majority of marsupials are plant feeders; originally, they probably all were; now there are carnivorous ones such as the Tasmanian wolf (Thylacinus) which has been nearly exterminated because of sheep killing.

Among the pouched mammals are mice, rats, squirrels, sloth-like "bears," koalas, bandicoots that suggest rabbits with longer tails, and kangaroos. Brood pouches are examples of convergence in evolution, the independent origin of similar functions in genetically unrelated plants and animals. The male sea horse, which is a fish with a brood pouch, and the female kangaroo, a mammal, illustrate convergence. These animals are widely different and only distantly related, yet both carry their young in pouches.

Newborn marsupials are very small and immature. The great kangaroo, *Macropus major,* is about 1 inch long when it is born and enters the pouch. There it becomes attached to one of the nipples and milk is pumped into its mouth by the contractions of muscles about the mammary gland. In this kangaroo, the development before birth lasts for only 5 or 6 weeks. There is little food in the egg and no adequate supply from the mother. After birth, the young joey is carried in the pouch for about eight months. During the last part of its stay, it leans out of the opening and sometimes crops grass as its mother grazes, often jumping out and in again, reluctant to leave its carriage.

Placental Mammals—Subclass 3, Placentalia. The members of this group include all the other mammals, the cats, elephants, polar bears, and others throughout the earth. There are about 3500 species of placental mammals in

FIG. 37.5. *Upper,* duckbill (Ornithorhynchus). A semi-aquatic egg-laying mammal, about the size of a large cat, that lives only in Eastern Australia. *Lower,* five-toed echidna or spiny anteater, also an egg layer. As adults neither duckbills nor echidnas have true teeth; the duckbill lives on worms and small mollusks; the echidna has a long beak with which it captures ants. During the period of rearing young a fold of skin forms a pouch in which the one or two eggs are incubated. After hatching, the young ones enter the pouch and from certain areas of the skin lick the milk secreted by the milk glands which are specialized sweat glands. (Courtesy, Australian News and Information Service, New York.)

FIG. 37.6. Koala, an Australian marsupial, at ease. It lives entirely in trees and its feet, the spread and separation of the toes, are adapted for clinging to branches. Koalas feed entirely on the leaves of a few species of Eucalyptus trees. Their only water supply is from the trees and their name koala is an old Australian word meaning "no drink." (Courtesy, Australian News and Information Service, New York.)

contrast to the now scarcely 150 species of marsupials. The great key to their success is the nourishment of the young before birth by means of the *placenta,* the organ formed partly on the pattern of the old reptilian allantois (Fig. 35.2). By means of the placenta, food and other needs of the growing embryo are provided for and waste products pass through it into the blood of the mother (Fig. 19.18). The young marsupial encounters the setbacks of a seedling that is transplanted midway in its early growth, but for the young placental mammal there is no transplanting.

Representative Groups of Placental Mammals

One or another of these mammals is adjusted to all the major phases of environment, air, water, and land. They can live in arctic, temperate, or tropical climates; they are fitted to manifold special niches in swamps and plains; to life in tropical forests and rocky mountain slopes—on deserts and in the ocean. An animal's diet, habitat, and general way of living are reflected particularly in the character of its locomotor appendages and in the number and

Fig. 37.7. Kangaroo (Macropus). The joey is leaning out of the pouch or marsupium. At this age the joey jumps out of the pouch, crops grass as its mother does and clambers in again. Koalas and kangaroos are the most pictured of the marsupials of Australia, but there are many other marsupials—among them pouched rats, moles, anteaters and flying opossums. They have retained characteristics that were general in mammals more than 70 million years ago. (Courtesy, Young: *The Life of The Vertebrates*. Oxford, England, The Clarendon Press, 1950.)

type of its teeth. The placental mammals are arranged in orders, the number differing slightly with the valuations given by the classifier. Groups called orders in one system may be suborders in another. The names, general habitat, and diet, are given here for the orders to which the better-known placental mammals belong.

Insectivora—Moles and Shrews (Fig. 37.9). Moles are stout-bodied burrowers with pointed noses, hardly visible eyes and ears, and a hunger for worms and insects. Their total length is five to nine inches. Shrews are the smallest of North American mammals, high strung, constantly moving, secretive, common but seldom seen, and fierce in their attacks on insects and mice. The length of various species of shrews ranges from three to six inches.

Chiroptera—The Only Flying Mammals (Fig. 37.10). The Chiroptera include the large fruit bats of the Eastern Hemisphere and small ones, that are chiefly insectivorous. The wings are formed of webs of skin and instead of being supported by a single long finger as in the wings of ancient reptiles, those of bats are supported by nearly the whole hand. Bats are skilled night flyers, avoiding all obstacles. As they fly, they constantly utter cries inaudible to the human ear. These are reflected back from objects as ultrasonic echoes that are detected by the bats (Fig. 17.8).

Rodentia—Gnawing Mammals. This large group includes the woodchucks and ground squirrels, chipmunks, squirrels, mice, rats, muskrats, porcupines,

FIG. 37.8. Opossum (*Didelphis virginiana*). A prehensile tailed marsupial about the size of a large cat, common in the southern United States. When it is born the young opossum is strikingly undeveloped and considerably smaller than the honey-bee. At birth, it immediately clambers into the pouch, similar to the more familiar one of kangaroos. It climbs by hand-over-hand movement through its mother's hair until it reaches the pouch where it remains attached to a nipple for over two months. (Courtesy, American Museum of Natural History, New York.)

Fig. 37.9. Common shrew (*Sorex vulgaris*). One of the smallest and commonest of mammals. Shrews are quick and ferocious, seldom seen although they may live in a bushy bank in the dooryard. They most nearly represent the ancestors of placental mammals. (After Flower and Lydekker. Courtesy, Rand: *The Chordates*. Philadelphia, The Blakiston Co., 1950.)

Fig. 37.10. Long-eared bat (Corynorhinus) pursues a moth. Bats are the only mammals that have attained the power to fly and according to the evidence of fossils they were flying 50 million years ago. In the wings of bats the thumb is always separate from the rest of the wing. When a bat crawls its thumb helps to hook its body along. Note the curled tail-membrane with which some bats capture their prey. (Courtesy, Hamilton: *American Mammals*. New York, McGraw-Hill Book Co., 1939.)

chinchillas, and guinea pigs. There are about 3000 species, more than in any other order of mammals. All of them feed chiefly on common plants and plant products. They have one pair of chisellike incisor teeth in each jaw, and molars but no canines. They are mainly small animals; the largest living rodent is the South American capybara, about four feet long, a semiaquatic animal that suggests an overgrown guinea pig.

Lagomorpha—Gnawing Mammals (Fig. 37.11). These rabbits, hares and pikas were formerly classified as a suborder of Rodentia. On the basis of certain structures they have now been placed in a separate order. The cutting teeth include 2 pairs of upper incisors and one pair of lower ones. Pikas are not coneys, though sometimes called so. The true coney (Procavia) of Syria and Africa, the Hyrax and others, resemble guinea pigs with hooflike nails and belong to the Order Hydracoidea.

Xenarthra (old name Edentata). Xenarthra meaning strange joints applies to peculiar articulations of certain vertebrae. The order includes the tree sloths, armadillos, and South American anteaters (Fig. 5.3).

Carnivora (Figs. 37.12, 37.13). Dogs, wolves, foxes, raccoons, the Asiatic pandas, weasels, minks, skunks, otters, mongooses, hyenas, cats, lynxes, lions, tigers, and panthers are all carnivores. Aside from their strong upper and lower canine teeth, the carnivores are not peculiarly specialized. The brain is well developed. A suborder includes the marine carnivores—sea lions, seals

Fig. 37.11. Pika (Ochotona). A little tailless rabbit, but 7 inches long and 3 inches at shoulder height. It lives in rock piles at high elevations in western North America. Its high squeak is familiar about Lake Louise, Yosemite and other mountain parks. (Courtesy, Seton: *Lives of Game Animals.* Garden City, Doubleday, Doran and Co., 1929.)

and walruses. When a sea lion is hungry it sinks to the sea bottom, usually in the shallows, stands on its head and grubs up clams and sea snails with its tusks.

Perissodactyla (Fig. 37.14). Horse, ass, zebra, tapir, and rhinoceros are all perissodactyls (odd-toed). Animals in this and the next two orders have hoofs. Formerly, they were included in one order Ungulata (hoofed) but are now believed to be less closely related than their feet would suggest. All hoofed

FIG. 37.12. Mink (*Putorius vison*). The mink, about the size of a slender cat, is a crafty killer of muskrats, ducks, chickens and fishes, seldom hunting far from a lake or stream. Its fur is soft and the glistening guard hairs have long captured human eyes and pocketbooks. (Courtesy, Rand: *The Chordates*. Philadelphia, The Blakiston Co., 1950.)

animals are herbivores. In members of this group, the main weight falls upon the tip of the third digit. In horses, it is the only one that touches the ground; the second and fourth are splint bones attached to it (Fig. 38.6). Tapirs have four digits (thumb lacking) on the front feet and three on the hind ones. The snout of the tapir is an example of similar ones in the elephant, proboscis monkey, and others, that show convergent evolution. Tapirs are natives of Central and South America and Malaysia.

Artiodactyla (Fig. 37.15). Pigs, peccaries, hippopotamuses, and cud-chewers such as camels, deer, giraffes, cattle, sheep and goats, chamois, and others are all even-toed. Their weight is carried by the third and fourth digits which are equally developed. The teeth are usually of the plant-feeding type.

Proboscidea. Elephants are the most highly specialized of living mammals (Fig. 37.16). With its trunk, an elephant can lift logs, delicately examine the texture of a leaf, pick up a peanut, suck up a drink of water and pour it into the mouth, or give itself a shower bath (Fig. 5.3). An elephant bears its weight on all five toes of each foot. They are bound together with connective tissue so that the sole is a large hooflike expanse. The teeth are exceptional in that one pair of upper incisors becomes the tusks and there are no canines. The development of the cheek teeth is peculiar and slow; finally, they acquire great

Fig. 37.13. Walrus (Odobenus). An arctic marine carnivore with a massive body of 2000 pounds or more, small head, ill-favored face and upper canine teeth grown into tusks 2 feet long. Above the tusks its lazy gentle disposition is apparent. It is the original model of the "walrus mustache." (Courtesy, American Museum of Natural History, New York.)

size, as much as three inches across the crown. Elephants eat large amounts of herbage but do no after-meal chewing like cattle.

Cetacea. Toothed whales, porpoises and dolphins, and whale-bone whales are all typically marine. Some are gigantic, the largest living animals. All are streamlined, fish-shaped. The skin is extremely thick, underlaid with fatty blubber, and almost or entirely hairless in the adults, but hairy in the young.

All of the toothed whales (Fig. 37.17), porpoises, and dolphins are carnivorous, having simple pointed teeth—numerous in some species, few in others. Toothed whales are the killers; the males run in schools in the Atlantic and Pacific oceans and far into the antarctic; the females are said to stay in the tropics. Dolphins are small-toothed whales, five to 14 feet long; one of them is the "killer whale," regarded as the most ferocious mammal in the sea.

The whale-bone whales feed upon the minute plants and animals that live in surface waters. The adults have no teeth. In place of them are plates of horn,

FIG. 37.14. Living relatives of the horse. *Upper,* American tapir and young; note the break of color on the young one comparable to the spots on a young robin. *Lower,* African black rhinoceros, pair and young. Like horses (zebras and asses) they are hoofed animals whose weight is borne on one hoof. (Order Perissodactyla.) According to the fossils the living tapirs have not changed in essentials since the time, at least 20 million years ago, when their ancestors resembled the small ancient horse (Eohippus). Their only special structure is the proboscis, more of a promise than an achievement. Rhinoceros history is more complex than that of tapirs and many types have perished including those that could run. (Courtesy, American Musuem of Natural History, New York.)

FIG. 37.15. *Upper,* northern white-tailed deer (*Odocoileus virginianus*) (bore-alis). Southern New England and New York through south-eastern Canada and westward. *Lower,* Virginia whitetailed deer (*Odocoileus virginianus virginianus*). From southern New Jersey to east central Florida. These are members of the Artiodactyla, the great order of even-toed hoofed mammals that includes such extremes as the pig and hippopotamus, and all the cud chewers whether oxen or gazelles. (Courtesy, Mochi and Carter: *Hoofed Mammals of The World.* New York, Charles Scribner's Sons, 1953.)

known as whale bone, that hang from the upper jaw like curtains, their fringed edges sweeping down to the floor of the mouth (Fig. 37.18). When a whale is feeding, it swims at the surface with its mouth open, collects a mouthful of the plankton-filled water, expels the water between the close set plates, and keeps the plankton.

Whales may dive 3,600 feet or more when wounded and doubtless do so at other times. When harpooned, a baleen whale can carry a line straight down for a half a mile, a depth where the pressure is half a ton—on every

FIG. 37.16. African elephants, a group in the American Museum of Natural History, New York. Mounted by Carl Akeley, one of his many examples of taxidermy as a fine art. For a fuller appreciation of the work of Akeley and that of others in the African Hall read *Frontiers of Enchantment* by W. R. Leigh (Simon & Schuster, 1938) who was with Akeley in Africa and who painted many of the backgrounds in the African Hall of the American Museum of Natural History. (Courtesy, American Museum of Natural History, New York.)

inch of its body. From such depths, it can return immediately to the surface. Yet it shows no symptoms of the accumulation of nitrogen bubbles in the veins which afflicts human divers who rise too quickly to the surface. Whales can stay submerged an hour or more though they usually stay down only a fraction of this time. They have varied equipments for this; one is the quality of the hemoglobin of their blood which has a long hold on oxygen. The spout-

FIG. 37.17. Sperm whale or cachelot (*Physeter macrocephalus*). The head is a third the length of the body which is about 65 feet. There are sharp clutching teeth on the lower jaw but none on the upper. A great cavity in the expanded snout holds about a ton of the highly valued oil from which vitamins are extracted for use in margarine. Moby Dick was a sperm whale. (Courtesy, Rand: *The Chordates*. Philadelphia, The Blakiston Co., 1950.)

FIG. 37.18. Jaws of whale-bone whale. Its food of minute animals and plants is caught on the horny plates, called whale bone. (Courtesy, American Museum of Natural History, New York.)

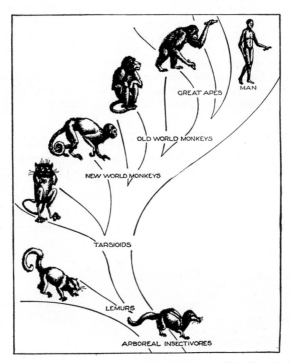

FIG. 37.19. A simplified family tree of the primates. (Reprinted from *Man and the Vertebrates* by A. S. Romer by permission of The University of Chicago Press. Copyright 1941.)

ing of whales is the expiration of warm air from the lungs condensed by the coolness of the surface water.

Primates. Lemurs, monkeys, apes and man are all primates (Figs. 37.19, 37.20, 37.21, 37.22, 37.23). Primates take hold of things with their hands. Their coordination of eyes and hands is one of their basic characteristics. The remote ancestors of man lived in trees, constantly climbing, gripping a branch, aiming at another branch and leaping to it, repeatedly catching a swinging vine and balancing upon it. They required an effectual combination of eye, hand, and brain work. Those tree dwellers were trapeze performers with mobile forelimbs that reached and stable hind ones that pushed. As the ages passed some, probably the smaller ones, tree shrews, lemurs, monkeys, and others remained in the trees; larger ones took to the ground. Among the latter were the ancestors of the manlike apes, and after untold generations of them there were prehistoric human beings.

FIG. 37.20. *Left,* lemur (Galago) and *right,* Tarsius—two members of the Order Primates which includes mankind. All primates have four generalized limbs each with five digits bearing nails. Lemurs are the most primitive of primates, small nocturnal animals that live in trees especially in Madagascar; some are as small as a mouse, others as large as a cat. Their right to belong in the primates is in the shortening of the jaws and greater size of the brain. Tarsius shows signs of relation to the higher primates, most of them associated with its arboreal life. Like those of many nocturnal animals its eyes are very large. They are turned completely forward as in the human face and close to the nose. Like other tree dwellers the capacity of the eyes has increased, that of the nose decreased. The upper lip is uncut and its shape suggests that of monkeys and man. (*Left,* courtesy, American Museum of Natural History, New York. *Right,* after Vogt and Specht. Courtesy, Rand: *The Chordates.* Philadelphia, The Blakiston Co., 1950.)

Fig. 37.21 *Center,* the gibbon is the smallest (about three feet tall) of the four manlike apes—gibbon, orangutan, gorilla and chimpanzee. The orang (*top*) has a small opposable thumb suggesting the human hand and hand-like feet. A large male gorilla (*left*) weighs about 600 pounds. *Right,* a young chimpanzee. (Courtesy, Museum of Comparative Zoology, Harvard University.)

Prehistoric Man

Although mankind must have appeared much earlier, its history recorded by fossils and other remains begins with the "ice age" or Pleistocene Epoch (Table 38.1).

The Ice Age was a time of many changes; lands were lifted from the sea; mountains were made; climates were changed; whole populations of plants and animals were moved, many of them destroyed and new ones formed. Four ice sheets spread over the northern lands and each time melted back. The time since the last ice sheet is called post glacial or recent. According to some theories of glacial origins, ice will be back again in about 50,000 years. The dawning humanity shared in the changes of the Ice Age. Some were isolated and subjected to special changes; others came together and interbred; many must have emigrated toward the south. Human populations increased and became diverse. They mixed and separated and mixed again as they have ever since.

The characteristics of prehistoric man have been reconstructed from the usually fragmentary remains which have been discovered, chiefly in Asia and Europe. New finds are still being made from time to time. At present the prehistoric record of human ancestry rests mainly upon the following types all extinct.

Java Ape Man—*Pithecanthropus erectus.* Several bones have been found in Java from earth of the Pleistocene Epoch about one million years ago (Table 38.1). In 1940, a skull was discovered. The Java man probably stood erect,

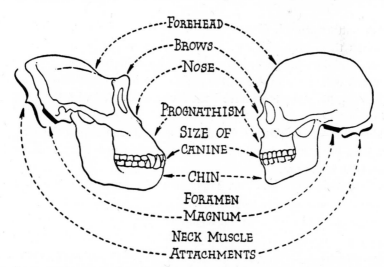

FIG. 37.22. Skull of gorilla showing generalized anthropoid ape characters contrasted with skull of man showing specialized ones. The prognathism, i.e., the protrusion of the jaws, is strikingly greater in the ape. (Courtesy, Howells: *Mankind So Far.* New York, Doubleday and Co., 1952.

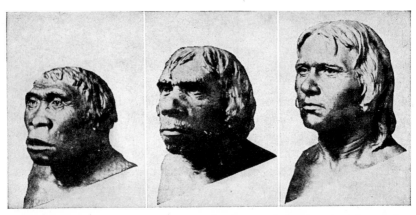

FIG. 37.23. Concepts of the possible appearance of three ancient types of man calculated from fossil remains. Hair and flesh have been added. *Left,* the "erect ape man" or *Pithecanthropus erectus* whose remains were first found in Java, from deposits by some estimates said to be about 500,000 years old. From other such bones it is believed that *erectus* stood erect not with an apelike droop. *Center,* Neanderthal man, *Homo neanderthalensis* was the first fossil type of man discovered and is still the best known of the *sub-human* types. The first such fossil was found in western Germany, in the Neander Valley. Since then more complete remains of this race have been found at various places in Europe and the skeleton is almost completely known. *Right,* Cro-Magnons, *Homo sapiens.* The Cro-Magnon race may have been established by 40,000 B.C. and persisted until perhaps 13,000 years B.C. The name Cro-Magnon is from that of the French rock shelter where a typical example of the race was found. Cro-Magnon artists wrought paintings and carvings upon the walls of caves that are vivid and life-like after these thousands of years. (Restorations by Dr. J. H. McGregor.)

but with outthrust head. Comparison of the skulls of a gorilla and the Java man shows them both chinless, the brow-ridge of the man lower, and the front teeth smaller though tusklike compared with those of modern man. The brain cavity is larger than that of the gorilla, but is only two-thirds that of any modern man. No stone tools have been found associated with the Java man's remains.

Peking Man—*Sinanthropus.* Teeth and several crania from the Pleistocene Epoch have been dug up and with them were numerous stone tools and evidences of the use of fire.

Piltdown Man—*Eoanthropus.* Fragments of a cranium, a jaw, and a few teeth were discovered near Piltdown, in Sussex, England, in 1908. The forehead is upright, and the brow-ridge slight. The upper part of the face is human, the lower part apelike. Tools of chipped flint were discovered in the vicinity.

For several years curiosity, and respectful study were excited by the remains. Authorities in paleontology wrote about it. Suspicions of its genuineness finally developed. In 1953 a new examination proved the jaw to be that of a modern chimpanzee and the worn surfaces of the teeth due to modern scraping. *The Piltdown Man* was changed to *The Piltdown Fraud*. The guilty party has not been discovered.

Heidelberg Man—*Homo heidelbergensis*. The remains consist of one complete lower jaw with teeth. Evidently the jaw muscles were powerful.

Neanderthal Man—*Homo neanderthalensis*. Bones of nearly 100 individuals come from various localities in Europe but the type is described from those found in the Neanderthal Valley in Germany (Fig. 37.23). The impressions of the convolutions of the brain on the interior of the cranium are simpler than in modern man. Skeletons found on the floors of caves along with tools and weapons of chipped stone are estimated to be about 100,000 years old.

Rhodesian Man—*Homo rhodesiensis*. The species is known only from a cranium in a cave in Rhodesia, South Africa. The teeth are distinctly human.

Cro-Magnon Man—*Homo sapiens fossilis*. Nearly complete skeletons have been found in southwestern Europe, along with stone implements, sculpture, and paintings of wild animals in the famous caves of France and Spain (Fig. 37.24). Cro-Magnon paintings are startlingly realistic, especially in the effects of motion and hunting with stone points and bows. The estimated date of Cro-Magnons is about 60,000 B.C.

Modern Man—*Homo sapiens* (*Wise Man*). All members of the human population of the earth belong to a single species. There are no significant structural differences between them and all interbreed. Without regard for culture, they are estimated to show 99.44 per cent of likeness and 0.56 of difference. *Homo sapiens* is the only surviving species of those which laid the way for its development, those that made the tools and weapons that are experiences of mind preserved in stone and later in metal. These were passed on from one generation to another and tied the past to the present. Time went on and more tools were made; speech developed; and pictures were painted in the caves. All of these contributed to continuity of ideas. Gradually, the species *Homo sapiens* came into being, unique upon the earth, perhaps anywhere.

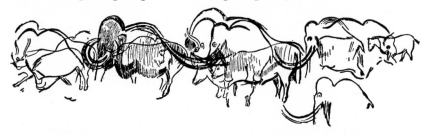

FIG. 37.24. Paintings made by prehistoric man in the Cavern of Font-de-Gaume in the Dordogne region of southwestern France. On the sides and ceiling of a smooth-walled cave the artists engraved and painted in black, red and brown, figures of more than 80 animals. In this cave paintings are made over one another and the earliest are the crudest. The work was probably done from memory by the light of a torch or a grease lamp. (After Breuil. Courtesy, Cleland: *Our Prehistoric Ancestors*. New York, Coward McCann, 1928.)

Part VI

Evolution and Conservation

38

Organic Evolution—Conservation

Organic Evolution

The basic resemblance of living things comes from their common origins and countless kinships. Their extraordinary complexity and variety are due to changes in them that have taken place during past ages and are continuing. Living matter is known only as it appears in different species of organisms. A species is a group of nearly related plants or animals that agree in certain distinguishing characteristics. They interbreed freely and their characteristics are inherited by their offspring. Species are inheritable patterns of life, repeated in generation after generation, though never exactly. They are patterns and processes that require time to become established. No species of bird came into being in a moment. Organic evolution is history.

ORIGIN OF LIFE

We do not know how life began. Neither do we yet know what keeps it going.

It is certain that the novelty of living matter is in the way it is put together, its organization, not the materials. Not one of these is unique (Chap. 3). The beginning of life might have been in the organization of a complex molecule containing carbon, and perhaps capable of affecting other molecules. The changes from the organization of such a molecule to that of the simplest protozoan would be greater than those between a protozoan and man.

BEGINNINGS OF LIFE

We do not know when life began. Measurements of the radioactivity of certain minerals have placed the age of rocks containing them at two billion years (Fig. 38.1; Table 38.1), and there is evidence that these rocks are by no means the youngest. A billion years and more may have passed before they

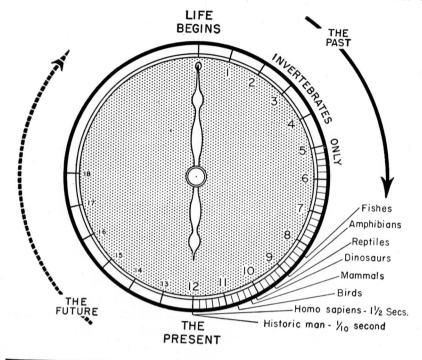

LIFE CLOCK   ONE HOUR = 100,000,000 YEARS
ONE MINUTE = 1,660,000 YEARS

If life's past, present and future are plotted on a 24-hour
clock, modern man appeared in the world about 1½ seconds ago.

FIG. 38.1. Life clock scaled to 12 hours showing the first appearance of various vertebrates in the history of life on the earth. Only invertebrates existed in the earlier three-fourths of the 12-hour day which represents time from the beginning of life to the present. New estimates (1954) of the age of the earth place its beginning at 5,000,000,000 years and the beginning of life at 3,500,000 to 4,000,000 years. (Redrawn after Ritchie, *New York Times,* Sept. 29, 1940.)

existed. There are no fossils of the first soft bits of living matter whose development must have taken eons of time. The oldest fossils are those of simple water plants that are more than one billion years old. After they appeared there seems to have been a tremendously long period before living organisms were numerous and varied enough to leave a continuous fossil record.

Evolution is an unimaginably long process that includes periods of profound geologic change. In some of these, the currents of life seem to have moved more rapidly; in others, they flowed slowly and evolutionary changes were slight. Fossils in the Cambrian Period mark the beginning of an upswing of change (Table 38.1).

The earth's past history has been divided into eras according to the evo-

Table 38.1

THE TIME SCALE OF EARTH HISTORY AND OF LIFE

Millions of Years Since Beginning	Eras	Periods	Epochs	Some Features of the Life Record
.025	Cenozoic	Quaternary	Recent	Man
1			Pleistocene	
12		Tertiary	Pliocene	Mammals and birds numerous
28			Miocene	
39			Oligocene	
58			Eocene	
75			Paleocene	
135	Mesozoic	Cretaceous		Flowering Plants
165		Jurassic	(Epoch divisions not necessary for present purposes)	Birds arise
205		Triassic		Mammals arise
230	Paleozoic	Permian		Reptiles numerous
255		Pennsylvanian		Archaic coal forests
280		Mississippian		Bony fishes numerous
325		Devonian		Crisis in marine life
360		Silurian		Aquatic vertebrates numerous, rise of true fishes, rise of land animals and plants
425		Ordovician		First vertebrates
505		Cambrian (Period divisions not well established)		All basic types of aquatic animals appear — First abundant fossils
2000	Pre-cambrian			Fossils few and obscure — Origin of life (not recorded)
?	(Unknown ages, before formation of rocks now exposed in crust of the earth)			

Courtesy, G. G. Simpson, *The Meaning of Evolution*, New Haven, Conn., Yale University Press, 1950.

lutionary advancement of life, such as Pre-cambrian, Paleozoic (primitive life), Mesozoic (intermediate life), and Cenozoic (modern life); even the Cenozoic Era extends back millions of years. The eras are divided into periods or epochs named for the locality where the rocks formed in that period were found or are best developed. Thus Cambrian, Ordovician, Silurian, and Devonian take their names from ancient inhabitants of England or Wales. Jurassic refers to the Jura Mountains in Switzerland and Cretaceous to the chalk deposits in western Europe. The limits of all these eras, periods, and so on are due to changes of conditions especially of climate caused by that profound shifting of the earth's crust that gave rise to mountains, moved the lines between sea and land, and caused destruction or changes in the inhabitants.

INCREASE OF LIFE

From its beginning, life increased. It began spreading over the earth and has never stopped. There were animals in the sea during the Cambrian Period but none on land or in the air. Now, through great expanses of the earth every handful of soil is alive with organisms, microscopic or otherwise; the tropics and all summer airs resound with songs of birds and the hum of insects. The history of plants and animals is the story of increase, and the invasion and filling of habitable space (Fig. 38.2). New occupants opened as well as closed the way to others. Wherever plants grew on land the plant-eating animals followed, and where the plant eaters were the carnivores came and preyed upon them. Little animals lived in the spaces between large ones. Insignificantly small mammals hid among the giant dinosaurs of the Late Reptilian Age. Long time residents of the water, such as the protozoans, moved into the pools where the newly come large animals fed and lounged. Certain of the protozoans moved into the larger animals and finally became parasites. Animals took the places left by other animals through desertion or death. As mammals overspread the earth, porpoises and dolphins took possession of the seas in which the great swimming reptiles (ichthyosaurs) had lived before them. Replacements were not exact for environments changed.

All living plants and animals have behind them unbroken streams of life that come from beginnings which we may surmise but do not know.

THE ENVIRONMENT AND THE ORGANISM

Adaptations. An adaptive structure or characteristic of an organism is one that is useful to it under the conditions in which it lives. Two mechanisms by which adaptations become established are inheritance and natural selection or the selective action by the environment. This question of how living things come to be the way they are is far from answered although many facts are known. Adaptation is characteristic of all living organisms and is one of the key puzzles of nature.

Fig. 38.2. The gradual clambering on to the land, a restoration of early amphibians (labyrinthodonts) of ancient Carboniferous times, the period of coal deposits. The history of plants and animals is the story of increase, and the invasion and filling of habitable space. Painting by F. L. Jaques. (Courtesy, American Museum of Natural History, New York.)

CONDITIONS AND VARIETIES OF ADAPTATIONS. Adaptations of one kind shut out others. Australian koalas ("teddy bears") live where eucalyptus trees are abundant and they are adapted to a pure diet of their leaves. They cannot live on anything else. Birds use their bills and feet to manipulate their food but those that are highly efficient tools for one skill are worthless for some other —the beak and talons of a hawk are poor seed pickers (Fig. 36.7).

An anteater that can poke its snout into an anthill and collect a dozen ants on its sticky tongue could scarcely use it to catch a grasshopper (Fig. 5.3). Such a particular tool is overspecialized, on a byroad, even a dead end. It allows its owner only one very particular kind of food. An anteater must have ants or starve. The zigzag course of evolution is full of byroads and pockets of adjustments so perfectly special that they come to a standstill in their perfection. Among them are the sponges with their elaboration of water tubes and the starfishes with their structures locked to the number five.

ADAPTATIONS OF PARTICULAR STRUCTURES IN DIFFERENT SPECIES. The fore limbs of vertebrates show striking and varied adjustments to use in each of the three basic environments—water, air and land. The relation of the bones

DEVELOPMENT OF FLIPPER

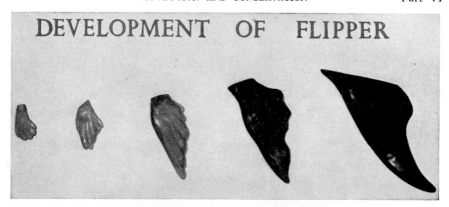

FIG. 38.3. Models of the developing left front flipper of a whale. Note the five digits in the first stage shown, more like a paw or hand than a flipper. In their earlier development the limbs of whales are strikingly like those of their ancestors, the land mammals. Later they become the flippers whose shape is adjusted to swimming. Within the flipper, however, the bones are similar in location and relationship to those of the ancestors of whales that lived on land. (Courtesy, British Museum, South Kensington, London, England.)

to one another is essentially the same, that is, the parts are homologous in spite of their striking differences in form and function (Fig. 38.3). The basic fore limb of land vertebrates is five-toed and adapted for walking. It has undergone great changes in different environments and yet has kept a basic plan (Figs. 38.4, 38.5). It may be close to the type, five-toed and soft padded, the silent walking foot of cats; or farther from the type, the single tiptoe running foot of horses (Fig. 38.6); the five-fingered grasping hand of man; the wing of a bird with thumb and first two fingers corresponding to the human hand; the bat's wing supported by four long fingers; and the fleshy flipper of whales and seals (Fig. 38.3). Wings have developed three times during the evolution of vertebrates—in the ancient flying reptiles, in birds, and in bats. They are examples of convergent evolution in the air. The structure arose from the same ancestral stock and retained the same ground plan but differed in expression. In other cases, a water environment offered an opportunity for adaptation in three different classes of animals (Fig. 38.4).

RACIAL LONG LIFE. Long ago certain animals reached an almost perfect state of adaptation to environments in which there have been no essential changes. These animals have been unstirred to further evolution. For generation after generation, through millions of years, they have scarcely changed. Among these museum pieces of antiquity are the little reptile Sphenodon (Fig. 35.4) which closely resembles the fossils of its ancestors of the Jurassic Period (Table 38.1), the opossum, the "living fossil" Lingula (Fig. 27.15) so like its brachiopod ancestors that are known from their fossil remains of 400 million years ago, and the common edible oysters very like their ancestors of

Fig. 38.4. Convergent evolution (*upper*) by a fish, the shark; (*center*) by a reptile (ancient Icthyosaurus); (*bottom*) and a mammal, the dolphin. They all live or did live in the sea and all are fish-shaped although only distantly related. (Courtesy, Moody: *Introduction to Evolution*. New York, Harper & Bros., 1953.)

more than 200 million years ago. Certain of these ancient animals had offspring that started side lines of descent. Some of these prospered and others disappeared. Those in the main lines lived on in uneventful safety as we see them now.

Nonadaptive Trends. These are tendencies for certain characteristics to keep developing until they become useless or dangerous. Great increase in size is one of these. Growth with increase in size is universal in living organisms. It usually reaches a slightly variable limit evidently an adaptation for the plant or animal and this is repeated generation after generation. We think of a mouse of one size, a horse of another. In contrast to this was the size of the dinosaurs, with Brontosaurus, 75 feet long, hazardous especially for land animals. There were other causes for their extinction, but giantism must have been an important one. The heavy, multibranched antlers of deer are claimed as nonadaptive features. In connection with adaptation, as with nonadaptation, it is realized that many structures are useless when they begin to develop and are not large enough to be selected by the environment till long afterward. In "The Origin of Species" Darwin pointed out that nonadaptation was an unexplained difficulty in the working of natural selection in evolution.

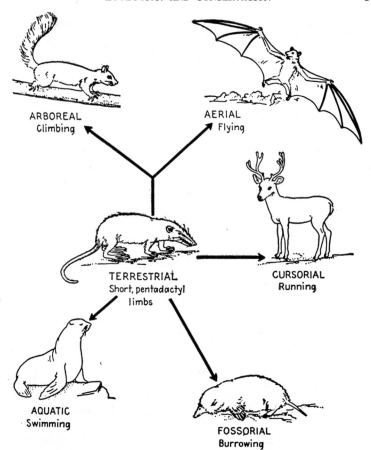

FIG. 38.5. The structure of the limbs of mammals that live in different environments. At the center is a primitive 5-toed terrestrial mammal. The other figures show other mammals related to the central one but adjusted to particular environments and ways of living in them. This is called *adaptive radiation*. (Courtesy, Moody: *Introduction to Evolution*. New York, Harper & Bros., 1953.)

HEREDITY—A FORCE IN EVOLUTION

Heredity produces both unity and diversity. It maintains old fundamental structures and activities and it establishes the new features known as mutations that partly account for the entrancing variety of nature.

Inheritance of Ancestral Pattern in Embryos. Except in some special types of reproduction, every multicellular animal begins life as one cell, a fertilized egg which divides into two cells, and goes on according to the course of its ancestors. The embryos of various invertebrates show striking similarities, maintained by inheritance and expressive of kinship. Those of various groups of animals are figured and described in Part 5, Evolution of Animals. Inheritance of ancestral pattern in embryos includes only the oldest and most fundamental structures. In the vertebrates, these are the notochord, the ver-

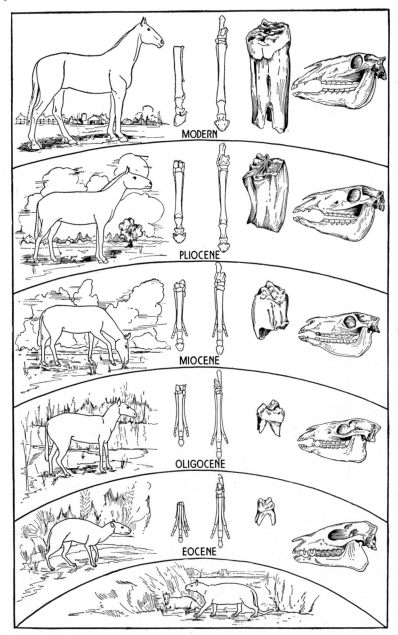

MODERN

PLIOCENE

MIOCENE

OLIGOCENE

EOCENE

FIG. 38.6. Evolution of the horse. Within each section from left to right the drawings show: a reconstruction of an ancestor of the horse in the surroundings in which it is believed to have lived; fossil remains of the animal's fore and hind feet displaying the progressive reduction in the lateral digits; one of the molar teeth and the skull. Only the teeth are drawn to scale. The oldest horse (eohippus) in the bottom section, was about the size of a fox terrier (12 inches tall). (Courtesy, Rogers, Hubbell, and Byers: *Man and the Biological World,* ed. 2. New York, McGraw-Hill Book Co., 1952.)

tebrae, gill slits, aortic arches, and two-chambered heart that exist for different lengths of time.

The top line of drawings in figure 38.7 shows young embryos with fundamental structures that are common to all vertebrates—a striking presentation of similarities. Figures in the next line show that the body form of the fish is not shared by the cow. Finally, in each of the oldest embryos there are one or more structures that are unique, the shell of the turtle, wing of the bird, snout of the pig, and the domed head of man. Unity is apparent in the younger embryos. Diversity is striking in the older ones.

Vestigial Organs. These are small, useless vestiges of structures that may be well-developed and functional in near kin and ancestors of their owners. They are maintained by heredity and the conservatism of living matter—treasured clocks that have stopped ticking. The human body has a collection of several dozen such structures. Among them are the ear muscles so feeble in man, so active in horses; the vermiform appendix, a nuisance in man, a digestive caecum in rabbits; and the nictitating membrane, a little fold of flesh in the inner angle of the human eye, a protective membrane that may instantly slip over the eye of a bird.

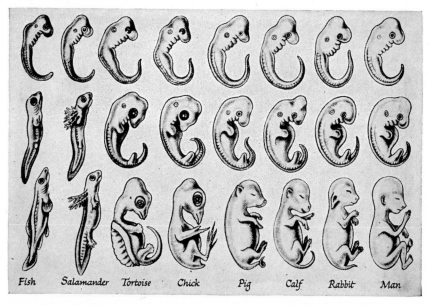

Fish   Salamander   Tortoise   Chick   Pig   Calf   Rabbit   Man

FIG. 38.7. Vertebrate embryos showing the inheritance of a unified basic plan followed by diverse structure which easily identify the animals. Embryos in three successive and comparable stages of development. *Upper row,* all are in general much alike. *Middle,* lower vertebrates, fish and salamander show differences sooner than mammals, pig to man. *Bottom,* all types are recognizable. These figures originally after Haeckel lack detail and certain points of accuracy but they excel in emphasizing essential agreements and ultimate differences. (Courtesy, Pauli: *The World of Life.* Boston, Houghton Mifflin Co., 1949.)

Mutations. Evolutionary changes consist of changes in heredity. Mutations are probably pre-eminent among them. They are sudden inheritable characteristics caused by changes in genes, the chemical units of the chromosomes. Mutations are discussed elsewhere (Chap. 20). This note is given here in view of their place in evolution. Probably all genes mutate at some time; some of them much oftener than others. Their frequency may be changed experimentally, and also in nature, by heat, radiation, and other influences. Mutations differ in extent; they may be "large," those having the greatest effect on the animal, such as brittle bones in man, or they may be "small" such as narrow nostrils in man. The effects of mutations of the genes have no evident relationship to the adaptation of the animal. They appear to be random changes. This is true of experimental mutations; those caused by applications of heat have no relation to adaptation to the temperature of the environment. For an animal that is not well adapted to its life in a certain place, some random mutation, however, might be the very one that would improve matters.

Evolution and the Kinships of Animals and Man

By many evidences, it is clear that all protoplasm has the same basic organization, and that all living things that exist or have existed are related including man.

Humanity is bound to other animals by many and deep kinships. Nevertheless man is unique among all animals, in flexibility of behavior, in control of the environment, in social organization, in degree of reasoning power, and in other qualities of mind and its expression.

Humanity is unique in having two inheritances that are highly different, yet blend on their borders. One of them is concerned with organic evolution, with features such as the build and grip of the hand, the size and activity of the brain. The other is a newer kind of social evolution built on cultures passed on by legends and records even through long lapses of time (Fig. 38.8). Past experiences are preserved, available for help and warning. The records of them have accumulated greatly and constitute a complex story of ups and downs of human thought and deed. Human beings alone are aware of their own evolution and their possible ability to direct it. In order to do so, they must use their double inheritance especially that of experience in which at sometime ethics appeared.

Separate Creations

The first time a puppy sees a strange animal in the grass he shies back. Then, curiosity overcomes him and he goes closer. From earliest times, human beings have been afraid of things. But, as with the puppy curiosity has prevailed; mankind has drawn closer, inquired and tried to explain.

In the sixth, fifth, and fourth centuries B.C., Aristotle and other Greek

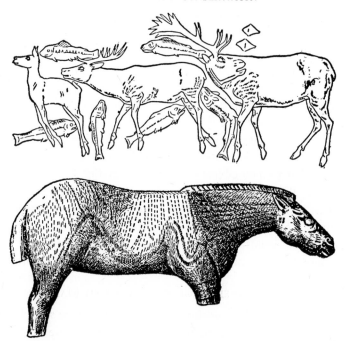

FIG. 38.8. Cro-Magnon art. *Upper,* a partial restoration of what has been termed
"the earliest picture in the world because it is a composition" (After Lankester).
It is an engraving on the antler of a deer representing a group of deer advancing.
The largest stag looks backward, his mouth open and "blowing." *Lower,* figure of
a wild horse carved in ivory from Lourdes, France. The relatively abundant skeletal remains of the Cro-Magnons indicate that they may belong to our own species
Homo sapiens. They lived in Europe perhaps as early as 40,000 B.C. and their
culture seems to have persisted until about 13,000 B.C. The name Cro-Magnon
is that of a French rock shelter where several of their remains were found. (Courtesy, Cleland: *Our Prehistoric Ancestors.* New York, Coward McCann, 1928.)

philosophers described animals and set them in a progression from imperfect
to perfect—a procession with one behind the other and few questions asked.
There was little or no meddling into the relationships between them.

Arrangements of animals according to perfection and separateness became
fixed in general thinking. For 15 centuries and more of the Christian era,
special creation, the separateness of different kinds of animals, was held essential to Christian belief. It pleaded for unity on the one hand and supported
separateness on the other. Toward the end of this long era, there were now
and then signs of a change.

FROM SEPARATENESS TO RELATIONSHIP

The first general theory of evolution (1809) was that of Jean Lamarck
(1744–1829), a French zoologist. Its basic plan was the sequence of living
organisms from less to greater perfection. This had been held long before

Lamarck, but not as an evolution which he proposed for the first time and for which he deserves great credit. He observed that the progress toward perfection in no wise followed a straight line, but was uneven and branched. He held that the results of use or disuse of a structure, an arm or an eye, would be inherited by the offspring and succeeding generations. This easy entrance of recent change was emphasized and the theory became known as that of acquired characters. By thousands of experiments and histories of succeeding generations it has since been shown that acquired characters are not inherited, at least in any such way as Lamarck maintained. The tails of horses may be docked for generations but the tails of their descendants still grow long. Lamarck's theory fell into disrepute because of its mistaken explanation. Notwithstanding this it drew attention to adaptation, exemplified by the honeybee that fits the flower. Such adaptation was the same material to which Darwin later applied natural selection.

FRANKLIN AND MALTHUS

Roughly within the span of Lamarck's lifetime, many another person was thinking about the multiplicity of plants and animals and the great numbers in human populations. There is room to mention only two of them, Franklin and Malthus. In view of the great increase in the population of the American Colonies, Benjamin Franklin (1706–1790) concluded (1751) that there is no bound to the prolific nature of plants and animals except that which is caused by crowding and competition for food. A similar principle was upheld by Thomas Malthus in his Essay on Population (1798). Unless humanity restricts its own rate of increase, war and hunger will do it. Malthus had been an Anglican priest and when the essay was written he was teaching political economy in Great Britain. He foresaw the disapproval that his book would excite. But time never allowed him to know the constructive interest which it was to kindle in the mind of Charles Darwin nor the important steppingstone that it would be for the Theory of Natural Selection.

CHARLES DARWIN

Charles Darwin (1809–1882) proposed the most adequate and influential theory of organic evolution which has ever been stated. His materials were plants and animals growing in their natural surroundings in various countries and climates. His tools were keen observation and sound reasoning. His unlimited use of these was his genius.

Darwin's school education led him into changes in professional training, and from his own testimony into a waste of time in taking courses, including preparation for medicine. He was an independent observer and thinker in his chosen field of natural history. It was through this that he became friends with some of the great scholars of Cambridge University, especially Professor J. S.

Henslow whose encouragement of Darwin was lifelong. In the British scheme of education, students have always been expected to learn and think for themselves. Darwin was happy in doing this.

What he termed "the most important event of my life" began in the autumn of 1831, a few months after he was graduated from Cambridge University, at 22 years of age. In his student days, he had called himself a naturalist (the old name for ecologist). He now became the official naturalist on the five-year voyage of "the Beagle" (1831–1836) (Fig. 38.9). This was to be an expedition to learn of the plants and animals of South America, its coastal waters and the famous Galapagos Islands, and to visit Africa, Australia and New Zealand. There Darwin saw and lived with plants and animals in their own homes. He felt the urge and press of tropical abundance. In the rain forests, he saw crowded plants reaching for light, heard the deafening hum and clatter of myriads of insects, and on the coral reefs he walked over packed coral animals in numbers beyond thinking. He had already learned to observe and think. He kept voluminous notes of what he had seen and of what he had thought.

FIG. 38.9. Charles Darwin in his thirty-first year, 1840. From a water color by George Richmond, R.A. On October 2, 1836 Darwin had returned to England after his five-year voyage on "the Beagle" which was the making of the Charles Darwin that the world was to know. Between 1836 and 1840 ideas about the multiplicity of kinds of life were coming into his mind. They persisted and in the *Origin of Species* (1859) brought to the world the fact that human beings are fellow voyagers with other animals in the great kinship of evolution. (Courtesy, West: *Charles Darwin, A Portrait.* New Haven, Yale University Press, 1938.)

Back in England, in London for a time, and later living in nearby Down, he pondered upon the plants and animals that grew crowded together. He also read the essay in which Malthus told of the human populations that became too large for the space available to them (1838). This suggested a plan. Some organisms must be winnowed out by their natural surroundings; thus, others would be benefited. There would be a natural selection.

In 1844, Darwin wrote a summary of his theory but continued to gather facts from his own observations and those of others. In the meanwhile, Alfred R. Wallace (1823–1913), another English naturalist, arrived independently at conclusions similar to those of Darwin. He had reached his conclusion also after an exploring trip through the tropics. By mutual agreement and especially through the desire of Darwin, the respective views of Darwin and Wallace were read to the Linnaean Society, in London, on June 30th, 1858. Wallace shared with Darwin the credit of propounding the theory of natural selection and there was sincere friendliness between the two naturalists. Now, Darwin has become famous throughout the world for a theory supported by thousands of observations and years of study. And now, Wallace is relatively little known for a conclusion which he arrived at honestly, independently and quickly, but with little critical treatment and relatively few examples for proof.

Changes Preserved by Selection. The Origin of Species by Natural Selection, or the Preservation of Favoured Races in the Struggle of Life, by Charles Darwin was published in 1859. It is regarded as the most widely influential book of the nineteenth century and the leading classic in biology. Its effect upon sciences and society in general was due to the vital nature of the theory and no less to the convincing presentation of facts supporting it. The following summary contains the essence of the theory.

1. Variations occur in individuals and species.

2. The numbers of every species tend to become enormously large, yet the population of each remains nearly constant because of the effects of climate, competition of other organisms, and other factors that eliminate many individuals.

3. This involves a struggle for existence. During this struggle, individuals in which variations are favorable continue to live and produce their kind whereas those having variations that are unsuitable in nature are eliminated.

4. A process of selection by the environment or natural selection operates.

5. There is a natural preservation of those that fit into a certain niche in nature, a survival of the fittest.

Within a year after "The Origin of Species" was published Darwin admitted that it would have been better to use "natural preservation" as a key phrase for the theory.

The majority of biologists accept Darwin's theory as the most adequate statement of evolution. Disagreements with it have been based upon the better understanding of processes that have been investigated since Darwin's time, especially inheritance. Darwin himself was aware of the gaps in knowledge and very wisely pointed them out. One of the finest results of his theory has been the investigation it has set in action. Among the results is the clearer understanding of heritable changes and the ways by which they are passed on from one generation to another. These are discussed in "The Physical Basis of Heredity" (Chap. 20) under "Changes in the Genes—Mutations" and other topics. Now it is known that mutations (changes) occur in genes (the physical units of heredity), and that the chromosomes which contain them may be rearranged. This alters the assortment of genes and hence the characteristics that are passed on to further generations. Darwin knew nothing of all this but he suspected that there was much to be discovered.

Conservation

Humanity is facing two very old problems, living with itself and living with its natural surroundings. Conservation is one way of working out these problems, an appreciation and intelligent care of living things and their environments. It is applied Ecology (Fig. 38.10).

Conservation brings many rewards. The rarest of them is the interest and enjoyment of unspoiled landscapes and the plants and animals growing in their natural places and in relationships, made right by ages of trial. Humanity created civilization out of the wilderness. Now that the wilderness is almost gone, we are beginning to be lonesome for it. We shall keep a refuge for our minds if we conserve the remnants. Psychologists suspect this; fishermen know it.

Writers and speakers discuss food and distribution of food. They discuss the present extraordinary rise of population and ways in which larger populations shall be fed. They calculate the space that may be necessary to raise more wheat and cattle. They do not give enough thought to the quality and quantity of space for human beings, spaces to whet their curiosity and adventure, to show them natural beauty, to give them places that are far from crowds. Conservation must guard the open spaces. A full stomach is not a cure-all.

The results of conservation that are best known are concerned with the care and economy of natural resources that are vital to communities, and to agriculture and industries. An awareness of the importance of saving the grass roots is increasing; fortunately one of its byproducts is the saving of minds.

NATURAL RESOURCES

Natural resources are everything in nature that is used to sustain life. Those called nonrenewable resources include metals, petroleum, gas, and coal, and the energy of the sun, abundant beyond imagination. It has taken ages to produce them and, except for atomic energy, substitutes in any practicable amounts are not available. The program of conservation for such material is:

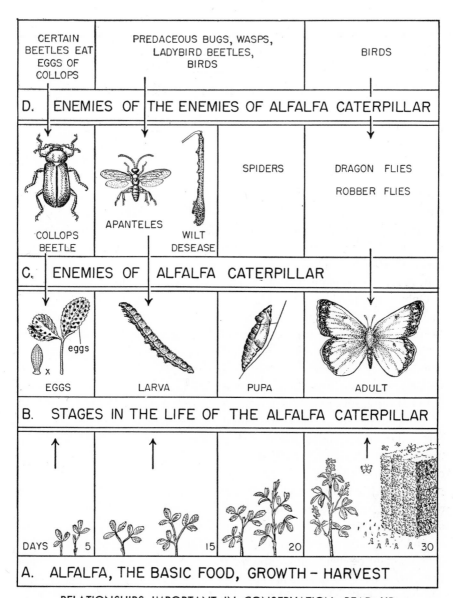

| CERTAIN BEETLES EAT EGGS OF COLLOPS | PREDACEOUS BUGS, WASPS, LADYBIRD BEETLES, BIRDS | BIRDS |

D. ENEMIES OF THE ENEMIES OF ALFALFA CATERPILLAR

COLLOPS BEETLE   APANTELES   WILT DESEASE   SPIDERS   DRAGON FLIES   ROBBER FLIES

C. ENEMIES OF ALFALFA CATERPILLAR

eggs   x   EGGS   LARVA   PUPA   ADULT

B. STAGES IN THE LIFE OF THE ALFALFA CATERPILLAR

DAYS 5   15   20   30

A. ALFALFA, THE BASIC FOOD, GROWTH – HARVEST

RELATIONSHIPS IMPORTANT IN CONSERVATION. READ UP

Fig. 38.10. The relationships of alfalfa plants and the various animals associated with them are an example of the natural control of populations. Change in one population brings changes in others. Knowledge of such relationships is essential for **conservation.** *A,* in favorable climates the widely cultivated clover-like alfalfa grows to full size in 30 days. *B,* the lifetime, egg to adult of the orange and yellow butterflies (*Colias philodice eurytheme*) is also about 30 days. In the populations of alfalfa plants and alfalfa butterflies however, there are always various stages of development. The butterflies lay their eggs mainly on young plants. The caterpillars feed heavily on all the plants. The pupae are fastened to the stems. *C,* main enemies of the caterpillars and adults. Pupae suffer least. *D,* the enemies of enemies of the alfalfa pests; *each group keeps other groups from the destruction of over-population.* (Based on Smith, Bryan and Allen: "The Relation of Flights of Colias to Larval Population Density," *Ecology,* **30:**288–297; *U. S. D. A. Bull. 124,* and personal communication.)

avoid waste of the product. Coal can be burned once; the products of the fire do not return to coal again. What a difference in the heating bills if oil or coal could be reburned! What a difference when atomic energy can be turned to peaceful ends!

Renewable Resources. Soil, water, air, and living organisms of all kinds are renewable resources. Air and water can be used over again; soil and living organisms are in certain ways renewable. In one or another situation, all of these need care in order to preserve their greatest usefulness; air needs the least; soil and living organisms the most. There are excellent books that deal with the earth's natural resources, with definite methods, e.g., of keeping streams clean enough for fishes, and of guarding the trees in house lots as well as forests. There are books that deal with the extraordinary increase in human populations of the earth and its relation to space and other possessions and to war. A few are mentioned in the Reading List for this chapter.

Only one natural resource, the soil, may be further mentioned here. It is one of the most important and rapidly disappearing resources of them all. Natural soil is made of particles of weathered rocks mixed with organic matter —the scattered substance of dead plants and animals intimately associated with living ones, myriads of bacteria, roots searching for water, and burrowing animals, microscopic and otherwise. Such soil occurs only in the shallow upper layers of the earth's crust. It is the fertile layer that pulsates with daily changes of temperature and activity of life, and the deeper changes of seasonal temperature and moisture, and animal migrations. There are chemical cycles of dearth and abundance of a given substance, e.g., perhaps calcium compounds weathered from limestone and transported by water. Calcium may be picked up by roots, locked in the plant for its lifetime, then returned to the soil from the dead and softened tissues. Other substances come and go—carbon, nitrogen, sulfur, and others. Soil formation is carried on by the energy of the sun and secondarily by the energy liberated from weathering rock and broken tissues. This fountain of energy flows upward from the fertile soil through the plants that grow out of it, from the insects that live upon the plants, through the birds and rodents that feed upon the plants and insects, and on into the carnivores— shrews that devour insects, and cats that eat field mice. This upward stream of energy flows through a chain of food. It returns to the soil in the byproducts of living and in the dead bodies of plants and animals.

By natural methods, it takes hundreds of years to make an inch or two of fertile topsoil. By human means, it takes work and money and years, more in some regions than others. It is estimated that since farming started in the United States one third of the whole area of topsoil has been lost, overworked, carried by wind, washed into the rivers, and taken into the sea. Under the good topsoil, there is another layer of soil, poor but present. Land may be dangerously hurt; but not finally destroyed. Conservation of soil is an effort to renew its pulsating energy.

Appendix

<hr>

Scheme of Classification

Example: Man—Homo sapiens

Phylum	Chordata
Subphylum	Craniata—Vertebrata
Class	Mammalia
Order	Primates
Family	Hominidae
Genus	Homo
Species	sapiens

A *species* is the smallest standard group into which plants or animals are classified. Members of a species are alike except for relatively slight, more or less inconstant differences and can interbreed. A *genus* includes a number of species that have many features in common. Similarly, a *family* is a group of genera, an *order* a group of families, a *class* a group of orders, and finally a *phylum* a group of classes that have fundamental likenesses. Thus the *phyla* are the largest groups into which the plant or animal kingdom is divided.

Throughout their history classifications have varied with the knowledge of the classifier. They still vary especially in the genera and species, hence there is no one true or best classification.

The Plant Kingdom

Several tables have been consulted and parts included in the following table; especially those in T. I. Storer, General Zoology, 2nd. ed., New York, McGraw-Hill Co., 1951. C. A. Villee, Biology, 2nd. ed., Philadelphia, W. B. Saunders Co., 1953, and Zoological Names. Prepared for Sect. F., Am. Assoc. for the Advancement of Science, 1949.

Phylum Thallophyta. The simplest plants, without true roots, stems or leaves (about 107,000 species).

Subphylum Schizophyta
  Class Bacteria
  Class Cyanophyceae—blue-green algae. Most primitive plants.
Subphylum Algae. Thallophytes with chlorophyll.

795

Class Chlorophyceae—green algae, with definite nuclei and chloroplasts. Ex. Volvox, Spirogyra

Class Phaeophyceae. The brown algae, large seaweeds.

Class Rhodophyceae. The red algae, usually marine plants.

Class Bacillariaceae. Diatoms.

Subphylum Fungi. Thallophytes without chlorophyll, either parasites or saprophytes

Class Myxomycetes. Slime molds. The body is a blob of protoplasm containing many nuclei, but not perfectly divided into cells.

Class Phycomycetes. Bread molds and leaf molds.

Class Ascomycetes. Yeasts, mildews and cheese molds. Ex. Penicillium.

Class Basidiomycetes. Mushrooms, rusts, smuts.

Phylum Bryophyta. Multicellular plants, with a marked alternation of sexual and asexual generations (23,000 species).

Class Hepaticae. Liverworts.

Class Musci. Mosses.

Phylum Pteridophyta. Multicellular, terrestrial plants, with true roots, stems and leaves, and with alternation of sexual and asexual generations. The asexual generation is more prominent.

Class Lycopodineae. Clubmosses, ground pines.

Class Equisetineae. Horsetails.

Class Filicineae. Ferns.

Phylum Spermatophyta. Multicellular plants with well-developed roots, stems and leaves. The familiar dominant is the sporophyte or asexual plant. Trees, shrubs, and seed plants.

Subphylum Gymnospermae. Without flowers; the seeds are borne on the surface of the cone scales. Order Coniferales. Evergreen trees and shrubs, pines, firs, with needle-shaped leaves.

Subphylum Angiospermae. Flowering plants with seeds enclosed in ovary.

Class Dicotyledoneae. Most flowering plants. Embryos with two seed leaves or cotyledons.

Order Rosales, rose, apple, strawberry, cherry and others. A dozen and more orders containing great numbers of familiar flowering plants.

Class Monocotyledonae. Leaves with parallel veins. Embryos with one seed leaf. Grasses, lilies, and orchids.

The Animal Kingdom

Animals rarely have stiff cell walls and do not have chlorophyll. The exceptions are mainly border line organisms such as Euglenas that are brilliant green.

Phylum Protozoa. The simplest animals, one-celled, microscopic, some of them living in colonies. Many are free-living; others are parasitic. Ameba, Vorticella (colonial).

Class Flagellata. Protozoans that swim by flagella. The group probably most nearly related to one-celled plants. Euglenas.

Class Rhizopoda. Protozoans that move by pseudopodia. Amebas.

Class Sporozoa. Parasitic protozoans. Malarial parasites.

Class Ciliata. Protozoans that move by means of cilia. Paramecia.

Phylum Porifera. The sponges, the simplest of the many-celled animals, in many ways resembling colonies of protozoans. Fresh-water and marine forms.

Class Calcarea. With limy skeletons. Scypha (formerly called Sycon).

Class Hexactinellida. With 6-rayed silicious spicules. Glass sponge.

Class Demispongiae. Skeletons of elastic spongin and with silicious spicules. Bath sponge.

Phylum Coelenterata.

Class Hydrozoa. Hydralike animals, either single or colonial. Nearly all marine. Hydra.

Class Scyphozoa. Jellyfishes. Aurelia. Marine.

Class Anthozoa. Corals and sea anemones. Marine.

Phylum Ctenophora. Comb jellies or sea gooseberries. Marine.

Phylum Platyhelminthes. Flatworms.

Class Turbellaria. Nonparasitic flatworms. Planarians.

Class Trematoda. Many are internal parasites. Flukes.

Class Cestoda. Tapeworms. Parasites.

Phylum Nemertinea. Ribbon worms. Free-living. Most of them marine.

Phylum Nematomorpha. Horsehair worms. Aquatic and parasitic.

Phylum Acanthocephala. Spiny-headed worms. Parasites.

Phylum Phoronida. Marine tube dwellers.

Phylum Gastrotricha. Microscopic. In fresh and salt waters.

Phylum Chaetognatha. Glassworms, arrow worms. Marine.

Phylum Brachiopoda. Lamp shells, about 225 living species from the great numbers that once existed. Marine.

Phylum Rotifera. Rotifers, wheel animalcules. Abound in fresh water.

Phylum Bryozoa. Bryozoans, moss animals. Most of them marine.

Phylum Nematoda. Roundworms. In soil, water, roots of plants, parasitic in animals. Trichina, hookworm.

Phylum Annelida. Segmented worms. Soil, and fresh and salt waters.

Class Polychaeta. Most of them marine. Clamworms, Nereis.

Class Oligochaeta. Fresh water and land. Earthworm.

Class Hirudinea. Fresh and salt water and land. Leeches.

Phylum Arthropoda. Joint-footed animals.

Class Onychophora. Few species known. Little known tropical animals, intermediate between annelids and arthropods. Peripatus.

Class Crustacea. Lobsters, crabs, crayfishes, water fleas, sowbugs. Fresh and salt water and land.

Class Chilopoda. Centipedes. On land, mainly tropical.

Class Diplopoda. Millipedes, thousand-legged worms. Land in damp places.

Class Arachnoidea. Spiders, scorpions, mites, ticks, horseshoe crabs.

Class Insecta. Probably the largest group of animals. Grasshoppers, termites, dragon flies, water-striders, lice, fleas, beetles, butterflies and moths and others.

Phylum Mollusca. Mollusks. Fresh and salt water and land.

Class Amphineura. Chitons, shell composed of 8 plates. Marine.

Class Gastropoda. Snails, slugs, abalones. Fresh and salt water, and land.

Class Pelecypoda. Clams, mussels, oysters, scallops. Fresh and salt water.

Class Cephalopoda. Squids, cuttlefishes, octopuses. Marine.

Phylum Echinodermata. All marine.

Class Asteroidea. Starfishes.

Class Ophiuroidea. Brittle stars.

Class Echinoidea. Sea urchins and sand dollars.

Class Holothuroidea. Sea cucumbers.

Class Crinoidea. Sea lilies. Most of the group known only as fossils.

Phylum Chordata. Chordates, bilaterally symmetrical animals with a notochord. Fresh and salt water and land.

Subphylum Hemichorda. Acorn worms. During their development they resemble larvae of echinoderms. Marine.

Subphylum Urochorda. Sea squirts (tunicates). Marine.

Subphylum Cephalochorda. Amphioxus. Marine.

Subphylum Vertebrata. Vertebrates. Those with a definite head, a well-developed brain and a chain of supporting bones, the vertebrae.

Class Cyclostomata. Lampreys. Vertebrates without jaws or paired fins.

Class Chondrichthyses. Sharks, rays, skates and other fishes with cartilaginous skeletons.

Class Osteichthys. Sturgeon, garpike, lung fish, herring, mackerel, and other fishes with bony skeletons.

Class Amphibia. Amphibians.

Order Urodela. Tailed amphibians, newts, salamanders.

Order Anura. Tailless amphibians, frogs, toads.

Order Apoda. Caecilians. Body wormshaped; no limbs. They live in the tropics.

Class Reptilia. Reptiles.

Order Rhynchocephalia. Primitive lizardlike reptile, only one living species, Sphenodon or tuatara of New Zealand.

Order Crocodilia. Crocodiles, alligators.

Order Chelonia (or Testudinata). Turtles, tortoises, terrapins.

Order Squamata. Lizards and snakes.

Class Aves. Birds. The only animals that have feathers.

Subclass Ratitae. Flightless birds. Ostrich, cassowary, emu, kiwi.

Subclass Carinatae. All can fly except the penguins and a few species in various orders. Penguins, cormorants, swans, ducks, geese, turkeys, hawks, eagles, vultures, pigeons, parrots, owls, hummingbirds, and all the perching birds such as sparrows and thrushes.

Class Mammalia. Mammals. The only animals that have true hair.

Subclass Prototheria. Egg-laying mammals, monotremes, duckbilled platypus, spiny anteater.

Subclass Metatheria. Pouched mammals, marsupials. Kangaroo, opossum, and others, nearly all of them native to Australia.

Subclass Eutheria. Placental mammals. Young developed in the body of the mother and attached to the uterus by a placenta.

Order Xenarthra. Armadillo, sloth.

Order Insectivora. Moles, shrews, hedgehogs.

Order Chiroptera. Bats.

Order Lagomorpha. Pikas, hares, rabbits.

Order Rodentia. Squirrels, rats, mice, beavers, gophers, etc.

Order Proboscidea. Elephants.

Order Hyracoidea. True coneys of Syria and Africa, e.g., Hyrax. Superficially resemble guinea pigs but related to hoofed animals.

Order Perissodactyla. Odd-toed hoofed mammals. Horses, zebras, rhinoceros, tapir.

Order Artiodactyla. Even-toed hoofed mammals. Pigs, hippopotamus, deer, giraffe, sheep, cattle, etc.

Order Cetacea. Whales, dolphins, porpoises.

Order Sirenia. Sea cows. Large plant-eating aquatic mammals.

Order Carnivora. Walruses, seals, dogs, cats, bears, weasels, foxes, wolves, etc.

Order Primates. Lemurs, tarsiers, monkeys, apes and man.

Equivalent Measurements

Table 1

UNITS OF WEIGHT

Metric	Avoirdupois
1 kilogram (kg.) or 1,000 grams (gm.)	2 pounds (lb.), 3¼ ounces (oz.)
1 gram (gm.) or 1,000 milligrams (mg.)	0.035 ounces (oz.) or 15.43 grains (gr.)
1 milligram (mg.) or 1,000 micrograms (μg)	0.015 grains (gr.)

Examples

A man may weigh 75 kilograms or 165 pounds. His heart weighs about 10½ ounces, or 300 grams. He began life as a fertilized egg about 0.1 millimeters in diameter and weighing about 0.5 of a microgram.

Table 2

UNITS OF LENGTH

Metric	English
1 meter or 100 centimeters (cm.)	3 feet (ft.), 3⅓ inches (in.)
1 centimeter (cm.) or 10 millimeters (mm.)	⅓ inch (in.)
1 millimeter or 1,000 microns (μ)	1/25 inch (in.)
1 micron (μ) or 1,000 millimicrons (mμ)	1/25, 400 inch (in.)

Examples

A 6 foot, 6¾-inch man is 2 meters tall. At birth he was about 20 inches, or 50 centimeters long. His red blood corpuscles are about 7.5 microns in diameter.

Table 3

UNITS OF VOLUME

Metric	Apothecaries' Measure
1 liter (l.) or 1,000 cubic centimeters (cc.)	1.06 quarts (qt.) or 2.11 pints (pt.)
1 cubic centimeter (cc.) or 1,000 cubic millimeters (cu.mm.)	0.034 fluid ounces (fl. oz.) or 0.27 fluid drams (fl.d.)
1 cubic millimeter (cu.mm.)	0.016 minim (min.) (1 min. = 1 drop)

Examples

A man who weighs 165 pounds (or 75 kilograms) has about 12⅔ pints, or 6 liters, of blood.

Suggested Reading

The references are GROUPED BY CHAPTERS with those in periodicals placed at the end of each group.

The references include well-seasoned books, and new ones, selected because they are important, well written and lively. Even in comparative anatomies there may be humor, detectable to readers who are sensitive to it.

1. RELATIONSHIPS OF THE LIVING WORLD

MENZEL, D. H.: *Our Sun.* Philadelphia, The Blakiston Company, 1949. (Its publication now [1955] controlled by Harvard Press, Cambridge, Mass.) A small, well-illustrated book based on the work of eminent astronomers.

KALMUS, HANS: "The Sun Navigation of Animals," *Scientific American,* **191**:74–78 (Oct. 1954). Such navigations as those of bees locating the direction to food by its angle with respect to the sun, and movements of starlings shown by experiment to be dependent on the sun.

2. LIFE IS A CONCERN OF MATTER AND ENERGY

CURIE, EVE: *Madame Curie.* Translated by Vincent Sheean. New York, Doubleday, Doran and Co., 1937. An account that expresses the dramatic quality of the original discovery of radium.

EDDINGTON, A. S.: *Stars and Atoms.* New Haven, Yale University Press, 1927. Astronomy and physics discussed with competence and appeal.

LEMON, HARVEY B.: *From Galileo to Cosmic Rays. A New Look at Physics.* Chicago, University of Chicago Press, 1946. Interpretation given in nontechnical language with familiar examples. Chapters on Electrons, Positive Rays, Protons and Isotopes, Radioactivity. Fully illustrated.

MOULTON, F. R., and J. J. SCHIFFERES, eds.: *The Autobiography of Science.* New York, Doubleday, Doran and Co., 1945. Great steps in science recorded in the original words (or translations) of those who achieved them.

WEAVER, W., ed.: *The Scientists Speak.* New York, Boni & Gaer, 1947. Eighty-one leading American scientists, most of them research workers in the branches they represent, have joined in this symposium. The separate discussions, each contained in two or three pages of this small book, are highly authoritative and clearly written.

KAMEN, M. D.: "Tracers," *Scientific American,* **180**:31–41 (1949).

3. LIVING MATTER AND CELLS

DE ROBERTIS, E. D. P., W. W. NOWINSKI, and F. A. SAEZ: *General Cytology,* 2nd ed. Philadelphia, W. B. Saunders Co., 1954. Advanced reference for chemical and physiochemical organization of the cell, submicroscopic organization, functions of organoids, plasma membrane and cell permeability, chromosomes and cell division.

HEILBRUNN, L. V.: *An Outline of General Physiology,* 3rd ed. Philadelphia, W. B. Saunders Co., 1952. Discussions on advanced level, with excellent examples. Chapters on: Chemical Aspect of Protoplasm, Osmosis, Enzymes and Metabolism, Growth.

SNYDER, L. H.: *The Principles of Heredity,* 4th ed. Boston, D. C. Heath & Co., 1951. Excellent reference.

SPEAR, F. G.: *Radiations and Living Cells.* New York, J. Wiley & Sons, 1953. A small book, clearly written and interesting to the intelligent reader. An introduction to the action of radiation on living cells, especially those of human tissues.

WILLMER, E. N.: *Tissue Culture,* 2nd ed. New York, J. Wiley & Sons, 1954. The growth and differentiation of normal tissues in artificial media. The essentials of the methods of culturing cells outside the body; a small book.

WILSON, E. B.: *The Cell in Development and Heredity,* 3rd ed. New York, The Macmillan Co., 1925. A classic by an important authority.

SINNOTT, E. W., and K. WILSON: *Botany: Principles and Problems,* 5th ed. New York, McGraw-Hill Book Co., 1954. An excellent and widely used book.

BONNER, JAMES: "Chemical Warfare Among the Plants," *Scientific American,* **180:** 48–51 (Mch. 1949). Remarkable plant relationships. Some plants have chemical weapons with which they attack their neighbors. Penicillin is a familiar one.

SCHROCKEN, V.: "Plant Hormones," *Scientific American,* **180:**40–43 (1949).

WILSON, M.: "Priestly," *Scientific American,* **191:**68–73 (Oct. 1954). This article is about Priestley as a scientist and even more as a person who struggled and suffered in the cause of civil, political, and religious liberty. What happened to him in 1791 savors of the present times.

4. PLANTS PROVIDE FOR THEMSELVES AND THE ANIMALS

AVERY, G. S., JR., and E. B. JOHNSON: *Hormones and Horticulture.* New York, McGraw-Hill Book Co., 1947. Chapters on Hormones and the Rooting of Cuttings, Hormone Treatment of Seeds.

BONNER, J. B., and A. W. GALSTON: *Principles of Plant Physiology.* San Francisco, W. H. Freeman & Co., 1952. Excellent account of photosynthesis.

FAIRCHILD, D.: *The World Was My Garden.* New York, Charles Scribner's Sons, 1938. The world travels of a naturalist who traced plants to their original homes and established valuable ones in this country.

MARTIN, A. C., H. S. ZIM, and A. L. NELSON: *American Wildlife and Plants.* New York, McGraw-Hill Book Co., 1951. A guide to the food habits of wildlife: the use of trees, shrubs, and smaller plants by the birds and mammals of the United States. It brings together the major research of the United States Fish and Wildlife Service on American wildlife in relation to plants.

PLATT, R.: *This Green World.* New York, Dodd, Mead and Co., 1946. Includes a highly interesting and intelligible explanation of autumn coloration of deciduous trees. A book to own.

PLATT, R.: *Our Flowering World.* New York, Dodd, Mead and Co., 1947. Chapters 5 through 12 describe the adversities that plants have survived through the ages: The Coal Age, Drifting Continents and the Ice Age. Vivid descriptions tell how the trees and flowers of today have traveled to their present locations.

5. ANIMALS AND THEIR ENVIRONMENTS

ALLEE, W. C., and K. P. SCHMIDT: *Ecological Animal Geography,* 2nd ed. New York, John Wiley & Sons, 1951. Animals in their environments, giving about equal space to sea, fresh water and land. Effect of civilization on the distribution of animals.

CARSON, R. L.: *The Sea Around Us.* New York, Oxford University Press, 1951. Among the chapters are: The Birth of an Island; Wind, Sun and the Spinning of the Earth. Brief, searching accounts that create a consciousness and vision of the sea.

CLARKE, G. L.: *Elements of Ecology.* New York, John Wiley & Sons, 1954. Excellent.

COTT, H. B.: *Adaptive Coloration in Animals.* New York, Oxford University Press, 1941. An inclusive reference book with many illustrations.

MACGINITIE, G. E., and N. MACGINITIE: *Natural History of Marine Animals.* New

York, McGraw-Hill Book Co., 1949. Firsthand observations, many but by no means all of them made on the Pacific Coast.

MORGAN, A. H.: *Fieldbook of Ponds and Streams.* New York, G. P. Putnam's Sons, 1930. Ponds and streams have lively populations. This book is an introduction to them.

MORGAN, A. H.: *Fieldbook of Animals in Winter.* New York, G. P. Putnam's Sons, 1939. Where and how animals spend the winter; "winter sleep" of hibernators, hoarded food, migrations, winter resorts in water and on land.

NEEDHAM, J. G.: *The Life of Inland Waters.* Ithaca, N. Y., Comstock Publishing Co., 1937. A book whose content and grace of language make reading it a discovery and pleasure.

NICE, M. M.: *The Watcher at the Nest.* New York, The Macmillan Co., 1939. The author is a foremost authority on the behavior of birds in their home territory.

ODUM, E. P.: *Fundamentals of Ecology.* Philadelphia, W. B. Saunders Co., 1953. Content well chosen and arranged, concise, a small book.

JOHNSON, F. H.: "Heat and Life," *Scientific Monthly,* **191:**64–68 (Sept. 1954). Life is limited to the zone between the freezing and boiling points of water where enzymes can exist and speed the reactions of metabolism.

KALMUS, HANS: "The Sun Navigation of Animals," *Scientific American,* **191:**74–78 (Oct. 1954). Such navigations as those of bees locating the direction to food by its angle with respect to the sun, and movements of starlings shown by experiment to be dependent on the sun.

6. MUTUAL RELATIONSHIPS OF ANIMALS

ALLEE, W. C.: "Animal Sociology," in *Encyclopedia Britannica,* 14th ed., 1947.

ALLEE, W. C.: *Cooperation Among Animals.* New York, Henry Schuman, Inc., 1951. Cooperation is demonstrated in animals from protozoans to man. A brief and stimulating discussion of relationships.

ALLEE, W. C., A. E. EMERSON, O. PARK, T. PARK, and K. P. SCHMIDT: *Principles of Animal Ecology.* Philadelphia, W. B. Saunders Co., 1949. Essential for everyone seriously interested in the relationships of plants and animals.

CHANDLER, A. C.: *Introduction to Parasitology,* 8th ed. New York, John Wiley & Sons, 1949. Excellent.

DOWDESWELL, W. H.: *Animal Ecology.* London, Methuen & Co., 1952. Excellent; it is brief, interesting, and inexpensive. Valuable for beginners of any age and training.

ELTON, C.: *The Ecology of Animals.* London, Methuen & Co., 1933. By a leading authority on populations, the Director of the Bureau of Animal Population at Oxford University.

TINBERGEN, N.: *Social Behavior in Animals.* London, Methuen & Co., 1953. A small book, clearly written, terse and interesting. Closes with hints for research in animal sociology.

TINBERGEN, N.: *The Study of Instinct.* Oxford, The Clarendon Press, 1951. Lectures given in New York in 1947 under the auspices of the American Museum of Natural History. They review the work done in animal behavior on the European continent in recent years; not easily accessible elsewhere.

WHEELER, W. M.: *Foibles of Insects and Men.* New York, Alfred A. Knopf, Inc., 1928. Observation, scholarship, and wit.

ZINSSER, H.: *Rats, Lice and History.* Boston, Little, Brown & Co., 1935. Also paper bound by Pocket Books, Inc. Parasites and typhus fever against a background of human history; told with scholarship, wit, and skill.

7. TISSUES

BREMER, J. L., and H. L. WEATHERFORD: *Textbook of Histology,* 6th ed. Philadelphia, The Blakiston Co., 1944. Arranged on an embryological basis.

HAM, A. W.: *Histology,* 2nd ed. Philadelphia, J. B. Lippincott Co., 1953. Emphasis on function. Excellent for general and medical reference.

MAXIMOW, A. A., and WM. BLOOM: *A Textbook of Histology*, 6th ed. Philadelphia, W. B. Saunders Co., 1952. Excellent. Especially for medical reference.

SHERRINGTON, C.: *Man on His Nature*. London and New York, Cambridge University Press, 1951. A small book, only for those who think. See Chapter 4, The Wisdom of the Body.

8. AN AGENT OF EVOLUTION—THE BODY COVERING

RAND, H. W.: *The Chordates*. Philadelphia, The Blakiston Co., 1950. See Chapter 16, Skin of Mammals.

ROMER, A. S.: *The Vertebrate Body*, 2nd ed. Philadelphia, W. B. Saunders Co., 1955. See Chapter 6, The Skin.

HAUSMAN, L. A.: "Structural Characters of the Hair of Mammals," *American Naturalist*, **54**:496–523 (1920). Figures show identification marks of hairs of various mammals. Structural causes of colors of hair and gray hair.

WISLOCKI, G. B.: "Studies on the Growth of Deer Antlers," *American Journal of Anatomy*, **71**:371–415 (1942). Interesting facts as well as a good example of investigation.

9. PROTECTION, SUPPORT, AND MOVEMENT—SKELETONS

RAND, H. W.: *The Chordates*. Philadelphia, The Blakiston Co., 1950. Comparative anatomy that portrays the evolution of the vertebrates. Excellent illustrations.

ROMER, A. S.: *The Vertebrate Body*, 2nd ed. Philadelphia, W. B. Saunders Co., 1955. The structure and evolution of systems in various types of vertebrates. See Chapter 7, The Skeleton.

SIMPSON, G. G.: *Horses*. New York, Oxford University Press, 1951. An account of the evolution of horses; for any intelligent reader.

SISSON, S.: *The Anatomy of the Domestic Animals*, 4th ed. Philadelphia, W. B. Saunders Co., 1953. General and veterinary reference.

CHUBB, S. H.: "How Animals Run: Some Interesting Laws Governing Animal Locomotion," *Natural History Magazine*, **29**:543–551 (1929).

10. MOVEMENT—MUSCLES

FULTON, J. F.: *Textbook of Physiology*, 16th ed. Philadelphia, W. B. Saunders Co., 1949. A standard advanced reference book.

GRAY, JAMES: *How Animals Move*. Cambridge, England, Cambridge University Press, 1953. Clearly expressed, highly interesting lectures with original illustrations. Originally given to British children. Appropriate and informing to adults.

HILL, A. V.: *Muscular Movement in Man*. New York, McGraw-Hill Book Co., 1927. A book to be known. The author writes with all possible simplicity about the fundamentals of muscular movement.

LANGLEY, L. L., and E. CHERASKIN: *The Physiology of Man*. New York, McGraw-Hill Book Co., 1954. A succinct presentation of the more important physiological processes.

PROSSER, C. L., et al.: *Comparative Animal Physiology*. Philadelphia, W. B. Saunders Co., 1950. Discussions of muscle of invertebrates with many references. See Chapter 16, Muscle and Electric Organs.

ROGERS, C. G.: *Textbook of Comparative Physiology*, 2nd ed. New York, McGraw-Hill Book Co., 1938. An old book that contains facts about invertebrates not easy to find elsewhere. See Chapter 15, Physiology of Movement.

SCHNEIDER, E. C., and P. V. KARPOVICH: *Physiology of Muscular Activity*, 3rd ed. Philadelphia, W. B. Saunders Co., 1948. Good reference for general structure and function, especially for practical, commonly asked questions. Brief.

SZENT-GYÖRGI, A.: *Nature of Life: A Study of Muscle*. New York, Academic Press Inc., 1948. Advanced.

11. Foods and Nutrition

BABKIN, B. P.: *Pavlov, A Biography.* Chicago, University of Chicago Press, 1949. A Russian scientist who was devoted to fact. His most notable investigations were made upon conditioned reflexes. In 1904 he received a Nobel prize for his work on the digestive system.

CANNON, W. B.: *The Wisdom of the Body,* rev. ed. New York, W. W. Norton & Co., Inc., 1939. The content of the body: thirst and hunger as means of assuring supplies, the constant balance of water, salt, sugar, protein, fat, and calcium contents; the constancy of body temperature; the natural defenses of the body. See Chapter 9, The Internal Environment and The Quality of Life.

CARLSON, A. J., and V. JOHNSON: *The Machinery of the Body,* 4th ed. Chicago, University of Chicago Press, 1954. Excellent reference.

GERARD, R. W., ed.: *Food for Life.* Chicago, University of Chicago Press, 1952. Chapters of note are: Preparation from Mouth to Cell; Enzymes Effective Agents; The Foods of Animals and Men.

SHERMAN, H. C.: *The Nutritional Improvement of Life.* New York, Columbia University Press, 1950. Traces the growth of man's awareness of nutrition; traces details of advances in major fields—energy foods, proteins and their amino acids, the mineral elements, and the vitamins; gives basic principles of nutrition, present-day approaches to malnutrition, vitamin deficiencies; describes the human body as a biochemical organism.

12. Circulation and Transportation—Body Fluids

AMBERSON, W. R., and D. C. SMITH: *Outline of Physiology,* 2nd ed. Baltimore, Williams & Wilkins Co., 1948. A standard reference book.

BEST, H. B., and N. B. TAYLOR: *The Living Body, A Text in Human Physiology,* 3rd ed. New York, Henry Holt & Co., 1952. A dependable, interesting, and useful book to own.

CARLSON, A. J., and V. JOHNSON: *Machinery of the Body,* 4th ed. Chicago, University of Chicago Press, 1954.

CLARK-KENNEDY, A. E.: *Stephen Hales (1677–1761). An Eighteenth Century Biography.* Cambridge, England, Cambridge University Press, 1929. Between his sermons Hales made observations on the circulation of blood which rank with those of Harvey. Classed as one of the best biographies of a scientific man written in recent years.

HAM, A. W.: *Histology,* 2nd ed. Philadelphia, J. B. Lippincott Co., 1953.

HARVEY, WILLIAM: *The Motion of the Heart and Blood.* (Original edition 1628). Translated with notes by C. D. Leake. Springfield, Ill., Charles C Thomas, Publisher, 1931. Harvey's own account of his experiments and conclusions.

MAXIMOW, A. A., and W. BLOOM: *A Textbook of Histology,* 6th ed. Philadelphia, W. B. Saunders Co., 1952.

13. The Release of Energy—Respiration

ARMSTRONG, H. G.: *Aviation Medicine,* 3rd ed. Baltimore, Williams & Wilkins Co., 1952.

GERARD, R. W.: *The Body Functions.* New York, John Wiley & Sons, 1941. Discussions are stimulating, clearly written, and brief.

KROGH, A.: *The Comparative Physiology of Respiratory Mechanisms.* The Cooper Foundation Lectures at Swarthmore College 1939. Philadelphia, University of Pennsylvania Press, 1941. Excellent reference, clear, authoritative, brief.

SCHNEIDER, E. C., and P. V. KARPOVICH: *Physiology of Muscular Activity,* 3rd ed. Philadelphia, W. B. Saunders Co., 1948. Good reference for respiration, blood content, and circulation.

STACKPOLE, C. E., and L. C. LEAVELL: *Textbook of Physiology.* New York, The Macmillan Co., 1953. See Section 4 on respiration. Brief and meaty, an excellent book to own.

14. The By-Products of Metabolism—Excretion

HAM, A. W.: *Histology,* 2nd ed. Philadelphia, J. B. Lippincott Co., 1953. Excellent account of excretion.

PROSSER, C. L., et al.: *Comparative Animal Physiology.* Philadelphia, W. B. Saunders Co., 1950. See especially, excretion of crayfish, pp. 29–32.

SMITH, HOMER W.: *From Fish to Philosopher.* Boston, Little, Brown and Co., 1953. One of the foremost authorities on the kidney traces the evolution of man by way of the evolution of the kidney. The kidney, more than any other organ, is responsible for maintaining the internal environment of the body. Excellent for the general reader.

STACKPOLE, C. E., and L. C. LEAVELL: *Textbook of Physiology.* New York, The Macmillan Co., 1953. See The Role of the Kidney.

HOWLAND, R. B.: "Experiments on the Contractile Vacuole of *Amoeba verrucosa* and *Paramoecium caudatum,*" *Journal of Experimental Zoology,* **40**:251–262 (1924).

SMITH, HOMER W.: "The Kidney," *Scientific American,* **188**:40–48 (1953). Excellent account of the evolution of the kidney.

15. Chemical Regulation—Endocrine Glands

ALLEN, E., C. H. DANFORTH, and E. A. DOISY: *Sex and Internal Secretions,* 2nd ed. Baltimore, The Williams & Wilkins Co., 1939. A standard advanced reference for the foundation work on endocrines.

AVERY, G. S., JR., and E. B. JOHNSON: *Hormones and Horticulture.* New York, McGraw-Hill Book Co., 1950. See note on Schocken and section on plant hormones.

BEACH, F. A.: *Hormones and Behavior.* New York, Paul B. Hoeber, Inc., 1948.

CORNER, G. W.: *The Hormones in Human Reproduction.* Princeton, Princeton University Press, 1942. An excellent account by a leading authority, well illustrated.

HAM, A. W.: *Histology,* 2nd ed. Philadelphia, J. B. Lippincott Co., 1953. An excellent account of the endocrines, with a particularly clear discussion of the pituitary gland.

HOSKINS, R. G.: *Endocrinology,* 2nd ed. New York, W. W. Norton & Co., Inc., 1950. The more significant facts of endocrinology as known at this date. One of the best general accounts for any intelligent reader.

PARKER, G. H.: *Animal Colour Changes and Their Neuro-Hormones.* Cambridge, England, Cambridge University Press, 1948. Inclusive, interesting, advanced.

STEVENSON, L.: *Sir Frederick Banting,* rev. ed. Springfield, Ill., Charles C Thomas, Publisher, 1947. Biography of the discoverer of insulin.

TURNER, C. D.: *General Endocrinology,* 2nd ed. Philadelphia. W. B. Saunders Co., 1955. A standard work on the endocrine glands of vertebrates and one chapter on those of invertebrates.

WIGGLESWORTH, V. B.: *Insect Physiology,* 4th ed. New York, John Wiley & Sons, Inc., 1950. Hormones chiefly in Chapter 7, Reproduction and Growth. A brief and inexpensive book containing chapters on the physiology of the main systems of the insect body.

BARGMANN, W., and E. SCHARRER: "The Site of Origin of the Hormones of the Posterior Pituitary," *American Scientist,* **39**:255–259 (1941).

CONSTANTINIDES, P. C., and N. CAREY: "The Alarm Reaction," *Scientific American,* **180**:20–23 (1949). The adrenal gland sends out its hormones in time of stress.

GRAY, G. W.: "Cortisone and ACTH," *Scientific American,* **182**:30–37 (1950).

HOAGLAND, H.: "Schizophrenia and Stress," *Scientific American,* **181**:44–47 (1949).

SCHOCKEN, V.: "Plant Hormones," *Scientific American,* **180**:40–43 (1949). A review of how plant hormones have been studied and applied. Subjects such as the effect of chemical substances (auxins) on the rooting of cuttings, stimulation of growth, and fruiting.

WILLIAMS, C. M.: "The Metamorphosis of Insects," *Scientific American,* **182**:24–28 (1950). Discussion of the important effects of endocrines on metamorphosis.

16. Conduction and Coordination—Nervous System

Adrian, E. D.: *The Physical Background of Perception.* Oxford, England, The Clarendon Press, 1947. A small book of lectures delivered at Magdalen College, Oxford University, by a master of the English language as well as of his subject. They were deemed appropriate for English University students. Among the titles are: The Brain and the Mind, Motor and Sensory Areas of the Brain, Sight and Hearing; The Electrical Activity of the Brain.

Best, C. H., and N. B. Taylor: *The Living Body, A Text in Human Physiology,* 3rd ed. New York, Henry Holt & Co., 1952. See the following chapters: The Physiology of Nerve and Muscle, The Central Nervous System, and The Special Senses.

Cobb, Stanley: *Foundations of Neuropsychiatry,* 5th ed. Baltimore, Williams & Wilkins Co., 1952.

Dennis, W., ed.: *Readings in the History of Psychology.* New York, Appleton-Century-Crofts, 1948.

Fulton, J. F.: *The Physiology of the Nervous System,* 3rd ed. London, Oxford University Press, 1949. A comprehensive advanced treatment on the functions of the nervous system.

Garrett, H. E.: *Great Experiments in Psychology,* 3rd ed. New York, Appleton-Century-Crofts, 1951.

Sherrington, C. S.: *Integrative Action of the Nervous System.* New Haven, Yale University Press, 1948.

Bodian, D.: "The Paralytic Plague," *Scientific American,* 183:22–26 (1950). The virus that causes the symptoms of poliomyelitis; its location in the brain and spinal cord; its behavior.

17. Responsiveness—The Sense Organs

Boring, E. G., H. S. Langfeld, and H. P. Weld, eds.: *Foundations of Psychology.* New York, John Wiley & Sons, 1948. Topics such as: color vision; hearing; taste and smell; perception of space by ultrasonic cries of bats; comparison of the bats' device with sonar instruments. Interest for general reader.

Davis, S. S., and H. Davis: *Hearing, Its Psychology and Physiology.* New York, John Wiley & Sons, 1938. An advanced, comprehensive reference.

Howell, A. B.: *Aquatic Mammals. Their Adaptations to Life in the Water.* Springfield, Ill., Charles C Thomas, Publisher, 1930. See Chapter 4, The Senses. The adjustments to water of eyes, ears, and other senses of marine mammals.

Walls, G. L.: *The Vertebrate Eye.* Bloomfield Hills, Mich., The Cranbrook Press, 1942. An inclusive reference, especially valuable because of its emphasis on ecology.

Wigglesworth, V. B.: *The Principles of Insect Physiology.* New York, E. P. Dutton & Co., Inc., 1939. An unexcelled authority. Discussions of sense organs of insects: Vision, Mechanical and Chemical Senses and Behavior. Many figures and extensive reference lists.

Griffin, D. R.: "The Navigation of Bats," *Scientific American,* 183:52–55 (1950). A description of the guidance of bats by the echoes of their own supersonic cries, inaudible to human ears.

Wald, G.: "Eye and Camera," *Scientific American,* 183:32–41 (1950). A comparison of the eye and camera, with a discussion of the basic physics and chemistry involved. Excellent.

18. Reproduction

Altenburg, Edgar: *Genetics.* New York, Henry Holt & Co., Inc., 1948. Reference for special topics, e.g., beginnings of sex, mating types, and reproduction of paramecia.

Bullough, W.: *Vertebrate Sexual Cycles.* New York, John Wiley & Sons, 1953. A generalized account with examples from different animals. Interesting, readable, brief.

Corner, G. W.: *The Hormones in Human Reproduction.* Princeton, N. J., Princeton University Press, 1942. An excellent presentation, interesting, finely written, scholarly, well illustrated, and brief. This and *Ourselves Unborn* by the same author are valuable to read and own. Both are for the general reader.

STONE, A., and H. STONE: *Manual of Marriage,* rev. ed. New York, Simon & Schuster, Inc., 1935. Excellent reference.

WALTER, H. E., and L. P. SAYLES: *Biology of the Vertebrates,* 3rd ed. New York, The Macmillan Co., 1949. A new edition of a comparative anatomy that has a long history of usefulness.

19. DEVELOPMENT

AREY, L. B.: *Developmental Anatomy,* 6th ed. Philadelphia, W. B. Saunders Co., 1954. A superbly illustrated up-to-date edition of a standard embryology.

BARTH, L. G.: *Embryology,* 2nd ed. New York, Dryden Press, 1954. Brief, fully illustrated with original, usually simple diagrams. Valuable for its emphasis on experimental embryology.

BRACHET, JEAN: *Chemical Embryology,* Trans. by L. G. Barth. New York, Interscience Publishers, Inc., 1950. Advanced treatise. Subjects such as: the relation of metabolism to cell division; chemical embryology of the invertebrates; chemical embryology of amphibian eggs.

CORNER, G. W.: *Ourselves Unborn.* New Haven, Yale University Press, 1944. For the general reader. A brief account of human development by a leading authority. Written with clarity and grace. Illustrated with excellent photographs. A book to own.

PATTEN, B. M.: *Human Embryology,* 2nd ed. New York, The Blakiston Co., 1953. Patten's embryologies are highly regarded and widely used.

PATTEN, B. M.: *Embryology of the Pig,* 3rd ed. Philadelphia, The Blakiston Co., 1948.

PATTEN, B. M.: *Early Embryology of the Chick,* 4th ed. Philadelphia, The Blakiston Co., 1951.

SHUMWAY, W.: *Introduction to Vertebrate Embryology,* 5th ed. New York, John Wiley & Sons, 1954. Amphioxus, frog, chick and mammal discussed comparatively.

WINDLE, W. F.: *Physiology of the Fetus.* Philadelphia, W. B. Saunders Co., 1940. Functions of the body in prenatal life.

20. THE PHYSICAL BASIS OF HEREDITY

CONKLIN, E. G.: *Heredity and Environment in the Development of Men,* 4th ed. Princeton, N. J., Princeton University Press, 1922. A classic not to be missed; suitable for those who think.

DUNN, L. C., and T. H. DOBZHANSKY: *Heredity, Race and Society.* New York, The New American Library of World Literature, 1950. Authentic, interesting and inexpensive.

GOLDSCHMIDT, R. B.: *Understanding Heredity, An Introduction to Genetics.* New York, John Wiley & Sons, 1952. Excellent. Brief yet it includes the significant items.

HOLT, R.: *George Washington Carver.* Garden City, N. Y., Doubleday, Doran & Co., 1943. A fascinating story of a Luther Burbank of the south.

ILTIS, HUGO: *Life of Mendel.* Translated by Eden and Cedar Paul. New York, W. W. Norton & Co., 1932.

MULLER, H. J., C. C. LITTLE, and L. H. SNYDER: *Genetics, Medicine and Man.* Ithaca, N. Y., Cornell University Press, 1947. Brief, authoritative and readable, with applications to evolution and public welfare.

PFEIFFER, J.: *Genetics, The Science of Heredity.* Public Affairs Pamphlet No. 165. Public Affairs Committee, 22 East 38th St., New York, 1950. Content well chosen and written.

SCHEINFELD, A.: *The New You and Heredity.* Philadelphia, J. B. Lippincott Co., 1950. Genetics in everyday life with familiar examples.

SINNOTT, E., L. C. DUNN, and T. DOBZHANSKY: *Principles of Genetics,* 4th ed. New York, McGraw-Hill Book Co., 1950. A standard text.

SNYDER, L. H.: *The Principles of Heredity,* 4th ed. Boston, D. C. Heath & Co., 1951. Excellent; has good teaching quality, and liveliness.

21. The Protozoans—Representatives of Unicellular Animals

DOBELL, C.: *Antony van Leeuwenhoek and his "Little Animals."* London, J. Bale Sons and Danielsson, 1932. An account of the founder of protozoology and bacteriology and his work (1632–1723).

GRANT, M. P.: *Microbiology and Human Progress.* New York, Rinehart Co., 1953. How the world of microscopic beings surrounds and travels with human ones in modern world affairs. The author believes that any citizen's culture and contributions to society are enriched by an understanding of the part taken by micro-organisms in its progress.

HYMAN, L. H.: *The Invertebrates, Protozoa through Ctenophora.* New York, McGraw-Hill Book Co., 1940. The standard advanced reference work in English on the invertebrates.

JAHN, T. A., and F. F. JAHN: *How to Know the Protozoa.* Dubuque, Iowa, W. C. Brown Co., 1949. A small, fully illustrated manual, interesting and easy to use, as easy as possible to make it.

JENNINGS, H. S.: *Behavior of the Lower Organisms.* New York, The Macmillan Co., 1915. A famous biologist's discussion of a subject on which he was a thought-provoking scholar.

LOCY, W. A.: *Biology and Its Makers,* 3rd ed. New York, Henry Holt & Co., 1915. Excellent accounts of Leeuwenhoek and other pioneers.

MACKIE, T. T., G. W. HUNTER, and C. B. WORTH: *Manual of Tropical Medicine,* 2nd ed. Philadelphia, W. B. Saunders Co., 1954. Comprehensive and advanced discussions of malaria, sleeping sickness and other diseases caused by protozoans.

WARSHAW, L. J.: *Malaria, The Biography of a Killer.* New York, Rinehart Co., 1949. Interesting, inclusive account of the parasites and the disease.

WICHTERMAN, RALPH: *The Biology of Paramecium.* New York, The Blakiston Co., 1952.

ALLEN, W. E.: "The Primary Food Supply of the Sea," *Quarterly Review of Biology,* **9:**161–180 (1934). A general survey of a subject of increasing importance. A valuable reference work with a list for further reading.

ALLEN, W. E.: "Red Water in La Jolla Bay (California) in 1945," *Transactions, American Microscopical Society,* **55:**149–153 (1946). "Red water" due to dinoflagellates (protozoans) has appeared now and again along the western coast of the United States.

HEGNER, R. W.: "The Interrelations of Protozoa and the Utricles (leaf traps) of Utricularia," *Biological Bulletin,* **50:**239–270 (1926). Also, "Protozoa of the Pitcher Plant," *Biological Bulletin,* **50:**271–276 (1926). The story of how plant traps catch and digest protozoans and other minute animals.

WOODRUFF, L. L.: "Eleven thousand generations of Paramecium," *Quarterly Review of Biology,* **1:**436–438 (1935). Generations of paramecia in which conjugation did not occur. Division followed endomixis.

22. Sponges—A Side Line of Evolution

BUCHSBAUM, R.: *Animals Without Backbones,* 2nd ed. Chicago, University of Chicago Press, 1948. This book presents the essentials of the structure and habits of sponges clearly and vividly.

HEGNER, R. W.: *Invertebrate Zoology.* New York, The Macmillan Co., 1933.

HYMAN, L. H.: *The Invertebrates, Protozoa through Ctenophora.* New York, McGraw-Hill Book Co., 1940. A leading authority, inclusive and thorough. Advanced.

MINER, R. W.: *Field Book of Seashore Life.* New York, G. P. Putnam's Sons, 1950. An excellent chapter on marine sponges.

POTTS, E.: *The Sponges (Porifera)* in Ward and Whipple's *Fresh-Water Biology.* New York, John Wiley & Sons, 1918.

RAMSAY, J. A.: *A Physiological Approach to the Lower Animals.* Cambridge, England, Cambridge University Press, 1952. Broad generalizations in the physiological approach to invertebrate animals. Subjects dealt with in short chapters are: Nutrition, Circulation, Respiration, Excretion, Muscle and Nerve, Sense Organs, Coordination, and Behavior. Brief and illuminating.

STUART, A. H.: *World Trade in Sponges.* Washington, U.S. Government Printing Office, 1948.

23. COELENTERATES—SIMPLE MULTICELLULAR ANIMALS

BUCHSBAUM, R.: *Animals Without Backbones,* 2nd ed. Chicago, University of Chicago Press, 1948.

HYMAN, L. H.: *The Invertebrates, Protozoa through Ctenophora.* New York, McGraw-Hill Book Co., 1940.

MACGINITIE, G. E., and N. MACGINITIE: *Natural History of Marine Animals.* New York, McGraw-Hill Book Co., 1949.

MINER, R. W.: *Fieldbook of Seashore Life.* New York, G. P. Putnam's Sons, 1950.

YONGE, C. M.: *A Year on the Great Barrier Reef.* New York, G. P. Putnam's Sons, 1930.

ROUDABUSH, R. L.: "Phenomenon of Regeneration in Everted Hydra," *Biological Bulletin,* **64:**253–258 (1933).

24. CTENOPHORES—COMB JELLIES OR SEA WALNUTS

HYMAN, L. H.: *The Invertebrates, Protozoa through Ctenophora.* New York, McGraw-Hill Book Co., 1940. Ctenophora pp. 662–696, figs. 209–221.

MAYER, A. G.: *Ctenophores of the Atlantic Coast of North America.* Carnegie Institution of Washington, Publication 162 (1912), 58 pp. 17 pls. See also titles for Chapter 23.

25. FLATWORMS—VANGUARD OF THE HIGHER ANIMALS

CHILD, C. M.: *Patterns and Problems of Development.* Chicago, University of Chicago Press, 1941. An advanced reference.

HYMAN, L. H.: *The Invertebrates, Platyhelminthes and Rhynchocoela.* New York, McGraw-Hill Book Co., 1951. Authoritative and inclusive. Extensive bibliography.

MACGINITIE, G. E., and N. MACGINITIE: *Natural History of Marine Animals.* New York, McGraw-Hill Book Co., 1949. Original observations, well told. For general reading.

MORGAN, T. H.: *Regeneration.* New York, The Macmillan Co., 1901. A classic in the subject. Out of print but in many college libraries.

26. ROUND WORMS—THE TUBULAR PLAN

CHANDLER, A. C.: *Introduction to Parasitology with Special Reference to the Parasites of Man,* 8th ed. New York, John Wiley & Sons, 1949. It contains a general account of animal parasites and excellent discussions of human parasites and the diseases which they cause.

COBB, N. A.: *Free Living Nematodes.* In Ward and Whipple: *Fresh-Water Biology.* New York, John Wiley & Sons, 1918. The ecology, and structure and functions of the nematodes of soil and fresh water. The keys are necessarily technical.

CRAIG, C. F., and E. C. FAUST: *Clinical Parasitology,* 5th ed. Philadelphia, Lea & Febiger, 1951. A readable and authentic account of human parasites.

ELTON, C.: *Animal Ecology,* 3rd ed. New York, The Macmillan Co., 1947. A small book that contains ideas and principles; pithy and stimulating.

GOODY, T.: *Plant Parasitic Nematodes.* New York, E. P. Dutton & Co., 1933.

HYMAN, L. H.: *The Invertebrates, Nematoda.* New York, McGraw-Hill Book Co., 1951.

STUNKARD, H. W.: "Parasitism as a Biological Phenomenon," *Scientific Monthly,* **28:**349–362 (1929). An excellent survey; characteristics of parasitism illustrated by examples.

27. An Aquatic Miscellany

BORRADAILE, L. A. et al.: *The Invertebrata.* New York, The Macmillan Co., 1932. An inclusive detailed treatment of types of animals. Discussions include functions and relationships with ecological notes.

MACGINITIE, G. E., and N. MACGINITIE: *Natural History of Marine Animals.* New York, McGraw-Hill Book Co., 1949. Original observations with life kept in the records. For both American coasts, especially the Pacific.

MINER, R. W.: *Field Book of Seashore Life.* New York, G. P. Putnam's Sons, 1950. A fieldbook of seashore animals from protozoans through the lower chordates. Descriptions and illustrations of 1300 species of animals of American coastal waters especially the Atlantic. Includes a list of references for the phyla in this chapter.

PRATT, H. S.: *A Manual of the Common Invertebrate Animals Exclusive of Insects,* rev. ed. Philadelphia, The Blakiston Co., 1935. Widely used, chiefly for identifications.

SVERDRUP, H. U., M. W. JOHNSON, and R. H. FLEMING: *The Oceans, Their Physics, Chemistry, and General Biology.* New York, Prentice-Hall Inc., 1942. A detailed treatise with extensive bibliographies for each chapter. Chapter 18, Interrelations of Marine Organisms, contains a general discussion of food relations in the ocean.

COE, W. R.: "Biology of the Nemerteans of the Atlantic Coast of North America," *Transactions of Connecticut Academy of Arts and Sciences,* Vol. 35 (1935).

28. Annelids—Pioneers in Segmentation

DARWIN, CHARLES: *The Formation of Vegetable Mould through the Action of Worms, with Observations on Their Habits,* 1st ed. London, John Murray, 1881. Later published as *Formation of Vegetable Mould.* New York, D. Appleton & Co. A classic that reveals Darwin's methods of observation and reasoning.

HARVEY, E. N.: *Living Light.* Princeton, Princeton University Press, 1940.

HARVEY, E. N.: *Bioluminescence.* New York, Academic Press, 1952.

MACGINITIE, G. E., and N. MACGINITIE: *Natural History of Marine Animals.* New York, McGraw-Hill Book Co., 1949. Many photographs. Lively, meaty accounts by experienced observers. Authors are at the Kerckoff Marine Laboratory, California Institute of Technology.

MINER, R. W.: *Field Book of Seashore Life.* New York, G. P. Putnam's Sons, 1950. An inclusive, fully illustrated handbook. Selected references.

ROGERS, C. G.: *Textbook of Comparative Physiology,* 2nd ed. New York, McGraw-Hill Book Co., 1938. Physiology of invertebrates; e.g., earthworm—respiration, chloragog cells.

LILLIE, F. R., and E. E. JUST: "Breeding Habits of the Heteronereis Form of *Nereis limbata* at Woods Hole, Mass.," *Biological Bulletin,* 24:147–168 (1913). Observations of the spawning swarms and bioluminescence of clamworms.

MOORE, J. P.: "The Control of Blood-sucking Leeches, with an Account of the Leeches of Palisades Interstate Park," *Roosevelt Wild Life Bulletin,* 2:1–55 (1923).

PROSSER, C. L.: "The Nervous System of the Earthworm," *Quarterly Review of Biology,* 9:181–200 (1934). Emphasis on experimental studies and function.

ROBERTSON, J. D.: "The Function of the Calciferous Glands of Earthworms," *Journal of Experimental Biology* (British), 13:279–297 (1936). Experimental environments and diets and their effects on the calciferous organs.

29. Arthropods—Crustaceans

HUXLEY, T. H.: *The Crayfish.* New York, D. Appleton & Co., 1880. A classic of clear, accurate description of structure. No attempt to present the living animal.

MACGINITIE, G. E., and N. MACGINITIE: *Natural History of Marine Animals.* New York, McGraw-Hill Book Co., 1949. Chapter 27, Arthropoda, is a lively, well-illustrated account that emphasizes the Pacific Coast fauna but includes much else.

MINER, R. W.: *Fieldbook of Seashore Life.* New York, G. P. Putnam's Sons, 1950. A compact introduction to the invertebrate animals of the Atlantic coastal waters of North America.

WARD, H. B., and G. C. WHIPPLE: *Fresh-Water Biology*. New York, John Wiley & Sons, 1918. Fresh-water crustaceans with abundant figures.

ANDREWS, E. A.: "Breeding Habits of Crayfish," *American Naturalist,* **38:**165–206 (1904).

HERRICK, F. H.: "Natural History of the American Lobster," *Bulletin U. S. Bureau of Fisheries,* **29:**149–408 (1911).

SCUDAMORE, H. H.: "The Influence of the Sinus Glands Upon Molting and Associated Changes in the Crayfish," *Physiological Zoology,* **20:**187–208 (1947). Endocrine control of calcium metabolism, formation of gastroliths, hardening of exoskeleton.

TACK, P. I.: "The Life History and Ecology of the Crayfish, *Cambarus immunis Hagen,*" *American Midland Naturalist,* **25:**420–446 (1941).

30. ARTHROPODS—INSECTS, SPIDERS, AND ALLIES

BAKER, E. W., and G. W. WHARTON: *An Introduction to Acarology*. New York, The Macmillan Co., 1952. An essential book for special study of mites.

BRUES, C. T.: *Insect Dietary, An Account of the Food Habits of Insects*. Cambridge, Mass., Harvard University Press, 1946. Facts with wit and philosophy added.

CHU, H. F.: *How to Know the Immature Insects*. Dubuque, Iowa, Wm. C. Brown Co., 1949. An illustrated key for identifying the orders and families of immature insects with suggestions for collecting, rearing and studying them.

CLAUSEN, LUCY W.: *Insect Fact and Folklore*. New York, The Macmillan Co., 1954. A highly entertaining book; various facts packed in among stories and anecdotes of great variety.

COMSTOCK, J. H.: *An Introduction to Entomology,* 9th ed. Ithaca, N. Y., Comstock Publishing Co., 1936. A highly valued standard text.

COMSTOCK, J. H.: *The Spider Book,* rev. ed. by W. J. Gertsch. New York, Doubleday, Doran & Co., 1940. Among other interesting accounts is the description of web making.

EMERTON, J. H.: *The Common Spiders of the United States*. Boston, Ginn & Co., 1902. A small, approachable book by a famous authority.

FABRE, J. H.: *The Life of the Spider*. New York, Dodd, Mead & Co., 1917. Charles Darwin termed Fabre an "incomparable observer."

FOLSOM, J. W., and R. A. WARDLE· *Entomology with Special Reference to Its Ecological Aspects,* 4th ed. Philadelphia, The Blakiston Co., 1934. Useful for reference.

GERTSCH, W. J.: *American Spiders*. New York, D. Van Nostrand Co., 1949. Finely illustrated by 32 color and 32 half-tone plates.

MATHESON, ROBERT: *Medical Entomology,* 2nd ed. Ithaca, N. Y., Comstock Publishing Co., 1950. Presents well-chosen facts with precision and clarity.

MATHESON, ROBERT: *Entomology for Introductory Courses,* 2nd ed. Ithaca, N. Y., Comstock Publishing Co., 1951. Excellent presentation of basic facts.

MICHENER, C. D., and M. H. MICHENER: *American Social Insects*. New York, D. Van Nostrand Co., 1951.

RIBBANDS, C. R.: *The Behavior and Social Life of Honeybees*. London, Bee Research Association, 1953. Emphasis on recent research and presentation in nontechnical language.

ROTHSCHILD, M., and T. CLAY: *Fleas, Flukes and Cuckoos*. London, Collins, 1952. A study of bird parasites. A revealing picture of relationships in one kind of world—the bodies of birds. Well illustrated and written with few technical terms. Extensive bibliography.

STEINHAUS, E. A.: *Insect Microbiology*. Ithaca, N. Y., Comstock Publishing Co., 1946. Sample titles of chapters: Rickettsiae; Fungi and Insects; Protozoa and Insects except Termites; Protozoa in Termites.

THORP, R. W., and W. D. WOODSON: *Black Widow*. Chapel Hill, N. C., University of North Carolina Press, 1945. A special study of a famous spider.

UNITED STATES DEPARTMENT OF AGRICULTURE: *Insects, The Yearbook of 1952*. Washington, D. C., U. S. Government Printing Office, 1952. A practical book about useful as well as harmful insects, insecticides, and crops. Seventy-two color plates of economically important insects. Extensive bibliography.

VON FRISCH, KARL: *Bees; Their Vision, Chemical Senses, and Language.* Ithaca, N. Y., Cornell University Press, 1950. A fascinating account.

VON FRISCH, KARL: *The Dancing Bees.* New York, Harcourt, Brace & Co., 1955.

WHEELER, W. M.: *Social Life among the Insects.* New York, Harcourt Brace & Co., 1923.

WHEELER, W. M.: *The Social Insects, Their Origin and Evolution.* New York, Harcourt Brace & Co., 1928. Wheeler's books stand high in literary flavor as well as upon his deep understanding of social insects.

WIGGLESWORTH, V. B.: *The Principles of Insect Physiology,* 4th ed. London, Methuen & Co., 1950.

WIGGLESWORTH, V. B.: *The Physiology of Insect Metamorphosis.* Cambridge, England, Cambridge University Press, 1954.

ZINNSER, HANS: *Rats, Lice and History.* New York, Pocket Books, Inc., 1945. Wit, poetry, historical and biological facts. From the preface: ". . . art and sciences have much in common and both may profit by mutual appraisal." Among the chapter subjects: a discussion of the relationship between science and art; on parasites and old and new diseases; on the louse; the birth, childhood and adolescence of typhus fever.

BAILEY, L.: "The Action of the Proventriculus of the Worker Honeybee, *Apis mellifera* L." *The Journal of Experimental Biology* (British), **29:**310–327 (1952).

WATERMAN, T. H.: "Flight Instruments in Insects," *American Scientist,* **38:**222–238 (1950).

WATERMAN, T. H.: "Polarized Light Navigation by Arthropods," *Transactions of the New York Academy of Sciences,* **14:**11–14 (1951).

31. MOLLUSKS—SPECIALISTS IN SECURITY

BLACK, J. D.: *Biological Conservation.* New York, The Blakiston Co., 1954. Wild life is interpreted to include invertebrates and other animals outside the game types. A practical introduction to conservation.

MACGINITIE, G. E., and N. MACGINITIE: *Natural History of Marine Animals.* New York, McGraw-Hill Book Co., 1949. Interesting, authentic and a pleasure to read.

MINER, R. W.: *Fieldbook of Seashore Life.* New York, G. P. Putnam's Sons, 1950. An excellent fully illustrated guide to the common invertebrates of the Atlantic coast.

MORGAN, A. H.: *Fieldbook of Ponds and Streams.* New York, G. P. Putnam's Sons, 1930. A brief chapter on the snails and mussels.

RICKETTS, E. F., and J. CALVIN: *Between Pacific Tides,* rev. ed. Stanford, Calif., Stanford University Press, 1948. An account of the habits and habitats of the common invertebrates of the Pacific coast.

ALEXANDER, A. E.: "Pearls through Artifice," *Scientific American,* **160:**228–229 (April, 1939).

GRAVE, B. H.: "Natural History of the Shipworm, *Teredo navalis,* at Woods Hole, Massachusetts," *Biological Bulletin,* **55:**260–282 (1928).

GUNTER, G.: "The Generic Status of Living Oysters and the Scientific Name of the Common American Species; Placed by Gunter as *Crassostrea virginica,*" *American Midland Naturalist,* **43:**438–449 (1950).

KORRINGA, P.: "Recent Advances in Oyster Biology," *Quarterly Review of Biology,* **27:**266–308; 339–365 (1952). An excellent survey of many aspects of the biology of oysters including "The American Oyster" known in many books as *Ostrea virginica* recently placed by some authors in a different genus, by Korringa as *Gryphaea virginica,* by Gunter as *Crassostrea virginica.*

32. ECHINODERMS—FORERUNNERS OF THE VERTEBRATES

AGASSIZ, ELIZABETH C.: *Louis Agassiz, His Life and Correspondence.* Boston, Houghton, Mifflin and Co., 1886. Agassiz kindled the spirit and built the foundation of the teaching of zoology in the United States. He was also an investigator and teacher of the structure and biology of echinoderms. This biography is one of several but none makes his time more alive.

MINER, R. W.: *Fieldbook of Seashore Life.* New York, G. P. Putnam's Sons, 1950. Useful for all groups of seashore animals. Fully illustrated.

COE, W. R.: "Echinoderms of Connecticut," *Connecticut State Geological and Natural History Survey Bull.,* **19**:1–152 (1912). Bibliography and excellent brief accounts and illustrations of general use on the Eastern coast of the United States.

JENNINGS, H. S.: "Behavior of the Starfish *Asterias forreri* Deloriol," *University of California Publications in Zoology,* **4**:53–185 (1907). Written by an authority in animal behavior.

MEAD, ALBERT D.: "The Natural History of the Star-fish," *Washington Bull. U. S. Bureau of Fisheries,* **19**:203–224 (1899). The most interesting account of the natural history of the common starfish. Available in many libraries.

33. INTRODUCTION TO THE VERTEBRATES—LOWER CHORDATES AND FISHES

BESTON, HENRY: *The Outermost House: A Year of Life on the Great Beach of Cape Cod.* New York, Rinehart and Co., 1949.

BREDER, C. M., JR.: *Fieldbook of Marine Fishes of the Atlantic Coast.* New York, G. P. Putnam's Sons 1929. Reliable, with a content and size for ready use.

CARSON, RACHEL L.: *The Sea Around Us.* New York, Oxford University Press, 1951. The book brings to the reader a sea as ancient and living, and as changeful as the sea really is.

CARSON, RACHEL L.: *Under the Sea-wind.* New York, Oxford University Press, 1952. Authentic life stories of fishes with the flavor left in—mackerel, herring, cod and their neighbors. The "River and the Sea" contains a life story of the eel.

CURTIS, BRIAN: *The Life Story of the Fish: His Morals and Manners,* 2nd ed. New York, Harcourt, Brace & Co., 1949. The author was formerly in charge of biological investigations of fresh-water fishes for the California State Division of Fish and Game. This book is an enjoyably clear and brief account told with humor, and based on firsthand acquaintance with living fishes.

DANIEL, J. F.: *The Elasmobranch Fishes,* 3rd ed. Berkeley, Calif., University of California Press, 1934.

JORDAN, DAVID S.: *Science Sketches,* 5th ed. Chicago, A. C. McClurg Co., 1916. Includes a famous "Story of Salmon," a classic of American fish stories. Out of print but in many libraries.

LAGORCE, J. O., ed.: *The Book of Fishes.* Washington, D. C., National Geographic Society, 1939. Chapters on fishes and fishways of the streams and coastal waters of North America. With 443 color portraits and 162 photographs from the *National Geographic Magazine.*

SMITH, HOMER W.: *Kamongo.* New York, The Viking Press, 1932. An account of the African lung fish. The author spent a year in Africa learning about the lung fish, then wrote *Kamongo* which has been read by thousands.

WALTON, ISAAK: *The Compleat Angler,* 5th ed. The classical account of the delights of a sport that has never gone out of fashion for men and should be in greater fashion for women.

GAGE, SIMON H.: "Lampreys and Their Ways," *Scientific Monthly,* **28**:401–416 (1929).

U. S. DEPARTMENT OF THE INTERIOR, FISH AND WILDLIFE SERVICE (Washington, D. C.), publishes reports and other publications that deal with fish and fisheries. Lists of these are sent upon request. Some publications are distributed free; others are for sale. The *Transactions of the American Fisheries Society, Reports of the North American Wild Life Conference,* and the periodical *Copeia* contain articles on all aspects of fishes. Various states distribute papers of interest to fishermen.

34. AMPHIBIANS—THE FROG, AN EXAMPLE OF THE VERTEBRATES

BARBOUR, T.: *Reptiles and Amphibians, Their Habits and Adaptations,* 2nd ed. Boston, Houghton, Mifflin & Co., 1934. Accounts of exotic amphibians by a great traveler with unique illustrations.

BISHOP, S. C.: *Handbook of Salamanders of the United States, Canada and Lower California.* Ithaca, N. Y., Comstock Publishing Co., 1943. Original observations, well illustrated. The only book on the subject.

DICKERSON, M. C.: *The Frog Book.* New York, Doubleday, Page and Co., 1920. An excellent book which has had a great career of use and is owned in personal, school and general libraries.

HOLMES, S. J.: *The Biology of the Frog,* 4th ed. New York, The Macmillan Co., 1927. A standard college text.

NOBLE, G. K.: *The Biology of the Amphibia.* New York, McGraw-Hill Book Co., 1931. An advanced reference; structure, function, life histories and classification.

RUGH, ROBERTS: *The Frog: Its Reproduction and Development.* Philadelphia, The Blakiston Co., 1951. An embryology which contains a chapter on the reproductive system of the adult frog. An advanced reference, finely illustrated.

WRIGHT, A. H., and A. A. WRIGHT: *Handbook of Frogs and Toads of the United States and Canada.* Ithaca, N. Y., Comstock Publishing Co., 1949. The standard modern work on the ecology, identification, and classification of frogs and toads. It contains an abundance of original observations and excellent photographs.

35. REPTILES—FIRST LAND VERTEBRATES

COLBERT, E. H.: *The Dinosaur Book.* New York, American Museum of Natural History, 1945. Fully illustrated by J. C. Germann and previously published drawings by C. R. Knight. An untechnical account based largely on fossils, with photographs of paintings in the American Museum, and including a reading list and glossary.

DITMARS, R. L.: *Reptiles of the World.* New York, The Macmillan Co.

DITMARS, R. L.: *The Reptiles of North America,* rev. ed. New York, Doubleday, Doran and Co., 1936. Firsthand observations of reptiles at the New York Zoological Park where the author was curator of reptiles; 400 photographs from life.

POPE, C. H.: *Snakes Alive and How They Live.* New York, The Viking Press, 1937. Excellent photographs; an ecological viewpoint; one chapter on snake venoms.

POPE, C. H.: *Turtles of the United States and Canada.* New York, A. A. Knopf, Inc., 1939. Both of the foregoing books by Pope are useful and interesting references for general readers.

ROMER, A. S.: *Man and the Vertebrates,* 3rd ed. Chicago, University of Chicago Press, 1941. From the standpoint of evolution with a good allowance for reptiles. Fully illustrated.

ROMER, A. S.: *Vertebrate Paleontology,* 2nd ed. Chicago, University of Chicago Press, 1945.

SCHMIDT, K. P., and D. D. DAVIS: *Fieldbook of Snakes of the United States and Canada.* New York, G. P. Putnam's Sons, 1941.

SMITH, H. M.: *Handbook of Lizards of the United States and Canada.* Ithaca, N. Y., Comstock Publishing Co., 1946.

SHARP, DALLAS LORE: "Turtle Eggs for Agassiz," *Atlantic Monthly,* **150:**537–545 (1932). A classic account of a hunt for incubating turtle eggs for Agassiz's work on the embryology of the turtle. First published, *Atlantic Monthly,* February, 1910.

36. BIRDS—CONQUEST OF THE AIR

ALLEN, A. A.: *Stalking Birds with Color Camera.* Washington, D. C., National Geographic Society, 1951. A magnificent collection of color photographs and descriptions by an outstanding authority.

ALLEN, G. M.: *Birds and Their Attributes.* Boston, Marshall Jones, 1925. One of the best non-technical books on the general biology of birds. Chapters deal with characteristic structures; food; ecological relations; eggs and nests; parasitic habit; senses and behavior; flight and migration. Recommended for any student of bird life.

AYMAR, GORDON: *Bird Flight.* New York, Dodd Mead & Co., 1935. A collection of 200 photographs.

BARTON, R.: *How to Watch Birds.* New York, McGraw-Hill Book Co., 1954. Interesting tips by a noted amateur ornithologist.

HERRICK, F. H.: *Audubon, the Naturalist.* New York, D. Appleton-Century Co., Inc., 1938. A one-volume edition of the biography published in 1917. An acquaintance with the most eminent of pioneer American ornithologists with glimpses of the naturalists whom he knew.

HICKEY, J. J.: *A Guide to Bird Watching.* New York, Oxford University Press, 1943. An introduction to bird study; how to identify birds in the field; where and when to look for them; how to acquire a good field glass and to keep records. Chapters on migration and bird banding and an annotated list of bird books.

HOWARD, H. ELIOT: *Territory in Bird Life.* London, John Murray, 1920. Authentic and thought provoking. Difficult to secure except in college or special libraries. Chapters on securing and defending the territory, its relation to song, to reproduction, to migration.

HOWARD, H. ELIOT: *The Nature of a Bird's World.* New York, The Macmillan Co., 1935. A brief, thought provoking book by a stimulating authority. Partly takes the place of the preceding reference.

LEOPOLD, ALDO: *Game Management.* New York, Charles Scribner's Sons, 1933. It is notable for its accumulation of facts, and clear style. It is said to be responsible for the founding of game management as an independent science and to be one of the most significant books in the field. The author was professor of game management at the University of Wisconsin, a leading authority and writer on conservation.

LINCOLN, F. C.: *Migration of Birds.* Garden City, N. Y., Doubleday & Co., 1952. A little book, up-to-date and written in direct, simple language.

NICE, MARGARET M.: *The Watcher at the Nest.* New York, The Macmillan Co., 1939. A thorough acquaintance with individual birds achieved by constant watching and recording. A unique study.

PETERSON, R. T.: *A Field Guide to the Birds,* 2nd ed. Boston, Houghton Mifflin Co., 1947. An excellent book for general field use with short descriptions of field marks, voice and range. It covers the area from the Dakotas and east Texas to the Atlantic Coast.

PETERSON, R. T.: *A Field Guide to Western Birds.* Boston, Houghton Mifflin Co., 1941. An excellent counterpart to the author's guide for eastern birds. It covers the western states, Washington and Oregon to New Mexico, including western Texas.

PETTINGILL, O. W., JR.: *A Laboratory and Field Manual of Ornithology.* Minneapolis, Minn., Burgess Publishing Co., 1945. Maps of life zones of birds. Definitions, keys, and descriptions. Plans of study designed by an expert.

GRIFFIN, D. R., and R. J. HOCH: "Experiments on Bird Navigation," *Science,* **107**:347–349 (April, 1948). Experiments on gannets et al. Results suggest: "The actual flight paths suggest exploration rather than absolute sense of direction."

WELTY, C.: "Birds as Flying Machines," *Scientific American,* **192**:88–95 (March, 1955). An interesting article on modifications in bird structure to adapt them for flying.

SPECIAL PERIODICALS. The leading North American ones are: *The Auk* (published by American Ornithologists Union); *The Condor* (Cooper Ornithological Club) for Western North America; *The Wilson Bulletin* (Wilson Ornithological Club) especially for the Middle West; *Bird Banding* (Northeastern Bird Banding Association). *The Audubon Magazine,* formerly *Bird Lore* is the official publication of the National Audubon Society. The headquarters of the Society are at Audubon House, 1130 Fifth Avenue, New York City. Members of the staff are helpful to anyone properly interested in bird life who may wish to consult them. The library is rich in books and periodicals.

37. MAMMALS AND MANKIND

ANTHONY, H. E.: *Fieldbook of North American Mammals.* New York, G. P. Putnam's Sons, 1928. Excellent reference in handy size.

CAHALANE, V. H.: *Mammals of North America.* New York, The Macmillan Co., 1947. Deals with groups of mammals, not with species. It is stored with firsthand information about the ways of mammals and written and illustrated to bring interest to anyone.

ELTON, C. S.: *Moles, Mice and Lemmings*. Oxford, England, The Clarendon Press, 1942. An important ecological study, especially of populations. Advanced and inclusive.

HAMILTON, W. J., JR.: *The Mammals of Eastern United States: An Account of Recent Land Mammals Occurring East of the Mississippi*. Ithaca, N. Y., Comstock Publishing Co., 1943. Concise and interesting. Many firsthand observations.

HARTMAN, CARL G.: *Possums*. Austin, University of Texas Press, 1952. The development, habits, history and folklore of the opossums of the south with many illustrations.

HOOTON, ERNEST A.: *Up from the Ape,* 3rd ed. New York, The Macmillan Co., 1946.

HOWELL, A. B.: *Aquatic Mammals*. Springfield, Ill., Charles C Thomas, 1930.

LEIGH, W. R.: *Frontiers of Enchantment*. New York, Simon and Schuster, 1938. An artist's account of the African country in which he painted scenes for Akeley Hall. See Figure 37.16.

MELVILLE, H.: *Moby Dick*. New York, The Modern Library, 1926. First ed. in 1851. The story of Moby Dick. A great whale is the symbol of adventure and courage. An allegory, a tale, and now a classic.

MOCHI, UGO and T. DONALD CARTER: *Hoofed Mammals of the World*. New York, Charles Scribner's Sons, 1953. The accurate and beautiful results of a pioneer technique in illustration. See Figure 37.15.

OSBORN, HENRY FAIRFIELD: *Men of the Old Stone Age,* 3rd ed. New York, Charles Scribner's Sons, 1918.

ROBERTSON, R. B.: *Of Whales and Men*. New York, A. A. Knopf, Inc., 1954. An account of whaling as it goes on today, the sea, the ships, the whales and whalers. It tells of the human mind and its culture unalarmed against the might of water, cold and animals.

ROMER, A. S.: *Man and the Vertebrates,* 3rd ed. Chicago, University of Chicago Press, 1941.

SETON, E. T.: *Lives of Game Animals,* 4 vols. New York, Doubleday, Doran & Co., 1929. Abundant illustrations by the artist author. A wealth of lively description and personal observation.

SIMPSON, G. G.: *The Principles of Classification and a Classification of the Mammals*. New York, American Museum of Natural History, 1945. Bulletin 85 of the museum.

YOUNG, J. Z.: *The Life of Vertebrates*. Oxford, Clarendon Press, 1950. The book is what its title says it is, the *life* of vertebrates. Excellent.

KELLOGG, R.: "The History of Whales, Their Adaptation to Life in the Water," *Quarterly Review of Biology,* 3:29–76 and 3:174–208 (1928). Their sight and hearing.

38. ORGANIC EVOLUTION—CONSERVATION

DARWIN, CHARLES: *The Origin of Species by Means of Natural Selection, or, the Preservation of Favoured Races in the Struggle for Life*. London, John Murray (Numerous editions, the first one, 1859).

GRAHAM, E. H.: *Natural Principles of Land Use*. New York, Oxford University Press, 1944. Short, finely illustrated survey of applied ecology.

HOWELLS, WILLIAM W.: *Mankind So Far*. New York, Doubleday & Co., 1952.

IRVINE, W.: *Apes, Angels, and Victorians*. New York, McGraw-Hill Book Co., 1954. The story of Darwin, Huxley, and evolution.

KELLOGG, C. E.: *The Soils That Support Us*. New York, The Macmillan Co., 1941. A layman's book, by a scientist who knows the soil and how to bring its fascination before the reader.

LEOPOLD, ALDO: *A Sand County Almanac*. New York, Oxford University Press, 1949. "There are some who can live without wild things and some who cannot. These essays are the delights and dilemmas of one who cannot." Widely known as an authority in the fields of ecology, conservation and forestry Leopold wrote with the integrity and flavor of the lines here quoted.

Moody, P. A.: *Introduction to Evolution.* New York, Harper & Bros., 1953. "Evolution as Seen in the Classification of Animals" is an unusual and valuable chapter in this readable book.

Osborn, Fairfield: *Our Plundered Planet.* Boston, Little, Brown & Co., 1948.

Raverat, G. M. (Darwin): *Period Piece; a Cambridge Childhood.* London, Faber & Faber, 1952. A thoroughly human reminiscence of the Darwin family. A fascinating tale.

Sears, Paul B.: *Charles Darwin, the Naturalist as a Cultural Force.* New York, Charles Scribner's Sons, 1950. A small and lively book that presents Darwin's way of living in present affairs and thinking.

Simpson, G. G.: *The Meaning of Evolution.* New Haven, Yale University Press, 1949. The best book on the general meaning of evolution.

Simpson, G. G.: *The Life of the Past, An Introduction to Paleontology.* New Haven, Yale University Press, 1953. Excellent for biologist and general reader.

Vogt, William: *Road to Survival.* New York, Wm. Sloane Associates, 1948. A dramatic analysis of human ecology and land use, a discussion of waste and the way to a rescue.

Wald, G.: *The Chemical Evolution of Vision.* Lancaster, Penna., The Science Press, 1946.

West, G.: *Charles Darwin, A Portrait.* New Haven, Yale University Press, 1938. Excellent. It should be better known.

Eisley, L. C.: "Fossil Man," *Scientific American,* **189**:65–72 (Dec. 1953). The bones of related animals offer no clue to the forces which caused the development of the unique human brain.

Index

Numbers in **boldface** type refer to pages on which illustrations occur. Complete scientific names of species are in *italic* type.

A

Abalone, **631**
Abomasum, **184**
Aboral surface, 655
Acanthocephala, **530**, 531, 797
Acanthometron, 441
Acarina, 593
Acoela, 507
Acorn worm, 663, **664, 665,** 798
Acquired characters, 414, 415, 789
Acromegaly, 272
ACTH, 267, 271, 272, 277, 304
Actinophrys sol, 441
Adaptations, 780–784, 789
Adaptive radiation, 784
Addison's disease, 267
Adenoids, **206,** 235
Adipose tissue, **115**
Adrenal glands, 200, **248, 256,** 264, **266,** 269, 271, 274, 348, **697, 709**
Adrenalin, 266, 273
Adrenocorticotrophic hormone (ACTH), 267, 271, 272, 277, 304
Aeroembolism, 226
Afferent neuron, **287, 295**
Age of the earth, **778**
Agglutinin, 209, 210
Agglutinogen, 209, 416
Aggregation, 100, **101**
Agranulocytes, **202,** 205, 207
Air bladder, 674
Air sacs, 608, 729, 744, **745**
Albino, 410
Albumin, 198, 746, 749
Alimentary canal, **179**
Allantois, 377–380, 752, 758
Allee, W. C., 93
Alligators, 716, 718, 722, **723,** 799
Alternation of generations, 443, 478
Alveoli, 232–235, **236, 237**
Amblystoma, 230, 683
  tigrinum, **685**
Ameba, 3, **21–23,** 34, **243,** 437, **438**–443

Ameba—(*Continued*)
  carolinensis, 437
  motion of, **430,** 438, **439**
  proteus, 437
  reaction to stimuli, 440
  reproduction of, 331, 440
Amebic dysentery, 430, 443
Amebocytes, 461, **463,** 464, 562
Ameboid cells, 639, 659
Amino acids, 31, 32, 65, 79, 169, 192, 194, 198, 199, 696
Amitosis, 43
Amiurus, 311
Amnion, 376, **377–379, 383, 613,** 666, 713
Amniotic fluid, 376
Amniotic sac, 377
Amphibia, 666, 681–713, 798
Amphineura, **631,** 633, **634,** 798
Amphioxus, 141, 363, **364, 365,** 664, **665,** 798
Amphitrite johnstoni, 554
Ampulla, 657
Amylase, 696
Amylopsin, 187, 191
Anadromous, 680
Anaerobic respiration, 227
Anaphase, **40**–42, 46, **365**
Anasa tristis, 406
Ancylostoma duodenale, **524**
Androgen, 343, 344, 348
Anemia, 204
Anemonia sulcate, 488
Animal pole of egg, 359, 361, 367, 368
Annelida, **227,** 552–571, **663,** 798
Anolis, 718, **719**
Anopheles, 445, **446,** 447, 528
Anoplura, 593
Ant lion, 598
Anteater, spiny, 755, **756,** 781, 799
Antennae, 601, **602,** 611, 619, **620**
  comb, **615,** 616
Anthozoa, **467,** 468

819